METHODS
OF
ALGEBRAIC GEOMETRY

METHODS

OF

ALGEBRAIC GEOMETRY

by

W. V. D. HODGE, M.A., F.R.S.

*Lowndean Professor of Astronomy and Geometry, and
Fellow of Pembroke College, Cambridge*

and

D. PEDOE, B.A., Ph.D.

*Sometime Charles Kingsley Bye-Fellow of
Magdalene College, Cambridge*

VOLUME I

BOOK I: ALGEBRAIC PRELIMINARIES
BOOK II: PROJECTIVE SPACE

CAMBRIDGE

AT THE UNIVERSITY PRESS

1947

Printed in Great Britain at the University Press, Cambridge
(Brooke Crutchley, University Printer)
and published by the Cambridge University Press
(Cambridge, and Bentley House, London)
Agents for U.S.A., Canada, and India: Macmillan

CONTENTS

BOOK II

PROJECTIVE SPACE

PREFACE

THIS VOLUME is the first part of a work designed to provide a convenient account of the foundations and methods of modern algebraic geometry. Since nearly every topic of algebraic geometry has some claim for inclusion it has been necessary, in order to keep the size of this volume within reasonable limits, to confine ourselves strictly to general methods, and to stop short of any detailed development of geometrical properties.

We have thought it desirable to begin with a section devoted to pure algebra, since the necessary algebraic topics are not easily accessible in English texts. After a preliminary chapter on the basic notions of algebra, we develop the theory of matrices. Some novelty has been given to this work by the fact that the ground field is not assumed to be commutative. The more general results obtained are used in Chapters V and VI to analyse the concepts on which projective geometry is based. Chapters III and IV, which will be required in a later volume, are devoted to a study of algebraic equations.

Book II is concerned with the definition and basic properties of projective space of n dimensions. Both the algebraic and the synthetic definitions are discussed, and the theory of matrices over a non-commutative field is used to show that a space based on the propositions of incidence can be represented by coordinates, without the introduction of any assumption equivalent to Pappus' theorem. The necessity of considering a large number of special cases has made Chapter VI rather long, but some space has been saved in the later parts of the chapter by merely mentioning the special cases and leaving the proofs to the reader, when they are sufficiently simple. It is hoped that this will not cause any difficulty. This Book concludes with a purely algebraic account of collineations and correlations. Certain elementary geometrical consequences are indicated, but a complete study of the geometrical problems involved would have taken us beyond our present objective.

It is hoped that Volume II will appear shortly. This will be devoted to the theory of algebraic varieties, and to the study of certain loci which arise in many geometrical problems.

We wish to express our thanks to Professor T. A. A. Broadbent of the Royal Naval College, Greenwich, who has read this volume in manuscript and in proof, and to Mr D. B. Scott of the University of Aberdeen, who has read it in proof. We must also thank the staff of the University Press for the care they have taken in the production of this book, and for their ready courtesy in meeting our wishes.

Note. The reference [II, §4, Th. II] is to Theorem II in §4 of Chapter II. If the reference is to the same chapter or section, the corresponding numeral or numerals will be omitted.

W. V. D. H.

D. P.

CAMBRIDGE
November 1946

BOOK I
ALGEBRAIC PRELIMINARIES

CHAPTER I
RINGS AND FIELDS

THE READER is assumed to be familiar with the use of homogeneous and non-homogeneous coordinates in geometry, when the
coordinates are real or complex numbers. When geometry is
developed with the help of these coordinates, results are obtained
by methods which belong to algebra, the differential calculus, and
so on. Those results which can be obtained by purely algebraic
processes (and they include many which are usually obtained by
the methods of the calculus) make up the subject with which we
are concerned in this work.

The operations of algebra we shall study are those of addition,
subtraction, multiplication, division, and the solution of algebraic
equations. While ordinary complex numbers are the most familiar
elements for which these operations are defined, there are more
general sets of elements for which it is possible to define them. By
allowing our coordinates to belong to these sets, a more general
geometry is obtained. We thus arrive at the definition of a more
general space than that considered in elementary geometry, and
the study of this space is the purpose of this work.

In this and succeeding chapters we consider sets of elements for
which some or all of the algebraic operations cited above are defined,
and step by step we arrive at a characterisation of the sets of elements
from which our coordinates may be chosen. These sets are known in
algebra as *fields*. In order, however, that the geometry which we
derive may conform to the general pattern which appears when the
field is that of the complex numbers, we shall find it desirable to
impose certain restrictions on the fields considered. These restrictions are not all imposed simultaneously, but in succession; and
only when we have proceeded under the limitations already adopted
as far as our subject demands do we impose a new condition. The
mathematical advantages of such a method are evident.

1. Groups. Consider a set S of elements, which we denote by $a, b, c, \ldots$. A law by which, given any ordered pair of elements a and b of S, possibly not distinct, we can derive a unique element c of S, is called a *law of composition* for S. A non-vacuous set S of elements with a law of composition which satisfies certain conditions, explained below, is called a *group*.

We denote the element resulting from the combination of a and b (in the given order) by ab; if the resulting element of S is c, we write

$$ab = c.$$

ab is a uniquely defined element of S, but may be different from ba.

The law of composition is said to be *associative* if, given any three elements a, b, c of S, we have the equation

$$(ab)c = a(bc).$$

We then write this element as abc.

The conditions that a set S, with a given law of composition, should form a group are that

(i) the law of composition is associative;

(ii) given any two elements a, b of S, there exist elements x, y such that

$$ax = b \quad \text{and} \quad ya = b.$$

As an example of a group, consider the possible derangements of the integers $1, 2, 3$. If α, β, γ is any derangement of these integers, we denote the operation of replacing $1, 2, 3$ by α, β, γ by the symbol

$$\begin{pmatrix} 1 & 2 & 3 \\ \alpha & \beta & \gamma \end{pmatrix}.$$

The successive application of any two of the six possible operations is equivalent to some single operation of the set, and hence a law of composition for the set of operations is defined. If we denote the six operations

$$\begin{pmatrix} 1 & 2 & 3 \\ 1 & 2 & 3 \end{pmatrix}, \quad \begin{pmatrix} 1 & 2 & 3 \\ 2 & 3 & 1 \end{pmatrix}, \quad \begin{pmatrix} 1 & 2 & 3 \\ 3 & 1 & 2 \end{pmatrix},$$

$$\begin{pmatrix} 1 & 2 & 3 \\ 1 & 3 & 2 \end{pmatrix}, \quad \begin{pmatrix} 1 & 2 & 3 \\ 3 & 2 & 1 \end{pmatrix}, \quad \begin{pmatrix} 1 & 2 & 3 \\ 2 & 1 & 3 \end{pmatrix}$$

by a, b, c, d, e, f respectively, and denote the result of performing first the substitution x and then the substitution y by xy, the complete law of composition is given by the table of double entry:

	a	b	c	d	e	f
a	a	b	c	d	e	f
b	b	c	a	e	f	d
c	c	a	b	f	d	e
d	d	f	e	a	c	b
e	e	d	f	b	a	c
f	f	e	d	c	b	a

where the entry in the row containing x and the column containing y is xy. From the table, or directly from the definition, it is at once seen that the law of composition is associative. Again, since each row contains all six elements, the equation

$$px = q$$

always has a solution; the corresponding result for the equation

$$yp = q$$

follows from the fact that each column contains all six elements. Hence the six elements, with the law of composition, form a group.

We notice in this group that $bd = e$, but $db = f$. Hence the equation $xy = yx$ does not hold for all pairs of elements in the group. Such a group is called *non-commutative*. If, in a given group, the equation $xy = yx$ is always true, we say the group is *commutative*, or *Abelian*. A very simple example of such a group is provided by the natural integers (positive, zero and negative), the law of composition being ordinary addition of integers.

It is often convenient, when dealing with commutative groups, to use the symbol of addition for the law of composition, writing $a+b$ instead of ab. We then call the group an *additive* group. It is important to remember that this notation is never used for a non-commutative group.

We now obtain certain properties common to all groups. From condition (ii) we know that, given any element a, there exist elements e and f such that

$$ae = a, \quad fa = a.$$

Let b be any element of S. Then there exist elements c, d such that

$$ac = b, \quad da = b.$$

From condition (i) we have

$$be = (da)e = d(ae) = da = b,$$
$$fb = f(ac) = (fa)c = ac = b.$$

In particular, in the first of these equations put $b = f$, and in the second put $b = e$. Then $f = fe$, and $fe = e$. Hence $e = f$. If there is another element e' with the properties of e,

$$e'e = e', \quad \text{and} \quad e'e = e,$$

and therefore e is unique. We have thus established the existence of a unique element e of the group such that

$$ae = a = ea$$

for every element of the group. This element e is called the *unity* of the group. In the case of an additive group it is usually called the *zero* of the group, and denoted by 0.

Now consider the equation

$$ax = e,$$

where a is any element of the group, e being the unity. By (ii) this has a solution x. Then

$$xax = xe = x,$$

and therefore the element $f = xa$ has the property $fx = x$, for the x considered. But, by an argument used above, $fb = b$ for any b in the group. In fact, let c be an element satisfying the equation $xc = b$. Then

$$fb = fxc = xc = b.$$

It follows, taking $b = e$, that $f = e$. Therefore $xa = e$. If y is any element such that

$$ay = e = ya,$$

then

$$y = ye = yax = ex = x.$$

Hence x is uniquely defined by the equations

$$ax = e = xa.$$

This element is called the *inverse* of a, and is denoted by a^{-1}. (In the case of an additive group it is called the *negative* of a, and denoted by $-a$. We then write $b - a$ for $b + (-a)$.)

We now show that the equations

$$ax = b, \quad ya = b,$$

where a, b are any elements of the group, serve to define x and y uniquely. For

$$x = ex = a^{-1}ax = a^{-1}b,$$

and

$$y = ye = yaa^{-1} = ba^{-1}.$$

Hence x and y are determined explicitly. In particular the equation

$$a^{-1}x = e$$

has a unique solution. But

$$a^{-1}a = e.$$

The solution is therefore $x = a$. Therefore

$$(a^{-1})^{-1} = a.$$

In the case of an additive group this becomes

$$-(-a) = a.$$

A non-vacuous subset s of S may, with the law of composition assumed for the elements of S, also form a group. This is called a *subgroup* of the given group. The following conditions are evidently necessary and sufficient for the elements of s to form a subgroup:

(i) if s contains elements a, b, it contains ab;

(ii) if s contains an element a, it also contains a^{-1}.

We conclude this section with a brief reference to an evident generalisation of the example of a group described above, namely, the *symmetric* group whose elements are the permutations of the numbers $1, 2, 3, ..., n$. The law of composition is defined as in the example. An important subgroup of this group is the *alternating group*. To define the alternating group we assume the definition of polynomials in the n indeterminates $x_1, ..., x_n$ which will be given in § 5. Consider the polynomial

$$\Delta = \prod_{i<k} (x_i - x_k) \quad (i, k = 1, 2, ..., n).$$

If the suffixes $1, 2, ..., n$ are permuted, it is easily seen that the polynomial Δ is either unchanged (except for the order of the factors) or becomes $-\Delta$. Permutations which leave Δ invariant are called *even* permutations, the others are called *odd* permutations.

A *transposition*, that is, a permutation which interchanges two suffixes only, is seen to be an *odd* permutation. Any permutation can be regarded as the product of transpositions. Such a decomposition of a permutation into transpositions is not unique, but the parity of the number of transpositions for a given permutation is independent of the method of decomposition. The product of two even or two odd permutations is even; the product of an even and an odd permutation is an odd permutation. Hence the set of *even* permutations of the symmetric group forms a subgroup, which is called the *alternating group*, and the number of even permutations in the symmetric group is equal to the number of odd permutations.

2. Rings. A set of elements may have more than one law of composition. We shall be particularly concerned with sets having two laws of composition, under one of which the set forms a commutative group. We write this group as an additive group, and refer to the corresponding law as the *addition law* of the set. The zero of the group is called the zero of the set.

The second law of composition is called the *multiplication law*, and the result of combining elements a, b of the set by this law is denoted by the product ab. Multiplication need not be commutative, but we shall require it to be associative. It is said to be *distributive over addition* if

$$a(b+c) = ab+ac, \quad \text{and} \quad (b+c)a = ba+ca,$$

for all a, b, c in the set.

A *ring*, then, is a set of elements with two laws of composition, addition and multiplication, with the properties:

  (i) the set is an additive group with respect to addition;

  (ii) multiplication is associative, and distributive over addition.

The following examples will illustrate the various possibilities which may arise in the study of rings. In the first four cases the laws of composition for the elements involved are addition and multiplication as usually defined:

  I.   The set of all complex numbers.
  II. The set of all integers, positive, zero, and negative.
  III. The set of all even integers.
  IV. The set of all integers, reduced *modulo* the integer m.

V. The set of all matrices of q rows and columns whose elements are complex numbers. A matrix of this type is the array

$$\begin{pmatrix} \alpha_{11} & \alpha_{12} & \cdot & \alpha_{1q} \\ \alpha_{21} & \alpha_{22} & \cdot & \alpha_{2q} \\ & \cdot & \cdot & \cdot \\ \alpha_{q1} & \alpha_{q2} & \cdot & \alpha_{qq} \end{pmatrix},$$

where each α_{ij} is a complex number. Addition is defined by the rule

$$\begin{pmatrix} \alpha_{11} & \alpha_{12} & \cdot & \alpha_{1q} \\ \alpha_{21} & \alpha_{22} & \cdot & \alpha_{2q} \\ & \cdot & \cdot & \cdot \\ \alpha_{q1} & \alpha_{q2} & \cdot & \alpha_{qq} \end{pmatrix} + \begin{pmatrix} \beta_{11} & \beta_{12} & \cdot & \beta_{1q} \\ \beta_{21} & \beta_{22} & \cdot & \beta_{2q} \\ & \cdot & \cdot & \cdot \\ \beta_{q1} & \beta_{q2} & \cdot & \beta_{qq} \end{pmatrix}$$

$$= \begin{pmatrix} \alpha_{11}+\beta_{11} & \alpha_{12}+\beta_{12} & \cdot & \alpha_{1q}+\beta_{1q} \\ \alpha_{21}+\beta_{21} & \alpha_{22}+\beta_{22} & \cdot & \alpha_{2q}+\beta_{2q} \\ & \cdot & \cdot & \cdot \\ \alpha_{q1}+\beta_{q1} & \alpha_{q2}+\beta_{q2} & \cdot & \alpha_{qq}+\beta_{qq} \end{pmatrix},$$

and multiplication by the rule

$$\begin{pmatrix} \alpha_{11} & \alpha_{12} & \cdot & \alpha_{1q} \\ \alpha_{21} & \alpha_{22} & \cdot & \alpha_{2q} \\ & \cdot & \cdot & \cdot \\ \alpha_{q1} & \alpha_{q2} & \cdot & \alpha_{qq} \end{pmatrix} \begin{pmatrix} \beta_{11} & \beta_{12} & \cdot & \beta_{1q} \\ \beta_{21} & \beta_{22} & \cdot & \beta_{2q} \\ & \cdot & \cdot & \cdot \\ \beta_{q1} & \beta_{q2} & \cdot & \beta_{qq} \end{pmatrix} = \begin{pmatrix} \gamma_{11} & \gamma_{12} & \cdot & \gamma_{1q} \\ \gamma_{21} & \gamma_{22} & \cdot & \gamma_{2q} \\ & \cdot & \cdot & \cdot \\ \gamma_{q1} & \gamma_{q2} & \cdot & \gamma_{qq} \end{pmatrix},$$

where

$$\gamma_{ij} = \sum_{k=1}^{q} \alpha_{ik}\beta_{kj}.$$

The reader may easily verify that these sets, with the prescribed laws of addition and multiplication, form rings. Further study reveals certain features common to some of the rings, but not necessarily to all.

(i) In the cases I, II, III and IV the zero of the ring is the number 0. In case V the zero is the zero matrix

$$0 = \begin{pmatrix} 0 & 0 & \cdot & 0 \\ 0 & 0 & \cdot & 0 \\ \cdot & \cdot & \cdot & \cdot \\ 0 & 0 & \cdot & 0 \end{pmatrix}.$$

In all five cases

$$a.0 = 0 = 0.a$$

for all elements a of the ring.

(ii) In cases I, II and IV let e be the integer 1, and in case V let

$$e = \begin{pmatrix} 1 & 0 & . & 0 \\ 0 & 1 & . & 0 \\ . & . & . & . \\ 0 & 0 & . & 1 \end{pmatrix};$$

in each of these cases e has the property given by the equations

$$ae = a = ea$$

for every element a of the ring. When such an element e exists, it will be shown to be unique. It is called the *unity* of the ring. In case III there is no element of the ring with this property.

(iii) In all but the last case multiplication is commutative. In case V it is non-commutative, since, if $q > 1$,

$$\begin{pmatrix} 1 & 0 & . & 0 \\ 0 & 0 & . & 0 \\ . & . & . & . \\ 0 & 0 & . & 0 \end{pmatrix} \begin{pmatrix} \alpha_{11} & \alpha_{12} & . & \alpha_{1q} \\ \alpha_{21} & \alpha_{22} & . & \alpha_{2q} \\ . & . & . & . \\ \alpha_{q1} & \alpha_{q2} & . & \alpha_{qq} \end{pmatrix} = \begin{pmatrix} \alpha_{11} & \alpha_{12} & . & \alpha_{1q} \\ 0 & 0 & . & 0 \\ . & . & . & . \\ 0 & 0 & . & 0 \end{pmatrix},$$

and

$$\begin{pmatrix} \alpha_{11} & \alpha_{12} & . & \alpha_{1q} \\ \alpha_{21} & \alpha_{22} & . & \alpha_{2q} \\ . & . & . & . \\ \alpha_{q1} & \alpha_{q2} & . & \alpha_{qq} \end{pmatrix} \begin{pmatrix} 1 & 0 & . & 0 \\ 0 & 0 & . & 0 \\ . & . & . & . \\ 0 & 0 & . & 0 \end{pmatrix} = \begin{pmatrix} \alpha_{11} & 0 & . & 0 \\ \alpha_{21} & 0 & . & 0 \\ . & . & . & . \\ \alpha_{q1} & 0 & . & 0 \end{pmatrix}.$$

(iv) In cases I, II and III, if a and b are two elements of the ring such that

$$ab = 0,$$

then either $a = 0$ or $b = 0$.

This property holds for the ring IV if and only if m is a prime number. If $m = pq$, where neither p nor q is 1, then p and q are two non-zero elements of the ring such that $pq = 0$. On the other hand, if m is prime and $ab = 0$, so that

$$ab = cm,$$

it follows, by the unique factorisation properties of ordinary integers, that either a or b is divisible by m.

The property we are discussing does not hold in case V if $q > 1$. For

$$\begin{pmatrix} 1 & 0 & . & 0 \\ 0 & 0 & . & 0 \\ . & . & . & . \\ 0 & 0 & . & 0 \end{pmatrix} \begin{pmatrix} 0 & 0 & . & 0 \\ 0 & 1 & . & 0 \\ . & . & . & . \\ 0 & 0 & . & 0 \end{pmatrix} = 0,$$

and neither factor is the zero of the ring.

(v) In case I there is associated with every element a of the ring, other than the zero, a unique inverse a^{-1} such that

$$aa^{-1} = a^{-1}a = e.$$

The rings II and V do not have this property, and it can be shown quite simply that the ring IV has the property only when m is a prime number. The property is meaningless in case III since the ring has not unity.

(vi) If we write

$$a+a = 2a, \quad a+2a = 3a, \quad \text{etc.,}$$

the elements $a, 2a, 3a, \ldots (a \neq 0)$ are all distinct, except in case IV, when

$$ma = 0$$

for all elements a in the ring.

It will be observed that only in (i) did we have a property common to the five rings, namely, the zero has the property $a0 = 0 = 0a$. We now show that this property holds for all rings, and deduce other elementary results true for any ring.

Let a, b be any two elements of a ring R, and let 0 be the zero of R. Then

$$a+0 = a,$$

and therefore
$$ba = b(a+0) = ba+b0,$$

and also
$$ab = (a+0)b = ab+0b.$$

From the uniqueness of the zero of a ring it follows that

$$b0 = 0 = 0b,$$

these equations holding for any element b in R.

Again, we know that any equation

$$a+x = b$$

has a unique solution

$$x = b+(-a) = b-a$$

in R. Now

$$a(b-c)+ac = a(b-c+c)$$
$$= ab.$$

Hence
$$a(b-c) = ab-ac,$$

and similarly
$$(b-c)a = ba-ca.$$

Therefore, taking $b = 0$, we obtain the equations

$$a(-c) = -ac, \quad (-c)a = -ca$$

for all a, c in R. Again,

$$(-a)(-b) - ab = (-a)(-b) + (-a)b$$
$$= (-a)(-b+b)$$
$$= (-a)0 = 0,$$

and therefore $(-a)(-b) = ab.$

We have thus shown that the usual multiplicative properties of the minus sign hold in any ring.

We now define the relationship between two rings known as *isomorphism*. Let R and R^* be two rings such that to each element a of R there corresponds a unique element a^* of R^*, and such that any element a^* of R^* arises from exactly one element a of R. Such a correspondence is said to be *one-to-one*. Now suppose, in addition, that the correspondence is such that if a, b correspond respectively to a^*, b^*, then $a+b$ and ab correspond respectively to a^*+b^* and to a^*b^*. The correspondence is then called an *isomorphism*.

Isomorphism between rings is a relation of the class known as *equivalence relations*. Consider any set S of elements $\alpha, \beta, \gamma, \ldots$, and let there be a relation, which we denote by $\sim$, between the elements of S, so that, given any two elements α, β, we know whether $\alpha \sim \beta$ is true or false. If the relation $\sim$ is:

  (i) reflexive, that is, $\alpha \sim \alpha$ for all α in S;
  (ii) symmetric, that is, $\alpha \sim \beta$ implies $\beta \sim \alpha$;
  (iii) transitive, that is, if $\alpha \sim \beta$ and $\beta \sim \gamma$, then $\alpha \sim \gamma$;

we say it is an *equivalence relation*.

An equivalence relation between the elements of a set S divides S into subsets, no two of which have any elements in common. If α, β are in the same subset, $\alpha \sim \beta$. Every element of S lies in one of these subsets.

It is clear that if S is the set of all rings, and if $\alpha \sim \beta$ means that the ring α is isomorphic with the ring β, the relation is an equivalence relation. We shall often speak of two isomorphic rings as being equivalent, implying that if in our discussion we replace one ring by the other (making any necessary consequential substitutions) nothing in our conclusions is altered.

A subset S of the elements of a ring R is said to form a *subring* of R if the elements of S form a ring under the addition and multiplication laws of R. For this to be so it is necessary and sufficient that if a and b are any two elements of S, then $a - b$ and ab belong to S.

If S is a subring of R, R is said to be an *extension* of S. The following theorem is frequently used:

THEOREM I. *If A and B^* are two rings, and A is isomorphic with a subring B of B^*, there exists an extension A^* of A which is isomorphic with B^*, this isomorphism including that between A and B.*

Let C be a set of elements in a one-to-one correspondence Γ with those elements of B^* which are not in B, and let A^* consist of the elements of A and C. We have merely to define addition and multiplication in A^* so that A^* becomes a ring with the required properties. Let $a_1, a_2, \ldots$ be elements of A^*. To each a_i there corresponds a unique element b_i in B^*. If a_i is in A, b_i is the element of B corresponding to a_i in the isomorphism between A and B. If a_i is in C, b_i is that element of the set of elements of B^* not in B which corresponds to a_i in the correspondence Γ. Conversely, to any element b_i of B^* there corresponds a unique element a_i of A^*. Now, if a_1, a_2 are any two elements of A^*, we define $a_1 + a_2$ and $a_1 a_2$ as follows. To a_1 and a_2 there correspond b_1 and b_2 in B^*. Let

$$b_1 + b_2 = b_3, \quad b_1 b_2 = b_4,$$

and let a_3 and a_4 be the elements of A^* which correspond to b_3 and b_4. We then define

$$a_1 + a_2 = a_3, \quad a_1 a_2 = a_4.$$

Clearly A^* is a ring isomorphic with B^*. Moreover, the construction shows that A is a subring of A^*. Hence A^* has all the required properties.

We conclude this section by describing a particular type of subring which we shall meet in later chapters. Let R be any ring, I a subset of R with the following properties:

   (i) if a, b are in I, then $a - b$ is in I;

   (ii) if a is in I, r in R, then ra is in I.

We call I a *left-hand ideal* in R; a *right-hand ideal* is defined by reading ar instead of ra in (ii). The two ideals coincide when multiplication in R is commutative.

To show that if I is not vacuous it is a subring of R we remark that if r is in I conditions (i) and (ii) coincide with the conditions stated above for a subring. On the other hand, not all subrings are ideals, since the condition (ii) need not hold.

R itself is an ideal in R, and is called the unit ideal. The subset of R which consists only of the zero of R is also an ideal. These two ideals are usually called the *improper ideals* of R. A ring containing a *proper* ideal is the ring of integers (Example II, above). If m is any integer greater than 1, the set I of all integers of the form $\pm ma$, where a is an integer, clearly forms a proper ideal in this ring.

The existence of an ideal I in R enables us to define an equivalence relation in R. If a, b are two elements of R, we write

$$a = b\,(I)$$

if $a - b$ is in I. The reader may easily verify that this is an equivalence relation. It is a type of equivalence which will often appear subsequently.

3. Classification of rings.   Rings which are subject to no other conditions than those imposed by the definition given in §2 are too general to be of much interest in algebraic geometry. We limit the rings with which we deal by imposing fresh conditions which are, in fact, equivalent to requiring the rings to possess one or more of the properties noted in the remarks (ii), ..., (vi) on the examples of rings given in §2. Different restrictions lead to rings with quite different properties. We now consider some of the more important types of rings.

We saw that a ring R may or may not possess an element e with the property

$$ea = a = ae$$

for every element a in R. We now show that R cannot have two distinct elements e, f with this property. For, if

$$ea = a, \quad bf = b,$$

for all elements a, b in R, we may take $a = f$, $b = e$, and obtain the equations

$$f = ef = e.$$

If this unique element e exists in R, it is called the *unity* of R. All the rings we shall consider will be rings with unity, unless the contrary is stated explicitly. For the present we continue to denote the unity by e.

If a is any element of a ring R with unity, there may or there may not exist an element a^{-1} of R such that

$$aa^{-1} = e = a^{-1}a.$$

There cannot be two such inverse elements, for if

$$ax = e,$$

then

$$a^{-1}ax = a^{-1}e,$$

that is,

$$x = a^{-1}.$$

When such an inverse element a^{-1} exists, a is said to be *regular*, or to be a *unit* of R. Clearly e and $-e$ are units of R. On the other hand, the zero 0 is not a unit, since for every element a of R

$$a0 = 0.$$

Again, we have seen [§ 2, (iv)] that there are rings R in which there exist pairs of elements a, b, neither of which is zero, such that

$$ab = 0.$$

We call a a *left-hand divisor of zero*, b a *right-hand divisor of zero*. The divisor of zero a cannot be regular. For, if a has an inverse a^{-1},

$$b = a^{-1}ab = a^{-1}0 = 0,$$

contradicting our assumption that b is not zero. Similarly, b cannot be regular.

The two types of ring with which we shall be particularly concerned are the *integral domain* and the *field*. An integral domain is defined as a ring with unity, in which multiplication is commutative, and which has no divisors of zero. Examples I, II, and IV (in the case m prime) of § 2 are integral domains.

A field is defined as a ring with unity in which every non-zero element is regular. The ring of all complex numbers is clearly a field. By the result proved above a field cannot contain any divisors of zero. A *commutative field*—that is, a field in which multiplication is commutative—is an integral domain.

We shall eventually be able to confine our attention to commutative rings, but it is convenient to obtain certain results which are valid for non-commutative rings, as these will be used in an analysis of the postulates on which projective geometry is usually based. Therefore, except when we say so explicitly, we shall not assume our rings to be commutative.

In a ring R consider any element a. Write

$$a + a = 2a, \quad a + 2a = 3a, \quad \ldots,$$

noting that na is not a product, but the sum of n elements each equal to a. We have seen by an example that there exists a ring R for which we can find an integer m such that

$$ma = 0$$

for all elements a in R.

Now, let R be a ring with unity e, and suppose that for some positive integer n,

$$ne = 0.$$

Let m be the *smallest* positive integer satisfying this condition. Then, first of all, if a is any element of R,

$$
\begin{aligned}
ma &= a + a + \ldots + a \\
&= ea + ea + \ldots + ea \\
&= (e + e + \ldots + e)a \\
&= (me)a \\
&= 0.
\end{aligned}
$$

If m is not prime, and $m = pq$, then

$$pe \neq 0, \quad qe \neq 0,$$

but

$$
\begin{aligned}
peqe &= pqee \\
&= me = 0,
\end{aligned}
$$

and R has divisors of zero. The number m is called the *characteristic* of the ring R. We have proved that the characteristic (if there is one) of an integral domain or a field is a prime number.

If, for all non-zero integers n,

$$ne \neq 0,$$

the ring is *without characteristic*. (It is then often said to be of characteristic zero, but this terminology is not strictly correct.)

If a ring R with unity has characteristic m, the subset

$$0, \quad e, \quad 2e, \quad \ldots, \quad (m-1)e$$

forms a subring. For

$$
\begin{aligned}
ae - be &= (a - b)e \\
&= ce,
\end{aligned}
$$

where $c = a - b \,(modulo\, m)$,

and $(ae)(be) = de,$

where $d = ab \,(modulo\, m)$.

Thus R contains a subring isomorphic with the ring of integers reduced *modulo m*. By Th. I, §2, there is an extension of this ring isomorphic with R.

Similarly, if R is without characteristic, it is isomorphic with an extension of the ring of natural integers. It follows that a ring without characteristic contains an infinite number of elements.

In each case we identify R with its isomorph, and so in future we shall write the unity of the integral domain or field we are considering as 1.

Later on we shall confine ourselves to integral domains and fields without characteristic, but at present we do not make this restriction.

4. The quotient field of an integral domain.

It is a familiar result that the integral domain of the natural integers is embedded in a field, namely, the field of rational numbers. This is a special case of a general theorem which we shall frequently use.

THEOREM I. *Given an integral domain I, there exists a commutative field K which, regarded as a ring, contains I as a subring.*

The construction which we give for K gives the minimum field having the required property. This minimum field is defined uniquely, to within isomorphism.

The elements of I are denoted by $a, b, c, \ldots$, the zero and unity by 0 and 1. Consider the set of all ordered pairs (a, b) in which $b \neq 0$, and the relation denoted by $\sim$ between pairs where

$$(a, b) \sim (c, d)$$

stands for the equation

$$ad - bc = 0.$$

Since multiplication is commutative, it follows at once that this relation is reflexive and symmetric. It is also transitive. For, if

$$(a, b) \sim (c, d) \quad \text{and} \quad (c, d) \sim (e, f),$$

$$ad = bc \quad \text{and} \quad cf = de.$$

Therefore

$$adf = bcf = bde,$$

and so

$$d(af - be) = 0.$$

From our definition of an ordered pair, d is not zero. Since an integral domain contains no divisors of zero it follows that

$$af = be,$$

that is,

$$(a, b) \sim (e, f).$$

The relation is therefore an equivalence relation, and divides all pairs under consideration into classes. The class to which (a, b) belongs will be denoted indifferently by $[a, b]$ or $[c, d]$, where

$$(a, b) \sim (c, d).$$

We define the sum of a pair (a, b) and a pair (c, d) by the equation

$$(a, b) + (c, d) = (ad + bc, bd).$$

By hypothesis, b and d are not zero, and therefore $bd \neq 0$. The pair denoted as the sum is therefore admissible. It is evident that addition of pairs is commutative. Now let

$$(a, b) \sim (a', b'), \quad (c, d) \sim (c', d').$$

Then $\quad (a', b') + (c', d') = (a'd' + b'c', b'd') \sim (ad + bc, bd),$

since $\qquad\qquad (ad + bc)\, b'd' - (a'd' + b'c')\, bd$

$$= (ab' - a'b)\, dd' + (cd' - c'd)\, bb'$$

$$= 0.$$

Hence we may define the addition of *classes* by the equation

$$[a, b] + [c, d] = [ad + bc, bd].$$

Since

$$([a, b] + [c, d]) + [e, f] = [adf + bcf + bde, bdf]$$

$$= [a, b] + ([c, d] + [e, f]),$$

addition is associative. Also, the equation

$$[a, b] + x = [c, d]$$

has the solution

$$x = [bc - ad, bd].$$

Hence the classes form a commutative group under addition. The zero of the additive group is $[0, 1] = [0, a]$, where a is any non-zero element of I.

We now define multiplication of pairs by the equation

$$(a, b)\,(c, d) = (ac, bd).$$

Multiplication is clearly commutative. Also, if

$$(a, b) \sim (a', b'), \quad (c, d) \sim (c', d'),$$

then $\qquad\qquad (a'c', b'd') \sim (ac, bd),$

since $\qquad\qquad a'c'bd - acb'd'$

$$= (a'b - ab')\, c'd + (c'd - cd')\, ab'$$

$$= 0.$$

Thus we can define multiplication of *classes* by the equation

$$[a, b][c, d] = [ac, bd].$$

Multiplication can immediately be proved to be associative. Again,

$$\begin{aligned}
[a, b]([c, d] + [e, f]) &= [a, b][cf + de, df] \\
&= [acf + ade, bdf] \\
&= [abcf + abde, b^2 df] \\
&= [ac, bd] + [ae, bf] \\
&= [a, b][c, d] + [a, b][e, f].
\end{aligned}$$

Hence multiplication is distributive over addition. The set of classes of equivalent pairs, with addition and multiplication defined as above, therefore forms a commutative ring K^*. If a is any non-zero element of I,

$$(a, a) \sim (1, 1),$$

and so

$$[a, a] = [1, 1].$$

Since

$$[a, b][1, 1] = [a, b],$$

$[1, 1]$ is the unity of K^*. Finally, if $[a, b]$ is any non-zero element of K^*, both a and b are non-zero. Therefore $[b, a]$ is in K^*. But

$$[b, a][a, b] = [ab, ab] = [1, 1].$$

Therefore every non-zero element of K^* has an inverse. Thus K^* is a commutative field.

Now consider the elements of K^* which can be written as $[a, 1]$, and let them form the subset S. Since

$$[a, 1] - [b, 1] = [a - b, 1],$$

and

$$[a, 1][b, 1] = [ab, 1],$$

S forms a subring of K^* isomorphic with I. By §2, Th. I, there is an extension K of I which is isomorphic with K^*, and which is therefore a field. The element of K corresponding to $[a, b]$ of K^* is usually written a/b. If

$$\frac{a}{b} = \frac{c}{d},$$

then

$$ad = bc.$$

We also have

$$\frac{a}{1} = a.$$

The field K is the one required. It is usually called the *quotient field* of I. To complete the proof of our theorem we now show that any commutative field K' which contains I as a subring contains a subfield isomorphic with K.

We first observe that, by the definition of a field, the non-zero elements of K' form a group under multiplication. Hence the equation

$$bx = a \quad (b \neq 0),$$

where a, b are in K', has a unique solution in K'. We now show that the equations

$$bx = a, \quad dx = c,$$

where a, b, c, d are in I, and b and d are not zero, have the same solution in K' if and only if

$$ad = bc.$$

First, if this condition is satisfied, and x is a solution of the first equation, we have

$$bdx = ad = bc.$$

Therefore $\qquad\qquad\qquad b(dx - c) = 0,$

that is, $\qquad\qquad\qquad\qquad dx = c.$

Secondly, if the two equations have the same solution x, then

$$ad = bdx = bc.$$

Thus to every element x of K' which satisfies an equation

$$bx = a,$$

where a, b are in I, and $b \neq 0$, there corresponds a unique element a/b of K, and conversely. Moreover, if x, y correspond to a/b, c/d respectively, then

$$bx = a, \quad dy = c.$$

and therefore $\qquad\quad db(x + y) = ad + bc,$

and $\qquad\qquad\qquad\qquad bdxy = ab.$

Hence $x + y$ and xy correspond to $\dfrac{a}{b} + \dfrac{c}{d}$ and $\dfrac{a}{b}\dfrac{c}{d}$ respectively. The field K' therefore contains a subfield isomorphic with K.

From this theorem we deduce that K is the smallest field which contains I as a subring.

Finally, we note that if I is of characteristic p, the sum to p terms

$$1 + 1 + \dots + 1 = 0.$$

Hence
$$[1, 1] + [1, 1] + \dots + [1, 1] = 0,$$

and it follows that K is of characteristic p. On the other hand, if I is without characteristic,

$$[1, 1] + [1, 1] + \dots + [1, 1] = [1 + 1 + \dots + 1, 1] \neq [0, 1],$$

and hence K is without characteristic.

5. Polynomial rings.

We now discuss a method of extending a ring by the adjunction of an element x, called an indeterminate. The only case of any importance which we shall meet in this book is that in which the ring is an integral domain, and it will make for simplicity if we assume throughout this section that the basic ring from which we start is an integral domain I.

Let us consider the ordered sets

$$(a_0, a_1, \dots, a_r)$$

which consist of a finite number of elements a_i of I. Two sets

$$(a_0, a_1, \dots, a_r), \quad (b_0, b_1, \dots, b_s)$$

are said to be equivalent if

$$a_i = b_i \quad (i = 1, 2, \dots, \min(r, s)),$$
$$a_i = 0 \quad (i = s+1, \dots, r) \text{ when } r > s,$$
$$b_i = 0 \quad (i = r+1, \dots, s) \text{ when } s > r.$$

This relation is evidently reflexive, symmetric and transitive, and is therefore an equivalence relation. We define the addition of two sets by the equation

$$(a_0, a_1, \dots, a_r) + (b_0, b_1, \dots, b_s) = (c_0, c_1, \dots, c_t),$$

where $t = \max(r, s)$, and $c_i = a_i + b_i$, defining $a_i = 0$ for $i > r$ and $b_i = 0$ for $i > s$. It is easily seen that if either of the two sets is replaced by an equivalent set, the sum is replaced by an equivalent set. Multiplication of two sets is defined by the equation

$$(a_0, a_1, ..., a_r)(b_0, b_1, ..., b_s) = (d_0, d_1, ..., d_{r+s}),$$

where $\quad d_i = a_i b_0 + a_{i-1} b_1 + ... + a_0 b_i \quad (i = 0, ..., r+s),$

and, as above, we define $a_i = 0$ for $i > r$, and $b_i = 0$ for $i > s$. Again, the replacement of either set by an equivalent set converts the product set into an equivalent set. If we now consider the classes of ordered sets defined by the equivalence relation, we see that they form an additive group with respect to addition, the zero of the group being all sets equivalent to the set (0); also, multiplication is associative, and distributive over addition. Hence our classes of equivalent sets, with the two laws of composition we have defined, form a ring R, and it is easily seen that (1) is the unity of R. This ring R contains a subring which is isomorphic to I. The elements of this subring are (a). For

$$(a) + (b) = (a+b),$$

and $\qquad\qquad (a)(b) = (ab).$

Hence an isomorphism is set up if (a) is mapped on the element a of I.

Let us now consider the set $(0, 1)$. We see that

$$(0, 1)^2 = (0, 1)(0, 1) = (0, 0, 1),$$

$$(0, 1)^3 = (0, 1)^2 (0, 1) = (0, 0, 0, 1),$$

$$\cdot \qquad \cdot \qquad \cdot \qquad \cdot \qquad \cdot \qquad \cdot$$

$$(0, 1)^n = (0, 1)^{n-1}(0, 1) = (0, 0, 0, ..., 1),$$

where in the last set written the unity is preceded by n zeros. Since

$$(a)(0, 1)^n = (0, 0, 0, ..., a),$$

we may express the set $(a_0, a_1, ..., a_r)$ as follows:

$$(a_0, a_1, ..., a_r) = (a_0) + (a_1)(0, 1) + (a_2)(0, 1)^2 + ... + (a_r)(0, 1)^r.$$

Now let us denote by $I[x]$ the ring which is an extension of I and which is isomorphic with R [§ 2, Th. I], x being the element of the extension which is mapped on the set $(0, 1)$ of R. Then, from the above reasoning, the set $(a_0, a_1, ..., a_r)$ of R is mapped on the element $a_0 + a_1 x + a_2 x^2 + ... + a_r x^r$ of $I[x]$. These elements are called *polynomials*, with *coefficients* $a_0, a_1, ..., a_r$. If $a_r \neq 0$, the polynomial $a_0 + a_1 x + ... + a_r x^r$ is said to be of *degree* r.

We note that the zero (0) of R is mapped on the zero of I, and therefore the equation

$$a_0 + a_1 x + \ldots + a_r x^r = 0 \qquad (1)$$

is satisfied if and only if

$$a_0 = a_1 = \ldots = a_r = 0.$$

Because of this property of the element x, it is said to be an *indeterminate over I*.

In the representation of a polynomial we usually omit any term $a_i x^i$ in which $a_i = 0$, whether i exceeds or is less than the degree of the polynomial. In this sense $a_n x^n$ is a polynomial whose complete representation is $0 + 0x + \ldots + 0x^{n-1} + a_n x^n$. Furthermore,

$$a_0 + a_1 x^1 + \ldots + a_r x^r$$

can be regarded as the sum of the $r + 1$ polynomials

$$a_0, a_1 x, \ldots, a_r x^r.$$

Since also $a_i x^i$ is the product of a_i and x^i, and since for the polynomials $x, x^2, \ldots$ we have the multiplication law

$$x^p x^q = x^{p+q},$$

the ring $I[x]$ is obtained by introducing a new element x among the elements of I which can be multiplied commutatively by any element of I. We say that $I[x]$ is obtained from I by *adjoining the indeterminate x to I*. $I[x]$ is also called the ring of polynomials in x *over I*.

These results apply when I is any commutative ring with unity. We now proceed to draw conclusions concerning the ring $I[x]$ from the fact that I is an integral domain.

THEOREM I. *If I is an integral domain, so is $I[x]$.*

We have already seen that $I[x]$ is a commutative ring with unity. We must now show that $I[x]$ has no divisors of zero. If

$$f = a_0 + a_1 x + \ldots + a_m x^m,$$

and

$$g = b_0 + b_1 x + \ldots + b_n x^n$$

are two non-zero polynomials, we may assume $a_m \neq 0$, $b_n \neq 0$. Then

$$fg = c_0 + c_1 x + \ldots + c_{m+n} x^{m+n},$$

where $c_{m+n} = a_m b_n \neq 0$, since I has no divisors of zero. Hence $fg \neq 0$. In other words, if $fg = 0$, and $f \neq 0$, we must have $g = 0$. Therefore $I[x]$ has no divisors of zero.

The process of adjoining an indeterminate to an integral domain to obtain another, more extensive, integral domain may be repeated. If $J = I[x_1]$, $J[x_2]$ is an integral domain. Its elements are polynomials

$$\alpha_0 + \alpha_1 x_2 + \ldots + \alpha_n x_2^n,$$

where

$$\alpha_i = a_{i0} + a_{i1} x_1 + \ldots + a_{im} x_1^m$$

is in $I[x_1]$, and m is the maximum of the degrees of $\alpha_0, \ldots, \alpha_n$. The elements a_{ij} lie in I. Hence, the elements of $J[x_2]$ can be written in the form

$$\sum_{i=0}^{n} \sum_{j=0}^{m} a_{ij} x_2^i x_1^j,$$

in which each term $a_{ij} x_2^i x_1^j$ is the commutative product of a_{ij}, x_2^i, x_1^j. If J' is the integral domain $I[x_2]$, the elements of $J'[x_1]$ are of the form

$$\sum_{i=0}^{m} \sum_{j=0}^{n} b_{ij} x_1^i x_2^j,$$

and the integral domains $J[x_2]$ and $J'[x_1]$ are easily proved to be equivalent. We denote this integral domain by $I[x_1, x_2]$.

Proceeding in this way, we can adjoin indeterminates $x_1, x_2, \ldots, x_r$ in turn to I. The resulting ring $I[x_1, \ldots, x_r]$ is independent of the order in which the indeterminates are adjoined. For the elements of this ring are of the form

$$\sum_{i_1=0}^{n_1} \ldots \sum_{i_r=0}^{n_r} a_{i_1 \ldots i_r} x_1^{i_1} \ldots x_r^{i_r},$$

the term written explicitly being the commutative product of $a_{i_1 \ldots i_r}$, $x_1^{i_1}, \ldots, x_r^{i_r}$. Also, $I[x_1, \ldots, x_r]$ is an integral domain. We have already proved this result when one indeterminate is adjoined to I. We assume it is true when $r-1$ indeterminates are adjoined. The result is assumed true for $J = I[x_1, \ldots, x_{r-1}]$, and by Th. I is therefore true for $J[x_r]$. But $J[x_r] = I[x_1, \ldots, x_r]$. Hence we have

THEOREM II. *If I is an integral domain, so is $I[x_1, \ldots, x_r]$.*

We conclude this section by introducing an important operation on polynomials in $I[x_1, \ldots, x_r]$ known as *specialisation*. Let

$$f = \sum_{i_1=0}^{n_1} \ldots \sum_{i_r=0}^{n_r} a_{i_1 \ldots i_r} x_1^{i_1} \ldots x_r^{i_r}$$

be any polynomial in our integral domain. We select any number j $(0 \leqslant j \leqslant r)$ of the indeterminates $x_1, \ldots, x_r$, say, for example,

$x_1, \ldots, x_j$. Let $\alpha_1, \ldots, \alpha_j$ be any elements of I. Then if in f we replace $x_1, \ldots, x_j$ by $\alpha_1, \ldots, \alpha_j$ respectively, f becomes

$$f^* = \sum_{i_{j+1}=0}^{n_{j+1}} \ldots \sum_{i_r=0}^{n_r} b_{i_{j+1}\ldots i_r} x_{j+1}^{i_{j+1}} \ldots x_r^{i_r},$$

where
$$b_{i_{j+1}\ldots i_r} = \sum_{i_1=0}^{n_1} \ldots \sum_{i_j=0}^{n_j} a_{i_1 \ldots i_j i_{j+1} \ldots i_r} \alpha_1^{i_1} \ldots \alpha_j^{i_j}$$

is in I. (α^i is, of course, the product of i factors each equal to α.) Then f is said to *specialise* to a polynomial f^* in $I[x_{j+1}, \ldots, x_r]$. We use the notation

$$f \to f^*, \quad x_1 \to \alpha_1, \ldots, x_j \to \alpha_j$$

to describe the specialisation.

By using the fact that equations such as

$$f + g = h, \quad fg = k$$

express relations between the coefficients of f, g, h and k which do not involve the indeterminates $x_1, \ldots, x_r$, we see at once that if, for any specialisation of the indeterminates,

$$f \to f^*, \quad g \to g^*, \quad h \to h^*, \quad k \to k^*,$$

then
$$f^* + g^* = h^*, \quad f^*g^* = k^*.$$

The converse of this result is not, of course, true.

Note. While we do not have to consider polynomials whose coefficients are in a non-commutative ring, it should be pointed out that a theory of such polynomials exists. The only result of this theory which we shall use is the following. Let

$$f = a_0 x^m + a_1 x^{m-1} + \ldots + a_m,$$

where a_i is in a non-commutative ring K, x is indeterminate and is assumed to commute with every element of K. Then if α is any element of K, there exist polynomials

$$p = b_0 x^{m-1} + \ldots + b_{m-1}, \quad q = c_0 x^{m-1} + \ldots + c_{m-1},$$

and elements b_m, c_m of K such that

$$f = (x - \alpha)(b_0 x^{m-1} + \ldots + b_{m-1}) + b_m$$
$$= (c_0 x^{m-1} + \ldots + c_{m-1})(x - \alpha) + c_m.$$

Indeed, we need only take

$$\left. \begin{array}{l} b_i = \alpha^i a_0 + \alpha^{i-1} a_1 + \ldots + a_i, \\ c_i = a_0 \alpha^i + a_1 \alpha^{i-1} + \ldots + a_i \end{array} \right\} \quad (i = 1, \ldots, m).$$

6. The division algorithm. In this section I denotes an integral domain, K a commutative field, and $I[x]$, $K[x]$ the rings obtained by adjoining the indeterminate x to I, K respectively.

Let
$$f = a_0 + a_1 x + \ldots + a_m x^m,$$
$$g = b_0 + b_1 x + \ldots + b_n x^n \quad (n \leqslant m)$$

be two polynomials in $I[x]$ of degrees m, n respectively, and let us suppose, in the first place, that $b_n = 1$. Then, clearly,

$$f_1 = f - a_m x^{m-n} g$$

is a polynomial in $I[x]$ of degree $m_1 < m$. If $n \leqslant m_1$, and if
$$f_1 = a_0' + a_1' x + \ldots + a_{m_1}' x^{m_1},$$

then
$$f_2 = f_1 - a_{m_1}' x^{m_1 - n} g$$
$$= f - (a_m x^{m-n} + a_{m_1}' x^{m_1 - n}) g$$

is a polynomial of degree $m_2 < m_1$. Proceeding in this way we arrive, in all cases, at a polynomial q of degree $m - n$ such that

$$r = f - qg$$

is a polynomial of degree less than n, the degree of g.

This result can be generalised to include the case in which b_n is a regular element of I. For, if $b_n^{-1} b_n = 1$,

$$g' = b_n^{-1} g$$

is a polynomial of degree n in which the term in x^n has coefficient unity. Then there exists a polynomial q' such that

$$r = f - q'g' = f - (q' b_n^{-1}) g$$
$$= f - qg$$

is of degree less than n.

We now show that the polynomials q, r obtained in this way are unique. For if q', r' are any two polynomials such that $r' = f - q'g$ is of degree less than n, we have the equation

$$r - r' = (q' - q) g.$$

But the degree of $r - r'$ is less than n, and the degree of $(q' - q) g$ is at least n, unless $q' = q$. Hence, unless $q' = q$, we have a polynomial of degree less than n equal to a polynomial of degree at least n. This is impossible, and therefore $q = q'$, and consequently $r = r'$.

The process given above for determining q and r is called the *division algorithm*.

A special case of the result just proved is the *Remainder Theorem*. If c is any element of I, take $g = x - c$. Then there exists a polynomial q such that

$$f - q(x - c) = r$$

is in I. This equation remains true when we make the specialisation $x \to c$. Hence

$$r = f(c),$$

where $f(c)$ is the result of replacing x by c in f.

Returning to the division algorithm, it may happen that $r = 0$. We then have three non-zero polynomials f, g, q in $I[x]$ such that

$$f = gq.$$

g and q are said to be *divisors* of f, and f is a *multiple* of g and of q. If the degrees of both g and q are greater than zero, both g and q are said to be *proper* divisors of f.

We now suppose that I is a field K. Since every non-zero element of K is regular, the division algorithm can be applied to any pair of polynomials f_0, f_1 of $K[x]$. By repeated applications of the division algorithm we shall construct a sequence of polynomials f_2, f_3, ... We shall denote the degree of f_i by m_i, and suppose that $m_0 \geqslant m_1$. Our purpose is to obtain information on the common divisors of f_0 and f_1. Applying the algorithm to f_0, f_1 we get the equation

$$f_0 = q_1 f_1 + f_2,$$

where $m_2 < m_1$. If f_2 is not zero we apply the algorithm to f_1, f_2, obtaining the equation

$$f_1 = q_2 f_2 + f_3,$$

and proceed thus until we have

$$f_{s-1} = q_s f_s + f_{s+1},$$

where f_{s+1} is zero. We reach this stage after at most $m_1 + 1$ applications of the algorithm.

Now, let g be a divisor of f_0 and of f_1. Then, if

$$f_0 = h_0 g,$$
and
$$f_1 = h_1 g,$$
we have
$$f_2 = h_2 g,$$
where
$$h_2 = h_0 - q_1 h_1.$$

Hence $\qquad\qquad\qquad f_3 = h_3 g,$

where $\qquad\qquad\qquad h_3 = h_1 - q_2 h_2,$

and so on. Finally
$$f_s = h_s g,$$

where $\qquad\qquad\qquad h_s = h_{s-2} - q_{s-1} h_{s-1}.$

Thus any common divisor of f_0 and f_1 is a divisor of the set of polynomials $f_2, \ldots, f_s$. Conversely, let g be a divisor of f_s. Then since

$$f_s = h_s g,$$

we have $\qquad f_{s-1} = q_s f_s = q_s h_s g = h_{s-1} g,$ say,

$$f_{s-2} = (q_{s-1} h_{s-1} + h_s) g = h_{s-2} g, \text{ say,}$$

and so on, until finally we obtain

$$f_1 = h_1 g,$$

and $\qquad\qquad\qquad f_0 = h_0 g.$

Thus any divisor of f_s is a common divisor of f_0 and f_1.

Since any common divisor of f_0 and f_1 is a divisor of f_s, the degree of such a divisor g cannot exceed m_s, the degree of f_s. On the other hand, f_s is itself a divisor of f_s, and therefore of f_0 and f_1. These polynomials therefore have a common divisor of degree m_s, and have no common divisor of higher degree. We call f_s, or af_s, where a is any non-zero element of K, the *highest common divisor* of f_0 and f_1.

The division algorithm enables us to express f_s in terms of f_0, f_1 as follows. We have the equations
$$f_2 = f_0 - q_1 f_1,$$
$$f_3 = f_1 - q_2 f_2$$
$$= -q_2 f_0 + (1 + q_1 q_2) f_1,$$

and by a simple induction we find that

$$f_s = a f_0 + b f_1,$$

where a, b are polynomials in $K[x]$.

If f_0, f_1 have no divisors of degree greater than zero, f_0, f_1 are said to be *relatively prime* elements of $K[x]$. Then $m_s = 0$, and f_s is a non-zero element of K. Let its inverse be g. Then

$$1 = f_s g = a g f_0 + b g f_1,$$

that is, $\qquad\qquad\qquad 1 = A f_0 + B f_1,$

where A, B are polynomials in $K[x]$.

A non-zero element of $K[x]$ which has no proper divisors is called a *prime* element of $K[x]$, or an *irreducible polynomial*. Our work above now enables us to prove

THEOREM I. *If f is an irreducible polynomial in $K[x]$, and g, h are polynomials in $K[x]$ such that f is not a divisor of g, but f is a divisor of gh, then f must be a divisor of h.*

Since f is not a divisor of g, the degree of any common divisor of these two polynomials is less than the degree of f. But f is irreducible. Therefore the only divisors of f have degree zero. Hence f and g are relatively prime, and so we can find polynomials a, b such that

$$1 = af + bg.$$

Therefore
$$h = afh + bgh.$$

But f divides gh. Therefore, for some polynomial k,

$$gh = fk.$$

Hence
$$h = (ah + bk)f,$$

showing that f is a divisor of h.

We note here that the term *factor* is often used in the same sense as *divisor*, so that we may refer to the *highest common factor* of two polynomials instead of to their highest common divisor.

We conclude this section with a theorem of frequent application. Let K^* be an extension of the field K, and suppose that f, g are polynomials in $K[x]$, and therefore in $K^*[x]$. If f, g are regarded as polynomials in $K^*[x]$, the process of the division algorithm, when applied to f and g, is carried out entirely in the subring $K[x]$. Hence the process of finding the highest common factor of f and g in $K^*[x]$ can be carried out entirely in $K[x]$. Thus the highest common factor of f and g in $K[x]$ is the highest common factor in $K^*[x]$, and, conversely, the highest common factor of f and g in $K^*[x]$, when multiplied by a suitable element of K^*, is in $K[x]$, and is the highest common factor of f and g in this ring. Hence, in particular, we obtain

THEOREM II. *If K^* is an extension field of the field K, and if f, g are two polynomials in $K[x]$ which are relatively prime, then f, g are still relatively prime when regarded as polynomials in $K^*[x]$.*

7. Factorisation in an integral domain. We have defined a *unit* or *regular element* of an integral domain I to be an element a which has an inverse a^{-1} in I, so that

$$aa^{-1} = 1.$$

We saw that the inverse is necessarily unique.

Clearly, 1 and -1 are always units of I. There exist integral domains, such as the ring of natural integers, with no other units. If, however, the integral domain is a field, every non-zero element in it is a unit. We shall make use of the following results in the sequel:

THEOREM I. *The product of any finite number of units is a unit. If the product of any finite number of elements of I is a unit, each element in the product is a unit.*

Let $\epsilon_1, ..., \epsilon_r$ be units, $\epsilon_1^{-1}, ..., \epsilon_r^{-1}$ their respective inverses. Then

$$\epsilon_1 ... \epsilon_r \epsilon_1^{-1} ... \epsilon_r^{-1} = \epsilon_1 \epsilon_1^{-1} \epsilon_2 \epsilon_2^{-1} ... \epsilon_r \epsilon_r^{-1} = 1.$$

Hence $\epsilon_1 ... \epsilon_r$ is a unit.

If $$a_1 ... a_r = \epsilon$$

is a unit, then $$a_1 ... a_r \epsilon^{-1} = 1.$$

That is, $$a_i(a_1 ... a_{i-1} \epsilon^{-1} a_{i+1} ... a_r) = 1.$$

Therefore a_i is a unit.

We now define the term *factor*. If any non-zero element a of an integral domain I can be written as

$$a = bc, \qquad (1)$$

where b, c are in I, these elements are said to be *factors* of a, and a is said to be a *multiple* of b and c. When a is written in the form (1) it is said to be *decomposed* into the factors b and c. If one of the factors is a unit, the decomposition is said to be *trivial*. Since every I has at least one unit ϵ_1, every element of I has at least one trivial decomposition $$a = \epsilon_1(\epsilon_1^{-1} a).$$

An element of I which is not a unit may or may not have a non-trivial decomposition. If it has only trivial decompositions it is called a *prime element* of I. (If I is the polynomial ring $K[x]$, the prime elements are the irreducible polynomials of degree greater than zero.) We prove that *if any product $a_1 ... a_r$ of elements in I is a prime, then one of the factors is a prime, and the rest are units.* For if $$b = a_1 ... a_r,$$

and each a_i is a unit, so is b [Th. I]. This is contrary to the definition of a prime. Hence one a_i at least, suppose it is a_1, cannot be a unit. Then since b is prime, $$b = a_1(a_2 ... a_r)$$

can only be a trivial decomposition. But a_1 is not a unit. It follows that $a_2 ... a_r$ is a unit, and therefore, by Th. I, that $a_2, a_3, ..., a_r$ are all units.

An element a of I is said to be *completely factorised* if it is expressed as the finite product

$$a = a_1 \dots a_r,$$

where each a_i is *either a unit or a prime*. By Th. I we can combine all the factors which are units into a single one. We then write this first, using a Greek letter to denote it, so that

$$a = \alpha a_1 \dots a_r$$

implies that α is a unit, $a_1, \dots, a_r$ are primes. In particular cases, of course, α may be unity.

Two complete factorisations of the same element

$$a = \alpha a_1 \dots a_r, \quad a = \beta b_1 \dots b_s$$

are said to be *equivalent* if $r = s$, and for a suitable reordering of the factors

$$b_i = \epsilon_i a_i \quad (i = 1, \dots, r),$$

where $\epsilon_1, \dots, \epsilon_r$ are units. We now give the following definition:

If an integral domain is such that every non-zero element can be completely factorised, and all complete factorisations of a given element are equivalent, it is called a *unique factorisation domain*. We shall abbreviate this to u.f.d.

The ring of the ordinary integers is a well-known example of a u.f.d. But we now give an example of a ring, in which not all elements are units, which is *not* a u.f.d. Consider the set S of complex numbers which can be written in the form

$$a = \alpha + \beta \sqrt{-3},$$

where α and β are integers. It is immediately verified that this set is closed under the operations of addition and multiplication, and it is easily shown that it forms an integral domain. This integral domain is, of course, a subring of the ring of complex numbers. We define the *norm* $N(a)$ of a by the rule

$$N(a) = \alpha^2 + 3\beta^2.$$

$N(a)$ is always a non-negative integer. The following properties are rapidly verifiable:

(i) $N(a) = 0$ if and only if $a = 0$;

   $N(a) = 1$ if and only if $a = \pm 1$;

   $N(a) \neq 2$ for any a in S;

   $N(a) = 3$ if and only if $a = \pm \sqrt{-3}$;

   $N(a) = 4$ if and only if $a = \pm 2$, or $a = \pm 1 \pm \sqrt{-3}$.

(ii) $$N(a)N(b) = N(ab).$$

Since $N(1) = 1$, we deduce that if $ab = 1$,

$$N(a)N(b) = 1.$$

Hence $$N(a) = N(b) = 1,$$

that is, by (i), $$a = \pm 1, \quad b = \pm 1.$$

Therefore the only units of the ring are $+1$ and -1.

Again, if

$$a = a_1 \dots a_r$$

is a factorisation of a in which no factor is a unit, it follows from the fact that

$$N(a) = N(a_1) \dots N(a_r)$$

that r cannot exceed the number of prime factors of $N(a)$. It follows from this that a can be completely factorised.

(iii) The numbers ± 2, $\pm 1 \pm \sqrt{-3}$ are all primes. For if any one of them could be written as bc, where neither b nor c is a unit, we should have

$$N(b)N(c) = 4,$$

while $$N(b) > 1 \quad \text{and} \quad N(c) > 1.$$

Therefore $$N(b) = N(c) = 2,$$

and we saw in (i) that there are no elements in the ring with norm equal to 2. The elements in question are therefore all primes. Now, since the only units are $+1$ and -1, we cannot have the equation

$$1 \pm \sqrt{-3} = \epsilon 2,$$

where ϵ is a unit. Therefore the factorisations

$$(2)(2) = 4 = (1 + \sqrt{-3})(1 - \sqrt{-3})$$

are not equivalent factorisations of 4. The ring S is therefore not a u.f.d.

We now return to the integral domain I, and assume that it is a u.f.d. We prove that any two elements a, b of I have a unique highest common factor. First of all let us call two primes p, q *equivalent* if there exists a unit ϵ such that

$$p = \epsilon q.$$

Now let us examine the consequences of assuming that an element c is a factor of an element d, so that

$$d = ce.$$

Let
$$c = \gamma c_1 \ldots c_r,$$
$$d = \delta d_1 \ldots d_s,$$
$$e = \epsilon e_1 \ldots e_t$$

be complete factorisations of c, d, e in which, as we agreed, γ, δ, ϵ denote units, all the remaining factors being primes. Then from the equation
$$\delta d_1 \ldots d_s = \gamma \epsilon c_1 \ldots c_r e_1 \ldots e_t$$

we deduce that $r + t = s$, and that the primes $c_1, \ldots, c_r$ are equivalent to r distinct primes of the set $d_1, \ldots, d_s$.

Now let
$$a = \alpha a_1 \ldots a_r, \quad b = \beta b_1 \ldots b_s$$

be the complete factorisations of two elements a, b of I, and suppose that, by suitably choosing the arrangement of the factors, and the unit multipliers of the primes, we can say that
$$a_i = b_i \quad (i = 1, \ldots, t),$$

but a_j and b_k are not equivalent for any j and k greater than t. By what has been proved above, any factor of a is the product of a unit and a certain number of the a_i, and similarly, any factor of b is the product of a unit and a certain number of the b_i. From the fact that I is a u.f.d. it follows that if d is a factor of *both* a and b, d can be written
$$d = \delta a_{i_1} \ldots a_{i_l},$$

where $1 \leqslant i_1 < i_2 \ldots < i_l \leqslant t$. Hence d is a factor of
$$D = a_1 \ldots a_t,$$

which is itself a factor of a and b. This element D is called the highest common factor of a and b, and is uniquely defined, save for a unit factor. We now prove

THEOREM II. *If $a_1, \ldots, a_n$ are any n elements of I, there is an element d, determined to within a unit factor, which is a factor of each a_i, and is such that any factor common to all the a_i is a factor of d.*

We shall call d the highest common factor of $a_1, \ldots, a_n$. The theorem has already been proved when $n = 2$. Let us suppose that it is true for $n - 1$ elements of I, $a_1, \ldots, a_{n-1}$, and let d_n be their highest common factor. Let d be the highest common factor of d_n and a_n. Then d is a factor of a_n, and of d_n, which is itself a factor of $a_1, \ldots, a_{n-1}$. Hence d is a factor of $a_1, \ldots, a_{n-1}, a_n$. Conversely, if e is any factor of $a_1, \ldots, a_{n-1}, a_n$, it is a factor of d_n and a_n, and hence of d. It only remains to prove that d is unique. Now, if d' is another element of I with the properties of d, d' is a factor of $a_1, \dots, a_n$, and therefore of d. Therefore

$$d = ad',$$

where a is in I. Similarly

$$d' = bd,$$

where b is in I, and hence

$$d = abd,$$

giving

$$ab = 1,$$

so that a and b are units.

We conclude this section with the important

THEOREM III. *If K is any commutative field, $K[x]$ is a u.f.d.*

We first prove that any polynomial in $K[x]$ of degree $n > 0$ can be written as the product of a finite number of prime factors. We proceed by induction on n.

If $n = 1$ there is nothing to prove, since, if f is of degree 1, and

$$f = gh,$$

where g, h are of degrees l, m respectively,

$$l + m = 1.$$

Hence either g or h is of degree zero, and is therefore a unit, and the decomposition is a trivial one; that is, f is prime.

We therefore suppose the result true for polynomials of degree less than n. Now let f be of degree n. If it is irreducible, then it is already expressed as a product of prime factors. If it is reducible,

$$f = gh,$$

where g, h are of degrees l, m, say, and

$$l + m = n \quad (l < n,\ m < n).$$

By hypothesis g and h can be expressed as products of a finite number of prime factors. Hence f can be so expressed.

We now prove that all factorisations of f are equivalent. That is, if f is a polynomial of degree n which can be expressed in two ways as the product of prime factors

$$f = \alpha f_1 \dots f_r, \quad f = \beta g_1 \dots g_s \quad (\alpha, \beta \text{ in } K),$$

we prove that $r = s$, and after a rearrangement of the factors,

$$g_i = \gamma_i f_i \quad (i = 1, \dots, r).$$

We again proceed by induction on n. For $n = 1$ the result is trivial, since all polynomials of degree 1 are irreducible. Assume that the result is true for polynomials of degree less than n. Since

$$\alpha f_1 \ldots f_r = \beta g_1 \ldots g_s,$$

f_1 is a factor of g_1 or of $\beta g_2 \ldots g_s$ [§ 6, Th. I]. If it is a factor of the second polynomial, the same theorem tells us that it is a factor of g_2 or of $\beta g_3 \ldots g_s$. Continuing thus, f_1 is either a factor of some g_i or of β. This last conclusion is untenable, since f_1 has degree greater than zero, while β is of degree zero. Hence, by re-ordering the factors g_i, if necessary, we can say that

$$g_1 = \gamma_1 f_1.$$

Since g_1 (as well as f_1) is irreducible, γ_1 must be a unit. $K[x]$ is an integral domain, and so we can cancel the factor f_1, obtaining the equation
$$\alpha f_2 \ldots f_r = \beta \gamma_1 g_2 \ldots g_s$$

between two polynomials of degree less than n. By our induction hypothesis
$$r - 1 = s - 1, \quad \text{that is} \quad r = s,$$

and, after a suitable arrangement of the factors,

$$g_i = \gamma_i f_i \quad (i = 2, \ldots, r),$$

where the γ_i are units. This proves the theorem.

8. Factorisation in polynomial rings.

The main theorem of this section, which we shall prove with the help of three lemmas, is

THEOREM I. *If I is a u.f.d., so is $I[x]$.*

Let f be any non-zero polynomial in $I[x]$, and suppose that d is the highest common factor of the coefficients of f. We can write

$$f = dg,$$

where g is a polynomial in $I[x]$ whose coefficients have a unit as their highest common factor. Such a polynomial is called a *primitive* polynomial. It is clear that both g and d are uniquely determined, save for unit factors. The importance of primitive polynomials is brought out by the following lemma.

Lemma 1. *The product of two primitive polynomials is a primitive polynomial.*

Let $\qquad\qquad f = a_0 + a_1 x + \ldots + a_n x^n,$

and $\qquad\qquad g = b_0 + b_1 x + \ldots + b_m x^m$

be two primitive polynomials, and suppose that the product fg is not primitive. Then the coefficients of this polynomial have a common factor d which is not a unit. If p is a prime factor of d, p must divide all the coefficients of fg. Now, f is primitive, and so not all the coefficients of f can be divisible by p. Let a_r be the first coefficient which does not have p as a factor. Similarly, let b_s be the first coefficient of g not divisible by p. Consider the coefficient of x^{r+s} in the product fg. It is

$$c_{r+s} = a_r b_s + a_{r-1} b_{s+1} + a_{r+1} b_{s-1} + \ldots + a_0 b_{r+s} + a_{r+s} b_0$$
$$= a_r b_s + pc,$$

where c is in I. By hypothesis c_{r+s} has p as a factor, and therefore the product $a_r b_s$ must be divisible by p. The prime factors of $a_r b_s$, since I is a u.f.d., are the prime factors of a_r and of b_s. Therefore either a_r or b_s is divisible by p, contrary to hypothesis. Our assumption that fg is not primitive is therefore false.

Let K be the quotient field of I. By §7, Th. III, we know that $K[x]$ is a u.f.d. We use this theorem, together with properties of primitive polynomials, to establish our theorem. Let ϕ be any polynomial in $K[x]$, and suppose that

$$\phi = \alpha_0 + \alpha_1 x + \ldots + \alpha_n x^n,$$

where $\qquad\qquad \alpha_i = a_i / b_i \quad (a_i, b_i \text{ in } I).$

We now write the coefficients in ϕ with a common denominator

$$b = b_0 \ldots b_n.$$

If $\qquad\qquad c_i = b_0 \ldots b_{i-1} a_i b_{i+1} \ldots b_n,$

and $\qquad\qquad f = c_0 + c_1 x + \ldots + c_n x^n,$

then $\qquad\qquad \phi = f/b,$

the polynomial f lying in $I[x]$. If now

$$f = ag,$$

where g is primitive, we have expressed ϕ in the form

$$\phi = \frac{a}{b} g.$$

Lemma 2. *The primitive polynomial g is uniquely determined by the non-zero polynomial ϕ, save for a factor which is a unit of I.*

Suppose that $\phi = \dfrac{a}{b} g$ and also $\phi = \dfrac{c}{d} h$, where g and h are both primitive in $I[x]$. Then

$$adg = bch,$$

and therefore ad is a factor of the coefficient of every term in bch. But since h is primitive, the highest common factor of the coefficients is bc. Hence

$$bc = \epsilon ad,$$

where ϵ is in I. Similarly, since bc is a factor of ad,

$$ad = \epsilon' bc,$$

where ϵ' is in I. Therefore

$$bcad = (\epsilon\epsilon')\, bcad.$$

Since ϕ is not zero, and I is an integral domain,

$$\epsilon\epsilon' = 1,$$

and therefore ϵ is a unit. Hence

$$g = \epsilon h,$$

and the lemma is proved.

If now the polynomial ψ in $K[x]$ determines the primitive polynomial h, and $\psi = \dfrac{c}{d} h$, then

$$\phi\psi = \frac{ac}{bd} gh.$$

By Lemma 1, gh is primitive. Hence, by Lemma 2, the primitive polynomial determined by $\phi\psi$ is gh. We therefore obtain

Lemma 3. *If ϕ is an irreducible polynomial in $K[x]$, the corresponding primitive polynomial in $I[x]$ is irreducible, and conversely.*

With these preparations we now come to the proof of our theorem. Let f be any polynomial in $I[x]$, and let d be the highest common factor of the coefficients. Write

$$f = dF,$$

and consider F as a polynomial in $K[x]$, which is a u.f.d. Let the prime factors of F in $K[x]$ be $\phi_1, ..., \phi_r$. These are uniquely determined, save for units of K. If

$$\phi_i = \frac{a_i}{b_i} F_i,$$

where F_i is the corresponding primitive polynomial in $I[x]$, then, by the above lemma, F_i is irreducible in $I[x]$. We have

$$F = \frac{a_1 \dots a_r}{b_1 \dots b_r} F_1 \dots F_r,$$

that is, $\qquad\qquad b_1 \dots b_r F = a_1 \dots a_r F_1 \dots F_r.$

Since $F, F_1, \dots, F_r$ are primitive polynomials, $b_1 \dots b_r$ is a factor of $a_1 \dots a_r$, and conversely. Hence

$$a_1 \dots a_r = \epsilon b_1 \dots b_r,$$

where ϵ is a unit of I, and therefore

$$f = \epsilon d F_1 \dots F_r.$$

Writing $\qquad\qquad \epsilon d = \delta d_1 \dots d_s,$

where $d_1, \dots, d_s$ are primes, the equation

$$f = \delta d_1 \dots d_s F_1 \dots F_r \quad (\delta \text{ a unit})$$

expresses f as a product of prime factors. Now let

$$f = \epsilon e_1 \dots e_{s'} G_1 \dots G_{r'} \quad (\epsilon \text{ a unit})$$

be another representation of f as a product of irreducible factors in $I[x]$. By Lemma 3 the F_i, G_j are irreducible in $K[x]$, and therefore, since $K[x]$ is a u.f.d., we must have $r = r'$, and

$$G_i = \alpha_i F_i \quad (\alpha_i \text{ a unit of } K),$$

when the factors have been suitably arranged. By Lemma 2

$$\alpha_i = \epsilon_i,$$

where ϵ_i is a unit of I. Hence, finally,

$$\delta d_1 \dots d_s = \epsilon e_1 \dots e_{s'} \epsilon_1 \dots \epsilon_r,$$

where δ and $\epsilon e_1 \dots \epsilon_r$ are units, whilst the d_i, e_j are not units. But I is a u.f.d. Therefore $s = s'$, and after a suitable rearrangement of the factors, $\qquad d_i = \theta_i e_i \quad (\theta_i \text{ a unit of } I).$

This proves that $I[x]$ is a u.f.d.

By a simple process of induction we then deduce

THEOREM II. *If $K[x_1, \dots, x_r]$ is the ring obtained by adjoining the r indeterminates $x_1, \dots, x_r$ to the commutative field K, then $K[x_1, \dots, x_r]$ is a u.f.d.*

9. Examples of fields. In constructing the spaces whose geometry we propose to discuss, the first step is always the selection of a field K. It is therefore appropriate to end this chapter with a few examples of fields.

I. We have already noted that the complex numbers form a commutative field under the usual laws of addition and multiplication.

II. We know that the natural integers form an integral domain I. By § 4, this integral domain can be embedded in the quotient field of I, which is just the field of rational numbers.

Both these fields are commutative and without characteristic. We now give an example of a field with finite characteristic.

III. Let p be any prime integer. We saw in § 2 that the ordinary integers, reduced *modulo p*, form a commutative ring with unity. The zero 0 represents the set of integers which are multiples of p, and the unity 1 the set of integers equal to 1 (*modulo p*). We now show that every non-zero element of this ring has an inverse. If a is any integer not a multiple of p, a and p are mutually prime. Hence we can find integers b, c such that

$$ab - pc = 1.$$

If now
$$a' = a\,(modulo\,p), \quad b' = b\,(modulo\,p),$$

it follows that
$$a'b' = 1\,(modulo\,p).$$

The set of integers *modulo p* therefore form a field. This field is clearly of characteristic p. This example also illustrates the case of a field with a finite number of elements.

IV. Let I be any integral domain with elements $a, b, \ldots$. The quotient field K consists of elements a/b ($b \neq 0$). The polynomial ring $I[x]$, consisting of polynomials

$$a_0 + a_1 x + \ldots + a_n x^n,$$

is an integral domain. There is also an integral domain $K[x]$, consisting of polynomials

$$\frac{a_0}{b_0} + \frac{a_1}{b_1} x + \ldots + \frac{a_n}{b_n} x^n \quad (b_0 \ldots b_n \neq 0).$$

We show that the quotient fields of $I[x]$ and $K[x]$ are isomorphic.

To each element

$$\frac{f}{g} = \frac{a_0 + a_1 x + \ldots + a_n x^n}{b_0 + b_1 x + \ldots + b_m x^m}$$

of the quotient field of $I[x]$ there corresponds the unique element of the quotient field of $K[x]$ similarly represented. If f'/g' is another representation of this element in the quotient field of $I[x]$, so that $fg' = f'g$, the elements f/g and f'/g' are equal in both quotient fields.

Conversely, any polynomial in $K[x]$

$$\phi = \frac{a_0}{b_0} + \frac{a_1}{b_1} x + \ldots + \frac{a_n}{b_n} x^n$$

can be written

$$\phi = \frac{c_0 + c_1 x + \ldots + c_n x^n}{c} = \frac{f}{c},$$

where

$$c_i = b_0 \ldots b_{i-1} a_i b_{i+1} \ldots b_n, \quad c = b_0 \ldots b_n.$$

If, similarly,

$$\psi = \frac{d_0 + d_1 x + \ldots + d_m x^m}{d} = \frac{g}{d},$$

we have, in the quotient ring of $K[x]$,

$$\frac{\phi}{\psi} = \frac{d(c_0 + c_1 x + \ldots + c_n x^n)}{c(d_0 + d_1 x + \ldots + d_m x^m)},$$

so that ϕ/ψ determines an element of the quotient field of $I[x]$. If, similarly,

$$\phi' = \frac{f'}{c'},$$

and

$$\psi' = \frac{g'}{d'},$$

and

$$\phi\psi' = \phi'\psi,$$

then

$$c'dfg' = cd'f'g,$$

and therefore the element of the quotient field of $I[x]$ corresponding to ϕ/ψ is the same as that corresponding to ϕ'/ψ'. The correspondence between the two fields is therefore one-to-one. It can be immediately verified that it is an isomorphism.

The quotient field of $K[x]$ is denoted by $K(x)$. It is called *the field of rational functions, over K, of the indeterminate x.* By the above argument, the field of rational functions of x_2 over the field

$K(x_1)$ is isomorphic with (and can be identified with) the quotient field of $K[x_1, x_2]$. It is denoted by $K(x_1, x_2)$. Proceeding, we see that

$$K(x_1, ..., x_{r-1})(x_r) = K(x_1, ..., x_r)$$

is isomorphic with the quotient field of $K[x_1, ..., x_r]$. It is called *the field of rational functions of* $x_1, ..., x_r$ *over* K. It is evident that the characteristic of this field is equal to that of K.

V. Finally, we give an example of a non-commutative field.

Let K be the field of the real numbers. Defining matrices as in § 2, Example V, consider the set Q of matrices which are of the form

$$\begin{pmatrix} \alpha & \delta & -\beta & -\gamma \\ -\delta & \alpha & \gamma & -\beta \\ \beta & -\gamma & \alpha & -\delta \\ \gamma & \beta & \delta & \alpha \end{pmatrix},$$

where $\alpha, \beta, \gamma, \delta$ are in K. Clearly, the sum of two matrices of Q is a matrix of Q, and if a, b are matrices of Q, the equation

$$a + x = b$$

has the solution

$$x = b - a$$

in Q. Thus the set Q forms a group under the addition law. Next, if

$$a = \begin{pmatrix} \alpha & \delta & -\beta & -\gamma \\ -\delta & \alpha & \gamma & -\beta \\ \beta & -\gamma & \alpha & -\delta \\ \gamma & \beta & \delta & \alpha \end{pmatrix}, \quad a^* = \begin{pmatrix} \alpha^* & \delta^* & -\beta^* & -\gamma^* \\ -\delta^* & \alpha^* & \gamma^* & -\beta^* \\ \beta^* & -\gamma^* & \alpha^* & -\delta^* \\ \gamma^* & \beta^* & \delta^* & \alpha^* \end{pmatrix},$$

the product

$$aa^* = \begin{pmatrix} p & s & -q & -r \\ -s & p & r & -q \\ q & -r & p & -s \\ r & q & s & p \end{pmatrix},$$

where

$$p = \alpha\alpha^* - \beta\beta^* - \gamma\gamma^* - \delta\delta^*,$$
$$q = \beta\alpha^* + \alpha\beta^* - \delta\gamma^* + \gamma\delta^*,$$
$$r = \gamma\alpha^* + \delta\beta^* + \alpha\gamma^* - \beta\delta^*,$$
$$s = \delta\alpha^* - \gamma\beta^* + \beta\gamma^* + \alpha\delta^*,$$

and therefore aa^* is in Q.

Since multiplication of matrices is associative, and distributive over addition, the set Q forms a subring of the ring of matrices. The zero of Q is the matrix with $\alpha = \beta = \gamma = \delta = 0$, and the unity of Q is the matrix with $\alpha = 1$, $\beta = \gamma = \delta = 0$. If, now, $a \neq 0$, and a^* is given by

$$\alpha^* = \alpha(\alpha^2 + \beta^2 + \gamma^2 + \delta^2)^{-1},$$
$$\beta^* = -\beta(\alpha^2 + \beta^2 + \gamma^2 + \delta^2)^{-1},$$
$$\gamma^* = -\gamma(\alpha^2 + \beta^2 + \gamma^2 + \delta^2)^{-1},$$
$$\delta^* = -\delta(\alpha^2 + \beta^2 + \gamma^2 + \delta^2)^{-1},$$

we find that

$$aa^* = 1 = a^*a.$$

Therefore every non-zero element of the set Q is regular: Q is a field.

Let us write $1, i, j, k$ for the matrices corresponding to

$$\alpha = 1, \quad \beta = \gamma = \delta = 0; \qquad \beta = 1, \quad \gamma = \delta = \alpha = 0;$$
$$\gamma = 1, \quad \delta = \alpha = \beta = 0; \qquad \delta = 1, \quad \alpha = \beta = \gamma = 0,$$

respectively. Then the element a of Q written above is expressible in the form

$$a = \alpha + \beta i + \gamma j + \delta k,$$

and the product

$$(\alpha + \beta i + \gamma j + \delta k)(\alpha^* + \beta^* i + \gamma^* j + \delta^* k)$$

can be evaluated by multiplying out and using the relations

$$i^2 = j^2 = k^2 = -1,$$
$$jk = -kj = i,$$
$$ki = -ik = j,$$
$$ij = -ji = k.$$

In particular, since ij and ji are unequal, the field Q is not commutative. This field is usually called the field of *quaternions*.

CHAPTER II

LINEAR ALGEBRA, MATRICES, DETERMINANTS

In this chapter we investigate properties of a set of elements which can be combined according to certain rules to form elements of the same set. These rules involve the use of the elements of a field. In the applications which have to be made in later chapters we shall usually assume that the field used is commutative, and without characteristic. But the main results of this chapter are independent of any such assumption, and, unless an explicit statement is made to the contrary, our results will be true for any field whatsoever.

We begin our investigation by selecting a field, which we denote throughout by K. We shall often refer to K as the *ground field*.

1. Linear dependence. Having selected a ground field K, let L be a set of elements (not necessarily belonging to K) which have the following properties:

(i) there is a law of composition in L, denoted by $+$, under which the elements form an additive group; the zero of the group is denoted by $\mathbf{0}$;

(ii) corresponding to each element of K there is an operation which transforms any element of L into an element of L. If a is the element of K, $\mathbf{u}$ the element of L, the result of operating on $\mathbf{u}$ with a is an element of L which is written $a\mathbf{u}$;

(iii) the operations described above obey the following laws:

$$(a) \qquad 1\mathbf{u} = \mathbf{u},$$
$$(b) \qquad a(\mathbf{u}+\mathbf{v}) = a\mathbf{u}+a\mathbf{v},$$
$$(c) \qquad (a+b)\,\mathbf{u} = a\mathbf{u}+b\mathbf{u},$$
$$(d) \qquad a(b\mathbf{u}) = (ab)\,\mathbf{u}.$$

A set L having these properties is called a *left-hand linear set* over K.

From the definition, certain properties of linear sets can be immediately deduced. First,

$$\mathbf{u}+0\mathbf{u} = 1\mathbf{u}+0\mathbf{u} = (1+0)\,\mathbf{u} = 1\mathbf{u} = \mathbf{u},$$

for all $\mathbf{u}$ in L. Hence, for all $\mathbf{u}$ in L,

$$0\mathbf{u} = \mathbf{0}.$$

Corollary. $u + (-1)u = 1u + (-1)u = 0u = \mathbf{0}.$

Hence $(-1)u$ is the negative of u as defined in the additive group. Secondly, if a is a non-zero element of K,

$$\begin{aligned}
u + a\mathbf{0} &= aa^{-1}u + a\mathbf{0} \\
&= a(a^{-1}u + \mathbf{0}) \\
&= a(a^{-1}u) \\
&= u.
\end{aligned}$$

Hence $\qquad\qquad\qquad a\mathbf{0} = \mathbf{0}.$

This result is also true if $a = 0$, by the first result.

The converse of these results is immediate. If

$$au = \mathbf{0},$$

and $a \neq 0$, we have the equations

$$u = 1u = (a^{-1}a)u = a^{-1}(au) = a^{-1}\mathbf{0} = \mathbf{0}.$$

Hence, the equation $\qquad\qquad au = \mathbf{0}$

implies either $a = 0$ or $u = \mathbf{0}$.

Corollary. If $\qquad au = bu \quad$ and $\quad u \neq \mathbf{0},$

then $\qquad\qquad\qquad\qquad a = b;$

and if $\qquad\qquad au = av \quad$ and $\quad a \neq 0,$

then $\qquad\qquad\qquad\qquad u = v.$

A right-hand linear set can be defined as above, except that all operations are performed on the right. We can deduce similar results to those proved above for left-hand linear sets. In the case of a commutative field K we shall not distinguish between right-hand and left-hand linear sets, and we shall write

$$au = ua,$$

and talk simply of *linear sets*. But in the following work we shall *not* assume that K is commutative. However, it will be sufficient to confine our attention to left-hand linear sets, since from each property of these sets a corresponding property of right-hand linear sets will be immediately deducible. Whenever there is no risk of confusion we shall simply call the left-hand linear set L a *linear set*.

Any r members $u_1, ..., u_r$ of L are said to be *linearly dependent* over K if there exist elements $a_1, ..., a_r$ of K, not all zero, such that

$$a_1 u_1 + ... + a_r u_r = 0;$$

otherwise they are *linearly independent*.

We note that no finite set of elements of L which includes 0 can be linearly independent, since, if the other members of the set be $u_1, ..., u_r$, we always have the equation

$$a0 + 0u_1 + ... + 0u_r = 0 \quad (a \neq 0).$$

If $u_1, ..., u_r$ are linearly independent, then any subset $u_{i_1}, ..., u_{i_s}$ consists of linearly independent elements. For the linear dependence of the subset would involve the linear dependence of the whole set.

Any element v of L which can be expressed in the form

$$v = a_1 u_1 + ... + a_r u_r \quad (a_i \text{ in } K)$$

is said to be linearly dependent on $u_1, ..., u_r$. We shall denote the set of elements of L which are linearly dependent on $u_1, ..., u_r$ by the symbol $L(u_1, ..., u_r)$. The zero 0 is always in the set. We now prove

THEOREM I. $L(u_1, ..., u_r)$ *is a linear set.*

If u, v are in the set,

$$u = a_1 u_1 + ... + a_r u_r,$$

and

$$v = b_1 u_1 + ... + b_r u_r.$$

Then

$$u + v = (a_1 + b_1) u_1 + ... + (a_r + b_r) u_r.$$

Hence $u + v$ is in the set. Also

$$au = aa_1 u_1 + ... + aa_r u_r,$$

and therefore au lies in the set. Since the negative of u in the additive group is equal to $(-1)u$, we see that the set $L(u_1, ..., u_r)$ is an additive group and is closed under multiplication by elements of K. It is therefore a linear set.

THEOREM II. *If $u_1, ..., u_r$ are linearly independent, the expression*

$$v = a_1 u_1 + ... + a_r u_r$$

for any element of $L(u_1, ..., u_r)$ is unique. Conversely, if the expression is unique, $u_1, ..., u_r$ are linearly independent.

If any element v of $L(u_1, ..., u_r)$ can be written in two ways as

$$v = a_1 u_1 + ... + a_r u_r,$$

and
$$v = b_1 u_1 + ... + b_r u_r,$$

we see that $$0 = (a_1 - b_1) u_1 + ... + (a_r - b_r) u_r.$$

Since $u_1, ..., u_r$ are linearly independent, it follows that

$$a_i = b_i \quad (i = 1, ..., r).$$

Conversely, suppose that the representation is unique, but that

$$a_1 u_1 + ... + a_r u_r = 0.$$

Then $$v = b_1 u_1 + ... + b_r u_r$$
can also be written as

$$v = (b_1 + a_1) u_1 + ... + (b_r + a_r) u_r.$$

From $$b_i + a_i = b_i \quad (i = 1, ..., r),$$

we deduce that $$a_i = 0 \quad (i = 1, ..., r).$$

This proves that $u_1, ..., u_r$ are linearly independent.

THEOREM III. *If $v_1, ..., v_s$ lie in $L(u_1, ..., u_r)$, and $w_1, ..., w_t$ lie in $L(v_1, ..., v_s)$, then $w_1, ..., w_t$ lie in $L(u_1, ..., u_r)$.*

For, from the equations

$$v_i = a_{i1} u_1 + ... + a_{ir} u_r \quad (i = 1, ..., s),$$

and $$w_i = b_{i1} v_1 + ... + b_{is} v_s \quad (i = 1, ..., t),$$

we deduce that

$$w_i = c_{i1} u_1 + ... + c_{ir} u_r \quad (i = 1, ..., t),$$

where $$c_{ij} = \sum_{k=1}^{s} b_{ik} a_{kj}.$$

THEOREM IV. *In any finite set $u_1, ..., u_r$, not all 0, we can find a subset $u_{i_1}, ..., u_{i_s}$, which is linearly independent, and such that*

$$L(u_1, ..., u_r) = L(u_{i_1}, ..., u_{i_s}).$$

We prove this by induction on r. The theorem is evident if $r = 1$, since, by hypothesis, $u_1 \neq 0$, and is therefore linearly independent. Suppose now that the theorem is true for $r - 1$ elements, and consider the set $u_1, ..., u_r$. If these elements are linearly independent we choose them as the subset, and there is nothing to prove. Assume then that they are dependent, and that

$$a_1u_1 + \ldots + a_ru_r = 0,$$

where at least one $a_i \neq 0$. If $a_k \neq 0$, we see that

$$u_k = -a_k^{-1}a_1u_1 - \ldots - a_k^{-1}a_{k-1}u_{k-1} - a_k^{-1}a_{k+1}u_{k+1} - \ldots - a_k^{-1}a_ru_r.$$

Not all the elements $u_1, \ldots, u_{k-1}, u_{k+1}, \ldots, u_r$ can be 0, otherwise $u_k = 0$ also. We can therefore apply the induction hypothesis to $L(u_1, \ldots, u_{k-1}, u_{k+1}, \ldots, u_r)$, and we deduce that there exists a set of linearly independent elements $u_{i_1}, \ldots, u_{i_s}$ such that

$$L(u_1, \ldots, u_{k-1}, u_{k+1}, \ldots, u_r) = L(u_{i_1}, \ldots, u_{i_s}).$$

Clearly $L(u_{i_1}, \ldots, u_{i_s})$ is contained in $L(u_1, \ldots, u_r)$. Conversely, any element v of $L(u_1, \ldots, u_r)$ can be written in the form

$$v = b_1u_1 + \ldots + b_ku_k + \ldots + b_ru_r$$
$$= (b_1 - b_ka_k^{-1}a_1)u_1 + \ldots + (b_k - b_ka_k^{-1}a_k)u_k + \ldots + (b_r - b_ka_k^{-1}a_r)u_r,$$

and is therefore in

$$L(u_1, \ldots, u_{k-1}, u_{k+1}, \ldots, u_r) = L(u_{i_1}, \ldots, u_{i_s}).$$

Hence $\qquad L(u_1, \ldots, u_r) = L(u_{i_1}, \ldots, u_{i_s}),$

and the theorem is proved.

The elements $v_1, \ldots, v_s$, whether linearly independent or not, are said to form a *basis* for the linear set $L(u_1, \ldots, u_r)$ if

$$L(v_1, \ldots, v_s) = L(u_1, \ldots, u_r).$$

If the elements are linearly independent the basis is described as a *minimal basis*. We shall prove that the number of elements in a minimal basis for $L(u_1, \ldots, u_r)$ is the same for all minimal bases, and this number will be called the *dimension* of $L(u_1, \ldots, u_r)$.

The principal step in proving that the number of elements in a minimal basis is always the same is the result known as the *Exchange Theorem*. This has many applications in algebra.

THEOREM V. *If $v_1, \ldots, v_s$ are s linearly independent elements of $L(u_1, \ldots, u_r)$, there is a subset $u_{i_1}, \ldots, u_{i_s}$ of the basis $u_1, \ldots, u_r$, such that if we exchange this subset for $v_1, \ldots, v_s$ the new set of r elements is a basis for $L(u_1, \ldots, u_r)$.*

We prove this theorem by induction on s. Assume that the theorem is true for $v_1, \ldots, v_{s-1}$, and suppose that these elements have been exchanged with $u_{i_1}, \ldots, u_{i_{s-1}}$, where $i_1, \ldots, i_{s-1}, \ldots, i_r$ is a derangement of $1, \ldots, r$. Then, by hypothesis,

$$L(u_1, \ldots, u_r) = L(v_1, \ldots, v_{s-1}, u_{i_s}, \ldots, u_{i_r}),$$

and contains v_s. Hence

$$v_s = a_1 v_1 + \ldots + a_{s-1} v_{s-1} + a_s u_{i_s} + \ldots + a_r u_{i_r}. \tag{1}$$

Not all the elements $a_s, \ldots, a_r$ of K can be zero, since this equation would then imply the linear dependence of $v_1, \ldots, v_s$. We may, without loss of generality, assume that the derangement $i_1, \ldots, i_r$ has been chosen so that $a_s \neq 0$. We can then write

$$u_{i_s} = -a_s^{-1} a_1 v_1 - \ldots - a_s^{-1} a_{s-1} v_{s-1} + a_s^{-1} v_s$$
$$- a_s^{-1} a_{s+1} u_{i_{s+1}} - \ldots - a_s^{-1} a_r u_{i_r}. \tag{2}$$

Now, $v_1, \ldots, v_{s-1}, v_s, u_{i_{s+1}}, \ldots, u_{i_r}$ lie in $L(v_1, \ldots, v_{s-1}, u_{i_s}, \ldots, u_{i_r})$, and therefore, by Th. III,

$$L(v_1, \ldots, v_{s-1}, v_s, u_{i_{s+1}}, \ldots, u_{i_r}) \subseteq L(v_1, \ldots, v_{s-1}, u_{i_s}, \ldots, u_{i_r}).$$

But conversely, equation (2) shows that u_{i_s} lies in

$$L(v_1, \ldots, v_{s-1}, v_s, u_{i_{s+1}}, \ldots, u_{i_r}),$$

and therefore

$$L(v_1, \ldots, v_{s-1}, u_{i_s}, \ldots, u_{i_r}) \subseteq L(v_1, \ldots, v_{s-1}, v_s, u_{i_{s+1}}, \ldots, u_{i_r}).$$

Hence

$$L(u_1, \ldots, u_r) = L(v_1, \ldots, v_{s-1}, u_{i_s}, \ldots, u_{i_r})$$
$$= L(v_1, \ldots, v_{s-1}, v_s, u_{i_{s+1}}, \ldots, u_{i_r}).$$

The same reasoning can be applied to the case $s = 1$, when there has been no exchange. Hence the theorem is proved.

Corollaries

(1) If $u_1, \ldots, u_r$ is a minimal basis for $L(u_1, \ldots, u_r)$, and $v_1, \ldots, v_r$ are r linearly independent elements of this set, then

$$L(u_1, \ldots, u_r) = L(v_1, \ldots, v_r).$$

(2) If $v_1, \ldots, v_{r+1}$ are any $r+1$ elements of $L(u_1, \ldots, u_r)$, they are linearly dependent.

If any r of the elements v_i are linearly dependent, the corollary needs no proof. Suppose, then, that $v_1, \ldots, v_r$ are linearly independent. Then v_{r+1} is in $L(u_1, \ldots, u_r)$, which, by the Exchange Theorem, is the same as $L(v_1, \ldots, v_r)$. Therefore

$$v_{r+1} = a_1 v_1 + \ldots + a_r v_r,$$

and therefore $v_1, \ldots, v_{r+1}$ are linearly dependent.

Note that this proof does not assume that $u_1, \ldots, u_r$ form a minimal basis for $L(u_1, \ldots, u_r)$.

THEOREM VI. *The number of elements in a minimal basis for $L(u_1, \ldots, u_r)$ is the same for all bases.*

Let $v_1, \ldots, v_n$, and $w_1, \ldots, w_m$ be two minimal bases. Then

$$L(u_1, \ldots, u_r) = L(v_1, \ldots, v_n) = L(w_1, \ldots, w_m).$$

If $n > m$, Corollary (2) states that $v_1, \ldots, v_n$ are linearly dependent, and similarly, if $m > n$, $w_1, \ldots, w_m$ are linearly dependent. But, by definition, the elements of a minimal basis are linearly independent. Therefore $m = n$.

As stated above, this number is called the *dimension* of the linear set. As an evident corollary to the above theorem we have

(1) *If L, M are linear sets of finite dimensions l, m respectively, and $L \subseteq M$, then $l \leqslant m$. If $L \subseteq M$ and $l = m$, then $L = M$.*

We now give an important example of a left-hand linear set over a field K.

We consider the set of n-tuples

$$(a_1, \ldots, a_n)$$

consisting of n elements a_i of K. Two n-tuples

$$(a_1, \ldots, a_n) \quad \text{and} \quad (b_1, \ldots, b_n)$$

are equal if and only if

$$a_i = b_i \quad (i = 1, \ldots, n).$$

If $\qquad u = (a_1, \ldots, a_n), \quad \text{and} \quad v = (b_1, \ldots, b_n)$

are two n-tuples, we define $u + v$ by the equation

$$u + v = (a_1 + b_1, \ldots, a_n + b_n),$$

and au (a in K) by the equation

$$au = (aa_1, \ldots, aa_n).$$

With these definitions it is evident that n-tuples form a left-hand linear set. If

$$u_1 = (1, 0, 0, ..., 0),$$
$$u_2 = (0, 1, 0, ..., 0),$$
$$\cdot \qquad \cdot \qquad \cdot$$
$$u_n = (0, 0, 0, ..., 1),$$

then $u_1, ..., u_n$ are linearly independent, and any n-tuple $u = (a_1, ..., a_n)$ is given by the equation

$$u = a_1 u_1 + ... + a_n u_n.$$

Hence the set of n-tuples forms a linear set of finite dimension n, for which $u_1, ..., u_n$ are a minimal basis.

The elements of this linear set are usually called *left-hand vectors*, or *left-hand n-vectors* when we wish to emphasise the dimension of the set. We say that the set of vectors forms a *left-hand vector manifold*. In the same way we can define *right-hand vectors*, and, when the ground-field K is commutative, simply *vectors*.

THEOREM VII. *Any left-hand linear set* $L(u_1, ..., u_n)$ *of finite dimension n is isomorphic with the set of left-hand n-vectors.*

Since the linear set is of dimension n, $u_1, ..., u_n$ are linearly independent. Hence [Th. II] any element u of the set can be written in a unique way as

$$u = a_1 u_1 + ... + a_n u_n. \qquad (3)$$

There corresponds to u, therefore, the unique vector

$$(a_1, ..., a_n).$$

Conversely, the n-vector above determines the unique element of the linear set given by (3). The proof that this one-to-one correspondence is an isomorphism is trivial.

It will be noted that the correspondence between the linear set and the set of n-vectors depends on the choice of a minimal basis in the linear set.

In the remainder of this chapter, and in the applications to be made later, we shall have to consider simultaneously the properties of a finite number of subsets, each of finite dimension, belonging to some linear set L. Now, if we choose a minimal basis for each of these subsets, we have an aggregate which consists of a finite number of elements of L. These elements define a subset L' of L, of finite dimension, which contains each of the given subsets. All our operations will take place in L'. We may always assume, therefore, that we are dealing with a linear set L' of finite dimension. By Th. VII, L' is isomorphic with a vector manifold. For this reason we shall usually speak of the elements of L' as vectors, and in this sense the discussion in the following paragraphs is related to vectors. We shall not state the dimension of the manifold of vectors explicitly, since our results will not depend on it; but on occasion it may be necessary to assume that the dimension is 'sufficiently high'.

2. Matrices. A matrix of p rows and q columns over a field K (called, for brevity, a $p \times q$ matrix) is an array

$$A = \begin{pmatrix} a_{11} & a_{12} & . & a_{1q} \\ a_{21} & a_{22} & . & a_{2q} \\ . & . & . & . \\ a_{p1} & a_{p2} & . & a_{pq} \end{pmatrix} = (a_{rs})$$

of pq elements of K, arranged in rectangular form. In §2 of Chapter I we met, by way of example, the special case in which K is the field of complex numbers, and $p = q$.

The theory of matrices is closely related to the theory of vectors, and we shall use the results of the preceding section to develop properties of matrices. The connection with vectors is established in this way. We consider in some vector manifold of finite but sufficiently high dimension, which need not be specified, a set of q left-hand vectors $u_1, ..., u_q$. By means of the matrix A we can determine from these q vectors p vectors $v_1, ..., v_p$ where

$$v_i = a_{i1}u_1 + ... + a_{iq}u_q \quad (i = 1, ..., p). \tag{1}$$

Then $$L(v_1, ..., v_p) \subseteq L(u_1, ..., u_q). \tag{2}$$

The individual vectors v_i are uniquely determined from the vectors u_i by means of the matrix A. The set $v_1, ..., v_p$ is called the *transform* of the set $u_1, ..., u_q$ by A. We notice, on the other hand, that if we are given condition (2) the matrix A is uniquely determined if and only if $u_1, ..., u_q$ are linearly independent. This is an immediate consequence of §1, Th. II.

Sets of equations such as (1) will occur very often in this book, and it is convenient to have an abbreviated notation for them. If we generalise the notion of a matrix so that the elements may be vectors instead of elements of K, and let U, V be respectively the $q \times 1$ and $p \times 1$ matrices

$$U = \begin{pmatrix} u_1 \\ \cdot \\ u_q \end{pmatrix}, \qquad V = \begin{pmatrix} v_1 \\ \cdot \\ v_p \end{pmatrix},$$

we write (1) in the form

$$V = AU. \tag{3}$$

We shall see later that in writing AU for the $p \times 1$ matrix

$$\begin{pmatrix} a_{11}u_1 + \ldots + a_{1q}u_q \\ \cdot \qquad \ldots \\ a_{p1}u_1 + \ldots + a_{pq}u_q \end{pmatrix}$$

we are using a special case of the law of multiplication of matrices. Finally, in writing a $q \times 1$ matrix, such as U, in full, it is sometimes typographically convenient to write

$$U = [u_1, \ldots, u_q],$$

the square brackets indicating that the elements enclosed should be read as a matrix of one column.

Now let B be any other $p \times q$ matrix over K, and use it to define p vectors $w_1, \ldots, w_p$, where

$$[w_1, \ldots, w_p] = BU.$$

Then

$$v_i + w_i = (a_{i1} + b_{i1})u_1 + \ldots + (a_{iq} + b_{iq})u_q \quad (i = 1, \ldots, p).$$

These equations can be abbreviated to the equation

$$V + W = (A + B)U,$$

if the sum of two $p \times q$ matrices is defined by the equation

$$\begin{pmatrix} a_{11} & a_{12} & \cdot & a_{1q} \\ a_{21} & a_{22} & \cdot & a_{2q} \\ \cdot & \cdot & & \cdot \\ a_{p1} & a_{p2} & \cdot & a_{pq} \end{pmatrix} + \begin{pmatrix} b_{11} & b_{12} & \cdot & b_{1q} \\ b_{21} & b_{22} & \cdot & b_{2q} \\ \cdot & \cdot & & \cdot \\ b_{p1} & b_{p2} & \cdot & b_{pq} \end{pmatrix}$$

$$= \begin{pmatrix} a_{11}+b_{11} & a_{12}+b_{12} & \cdot & a_{1q}+b_{1q} \\ a_{21}+b_{21} & a_{22}+b_{22} & \cdot & a_{2q}+b_{2q} \\ \cdot & \cdot & & \cdot \\ a_{p1}+b_{p1} & a_{p2}+b_{p2} & \cdot & a_{pq}+b_{pq} \end{pmatrix}.$$

With this definition of addition for $p \times q$ matrices, we see that $p \times q$ matrices over K form an additive group. The zero of the group which, without risk of confusion, may be denoted by 0, is the zero $p \times q$ matrix, that is, the $p \times q$ matrix whose elements are all zero.

Now let A be a $p \times q$ matrix over K, and let B be a $q \times r$ matrix over K. Let $u_1, ..., u_r$ be r vectors and $v_1, ..., v_q$ the vectors defined by the equation

$$V = BU,$$

where now $U = [u_1, ..., u_r]$ and $V = [v_1, ..., v_q]$.

Similarly, consider the set of vectors

$$W = [w_1, ..., w_p]$$

defined by the equation

$$W = AV.$$

Then $L(w_1, ..., w_p) \subseteq L(v_1, ..., v_q) \subseteq L(u_1, ..., u_r),$

and hence there must be a $p \times r$ matrix C such that

$$W = CU.$$

As in § 1, Th. III, we may take

$$C = (c_{ij}),$$

where $c_{ij} = \sum_{k=1}^{q} a_{ik} b_{kj} \quad (i = 1, ..., p; j = 1, ..., r).$ (4)

If we formally eliminate V from the equations

$$W = AV, \quad V = BU$$

by writing $W = A(BU) = ABU,$

this suggests that we define the *product* AB of A and B to be the $p \times r$ matrix C, whose elements are given by means of (4). We see that the product of a $p \times q$ matrix and an $r \times s$ matrix is only defined when $q = r$, and that the result is a $p \times s$ matrix. If AB and BA are both defined they are not necessarily equal.

We note here that AB is said to be obtained from A by *post-multiplication* by B, and that AB is obtained from B by *pre-multiplication* by A.

Matrices do not form a ring, since the sum of two matrices is only defined when each is a $p \times q$ matrix, and the product is only defined when the number of columns in the first matrix is equal to the number of rows in the second matrix. If we restrict ourselves to square $n \times n$ matrices we do obtain a ring, as we shall see in the next section; but certain associative, distributive and commutative properties also hold for all rectangular matrices.

Let A, A_1, A_2 denote $p \times q$ matrices, let B, B_1, B_2 denote $q \times r$ matrices, and let C denote an $r \times s$ matrix. If

$$BC = D, \quad AD = E,$$

then
$$d_{ij} = \sum_{t=1}^{r} b_{it} c_{tj} \quad (i = 1, \ldots, q; j = 1, \ldots, s),$$

and therefore
$$e_{ij} = \sum_{u=1}^{q} a_{iu} d_{uj} \quad (i = 1, \ldots, p; j = 1, \ldots, s)$$

$$= \sum_{u=1}^{q} \sum_{t=1}^{r} a_{iu} b_{ut} c_{tj}$$

$$= \sum_{t=1}^{r} f_{it} c_{tj},$$

where $F = (f_{ij}) = AB$. Hence

$$A(BC) = (AB)C,$$

and the product can be written as ABC without ambiguity. This is *the associative law for the multiplication of matrices*.

By direct calculation we may easily prove that

$$A(B_1 + B_2) = AB_1 + AB_2,$$

and
$$(A_1 + A_2)B = A_1 B + A_2 B.$$

These are *the distributive laws for matrices*.

If A is a $p \times q$ matrix, and $i_1, \ldots, i_{p'}, j_1, \ldots, j_{q'}$ are any integers satisfying the relations

$$1 \leqslant i_1 < i_2 \ldots < i_{p'} \leqslant p,$$

$$1 \leqslant j_1 < j_2 \ldots < j_{q'} \leqslant q,$$

we can obtain from A a new matrix of type $p' \times q'$ by striking out all the elements which do not lie in the

$$i_1 \text{th}, i_2 \text{th}, \ldots, \quad \text{or} \quad i_{p'} \text{th rows},$$

and in the $j_1 \text{th}, j_2 \text{th}, \ldots, \quad \text{or} \quad j_{q'} \text{th columns}.$

The matrix we obtain is called a *submatrix* of A.

Now let $p_1, ..., p_s, q_1, ..., q_t$ be $s + t$ positive integers such that

$$\sum_1^s p_i = p, \quad \sum_1^t q_i = q.$$

Let the submatrix of A whose elements are in the

$$\left(\sum_{k=1}^{i-1} p_k + 1\right)\text{th}, \quad \left(\sum_{k=1}^{i-1} p_k + 2\right)\text{th}, \quad ..., \quad \left(\sum_{k=1}^{i} p_k\right)\text{th} \quad \text{rows},$$

and the $\left(\sum_{k=1}^{j-1} q_k + 1\right)\text{th}, \quad \left(\sum_{k=1}^{j-1} q_k + 2\right)\text{th}, \quad ..., \quad \left(\sum_{k=1}^{j} q_k\right)\text{th}$ columns

be denoted by A_{ij}. The submatrix A_{ij} is a $p_i \times q_j$ matrix, and in an obvious notation we can write

$$A = \begin{pmatrix} A_{11} & . & A_{1t} \\ . & . & . \\ A_{s1} & . & A_{st} \end{pmatrix}.$$

The matrix A may then be described as divided into *blocks*, corresponding to the numbers $p_1, ..., p_s, q_1, ..., q_t$.

If B is a $q \times r$ matrix, let $r_1, ..., r_u$ be a set of positive integers such that $\sum_1^u r_i = r$. We may then divide B into blocks corresponding to the numbers $q_1, ..., q_t; r_1, ..., r_u$, and write

$$B = \begin{pmatrix} B_{11} & . & B_{1u} \\ . & . & . \\ B_{t1} & . & B_{tu} \end{pmatrix}.$$

Now, A_{ik} is a $p_i \times q_k$ matrix, and B_{kj} is a $q_k \times r_j$ matrix. Hence $A_{ik} B_{kj}$ is defined, and is a $p_i \times r_j$ matrix. We can therefore define a $p_i \times r_j$ matrix C_{ij}, given by the equation

$$C_{ij} = \sum_{k=1}^{t} A_{ik} B_{kj}. \tag{5}$$

Consider the element in the lth row and mth column of C_{ij}. It is

$$\sum_{n=1}^{q} a_{hn} b_{nk},$$

where $\qquad h = \sum_{a=1}^{i-1} p_a + l, \quad k = \sum_{a=1}^{j-1} r_a + m.$

Thus

$$\begin{pmatrix} C_{11} & . & C_{1u} \\ . & . & . \\ C_{s1} & . & C_{su} \end{pmatrix}$$

is simply the division of $C = AB$ into blocks corresponding to the numbers $p_1, ..., p_s, r_1, ..., r_u$. We may therefore regard A and B as $s \times t$ and $t \times u$ matrices whose elements are matrices, and their product is defined by (5). This is a definition similar to that given in (4). But it must be remembered that (5) is only possible when the submatrices of A and of B are chosen in the way we have indicated.

Similar, but simpler, reasoning shows that if A and B are two $p \times q$ matrices divided into blocks corresponding to the *same* set of numbers, thus

$$A = \begin{pmatrix} A_{11} & . & A_{1t} \\ . & . & . \\ A_{s1} & . & A_{st} \end{pmatrix}, \quad B = \begin{pmatrix} B_{11} & . & B_{1t} \\ . & . & . \\ B_{s1} & . & B_{st} \end{pmatrix},$$

then

$$A + B = \begin{pmatrix} A_{11} + B_{11} & . & A_{1t} + B_{1t} \\ . & . & . \\ A_{s1} + B_{s1} & . & A_{st} + B_{st} \end{pmatrix}.$$

The device of considering matrices divided into blocks is often used. The operations discussed above are the only ones which will be employed, and the matrices concerned will always be matrices with elements in a field.

3. Square matrices. A matrix in which the number of rows is equal to the number of columns is said to be a square matrix. If we consider only $n \times n$ matrices, we see that two such matrices can always be added or multiplied, and the result is an $n \times n$ matrix. The properties demonstrated in § 2 enable us to say that $n \times n$ *matrices over K form a ring.* If we refer to I, § 2, Example V we see that the ring is non-commutative, and has divisors of zero. But it has unity, namely, the unit matrix

$$I_n = \begin{pmatrix} 1 & 0 & . & 0 \\ 0 & 1 & . & 0 \\ . & . & . & . \\ 0 & 0 & . & 1 \end{pmatrix} = (\delta_{ij}),$$

where $\delta_{ij} = 0 \quad (i \neq j)$,

and $\delta_{ii} = 1 \quad (i = 1, ..., n)$.

The symbol δ_{ij} defined in this way is frequently used in algebra. It is called the *Kronecker delta.*

In accordance with the terminology of I, § 3, an $n \times n$ matrix A is said to be *regular* if it has an inverse A^{-1} such that

$$AA^{-1} = A^{-1}A = I_n.$$

From the theory of rings developed in the previous chapter, we know that a matrix cannot have two distinct inverses. We also see that if both A and B are regular, having inverses A^{-1}, B^{-1} respectively, then AB is regular, with inverse $B^{-1}A^{-1}$. For

$$(AB)(B^{-1}A^{-1}) = ABB^{-1}A^{-1} = AI_nA^{-1} = AA^{-1} = I_n,$$

by the associative law. Similarly,

$$(B^{-1}A^{-1})(AB) = I_n.$$

We now obtain two theorems giving necessary and sufficient conditions for an $n \times n$ matrix A to be regular.

THEOREM I. *An $n \times n$ matrix is regular if and only if it transforms a set of n linearly independent left-hand vectors into a set of n linearly independent vectors.*

(1)   Let $u_1, \ldots, u_n$ be a set of n linearly independent vectors. Suppose that the n vectors

$$v_i = a_{i1}u_1 + \ldots + a_{in}u_n \quad (i = 1, \ldots, n)$$

are linearly independent. By § 1, Th. V, Cor. (1)

$$L(v_1, \ldots, v_n) = L(u_1, \ldots, u_n).$$

Hence

$$u_i = b_{i1}v_1 + \ldots + b_{in}v_n \quad (i = 1, \ldots, n),$$

where b_{ij} is in K. Then

$$v_i = \sum_{j=1}^{n} a_{ij}b_{j1}v_1 + \ldots + \sum_{j=1}^{n} a_{ij}b_{jn}v_n,$$

and

$$u_i = \sum_{j=1}^{n} b_{ij}a_{j1}u_1 + \ldots + \sum_{j=1}^{n} b_{ij}a_{jn}u_n.$$

Since both the sets $u_1, \ldots, u_n$ and $v_1, \ldots, v_n$ are sets of linearly independent vectors, each of the two equations above must be an identity. Therefore

$$\sum_{j=1}^{n} a_{ij}b_{jk} = \delta_{ik}, \quad \text{and} \quad \sum_{j=1}^{n} b_{ij}a_{jk} = \delta_{ik}.$$

In matrix notation this is simply

$$AB = I_n = BA.$$

Therefore $A = (a_{ij})$ has an inverse B, and is regular.

(2)   Now suppose that A is regular, and B is its inverse. Let $u_1, ..., u_n$ be a set of independent vectors, and let

$$v_i = a_{i1}u_1 + ... + a_{in}u_n \quad (i = 1, ..., n);$$

then $\qquad\qquad L(v_1, ..., v_n) \subseteq L(u_1, ..., u_n).$

Now $\qquad\qquad b_{i1}v_1 + ... + b_{in}v_n$

$$= \sum_{j=1}^{n} b_{ij}a_{j1}u_1 + ... + \sum_{j=1}^{n} b_{ij}a_{jn}u_n$$

$$= \delta_{i1}u_1 + ... + \delta_{in}u_n$$

$$= u_i.$$

Hence $\qquad\qquad L(u_1, ..., u_n) \subseteq L(v_1, ..., v_n),$

and therefore $\qquad L(u_1, ..., u_n) = L(v_1, ..., v_n).$

Since $u_1, ..., u_n$ are linearly independent, it follows from § 1, Th. VI, Cor. 1, that $v_1, ..., v_n$ are linearly independent. This completes the proof of the theorem.

If C is any $p \times q$ matrix $\quad C = (c_{ij}),$

we may regard the p rows of C

$$(c_{i1}, ..., c_{iq})$$

as p left-hand q-vectors. We speak of these as *the q-vectors given by the rows of C*, and we shall always regard them as *left-hand* vectors. Our second criterion for a regular matrix is given by

THEOREM II. *An $n \times n$ matrix A is regular if and only if the n-vectors given by the rows are linearly independent.*

As in the previous theorem we denote n linearly independent vectors by $u_1, ..., u_n$, and the transforms of these by A by $v_1, ..., v_n$.

(1)   Suppose that the n-vectors $(a_{i1}, ..., a_{in})$ are linearly independent. Then if

$$\sum_{i=1}^{n} b_i a_{ij} = 0 \quad (j = 1, ..., n),$$

we must have $\qquad b_i = 0 \quad (i = 1, ..., n).$

Now if $v_1, ..., v_n$ satisfy a relation

$$b_1 v_1 + ... + b_n v_n = 0 \quad (b_i \text{ in } K),$$

this implies that

$$\sum_{i=1}^{n} b_i a_{i1} u_1 + ... + \sum_{i=1}^{n} b_i a_{in} u_n = 0.$$

Since $u_1, \ldots, u_n$ are linearly independent,

$$\sum_{i=1}^{n} b_i a_{ij} = 0 \quad (j = 1, \ldots, n),$$

and therefore, by the above,

$$b_i = 0 \quad (i = 1, \ldots, n).$$

Therefore $v_1, \ldots, v_n$ are linearly independent, and, by Th. I, A is regular.

(2) Suppose that A is regular. Then $v_1, \ldots, v_n$ are linearly independent. Now, if the n-vectors $(a_{i1}, \ldots, a_{in})$ are linearly dependent, there exist elements $b_1, \ldots, b_n$ of K, not all zero, such that

$$\sum_{i=1}^{n} b_i a_{ij} = 0 \quad (j = 1, \ldots, n).$$

Then

$$b_1 v_1 + \ldots + b_n v_n$$

$$= \sum_{i=1}^{n} b_i a_{i1} u_1 + \ldots + \sum_{i=1}^{n} b_i a_{in} u_n$$

$$= 0.$$

This implies the linear dependence of $v_1, \ldots, v_n$. From this contradiction we deduce that the n-vectors given by the rows of A are linearly independent.

The methods used above also give us

THEOREM III. *If A is a $p \times n$ matrix, and the left-hand n-vectors determined by the rows of A determine a vector manifold of dimension r, the manifold $L(v_1, \ldots, v_p)$, where*

$$v_i = a_{i1} u_1 + \ldots + a_{in} u_n$$

is also of dimension r, provided that $u_1, \ldots, u_n$ are linearly independent.

If the vectors defined by the rows of A be

$$a_i = (a_{i1}, \ldots, a_{in}) \quad (i = 1, \ldots, p),$$

then $a_{i_1}, \ldots, a_{i_s}$, the vectors of any subset of the vectors $a_1, \ldots, a_p$ are linearly dependent or independent according as the corresponding vectors $v_{i_1}, \ldots, v_{i_s}$ are linearly dependent or independent, and conversely. For

$$\sum_{i_1, \ldots, i_s} b_i v_i = \sum_{i_1, \ldots, i_s} \sum_{j=1}^{n} (b_i a_{ij}) u_j = 0$$

if and only if

$$\sum_{i_1, \ldots, i_s} b_i a_{ij} = 0 \quad (j = 1, \ldots, n),$$

since $u_1, \ldots, u_n$ are linearly independent.

It follows that if the maximum number of independent vectors in the set $a_1, \ldots, a_p$ is r, the maximum number of independent vectors in the set $v_1, \ldots, v_p$ is also r. This proves the theorem.

THEOREM IV. *If A is a $p \times n$ matrix, and the p left-hand vectors determined by the rows of A are linearly independent, then $p \leqslant n$, and there exists an $(n-p) \times n$ matrix B such that the $n \times n$ matrix*

$$\begin{pmatrix} A \\ B \end{pmatrix}$$

is regular.

We have seen that a minimal basis for the manifold of n-vectors is given by the n vectors

$$(\delta_{i1}, \ldots, \delta_{in}) \quad (i = 1, \ldots, n).$$

It follows that the maximum number of linearly independent n-vectors is n. Therefore $p \leqslant n$. Now let $u_1, \ldots, u_n$ be n linearly independent vectors and let

$$v_i = a_{i1}u_1 + \ldots + a_{in}u_n \quad (i = 1, \ldots, p).$$

Then, as in the above theorem, $v_1, \ldots, v_p$ are linearly independent. Applying the Exchange Theorem [§ 1, Th. V], we deduce that there is a derangement $i_1, \ldots, i_n$ of the numbers $1, \ldots, n$ such that if

$$v_j = u_{i_j} \quad (j = p+1, \ldots, n),$$

then $v_1, \ldots, v_n$ form a basis for $L(u_1, \ldots, u_n)$. This basis is necessarily minimal. Hence, by Th. I,

$$v_i = c_{i1}u_1 + \ldots + c_{in}u_n \quad (i = 1, \ldots, n),$$

where $C = (c_{ij})$ is regular. But

$$C = \begin{pmatrix} A \\ B \end{pmatrix},$$

where B is the $(n-p) \times n$ matrix whose hth row is

$$(\delta_{i_{p+h}1}, \ldots, \delta_{i_{p+h}n}).$$

This establishes the theorem.

4. Transformations of a matrix. Now let A be a $p \times q$ matrix. If $u_1, \ldots, u_q$ are q linearly independent vectors, A transforms them into p vectors, $v_1, \ldots, v_p$, say, and

$$L(v_1, \ldots, v_p) \subseteq L(u_1, \ldots, u_q).$$

If we are concerned with the vector manifolds $L(v_1, \ldots, v_p)$ and

$L(u_1, ..., u_q)$, we are at liberty to change the bases in these manifolds without altering the manifolds themselves. Since $u_1, ..., u_q$ are assumed to be linearly independent, a new set of vectors $u_1^*, ..., u_q^*$ forms a minimal basis for $L(u_1, ..., u_q)$ if and only if

$$U = QU^*, \tag{1}$$

where, in the notation of §1, $U = [u_1, ..., u_q]$, $U^* = [u_1^*, ..., u_q^*]$, and Q is a regular $q \times q$ matrix [§ 3, Th. I].

If $v_1, ..., v_p$ are linearly independent, a similar argument applies to $L(v_1, ..., v_p)$. The set $v_1^*, ..., v_p^*$ is then a minimal basis for $L(v_1, ..., v_p)$ if and only if

$$V^* = PV, \tag{2}$$

where P is a regular $p \times p$ matrix. This result requires modification if $v_1, ..., v_p$ are *not* linearly independent. But in the case we are considering P is a regular $p \times p$ matrix, and if

$$V^* = PV, \quad \text{then} \quad V = P^{-1}V^*,$$

and therefore

$$L(v_1^*, ..., v_p^*) \subseteq L(v_1, ..., v_p) \subseteq L(v_1^*, ..., v_p^*),$$

so that

$$L(v_1^*, ..., v_p^*) = L(v_1, ..., v_p).$$

Hence, in order that the equation (2) should represent a change of basis in $L(v_1, ..., v_p)$, it is a *sufficient* condition that P should be regular. Simple examples show that it is not a necessary condition when $v_1, ..., v_p$ are not linearly independent.

Equations such as (1) or (2), where Q and P are regular matrices, are said to define *allowable transformations* of the bases $u_1, ..., u_q$ and $v_1, ..., v_p$ of $L(u_1, ..., u_q)$ and $L(v_1, ..., v_p)$ respectively. These allowable transformations replace the matrix equation

$$V = AU$$

(which connects $v_1, ..., v_p$ with $u_1, ..., u_q$) by

$$V^* = A^*U^*,$$

where

$$A^* = PAQ.$$

We note that

(i) $\qquad A = I_p A I_q;$

(ii) if $\qquad A^* = PAQ \quad (P \text{ and } Q \text{ regular}),$

then $\qquad A = P^{-1}A^*Q^{-1};$

(iii) if $\qquad A^* = PAQ \quad$ and $\quad A^{**} = P^*A^*Q^*,$

then $\qquad A^{**} = (P^*P)A(QQ^*).$

Thus the relation between A and A^* is reflexive, symmetric and transitive. It is therefore an equivalence relation [I, §2]. Our object in this section is to determine a set of *canonical forms* for $p \times q$ matrices. In other words, we shall obtain a set of $p \times q$ matrices with the properties

(1)   No two matrices of the set are equivalent, in the above sense.

(2)   There is a matrix of the set equivalent to *any* $p \times q$ matrix.

We first establish the existence of a numerical character which is invariant under our equivalence relation.

Let r_A denote the maximum number of q-vectors given by the rows of A which are linearly independent. If these q-vectors are all zero, $r_A = 0$. By §3, Th. III, we see that r_A is also the maximum number of linearly independent vectors of V. That is, the dimension of $L(v_1, ..., v_p)$ is r_A. But since

$$L(v_1, ..., v_p) = L(v_1^*, ..., v_p^*),$$

it follows that r_A is also the number of linearly independent vectors in the set $v_1^*, ..., v_p^*$. Therefore $r_A = r_{A^*}$. We notice that the equations

$$V^* = PAU, \quad V^* = PAQU^*$$

determine the same vectors of

$$L(u_1, ..., u_q) = L(u_1^*, ..., u_q^*).$$

Therefore the number of independent rows of PA is equal to the number of independent rows of $A^* = PAQ$, and both these are equal to the number of independent vectors in the set $v_1^*, ..., v_p^*$, which is r_A. Hence, calling the number r_A the *row-rank* of A, we have

THEOREM I. *The row-rank of a matrix A is equal to the row-rank of PAQ, where P and Q are regular matrices.*

This includes the cases in which $Q = I_q$, $P = I_p$, when we have, respectively, the matrices PA, and AQ. *Pre-multiplication or post-multiplication of A by a regular matrix does not alter its row-rank.*

Now, the replacement of the vectors $v_1, ..., v_p$ by the same vectors $v_{i_1}, ..., v_{i_p}$ in a different order is a transformation

$$V_1 = P_1 V,$$

where P_1 is a regular matrix. For, since every permutation of the numbers $1, ..., p$ has an inverse permutation, P_1 must have an inverse.

We choose P_1 so that the first r_A permuted vectors are linearly independent. Let us denote the permuted vectors by

$$v_{1,j} \quad (j = 1, ..., p).$$

Then since the vectors

$$v_{1,j} \quad (j = r_A + 1, ..., p)$$

are linearly dependent on the first r_A, we have the equations

$$v_{1,j} = \sum_{k=1}^{r_A} b_{jk} v_{1,k} \quad (j = r_A + 1, ..., p).$$

Let

$$B = \begin{pmatrix} b_{r_A+1\,1} & \cdot & b_{r_A+1\,r_A} \\ \cdot & \cdot & \cdot \\ b_{p\,1} & \cdot & b_{p\,r_A} \end{pmatrix},$$

and let

$$P_2 = \begin{pmatrix} I_{r_A} & 0 \\ -B & I_{p-r_A} \end{pmatrix}.$$

Since

$$\begin{pmatrix} I_{r_A} & 0 \\ -B & I_{p-r_A} \end{pmatrix}\begin{pmatrix} I_{r_A} & 0 \\ B & I_{p-r_A} \end{pmatrix} = I_p = \begin{pmatrix} I_{r_A} & 0 \\ B & I_{p-r_A} \end{pmatrix}\begin{pmatrix} I_{r_A} & 0 \\ -B & I_{p-r_A} \end{pmatrix},$$

the matrix P_2 is regular. If we now put

$$V_2 = P_2 V_1,$$

calling the transformed vectors $v_{2,1}, ..., v_{2,p}$, then of these, the

$$v_{2,i} \quad (i = 1, ..., r_A)$$

are linearly independent, but the rest are zero; that is,

$$v_{2,j} = 0 \quad (j = r_A + 1, ..., p).$$

Since

$$V_2 = P_2 V_1 = P_2 P_1 V = P_2 P_1 A U$$
$$= A_2 U,$$

say, and $u_1, ..., u_q$ are linearly independent, the last $p - r_A$ rows of A_2 must be zero. We therefore write

$$A_2 = \begin{pmatrix} C \\ 0 \end{pmatrix},$$

where C is a $r_A \times q$ matrix.

By the Exchange Theorem we can replace r_A of the vectors $u_1, ..., u_q$ by the linearly independent vectors $v_{2,1}, ..., v_{2,r_A}$, and thus obtain a new basis for $L(u_1, ..., u_q)$. Before doing this we make a transformation

$$U = Q_1 U_1$$

which merely permutes the vectors $u_1, ..., u_q$, so that those to be replaced are the first r_A vectors. The exchange is then represented by another transformation

$$U_1 = Q_2 U_2,$$

where Q_2 is regular. Hence, finally, we have

$$V_2 = A_2 U = A_2 Q_1 Q_2 U_2$$
$$= \begin{pmatrix} CQ_1 Q_2 \\ 0 \end{pmatrix} U_2;$$

that is,

$$V_2 = \begin{pmatrix} D \\ 0 \end{pmatrix} U_2,$$

say, where $D = (d_{ij}) = CQ_1 Q_2$. Now consider the first r_A of the p equations given by this last matrix equation. Since

$$v_{2,i} = u_{2,i} \quad (i = 1, ..., r_A),$$

we have

$$u_{2,i} = \sum_{j=1}^{q} d_{ij} u_{2,j} \quad (i = 1, ..., r_A).$$

Since $u_{2,1}, ..., u_{2,q}$ are linearly independent, we must have

$$d_{ij} = \delta_{ij} \quad (i = 1, ..., r_A).$$

Hence

$$\begin{pmatrix} D \\ 0 \end{pmatrix} = \begin{pmatrix} I_{r_A} & 0 \\ 0 & 0 \end{pmatrix}.$$

That is,

$$P_2 P_1 A Q_1 Q_2 = \begin{pmatrix} I_{r_A} & 0 \\ 0 & 0 \end{pmatrix}.$$

Since P_1, P_2, Q_1, Q_2 are regular matrices,

$$P = P_2 P_1 \quad \text{and} \quad Q = Q_1 Q_2$$

are regular. We have therefore proved

THEOREM II. *If A is a $p \times q$ matrix of row-rank r_A, A is equivalent to the matrix*

$$PAQ = \begin{pmatrix} I_{r_A} & 0 \\ 0 & 0 \end{pmatrix}.$$

It is sometimes convenient to effect the transformation (or reduction) of A to this canonical form by a series of elementary steps, or *elementary transformations*. We define these as the following transformations of the basis $w_1, ..., w_r$ (not assumed to be minimal) of a vector manifold $L(w_1, ..., w_r)$:

(i) the interchange of two elements w_i, w_j;

(ii) the multiplication of an element w_i of the basis by a non-zero element of K;

(iii) the addition to any element of the basis of any vector linearly dependent on the remaining $r-1$ elements of the basis. Each of these transformations of the basis is called an *elementary transformation*, and is represented by the equation

$$W^* = RW.$$

The matrix R is regular, for the inverse of an elementary transformation is easily constructed, and is itself an elementary transformation. It follows that the result of any number of elementary changes of basis replaces the basis by an equivalent basis, and is reversible.

We now consider the equation

$$V = AU,$$

that is,

$$v_i = \sum_{j=1}^{q} a_{ij} u_j \quad (i = 1, ..., p).$$

Unless $r_A = 0$, there is at least one element of A, say a_{ij}, which is not zero. By performing an elementary change of basis of type (i) on the bases $u_1, ..., u_q$ and $v_1, ..., v_p$, we obtain new bases, which we denote by

$$u_{1,1}, ..., u_{1,q} \quad \text{and} \quad v_{1,1}, ..., v_{1,p},$$

and a relation

$$V_1 = A_1 U_1 \quad (A_1 = (a_{1,ij})),$$

where $a_{1,11} = a_{ij} \neq 0$. By a transformation of type (ii) applied to $u_{1,1}$ we may arrange that $a_{1,11} = 1$. We then perform the transformation of type (iii) on $u_{11}, ..., u_{1q}$ which is given by the equations

$$u_{2,1} = u_{1,1} + \sum_{i=2}^{q} a_{1,1i} u_{1,i},$$

$$u_{2,j} = u_{1,j} \quad (j = 2, ..., q),$$

so that we now have the matrix equation

$$V_1 = A_2 U_2,$$

where
$$A_2 = \begin{pmatrix} I_1 & 0 \\ C & B \end{pmatrix},$$
and C is a $(p-1) \times 1$ matrix,
$$C = (c_{ij}) \quad (i = 2, \ldots, p, \, j = 1).$$

Now perform the transformation
$$v_{2,1} = v_{1,1},$$
$$v_{2,i} = v_{1,i} - c_{i1} v_{1,1} \quad (i = 2, \ldots, p),$$

on $v_{1,1}, \ldots, v_{1,p}$. This is a series of transformations of type (iii). We obtain the equation
$$V_2 = A_3 U_2,$$
where
$$A_3 = \begin{pmatrix} I_1 & 0 \\ 0 & B \end{pmatrix}.$$

Since the number of independent rows of A_3 is still r_A, it follows at once that B is of row-rank $r_A - 1$.

We now show by induction that the matrix A can be reduced to canonical form by elementary transformations on the bases of $L(v_1, \ldots, v_p)$ and $L(u_1, \ldots, u_q)$. There is nothing to prove when $r_A = 0$, since A must then be a zero matrix. Let us suppose that the theorem is true for any matrix whose row-rank is less than r_A. By what has been proved above we can reduce A, by elementary transformations, to the form
$$\begin{pmatrix} I_1 & 0 \\ 0 & B \end{pmatrix},$$

where B is of rank $r_A - 1$. By the induction hypothesis we can reduce B to canonical form by elementary transformations applied to $v_{2,2}, \ldots, v_{2,p}$ and $u_{2,2}, \ldots, u_{2,q}$. But these transformations can also be regarded as elementary transformations applied to $v_{2,1}, v_{2,2}, \ldots, v_{2,p}$ and $u_{2,1}, u_{2,2}, \ldots, u_{2,q}$. This proves the theorem.

As a corollary we have

THEOREM III. *Any allowable transformation*
$$U^* = PU$$

of the basis of a vector manifold $L(u_1, \ldots, u_q)$ *of dimension* q *is the result of a finite succession of elementary transformations.*

For we can apply the result proved above to the set of vectors $u_1^*, \ldots, u_q^*$ and to the set $u_1, \ldots, u_q$, and reduce the matrix P to canonical form. Suppose that a succession of elementary transformations, corresponding to matrices $Q_1, \ldots, Q_a$, on the vectors

$u_1^*, \ldots, u_q^*$, together with a set of elementary transformations, corresponding to matrices $R_1, \ldots, R_b$, on the vectors $u_1, \ldots, u_q$, transforms the first set of vectors into $v_1^*, \ldots, v_q^*$, and the second set into $v_1, \ldots, v_q$. Then if the matrix expressing the relation between the v_i^* and the v_j is in canonical form, we have the equations

$$v_i^* = v_i \quad (i = 1, \ldots, r_P),$$

But since P is regular, $r_P = q$. Therefore the transform of

$$U^* = PU$$

is

$$V^* = I_q V.$$

But

$$V^* = Q_a Q_{a-1} \cdots Q_1 U^*,$$

and

$$V = R_b R_{b-1} \cdots R_1 U.$$

Hence

$$Q_a Q_{a-1} \cdots Q_1 P R_1^{-1} \cdots R_b^{-1} = I_q,$$

that is,

$$P = Q_1^{-1} \cdots Q_a^{-1} R_b \cdots R_1.$$

Since Q_j is the matrix corresponding to an elementary transformation, so is Q_j^{-1}. This proves the theorem.

5. The rank of a matrix.

Until now, our theory of matrices has been based on the consideration of *left-hand* vectors, and in particular we have been led to consider the rows of a $p \times q$ matrix as left-hand q-vectors. We now consider how our results would be affected if we based our investigation on *right-hand* vectors.

The theory of right-hand vectors is immediately deducible from the results of § 1. If $x_1, \ldots, x_p$ are p such vectors, they are said to be linearly independent over K if the equation

$$x_1 a_1 + \ldots + x_p a_p = 0 \quad (a_i \text{ in } K)$$

implies the equations

$$a_i = 0 \quad (i = 1, \ldots, p).$$

Also, if

$$y = x_1 a_1 + \ldots + x_p a_p,$$

y is said to be linearly dependent on $x_1, \ldots, x_p$. We then prove the analogues of § 1, Th. I–VII, noting in Th. VII that a set of right-hand vectors of dimension p is isomorphic with the set of right-hand p-tuples

$$(a_1, \ldots, a_p),$$

in which multiplication on the right is the only kind admitted.

A $p \times q$ matrix A transforms the p right-hand vectors $x_1, ..., x_p$ into the q vectors $y_1, ..., y_q$, where

$$y_j = \sum_{i=1}^{p} x_i a_{ij} \quad (j = 1, ..., q).$$

Proceeding from this equation we can deduce results similar to those obtained in §§ 2–4. The most important one from our point of view is that if $x_1, ..., x_p$ are linearly independent, the number of linearly independent vectors in the set $y_1, ..., y_q$ is the number of linearly independent *columns* of A, *regarded as right-hand vectors*. We call this the *column-rank* of A. Just as in § 4 we show that if A is of column rank s_A, there exist regular matrices P and Q such that

$$PAQ = \begin{pmatrix} I_{s_A} & 0 \\ 0 & 0 \end{pmatrix}.$$

But we saw in § 4 that the row-rank of A is equal to the row-rank of PAQ, which in this case is clearly s_A. Hence we have

THEOREM I. *In any $p \times q$ matrix A the number of linearly independent rows, regarded as left-hand vectors, is equal to the number of linearly independent columns, regarded as right-hand vectors.*

This number we now call the *rank* of A. We recall that by § 3, Th. II, an $n \times n$ matrix is regular if and only if its rank is n.

The rows of A may be considered as *right-hand* vectors, and the columns as *left-hand* vectors if we interchange rows and columns. We define the *transpose* A' of A as the $q \times p$ matrix

$$A' = (a'_{ij}),$$

where $\quad\quad a'_{ij} = a_{ji} \quad (i = 1, ..., q; j = 1, ..., p).$

Clearly, the number of linearly independent rows of A', regarded as left-hand vectors, is equal to the number of linearly independent columns of A, regarded as left-hand vectors. The number of linearly independent columns of A', regarded as right-hand vectors, is equal to the number of linearly independent rows of A, regarded as right-hand vectors. By the theorem above these numbers are equal, and give the rank of A'. The consideration of the case when K is commutative, and left-hand and right-hand vectors are identical, gives us

THEOREM II. *If the ground field K is commutative, the rank of a matrix A is equal to the rank of its transpose A'.*

On the other hand, if K is not commutative, this theorem is not necessarily true. For K contains at least two elements a, b such that

$$ab \neq ba.$$

Neither a nor b is zero. Consider the 2×2 matrix

$$A = \begin{pmatrix} 1 & a \\ b & ab \end{pmatrix}.$$

If

$$p(1, a) + q(b, ab) = 0,$$

then

$$p + qb = 0,$$

and

$$pa + qab = 0.$$

Hence

$$-qba + qab = 0,$$

that is,

$$q(ab - ba) = 0.$$

Since K is a field, and $ab \neq ba$, we deduce that $q = 0$. Therefore

$$p = -qb = 0.$$

Hence the number of independent rows of A is 2, and its rank is 2. On the other hand, the equation

$$(1, a)p + (b, ab)q = 0$$

is satisfied by $p = b, q = -1$, and so the rank of A' is 1.

Our final theorem in this section is often useful:

THEOREM III. *If A is a $p \times q$ matrix of rank r, A contains a submatrix of type $r \times r$ which is of rank r. No submatrix of A is of rank greater than r.*

If A is of rank r it has r linearly independent rows. Every other row of A is linearly dependent on these. If the submatrix defined by the r independent rows be denoted by B, B is an $r \times q$ matrix of rank r. Recalling the proof of § 3, Th. IV, we see that there exists a $(q-r) \times q$ matrix C such that the matrix

$$D = \begin{pmatrix} B \\ C \end{pmatrix}$$

is regular, where the hth row of C is

$$(\delta_{i_{r+h}1}, \ldots, \delta_{i_{r+h}q}),$$

$(i_1, \ldots, i_q)$ being a derangement of $(1, \ldots, q)$. Since D is regular, its rank is q, and hence its columns are linearly independent, regarded as right-hand vectors. In particular, the i_1th, $\ldots, i_r$th columns are linearly independent. These columns contain only zeros in the last $(q-r)$ rows of D. It follows that the columns of the $r \times r$ submatrix E, which consists of the i_1th, ..., i_rth columns of B, are independent. That is, E is of rank r. Hence the first part of the theorem is proved.

If F is a submatrix of rank $s > r$, it contains s independent rows. Let these lie in the j_1th, ..., j_sth rows of A. Since $s > r$, there exist elements b_i of K, not all zero, such that

$$\Sigma b_i a_{ij} = 0 \quad (i = j_1, ..., j_s; \, j = 1, ..., q).$$

But since this summation includes values of j corresponding to the columns of F, it follows that the rows of F assumed to be independent are linearly dependent. From this contradiction we deduce the second part of our theorem.

6.   Homogeneous linear equations.   Let A be a $p \times q$ matrix over the field K. Consider the q-tuples $(x_1, ..., x_q)$ which satisfy the equations

$$a_{i1}x_1 + ... + a_{iq}x_q = 0 \quad (i = 1, ..., p). \tag{1}$$

If $y = (y_1, ..., y_q)$, and $z = (z_1, ..., z_q)$ are two q-tuples satisfying (1), then

$$yb + zc = (y_1 b + z_1 c, ..., y_q b + z_q c)$$

also satisfies (1), for any b and c in K. It follows that the q-tuples $(x_1, ..., x_q)$ which satisfy (1) form a *right-hand* vector manifold. Any vector of this manifold is called a *solution* of the *left-hand linear homogeneous equations* (1), in which $(x_1, ..., x_q)$ is called the *unknown*. We write the equations (1) in matrix notation as

$$Ax = 0, \tag{2}$$

where

$$x = [x_1, ..., x_q].$$

If A is of rank r there exist regular matrices P and Q such that

$$PAQ = \begin{pmatrix} I_r & 0 \\ 0 & 0 \end{pmatrix}.$$

Let $y = [y_1, ..., y_q]$ be a solution of (2), and let

$$z = Q^{-1}y.$$

Then

$$0 = PAy$$
$$= PAQz$$
$$= [z_1, ..., z_r, 0, ..., 0].$$

Hence

$$z_i = 0 \quad (i = 1, ..., r).$$

On the other hand, let $z_{r+1}, ..., z_q$ be any elements in any extension of K, and let
$$z = [0, ..., 0, z_{r+1}, ..., z_q],$$
and let
$$y = Qz.$$
Then
$$Ay = P^{-1}PAQz$$
$$= P^{-1} \begin{pmatrix} I_r & 0 \\ 0 & 0 \end{pmatrix} z$$
$$= 0.$$

Hence we obtain any solution of (2) as follows: let
$$z = [0, ..., 0, z_{r+1}, ..., z_q],$$
where $z_{r+1}, ..., z_q$ are indeterminate over K. Any solution y of (2) is obtained by a suitable specialisation of the indeterminates in Qz.

A basis for the manifold of solutions is obtained by taking
$$z = [0, ..., 0, \delta_{h\,r+1}, ..., \delta_{hq}] \quad (h = r+1, ..., q).$$

Hence the manifold of solutions has dimension $q - r$.

Let us call this manifold, which consists of right-hand vectors, R, and let L denote the manifold of left-hand vectors defined by the rows of the matrix A. If
$$a = (a_1, ..., a_q)$$
is any vector of L, we can write
$$a_i = \sum_{j=1}^{p} p_j a_{ji} \quad (i = 1, ..., q).$$
If y is any vector of R,
$$a_1 y_1 + ... + a_q y_q$$
$$= \sum_{j=1}^{p} p_j a_{j1} y_1 + ... + \sum_{j=1}^{p} p_j a_{jq} y_q$$
$$= \sum_{j=1}^{p} \sum_{i=1}^{q} p_j (a_{ji} y_i) = 0.$$

The two vectors a and y are said to be *apolar*.

The theory of *right-hand* linear homogeneous equations
$$\sum_{i=1}^{q} x_i b_{ij} = 0 \quad (j = 1, ..., s) \tag{3}$$
can be developed as above, and we can prove that if the matrix
$$B = (b_{ij})$$

is of rank t, the solutions form a left-hand vector manifold of dimension $q - t$. In particular, consider the case when the columns of B are right-hand q-vectors forming a basis for the manifold R of solutions of (2). Then

$$t = q - r,$$

and the solutions of (3) form a left-hand vector manifold of dimension

$$q - t = r.$$

But *any* vector of L is then a solution of (3), and it therefore follows that L is the manifold of solutions of (3).

Hence the manifold L and the manifold R are in a dual relationship, each defining the other uniquely.

We conclude this section by using the foregoing results to prove

THEOREM I. *If A is a $p \times q$ matrix of rank r_A, B a $q \times r$ matrix of rank r_B, then $C = AB$ is a $p \times r$ matrix of rank r_C, where*

$$r_A + r_B - q \leqslant r_C \leqslant \min(r_A, r_B).$$

(i) Since B is of rank r_B there exist regular matrices Q (of type $q \times q$) and R (of type $r \times r$) such that

$$B = Q \begin{pmatrix} I_{r_B} & 0 \\ 0 & 0 \end{pmatrix} R. \tag{4}$$

Also, by §4, Th. I,

$$C^* = CR^{-1}, \quad A^* = AQ \tag{5}$$

are of ranks r_C, r_A respectively. We write

$$A^* = (A_1^* \; A_2^*),$$

where A_1^* is a $p \times r_B$ matrix, and A_2^* a $p \times (q - r_B)$ matrix. Now A^* has r_A linearly independent columns, regarded as right-hand vectors. It follows that A_1^* has at least

$$r_A - (q - r_B)$$

linearly independent columns, since any set of r_A columns of A contains at least this number of columns of A_1^*. Hence, the rank of the matrix

$$(A_1^* \; 0)$$

is at least

$$r_A + r_B - q.$$

But
$$(A_1^* \quad 0) = (A_1^* \quad A_2^*) \begin{pmatrix} I_{r_B} & 0 \\ 0 & 0 \end{pmatrix}$$

$$= AQ \begin{pmatrix} I_{r_B} & 0 \\ 0 & 0 \end{pmatrix}$$

$$= ABR^{-1}, \quad \text{from (4)},$$

$$= CR^{-1}$$

$$= C^*, \quad \text{from (5)}.$$

Since C^* is of rank r_C, it follows that

$$r_A + r_B - q \leqslant r_C.$$

(ii) The solutions of the equations
$$Cx = 0, \tag{6}$$

form a right-hand vector manifold R of dimension $r - r_C$. If y is any solution of the equations
$$Bx = 0, \tag{7}$$

we have
$$Cy = ABy = 0.$$

Hence, any solution of (7) is a solution of (6). But the solutions of (7) form a vector manifold S of dimension $r - r_B$. Since

$$S \subseteq R,$$

it follows that
$$r - r_B \leqslant r - r_C;$$

that is
$$r_C \leqslant r_B.$$

If instead of considering equations (6) and (7) we considered the equations
$$xC = 0, \quad \text{and} \quad xA = 0,$$

we should obtain the relation
$$r_C \leqslant r_A.$$

Finally, then
$$r_C \leqslant \min(r_A, r_B),$$
and the proof is completed.

7. **Matrices over a commutative field.** The remainder of this chapter is devoted to the case in which the ground field K is commutative. Most of the results we shall obtain will be independent of the characteristic of the field, but some will be proved only in the case of a field without characteristic. Unless the contrary is stated,

K is assumed to be commutative, and no restriction is imposed on its characteristic.

The rank of a matrix A is now equal to the rank of its transpose A' [§5, Th. II]. Hence, in particular, if A is a regular $n \times n$ matrix, A' is also a regular $n \times n$ matrix. An $n \times n$ matrix of rank less than n is said to be *singular*, and the terms 'non-singular' and 'regular' are synonymous.

We consider how to obtain the transpose of the product AB of a $p \times q$ matrix A and a $q \times r$ matrix B. Let

$$AB = C,$$

where
$$c_{ij} = \sum_{k=1}^{q} a_{ik} b_{kj} \quad (i = 1, ..., p; \, j = 1, ..., r).$$

If C' is the transpose of C,

$$c'_{ij} = c_{ji}$$
$$= \sum_{k=1}^{q} a_{jk} b_{ki}$$
$$= \sum_{k=1}^{q} a'_{kj} b'_{ik}$$
$$= \sum_{k=1}^{q} b'_{ik} a'_{kj},$$

since K is commutative. Hence
$$C' = B'A'.$$

Now let A be a non-singular $n \times n$ matrix. A' is also non-singular, and therefore has an inverse
$$B = (A')^{-1}.$$

We then have
$$A'B = I_n = BA',$$

and hence
$$(A'B)' = I'_n = I_n = (BA')'.$$

But
$$(A')' = A,$$

and therefore
$$B'A = I_n = AB',$$

that is
$$B' = A^{-1}, \quad \text{or} \quad B = (A^{-1})'.$$

Hence, for any non-singular matrix A,
$$(A')^{-1} = (A^{-1})'.$$

We shall usually write this matrix as $\tilde{A}$, and call it the *complement* of A.

We now have three methods for obtaining $n \times n$ matrices from a non-singular $n \times n$ matrix A. These are: forming the inverse, the transpose, and the complement. If we denote by S the operation of forming the inverse, T that of forming the transpose, and U that of forming the complement, we have

$$TU = S = UT,$$
$$US = T = SU,$$
$$ST = U = TS,$$

and
$$S^2 = T^2 = U^2 = I,$$

where I is the identity operation which leaves A unaltered. The four operations I, S, T, U form an Abelian group.

Other properties of these operations which can be verified immediately are:

$$(A + B)' = A' + B',$$
$$(AB)^{-1} = B^{-1}A^{-1},$$
$$(\widetilde{AB}) = \tilde{A}\tilde{B},$$

where A, B are $n \times n$ matrices, which need not be regular for the first property to hold. It is only in the last case that K must be taken as commutative. The first two properties hold in any field.

8. Determinants.

When the ground field K is commutative we are able to define determinants exactly as in the case in which K is the field of complex numbers. Determinants over a commutative field K have many properties which are similar to those of determinants defined over the field of complex numbers. It will therefore be sufficient to give a brief outline of the main results which we shall need in the sequel.

We begin by defining certain symbols which are frequently used.

(i)   The symbol

$$\epsilon^{i_1 \cdots i_n} \quad (\text{or } \epsilon_{i_1 \ldots i_n})$$

is zero unless $i_1, \ldots, i_n$ is some derangement of the first n natural numbers. If the derangement is an even permutation [I, § 1],

$$\epsilon^{i_1 \cdots i_n} = \epsilon_{i_1 \ldots i_n} = 1.$$

If the derangement is an odd permutation,

$$\epsilon^{i_1 \cdots i_n} = \epsilon_{i_1 \ldots i_n} = -1.$$

Both notations will be used as may be convenient. In tensor theory there is an important difference to be observed in the uses of the two symbols, but this difference does not concern us.

(ii)   The symbol

$$\delta\,{}^{j_1\ldots\,j_p}_{i_1\ldots\,i_p}$$
$$(n)$$

is zero unless $i_1, \ldots, i_p$ and $j_1, \ldots, j_p$ are derangements of the *same* set of p *distinct* integers, each one of which lies between 1 and n (inclusive). When the derangements are of like parity,

$$\delta\,{}^{j_1\ldots\,j_p}_{i_1\ldots\,i_p} = 1,$$
$$(n)$$

and when they are of unlike parity,

$$\delta\,{}^{j_1\ldots\,j_p}_{i_1\ldots\,i_p} = -1.$$
$$(n)$$

Evidently
$$\delta\,{}^{i_1\ldots\,i_n}_{1\ldots\,n} = \epsilon^{i_1\ldots\,i_n}.$$
$$(n)$$

The (n) beneath the δ-symbol is usually omitted when there is no doubt about the value intended.

Now let $A = (a_{ij})$ be an $n \times n$ matrix. We define its determinant to be

$$\det A = \begin{vmatrix} a_{11} & a_{12} & \cdot & a_{1n} \\ a_{21} & a_{22} & \cdot & a_{2n} \\ \cdot & \cdot & \cdot & \cdot \\ a_{n1} & a_{n2} & \cdot & a_{nn} \end{vmatrix}$$

$$= \sum_{i_1=1}^{n} \ldots \sum_{i_n=1}^{n} \epsilon^{i_1\ldots\,i_n} a_{i_1 1} \ldots a_{i_n n}.$$

From this definition it follows at once that if $B = (b_{ij})$ is a $p \times q$ matrix, and A is the $n \times n$ submatrix whose elements are in the i_1th, ..., i_nth rows and j_1th, ..., j_nth columns of B, then

$$\det A = \sum_{k_1=1}^{p} \ldots \sum_{k_n=1}^{p} \delta\,{}^{k_1\ldots\,k_n}_{i_1\ldots\,i_n}\,{}_{(p)} b_{k_1 j_1} \ldots b_{k_n j_n}.$$

THEOREM I. *If A is an $n \times n$ matrix, A' its transpose,*

$$\det A = \det A'.$$

In the expression for $\det A$ consider any term

$$\epsilon^{i_1\ldots\,i_n} a_{i_1 1} \ldots a_{i_n n},$$

in which $\epsilon^{i_1 \cdots i_n}$ is not zero. Then $i_1, \ldots, i_n$ is a derangement of $1, \ldots, n$, defining a substitution [I, § 1]

$$\begin{pmatrix} 1 & 2 & . & n \\ i_1 & i_2 & . & i_n \end{pmatrix}.$$

Let the inverse substitution be

$$\begin{pmatrix} 1 & 2 & . & n \\ j_1 & j_2 & . & j_n \end{pmatrix}.$$

Then these substitutions have the same parity, and therefore

$$\epsilon^{i_1 \cdots i_n} = \epsilon^{j_1 \cdots j_n}.$$

If we rearrange the factors of $a_{i_1 1} \ldots a_{i_n n}$, we obtain the equation

$$a_{i_1 1} \ldots a_{i_n n} = a_{1 j_1} \ldots a_{n j_n},$$

and
$$\epsilon^{i_1 \cdots i_n} a_{i_1 1} \ldots a_{i_n n} = \epsilon^{j_1 \cdots j_n} a_{1 j_1} \ldots a_{n j_n}.$$

Conversely, any term

$$\epsilon^{j_1 \cdots j_n} a_{1 j_1} \ldots a_{n j_n}$$

in which the ϵ-symbol is not zero determines uniquely a term

$$\epsilon^{i_1 \cdots i_n} a_{i_1 1} \ldots a_{i_n n}.$$

Therefore

$$\det A = \sum_{i_1=1}^{n} \ldots \sum_{i_n=1}^{n} \epsilon^{i_1 \cdots i_n} a_{i_1 1} \ldots a_{i_n n}$$

$$= \sum_{j_1=1}^{n} \ldots \sum_{j_n=1}^{n} \epsilon^{j_1 \cdots j_n} a_{1 j_1} \ldots a_{1 j_n}$$

$$= \sum_{j_1=1}^{n} \ldots \sum_{j_n=1}^{n} \epsilon^{j_1 \cdots j_n} a'_{j_1 1} \ldots a'_{j_n n} = \det A'.$$

THEOREM II (*Laplace's expansion*):

$$\begin{vmatrix} a_{11} & a_{12} & . & a_{1n} \\ a_{21} & a_{22} & . & a_{2n} \\ . & . & . & . \\ a_{n1} & a_{n2} & . & a_{nn} \end{vmatrix} = \sum_i \rho_i \begin{vmatrix} a_{i_1 j_1} & . & a_{i_1 j_p} \\ . & . & . \\ a_{i_p j_1} & . & a_{i_p j_p} \end{vmatrix} \begin{vmatrix} a_{i_{p+1} j_{p+1}} & . & a_{i_{p+1} j_n} \\ . & . & . \\ a_{i_n j_{p+1}} & . & a_{i_n j_n} \end{vmatrix},$$

where $j_1, \ldots, j_n$ is any fixed derangement of $1, \ldots, n$, and the summation is over all possible divisions of $1, \ldots, n$ into two sets

$$i_1 < i_2 \ldots < i_p \quad \text{and} \quad i_{p+1} < \ldots < i_n$$

(so that there are $\binom{n}{p}$ terms) and $\rho_i = +1$ or -1 according as $i_1, \ldots, i_n$ and $j_1, \ldots, j_n$ are like or unlike derangements of $1, \ldots, n$.

By rearranging the factors a_{ij} in the expression for $\det A$ we find that

$$\det A = \sum_{i_1=1}^{n} \ldots \sum_{i_n=1}^{n} \epsilon^{i_1 \ldots i_n} a_{i_1 1} \ldots a_{i_n n}$$

$$= \sum_{i_1=1}^{n} \ldots \sum_{i_n=1}^{n} \epsilon^{i_1 \ldots i_n} a_{k_1 j_1} \ldots a_{k_n j_n}.$$

Since

$$\epsilon^{i_1 \ldots i_n} = \epsilon^{j_1 \ldots j_n} \epsilon^{k_1 \ldots k_n},$$

$$\det A = \epsilon^{j_1 \ldots j_n} \sum_{k_1=1}^{n} \ldots \sum_{k_n=1}^{n} \epsilon^{k_1 \ldots k_n} a_{k_1 j_1} \ldots a_{k_n j_n}.$$

In the summation on the right consider the $p! \times (n-p)!$ terms in which $k_1, \ldots, k_p$ are derangements of $i_1, \ldots, i_p$, and $k_{p+1}, \ldots, k_n$ are derangements of $i_{p+1}, \ldots, i_n$. These terms sum to

$$\delta^{j_1 \ldots j_n}_{i_1 \ldots i_n} \sum_{k_1=1}^{n} \ldots \sum_{k_n=1}^{n} \delta^{k_1 \ldots k_p}_{i_1 \ldots i_p} \delta^{k_{p+1} \ldots k_n}_{i_{p+1} \ldots i_n} a_{k_1 j_1} \ldots a_{k_n j_n}$$

$$= \delta^{j_1 \ldots j_n}_{i_1 \ldots i_n} \begin{vmatrix} a_{i_1 j_1} & \cdot & a_{i_1 j_p} \\ \cdot & \cdot & \cdot \\ a_{i_p j_1} & \cdot & a_{i_p j_p} \end{vmatrix} \begin{vmatrix} a_{i_{p+1} j_{p+1}} & \cdot & a_{i_{p+1} j_n} \\ \cdot & \cdot & \cdot \\ a_{i_n j_{p+1}} & \cdot & a_{i_n j_n} \end{vmatrix},$$

and hence

$$\det A = \sum_i \rho_i \begin{vmatrix} a_{i_1 j_1} & \cdot & a_{i_1 j_p} \\ \cdot & \cdot & \cdot \\ a_{i_p j_1} & \cdot & a_{i_p j_p} \end{vmatrix} \begin{vmatrix} a_{i_{p+1} j_{p+1}} & \cdot & a_{i_{p+1} j_n} \\ \cdot & \cdot & \cdot \\ a_{i_n j_{p+1}} & \cdot & a_{i_n j_n} \end{vmatrix}.$$

This result is usually referred to as *the Laplace expansion in terms of the determinants of the j_1th, $\ldots, j_p$th columns.*

Using Th. I we obtain a similar expression for $\det A$ in terms of determinants in p selected rows.

THEOREM III. *If two columns (rows) of a determinant are the same, the determinant is zero.*

We first prove the theorem for the case $n = 2$. By direct evaluation

$$\begin{vmatrix} a & a \\ b & b \end{vmatrix} = ab - ab = 0.$$

Now suppose that in a determinant of n rows and columns the hth and kth columns are identical. Expanding the determinant in terms of these two columns we have

$$
\begin{vmatrix} a_{11} & \cdot & a_{1n} \\ \cdot & \cdot & \cdot \\ a_{n1} & \cdot & a_{nn} \end{vmatrix} = \sum_i \pm \begin{vmatrix} a_{i_1 h} & a_{i_1 k} \\ a_{i_2 h} & a_{i_2 k} \end{vmatrix} \begin{vmatrix} a_{i_3 j_3} & \cdot & a_{i_3 j_n} \\ \cdot & \cdot & \cdot \\ a_{i_n j_3} & \cdot & a_{i_n j_n} \end{vmatrix},
$$

where $h, k, j_3, \ldots, j_n$ is a derangement of $1, \ldots, n$. Since

$$
\begin{vmatrix} a_{i_1 h} & a_{i_1 k} \\ a_{i_2 h} & a_{i_2 k} \end{vmatrix} = 0
$$

for all values of i_1, i_2, the theorem, as applied to columns, follows. The result for rows follows from Th. I.

If we expand $\det A$ in terms of the hth column,

$$
\det A = \sum_{i=1}^{n} (-1)^{i+h} a_{ih} \begin{vmatrix} a_{11} & \cdot & a_{1\,h-1} & a_{1\,h+1} & \cdot & a_{1n} \\ & \cdot & \cdot & \cdot & \cdot & \\ a_{i-11} & \cdot & a_{i-1\,h-1} & a_{i-1\,h+1} & \cdot & a_{i-1\,n} \\ a_{i+11} & \cdot & a_{i+1\,h-1} & a_{i+1\,h+1} & \cdot & a_{i+1\,n} \\ & \cdot & \cdot & \cdot & \cdot & \\ a_{n\,1} & \cdot & a_{n\,h-1} & a_{n\,h+1} & \cdot & a_{nn} \end{vmatrix}.
$$

If we write the coefficient of a_{ih} in this expression as A_{hi}, we have

$$
\sum_{i=1}^{n} a_{ih} A_{hi} = \det A.
$$

On the other hand, if $h \neq k$,

$$
\sum_{i=1}^{n} a_{ik} A_{hi} = \det B,
$$

where B is the matrix obtained from A by replacing the hth column by the kth column. By Th. III, $\det B = 0$, if $h \neq k$. Hence

$$
\sum_{i=1}^{n} a_{ik} A_{hi} = \delta_{hk} \det A.
$$

Expanding in terms of rows we get, similarly, the equation

$$
\sum_{i=1}^{n} a_{hi} A_{ik} = \delta_{hk} \det A.
$$

We call A_{ji} the *signed minor* or *cofactor* of a_{ij} in $\det A$.

We now prove

Theorem IV. *If A, B, C are $n \times n$ matrices, and $C = AB$, then*

$$\det C = \det A \, \det B.$$

If $C = (c_{ij}) = \left(\sum_{j_1=1}^{n} a_{ij_1} b_{j_1 j} \right)$,

$$\det C = \sum_{i_1=1}^{n} \cdots \sum_{i_n=1}^{n} \epsilon^{i_1 \cdots i_n} c_{i_1 1} \cdots c_{i_n n}$$

$$= \sum_{i_1=1}^{n} \cdots \sum_{i_n=1}^{n} \sum_{j_1=1}^{n} \cdots \sum_{j_n=1}^{n} \epsilon^{i_1 \cdots i_n} a_{i_1 j_1} b_{j_1 1} \cdots a_{i_n j_n} b_{j_n n}$$

$$= \sum_{i_1=1}^{n} \cdots \sum_{i_n=1}^{n} \sum_{j_1=1}^{n} \cdots \sum_{j_n=1}^{n} \epsilon^{i_1 \cdots i_n} (a_{i_1 j_1} \cdots a_{i_n j_n}) (b_{j_1 1} \cdots b_{j_n n})$$

$$= \sum_{j_1=1}^{n} \cdots \sum_{j_n=1}^{n} \epsilon^{j_1 \cdots j_n} \det A \, (b_{j_1 1} \cdots b_{j_n n})$$

$$= \det A \, \det B.$$

Theorem V. *If A is any matrix with n columns, B any matrix with n rows, any t-rowed determinant of the matrix AB is equal to a sum of terms, each of which is the product of a t-rowed determinant of A by a t-rowed determinant of B.*

Let $A = (a_{ij})$ be a $p \times n$ matrix, $B = (b_{ij})$ an $n \times q$ matrix, so that $C = (c_{ij}) = AB$ is a $p \times q$ matrix.

Any t-rowed determinant D extracted from C is of the form

$$D = \begin{vmatrix} c_{i_1 k_1} & \cdot & c_{i_1 k_t} \\ \cdot & \cdot & \cdot \\ c_{i_t k_1} & \cdot & c_{i_t k_t} \end{vmatrix},$$

that is

$$D = \sum_{\tau_1=1}^{p} \cdots \sum_{\tau_t=1}^{p} \delta^{\tau_1 \cdots \tau_t}_{i_1 \cdots i_t} c_{\tau_1 k_1} \cdots c_{\tau_t k_t}$$

$$= \sum_{\tau_1=1}^{p} \cdots \sum_{\tau_t=1}^{p} \sum_{j_1=1}^{n} \cdots \sum_{j_t=1}^{n} \delta^{\tau_1 \cdots \tau_t}_{i_1 \cdots i_t} a_{\tau_1 j_1} b_{j_1 k_1} \cdots a_{\tau_t j_t} b_{j_t k_t}$$

$$= \sum_{j_1=1}^{n} \cdots \sum_{j_t=1}^{n} \sum_{\tau_1=1}^{p} \cdots \sum_{\tau_t=1}^{p} \delta^{\tau_1 \cdots \tau_t}_{i_1 \cdots i_t} (a_{\tau_1 j_1} \cdots a_{\tau_t j_t}) (b_{j_1 k_1} \cdots b_{j_t k_t})$$

$$= \sum_{j_1=1}^{n} \cdots \sum_{j_t=1}^{n} \begin{vmatrix} a_{i_1 j_1} & \cdot & a_{i_1 j_t} \\ \cdot & \cdot & \cdot \\ a_{i_t j_1} & \cdot & a_{i_t j_t} \end{vmatrix} (b_{j_1 k_1} \cdots b_{j_t k_t}).$$

Now

$$
\begin{vmatrix} a_{i_1 j_1} & \cdot & a_{i_1 j_t} \\ \cdot & \cdot & \cdot \\ a_{i_t j_1} & \cdot & a_{i_t j_t} \end{vmatrix} = \sum_g \delta_{j_1 \ldots j_t}^{g_1 \ldots g_t} \begin{vmatrix} a_{i_1 g_1} & \cdot & a_{i_1 g_t} \\ \cdot & \cdot & \cdot \\ a_{i_t g_1} & \cdot & a_{i_t g_t} \end{vmatrix},
$$

where the summation $\sum\limits_g$ is over the $\binom{n}{t}$ sets of distinct $g_1, \ldots, g_t$ which can be chosen from the set $(1, \ldots, n)$. Hence

$$
D = \sum_g \sum_{j_1=1}^{n} \ldots \sum_{j_t=1}^{n} \begin{vmatrix} a_{i_1 g_1} & \cdot & a_{i_1 g_t} \\ \cdot & \cdot & \cdot \\ a_{i_t g_1} & \cdot & a_{i_t g_t} \end{vmatrix} \delta_{j_1 \ldots j_t}^{g_1 \ldots g_t} (b_{j_1 k_1} \ldots b_{j_t k_t})
$$

$$
= \sum_g \begin{vmatrix} a_{i_1 g_1} & \cdot & a_{i_1 g_t} \\ \cdot & \cdot & \cdot \\ a_{i_t g_1} & \cdot & a_{i_t g_t} \end{vmatrix} \begin{vmatrix} b_{g_1 k_1} & \cdot & b_{g_1 k_t} \\ \cdot & \cdot & \cdot \\ b_{g_1 k_t} & \cdot & b_{g_t k_t} \end{vmatrix}
$$

We have proved then that

$$
\begin{vmatrix} c_{i_1 k_1} & \cdot & c_{i_1 k_t} \\ \cdot & \cdot & \cdot \\ c_{i_1 k_t} & \cdot & c_{i_t k_t} \end{vmatrix} = \sum_g \begin{vmatrix} a_{i_1 g_1} & \cdot & a_{i_1 g_t} \\ \cdot & \cdot & \cdot \\ a_{i_t g_1} & \cdot & a_{i_t g_t} \end{vmatrix} \begin{vmatrix} b_{g_1 k_1} & \cdot & b_{g_1 k_t} \\ \cdot & \cdot & \cdot \\ b_{g_t k_1} & \cdot & b_{g_t k_t} \end{vmatrix},
$$

and this is the form in which we shall subsequently use this theorem.

The values of certain determinants will be needed in the next section, and we state these values here. They can be obtained at once, expanding the determinants by rows or columns.

(i)
$$
\begin{vmatrix} a_1 & 0 & \cdot & 0 \\ 0 & a_2 & \cdot & 0 \\ \cdot & \cdot & \cdot & \cdot \\ 0 & 0 & \cdot & a_n \end{vmatrix} = a_1 a_2 \ldots a_n.
$$

This determinant has non-zero elements only along the principal diagonal ($a_{ii} = a_i$, $a_{ij} = 0$ ($i \neq j$)).

(ii)
$$
\begin{vmatrix} a_1 & 0 & \cdot & \cdot & \cdot & \cdot & \cdot & \cdot \\ 0 & a_2 & & & & & & \\ \cdot & & \cdot & & & & & \\ 0 & & \cdot & a_h & & a & & \\ \cdot & & & & \cdot & & & \\ 0 & & & & & a_k & & \cdot \\ \cdot & & & & & & \cdot & \\ 0 & 0 & & & & & \cdot & a_n \end{vmatrix} = a_1 a_2 \ldots a_n.
$$

Non-zero elements occur only along the principal diagonal and in one other place ($a_{ii} = a_i$, $a_{hk} = a$ for a particular h, k).

(iii) If $A = (a_{ij})$, where

$$a_{ij} = \delta_{h_i j} \quad (1 \leqslant h_i \leqslant n;\ i = 1, \ldots, n;\ j = 1, \ldots, n),$$

then $$\det A = \epsilon^{h_1 \cdots h_n}.$$

With these preliminaries, we consider certain operations on a matrix A which correspond to the elementary transformations discussed in §4. The operations are:

(a) interchanging two rows of A, say the hth and kth rows;

(b) multiplying the elements of the hth row by an element a of K;

(c) adding to the elements of the hth row a linear combination of the corresponding elements of the other rows.

The operation (a) is equivalent to premultiplying A by the matrix

$$B = (\delta_{h_i j}) \quad (i, j = 1, \ldots, n),$$

where $(h_1, \ldots, h_n) = (1, \ldots, h-1, k, h+1, \ldots, k-1, h, k+1, \ldots, n)$.

That is, B is the unit matrix with the hth and kth rows interchanged. By (iii) above, $\det B = -1$, and therefore

If the two rows of a determinant are interchanged the sign of the determinant is changed.

Operation (b) is equivalent to premultiplying A by

$$B = \begin{pmatrix} b_1 & 0 & . & . & 0 \\ 0 & b_2 & . & . & 0 \\ . & . & . & . & . \\ 0 & . & . & b_{n-1} & 0 \\ 0 & . & . & . & b_n \end{pmatrix},$$

where $b_i = 1$ if $i \neq h$, $b_h = a$. By (i), $\det B = a$, and therefore

If the elements of a row of a determinant are multiplied by a constant a, the determinant is multiplied by a.

Operation (c) can be split up into a set of operations, each of which consists of adding to the hth row a multiple b_k of the corresponding element of the kth row, k taking the values $(1, \ldots, h-1, h+1, \ldots, n)$. For a given k each operation is equivalent to premultiplying A by a matrix B of the type considered in (ii) above. B has 1 in each place on the principal diagonal, b_k in the hth row and kth column, and zeros in all other places. But $\det B = 1$, and so

Adding to the elements of any row of A a linear combination of the corresponding elements of the remaining rows does not alter the value of $\det A$.

All these operations may be performed on *columns* instead of *rows*. If a given operation on rows is carried out by premultiplying A by a matrix B, postmultiplying A by B' gives the corresponding operation for *columns*. Since

$$\det B = \det B',$$

the results stated above remain true when 'column' is read for 'row'.

We now discuss some properties of the cofactors A_{ji} of the elements a_{ij} of a determinant. If

$$A = (a_{ij}),$$

the matrix $$A^* = (A_{ij})$$

is called the *adjugate* of A. We saw that

$$\sum_{i=1}^{n} a_{ik}A_{hi} = \sum_{i=1}^{n} a_{hi}A_{ik} = \delta_{hk}\det A.$$

Hence $$AA^* = (\det A)\,I_n = A^*A.$$

If, therefore, $\det A \neq 0$, the matrix

$$\left(\frac{A_{ij}}{\det A}\right)$$

is the inverse A^{-1} of A. The determinant of this matrix must be $(\det A)^{-1}$, for if A is regular, so that

$$A(A^{-1}) = I_n,$$

then $$\det A \det(A^{-1}) = \det I_n = 1,$$

and therefore $$\det(A^{-1}) = (\det A)^{-1}.$$

On the other hand, if A has an inverse B, we have

$$\det A \det B = 1, \quad \text{and hence} \quad \det A \neq 0.$$

We have thus proved

THEOREM VI. *An $n \times n$ matrix A is non-singular if and only if* $\det A$ *is not zero.*

Let us now examine the case in which $\det A = 0$. Then

$$\sum_{i=1}^{n} a_{hi}A_{ip} = 0 \quad (h, p = 1, \ldots, n).$$

Now the cofactor A_{jq} is itself a determinant, and contains all the rows and columns of A except the qth row and the jth column. If we multiply the above equation by the cofactor of a_{hk} in A_{jq}, and sum over the following values of h:

$$h = 1, \ldots, q-1, q+1, \ldots, n,$$

we obtain the equation

$$\sum_{i=1}^{n} A_{jq}\binom{i}{k} A_{ip} = 0,$$

where $A_{jq}\binom{i}{k}$ denotes the determinant obtained from A_{jq} by replacing the element a_{lk} by a_{li}, for each value of l. Since

$$A_{jq}\binom{k}{k} = A_{jq},$$

$$A_{jq}\binom{j}{k} = -A_{kq},$$

and otherwise

$$A_{jq}\binom{i}{k} = 0,$$

the equation

$$\sum_{i=1}^{n} A_{jq}\binom{i}{k} A_{ip} = 0$$

reduces to the equation

$$A_{jq}A_{kp} - A_{kq}A_{jp} = 0.$$

Hence any two rows (or columns) of the adjugate matrix A^* are proportional, and we have

THEOREM VII. *If* $\det A = 0$, *and* $p > 1$, *the determinant of any* $p \times p$ *submatrix of* A^* *is zero.*

We now prove

THEOREM VIII (*Jacobi's Theorem*):

$$\begin{vmatrix} A_{i_1 j_1} & \cdot & A_{i_1 j_p} \\ \cdot & \cdot & \cdot \\ A_{i_p j_1} & \cdot & A_{i_p j_p} \end{vmatrix} = \delta_{i_1 \ldots i_n}^{j_1 \ldots j_n} \begin{vmatrix} a_{j_{p+1} i_{p+1}} & \cdot & a_{j_{p+1} i_n} \\ \cdot & \cdot & \cdot \\ a_{j_n i_{p+1}} & \cdot & a_{j_n i_n} \end{vmatrix} (\det A)^{p-1},$$

where $i_1, \ldots, i_n$ *and* $j_1, \ldots, j_n$ *are any derangements of the set* $(1, \ldots, n)$.

Let B be the matrix obtained from A by interchanging the ith and jth rows of A. If, with the usual notation, the elements of the adjugate matrix B^* are represented by B_{rs}, it is easily seen that

$$B_{rs} = -A_{rs} \quad (s \neq i, j),$$

and
$$B_{ri} = -A_{rj},$$
$$B_{rj} = -A_{ri}.$$

Assuming Jacobi's Theorem to be true for the matrix B, we readily prove its truth for the matrix A, and conversely. A similar result is obtained by interchanging any two columns of A. Hence, if we prove the theorem when

$$i_k = j_k = k \quad (k = 1, \ldots, n),$$

the theorem as stated above follows.

If $p = 1$ the theorem is true, by definition of $A_{i_1 j_1}$. If $p > 1$ and $\det A = 0$, it follows from Theorem VII. Assume that $\det A \neq 0$. Then

$$
\begin{vmatrix}
A_{11} & . & A_{1p} & . & . & A_{nn} \\
. & . & . & . & . & . \\
A_{p1} & . & A_{pp} & . & . & A_{pn} \\
0 & . & 0 & 1 & . & 0 \\
. & . & . & . & . & . \\
0 & . & 0 & 0 & . & 1
\end{vmatrix}
\begin{vmatrix}
a_{11} & . & . & a_{1n} \\
. & . & . & . \\
. & . & . & . \\
. & . & . & . \\
. & . & . & . \\
a_{n1} & . & . & a_{nn}
\end{vmatrix}
$$

$$
=
\begin{vmatrix}
\det A & 0 & . & 0 & . & . & 0 \\
0 & \det A & . & . & . & . & . \\
. & . & . & . & . & . & . \\
0 & 0 & . & \det A & . & . & 0 \\
a_{p+11} & . & . & a_{p+1p} & . & . & a_{p+1n} \\
. & . & . & . & . & . & . \\
a_{n1} & . & . & a_{np} & . & . & a_{nn}
\end{vmatrix},
$$

and therefore

$$
\begin{vmatrix}
A_{11} & . & A_{1p} \\
. & . & . \\
A_{p1} & . & A_{pp}
\end{vmatrix}
\det A =
\begin{vmatrix}
a_{p+1\,p+1} & . & a_{p+1\,n} \\
. & . & . \\
a_{n\,p+1} & . & a_{nn}
\end{vmatrix}
(\det A)^p.
$$

Since $\det A \neq 0$, the theorem follows. As a special case we have the result
$$\det A^* = (\det A)^{n-1}.$$

We have already shown [Th. VI] that an $n \times n$ matrix A is non-singular, and therefore of rank n, if and only if $\det A$ is different from zero. We now obtain further results connecting determinants with the rank of any matrix. If A is a $p \times q$ matrix of rank r, there exists at least one $r \times r$ submatrix of A which is of rank r, and any $s \times s$ submatrix of A $(s > r)$ is of rank not greater than r, and therefore less than s [§5, Th. III]. It follows from Th. VI that the determinant of any $s \times s$ submatrix must be zero. Hence we have

THEOREM IX. *A $p \times q$ matrix A is of rank r if there exists in it an $r \times r$ submatrix with determinant different from zero, and if every $s \times s$ submatrix $(s > r)$ has zero determinant.*

If $A = (a_{ij})$, and

$$\begin{vmatrix} a_{i_1 j_1} & \cdot & a_{i_1 j_r} \\ \cdot & \cdot & \cdot \\ a_{i_r j_1} & \cdot & a_{i_r j_r} \end{vmatrix} \neq 0,$$

the matrix

$$\begin{pmatrix} a_{i_1 1} & \cdot & a_{i_1 q} \\ \cdot & \cdot & \cdot \\ a_{i_r 1} & \cdot & a_{i_r q} \end{pmatrix}$$

is of rank r. Hence the vectors given by the i_1th, ..., i_rth rows of A are linearly independent. But since A is of rank r, the vectors determined by the rows of A form a manifold of dimension r, and therefore any row is linearly dependent on the i_1th, ..., i_rth rows. It follows from this reasoning that to solve the equations

$$a_{i1} x_1 + \ldots + a_{iq} x_q = 0 \quad (i = 1, \ldots, p), \tag{1}$$

we have only to solve the equations for $i = i_1, \ldots, i_p$. To simplify the notation let us write

$$a_{i_\rho j} = b_{\rho j},$$

and consider the solution of the equations

$$b_{i1} x_1 + \ldots + b_{iq} x_q = 0 \quad (i = 1, \ldots, r). \tag{2}$$

Then

$$\begin{vmatrix} b_{1 j_1} & \cdot & b_{1 j_r} \\ \cdot & \cdot & \cdot \\ b_{r j_1} & \cdot & b_{r j_r} \end{vmatrix} \neq 0.$$

By renaming the x_i we may suppose that $j_\rho = \rho$ $(\rho = 1, \ldots, r)$. Now let B_{ji} be the cofactor of b_{ij} in

$$b = \begin{vmatrix} b_{11} & \cdot & b_{1r} \\ \cdot & \cdot & \cdot \\ b_{r1} & \cdot & b_{rr} \end{vmatrix}.$$

If $(x_1, \ldots, x_q)$ is any solution of the set of equations

$$b_{i1}x_1 + \ldots + b_{iq}x_q = 0 \quad (i = 1, \ldots, r), \tag{3}$$

then
$$\sum_{i=1}^{r} \sum_{j=1}^{q} B_{hi} b_{ij} x_j = 0 \quad (h = 1, \ldots, r),$$

that is,

$$bx_h + \sum_{j=r+1}^{q} \begin{vmatrix} b_{11} & . & b_{1\,h-1} & b_{1j} & b_{1\,h+1} & . & b_{1r} \\ . & & . & . & . & & . \\ b_{r1} & . & b_{r\,h-1} & b_{rj} & b_{r\,h+1} & . & b_{rr} \end{vmatrix} x_j = 0. \tag{4}$$

Conversely, let $x_{r+1}, \ldots, x_q$ be *any* $q-r$ elements of K, and let $x_1, \ldots, x_r$ be defined by the above equations (4). By direct substitution we see that $(x_1, \ldots, x_q)$ is then a solution of (3). Thus we see how to construct explicitly all the solutions of (1).

THEOREM X. *A necessary and sufficient condition that the non-homogeneous equations*

$$\sum_{j=1}^{q} a_{ij} x_j = c_i \quad (i = 1, \ldots, p)$$

have a solution is that the matrices

$$\begin{pmatrix} a_{11} & . & a_{1q} \\ . & & . \\ a_{p1} & . & a_{pq} \end{pmatrix} \quad \text{and} \quad \begin{pmatrix} a_{11} & . & a_{1q} & c_1 \\ . & & . & . \\ a_{p1} & . & a_{pq} & c_p \end{pmatrix}$$

have the same rank.

Let us refer to the two matrices in question as the matrix of coefficients and the augmented matrix. The rank of the augmented matrix cannot be less than that of the matrix of coefficients. If the equations have a solution, the last column of the augmented matrix is a linear combination of the remaining columns of the matrix. The rank of the augmented matrix is therefore equal to the rank of the matrix of coefficients. On the other hand, if we are given the equality of the ranks, we deduce that the last column of the augmented matrix is linearly dependent on the first q columns, and if the equations

$$c_i = \sum_{j=1}^{q} a_{ij} \xi_j \quad (i = 1, \ldots, p)$$

express this linear dependence, $(\xi_1, \ldots, \xi_q)$ is a solution of the given equations.

None of the results proved so far in this section requires any restriction on the characteristic of K. We conclude with a theorem which is only true if K is not of characteristic 2. First of all, an $n \times n$ matrix A is said to be *symmetric* if

$$A = A',$$

skew-symmetric if $\qquad A = -A'.$

If A is skew-symmetric,

$$\det A = \det(-A)'$$
$$= \det(-I_n)\det A'$$
$$= (-1)^n \det A.$$

Hence, if n is odd, $\qquad 2\det A = 0,$

and therefore, *if K is not of characteristic* 2,

$$\det A = 0.$$

On the other hand,
$$A = \begin{pmatrix} a & h & g \\ h & b & f \\ g & f & c \end{pmatrix}$$

is skew if K is of characteristic 2, since any element l of K satisfies the relation
$$l = -l.$$

But $\qquad \det A = abc + af^2 + bg^2 + ch^2,$

which is *not* zero for all a, b, c, f, g, h in K. In fact, if

$$a = b = c = 1; \quad f = g = h = 0,$$

$$\det A = 1.$$

This brief account of determinantal theory establishes the main results which we shall use in later chapters. We have shown that nearly all the results proved in textbooks for determinants whose elements are real or complex numbers extend to determinants over any commutative field. The many theorems on special methods of expansion, and on the value of determinants of special type (e.g. Vandermonde's determinant) which can be found in textbooks can easily be deduced from the above theorems for determinants over any commutative field. When necessary, such special results will be assumed in the sequel.

9. **λ-matrices.** Let K be a commutative field, and let λ be an indeterminate over K. In the following chapters we shall often have to consider matrices whose elements are polynomials in λ, and it is convenient to obtain here a number of results which will frequently be used.

Strictly speaking, we have so far only defined matrices over a field. We can, however, deduce the basic properties of matrices whose elements are in an integral domain I, say $K[\lambda]$, simply by regarding these matrices as forming a subset of the set of matrices whose elements are in the quotient field of the integral domain. Addition and multiplication of matrices of the subset give further matrices of the subset.

A matrix whose elements are in the integral domain $K[\lambda]$ is called a λ-*matrix*. An $n \times n$ λ-matrix which has an inverse which is also a λ-matrix is called a *regular* λ-matrix, of order n.

THEOREM I. *A necessary and sufficient condition for the $n \times n$ λ-matrix M to be a regular λ-matrix is that* det M *is a non-zero element of K.*

(i) Suppose that M is regular, and let N be its inverse. Since the elements of M and N are polynomials in λ, the determinants of these matrices are polynomials in λ. Let

$$\det M = f(\lambda), \quad \det N = g(\lambda),$$

where $f(\lambda)$ is of degree r, $g(\lambda)$ of degree s. Then since

$$MN = I_n,$$
$$\det M \det N = 1,$$

that is, $$f(\lambda)g(\lambda) = 1.$$

But one side of this equation is a polynomial of degree $r+s$, while the other side is a polynomial of degree 0. Hence

$$r = s = 0,$$

and $f(\lambda)$, $g(\lambda)$ are non-zero elements of K. The condition is therefore necessary.

(ii) Suppose that det $M = m$, where m is a non-zero element of K. Let $M = (m_{ij})$, and write

$$n_{ij} = (-)^{i+j} m^{-1} \begin{vmatrix} m_{11} & \cdot & m_{1\,i-1} & m_{1\,i+1} & \cdot & m_{1\,n} \\ & & \cdot & \cdot & & \\ m_{j-1\,1} & \cdot & m_{j-1\,i-1} & m_{j-1\,i+1} & \cdot & m_{j-1\,n} \\ m_{j+1\,1} & \cdot & m_{j+1\,i-1} & m_{j+1\,i+1} & \cdot & m_{j+1\,n} \\ \cdot & & \cdot & \cdot & & \cdot \\ m_{n\,1} & \cdot & m_{n\,i-1} & m_{n\,i+1} & \cdot & m_{n\,n} \end{vmatrix}.$$

Then $N = (n_{ij})$ is a λ-matrix, and [§8, Th. VI]

$$MN = I_n.$$

We now define *equivalent* λ-matrices. Two $p \times q$ λ-matrices A and B are said to be *equivalent* if there exist regular λ-matrices M and N, of orders p and q respectively, such that

$$A = MBN. \tag{1}$$

This relation is reflexive, since

$$A = I_p A I_q.$$

From (1) we have
$$B = M^{-1}AN^{-1},$$

and M^{-1}, N^{-1} are regular λ-matrices, since M, N are regular. The relation is therefore symmetric. Again, if besides (1) we also have

$$B = PCQ,$$

where P and Q are regular, then

$$A = (MP)\,C(QN),$$

where MP, QN are regular λ-matrices. The relation is therefore transitive, and it is thus an equivalence relation.

We wish to find a set of *canonical forms* for all $p \times q$ λ-matrices. As in §4 we say that a set of $p \times q$ λ-matrices is a set of *canonical forms* for the set of *all* $p \times q$ λ-matrices if

(*a*) no two matrices of the set are equivalent;

(*b*) there is a matrix of the set equivalent to *any* given $p \times q$ λ-matrix.

Clearly, if we can construct such a canonical set, and also find a method for determining the canonical form equivalent to any $p \times q$ λ-matrix, we shall have a method for determining whether two given λ-matrices are equivalent.

Our first step is to consider certain simple operations on a λ-matrix A. These are known as *elementary transformations* [cf. §4], and produce a λ-matrix B equivalent to A.

(i) Let $k_1, ..., k_p$ be any derangement of the integers $1, ..., p$, and let P be the $p \times p$ matrix

$$P = (\delta_{k_i j}) \quad (i, j = 1, ..., p).$$

Then $\det P = \pm 1$, and the matrix $B = PA$ is the matrix obtained from A by performing the permutation

$$\begin{pmatrix} 1 & 2 & . & p \\ k_1 & k_2 & . & k_p \end{pmatrix}$$

on the rows. Hence, the elementary transformation of A which consists of a permutation of the rows of A transforms A into an equivalent matrix.

(ii) A permutation of the columns of A transforms A into an equivalent matrix. The proof is similar to that in (i), the new matrix being of the form AQ.

(iii) Let R be the $p \times p$ matrix (r_{ij}) where

$$r_{ij} = \delta_{ij} \quad (i \neq h),$$
$$r_{hj} = f_j(\lambda) \quad (j = 1, ..., h-1, h+1, ..., p),$$

where $f_j(\lambda)$ is a polynomial in $K[\lambda]$, and

$$r_{hh} = f_h(\lambda) = a \quad (a \text{ in } K, \text{ and not zero}).$$

Then $\det R = a$, and R is therefore a regular λ-matrix. We obtain a matrix $B = RA$ equivalent to A by multiplying the hth row by a and adding to it $f_1(\lambda)$ times the first row, $f_2(\lambda)$ times the second row, ..., $f_{h-1}(\lambda)$ times the $(h-1)$th row, $f_{h+1}(\lambda)$ times the $(h+1)$th row, ..., $f_p(\lambda)$ times the pth row.

(iv) If a column of A is multiplied by a non-zero element of K, and to it we add a multiple (by a polynomial) of any other column, we obtain a matrix, equivalent to A, of the form AS. The proof is similar to that in (iii).

We now show how a matrix can be simplified by a series of elementary transformations until it is reduced to a canonical form.

Let A be a $p \times q$ λ-matrix. If it is the zero matrix, any matrix equivalent to it is clearly zero, and no reduction is possible. We therefore assume that at least one element of A is not zero, and by a permutation of rows and columns we bring a non-zero element of A to the top left-hand corner. Let this element a_{11} be of degree ρ in λ. We show that unless a_{11}, regarded as a polynomial in λ, is a factor of every element a_{ij} of A, we can transform A into an equivalent matrix C, where c_{11} is not zero and is of lower degree than a_{11}. Our transformation will be a series of elementary transformations.

(i) If, for some j, a_{11} is not a factor of a_{1j}, then

$$a_{1j} = a_{11}b(\lambda) + c(\lambda),$$

by the division algorithm, where $c(\lambda)$ is not zero, and is of lower degree than a_{11}. From the jth column we subtract $b(\lambda)$ times the first column, and then interchange the first and jth columns. The resulting matrix is equivalent to A, and has $c(\lambda)$ in the top left-hand corner.

(ii) If, for some i, a_{11} is not a factor of a_{i1}, we operate on rows instead of columns.

(iii) Suppose that a_{11} is a factor of all non-zero elements in the first row and column, but is not a factor of a_{hk} $(h, k > 1)$. Let $a_{i1} = b_i a_{11}$, and $a_{1j} = c_j a_{11}$. Then if we subtract from the ith row b_i times the first row, for each $i > 1$, and then subtract from the jth column c_j times the first column, for each $j > 1$, we obtain a matrix B equivalent to A in which

$$b_{11} = a_{11}, \quad b_{1j} = 0 \ (j > 1), \quad b_{i1} = 0 \ (i > 1),$$

while b_{hk} is still not divisible by b_{11}. Now add the hth row of B to the first row, and apply method (i). We obtain a matrix C equivalent to A, with $c_{11} \neq 0$, and of lower degree than a_{11}.

Since there is a finite upper bound to the degree in λ of the elements of the matrix A, the processes described above cannot be repeated more than a finite number of times. We eventually obtain a matrix B, say, equivalent to A, in which b_{11} is a factor of every element b_{ij}. By (iii) we can arrange that

$$b_{i1} = 0 \ (i > 1), \quad b_{1j} = 0 \ (j > 1).$$

Thus a series of elementary transformations has produced from A the equivalent matrix

$$PAQ = \begin{pmatrix} b_{11} & 0 & 0 & . & 0 \\ 0 & b_{22} & . & . & b_{2q} \\ 0 & . & . & . & . \\ . & . & . & . & . \\ 0 & b_{p2} & . & . & b_{pq} \end{pmatrix},$$

where b_{11} is a factor of all the elements b_{ij}.

If the submatrix

$$B_1 = \begin{pmatrix} b_{22} & . & b_{2q} \\ . & . & . \\ b_{p2} & . & b_{pq} \end{pmatrix}$$

is not zero, we can repeat the process given above, until we obtain an equivalent matrix

$$P_1 B_1 Q_1 = \begin{pmatrix} c_{22} & 0 \\ 0 & C_2 \end{pmatrix},$$

each element of C_2 containing c_{22} as a factor. Then

$$\begin{pmatrix} 1 & 0 \\ 0 & P_1 \end{pmatrix} PAQ \begin{pmatrix} 1 & 0 \\ 0 & Q_1 \end{pmatrix} = \begin{pmatrix} b_{11} & 0 & 0 \\ 0 & c_{22} & 0 \\ 0 & 0 & C_2 \end{pmatrix},$$

so that the elementary transformations on the submatrix B_1 can be considered as elementary transformations on A. Proceeding in this way we can transform A into an equivalent matrix in which the only non-zero elements are on the principal diagonal, and each element on the diagonal is a factor of all those following it. Finally, multiplying each row of this matrix by a non-zero constant, A is equivalent to the matrix

$$MAN = \begin{pmatrix} E_1(\lambda) & 0 & . & 0 & . & 0 \\ 0 & E_2(\lambda) & . & 0 & . & 0 \\ . & . & . & . & . & . \\ . & . & . & E_r(\lambda) & . & . \\ . & . & . & . & . & . \\ . & . & . & . & . & 0 \end{pmatrix}, \tag{2}$$

where each $E_i(\lambda)$ is a polynomial in λ with $+1$ as the coefficient of the highest power of λ, and $E_i(\lambda)$ is a factor of $E_{i+1}(\lambda)$. Since equivalent λ-matrices have the same rank, and the rank of the matrix MAN is evidently r, it follows that r is the rank of A.

Again, writing
$$MAN = E = (e_{ij}),$$

an evident extension of § 8, Th. V gives us the theorem

$$\begin{vmatrix} e_{i_1 j_1} & . & e_{i_1 j_t} \\ . & . & . \\ e_{i_t j_1} & . & e_{i_t j_t} \end{vmatrix} = \sum_\lambda \sum_\mu \begin{vmatrix} m_{i_1 \lambda_1} & . & m_{i_1 \lambda_t} \\ . & . & . \\ m_{i_t \lambda_1} & . & m_{i_t \lambda_t} \end{vmatrix} \begin{vmatrix} a_{\lambda_1 \mu_1} & . & a_{\lambda_1 \mu_t} \\ . & . & . \\ a_{\lambda_t \mu_1} & . & a_{\lambda_t \mu_t} \end{vmatrix} \begin{vmatrix} n_{\mu_1 j_1} & . & n_{\mu_1 j_t} \\ . & . & . \\ n_{\mu_t j_1} & . & n_{\mu_t j_t} \end{vmatrix}.$$

It follows that if $D_t(\lambda)$ is the highest common factor of the determinants of order t formed from A, $D_t(\lambda)$ is also a factor of each determinant of order t extracted from E. But since M, N are regular, the equation
$$MAN = E$$

can be written as
$$A = M^{-1}EN^{-1},$$

and therefore the highest common factor of determinants of order t formed from E divides each determinant of order t formed from A. Hence, save for a factor in K, this highest common factor is $D_t(\lambda)$. But from the properties of the polynomials $E_i(\lambda)$,

$$D_t(\lambda) = E_1(\lambda)\, E_2(\lambda) \ldots E_t(\lambda),$$

provided that the coefficient of the highest power of λ in $D_i(\lambda)$ is taken to be $+1$. Therefore

$$E_i(\lambda) = D_i(\lambda)/D_{i-1}(\lambda) \quad (i = 1, ..., r),$$

defining $$D_0(\lambda) = 1.$$

This last result shows us that the $E_i(\lambda)$ are uniquely defined by means of the highest common factors of the determinants of different orders extracted from A. Calling the $E_i(\lambda)$ *the invariant factors* of A we have now proved

THEOREM II. *If A is a $p \times q$ λ-matrix of rank r, and $E_1(\lambda), ..., E_r(\lambda)$ are its invariant factors, there exist regular λ-matrices M, N such that*

$$MAN = \begin{pmatrix} E_1(\lambda) & 0 & . & 0 & . & 0 \\ 0 & E_2(\lambda) & . & 0 & . & 0 \\ . & . & . & . & . & . \\ . & . & . & E_r(\lambda) & . & . \\ . & . & . & . & . & . \\ . & . & . & . & . & 0 \end{pmatrix}.$$

Since the inverse of a regular λ-matrix is a regular λ-matrix we also have

THEOREM III. *Two $p \times q$ λ-matrices A and B are equivalent if and only if they have the same invariant factors.*

Hence the set of matrices (2) is a set of canonical forms for $p \times q$ λ-matrices.

If the field K is such that every polynomial $f(\lambda)$ in $K[\lambda]$ can be written as a product of linear factors, it is sometimes convenient to use *elementary divisors* in place of invariant factors. We define these as follows. Let

$$E_1(\lambda) = (\lambda - \alpha_1)^{e_{11}} (\lambda - \alpha_2)^{e_{12}} ... (\lambda - \alpha_s)^{e_{1s}},$$
$$E_2(\lambda) = (\lambda - \alpha_1)^{e_{21}} (\lambda - \alpha_2)^{e_{22}} ... (\lambda - \alpha_s)^{e_{2s}},$$
$$\cdots\cdots\cdots\cdots\cdots\cdots\cdots\cdots\cdots\cdots\cdots$$
$$E_r(\lambda) = (\lambda - \alpha_1)^{e_{r1}} (\lambda - \alpha_2)^{e_{r2}} ... (\lambda - \alpha_s)^{e_{rs}},$$

where each $e_{ij} \geqslant 0$, and $\lambda - \alpha_1, ..., \lambda - \alpha_s$ are the distinct linear factors of $E_r(\lambda)$, that is, $e_{rj} > 0$ $(j = 1, ..., s)$. Then those factors

$$(\lambda - \alpha_1)^{e_{11}}, (\lambda - \alpha_1)^{e_{21}}, ..., (\lambda - \alpha_2)^{e_{12}}, ..., (\lambda - \alpha_s)^{e_{rs}},$$

for which the indices e_{ij} are greater than zero are called the *elementary divisors* of A. By definition, these are determined by the invariant factors.

Suppose, conversely, that we are given the elementary divisors of A, which is known to be of rank r. Let them be

$$(\lambda - \alpha)^{a_1}, (\lambda - \alpha)^{a_2}, \ldots, (\lambda - \alpha)^{a_l} \quad (a_1 \geqslant a_2 \geqslant \ldots \geqslant a_l),$$
$$(\lambda - \beta)^{b_1}, (\lambda - \beta)^{b_2}, \ldots, \quad\quad\quad (b_1 \geqslant b_2 \geqslant \ldots),$$
$$\ldots\ldots\ldots\ldots\ldots\ldots\ldots,$$
$$(\lambda - \delta)^{d_1}, (\lambda - \delta)^{d_2}, \ldots, \quad\quad\quad (d_1 \geqslant d_2 \geqslant \ldots).$$

Each invariant factor $E_i(\lambda)$ must be a product of these factors. Since $E_r(\lambda)$ contains $E_i(\lambda)$ as a factor $(i < r)$, $E_r(\lambda)$ must contain the highest power of $\lambda - \alpha$, the highest power of $\lambda - \beta$, etc. Hence

$$E_r(\lambda) = (\lambda - \alpha)^{a_1}(\lambda - \beta)^{b_1} \ldots (\lambda - \delta)^{d_1}.$$

Similarly, since $E_{r-1}(\lambda)$ is divisible by $E_i(\lambda)$ $(i < r - 1)$,

$$E_{r-1}(\lambda) = (\lambda - \alpha)^{a_2}(\lambda - \beta)^{b_2} \ldots (\lambda - \delta)^{d_2},$$

and so on. Once all the elementary divisors which are powers of $\lambda - \alpha$ are used up, the remaining $E_i(\lambda)$ do not contain $\lambda - \alpha$ as a factor. Similarly for $\lambda - \beta, \ldots$. When *all* the elementary divisors have been used up, the remaining invariant factors (if any) are $E_i(\lambda) = 1$. An equivalent form of Th. III, is therefore

THEOREM IV. *A necessary and sufficient condition that two $p \times q$ λ-matrices be equivalent is that they have the same rank and the same elementary divisors.*

Our next theorem is often useful in subsequent chapters.

THEOREM V. *If A, B are two $n \times n$ λ-matrices which can be written*

$$A = A_1\lambda - A_2, \quad B = B_1\lambda - B_2,$$

where A_1, A_2, B_1, B_2 are $n \times n$ matrices over K, and B_1 is non-singular, then the equivalence of A and B implies the existence of non-singular matrices P, Q over K such that

$$PAQ = B.$$

Since A and B are equivalent, there exist regular λ-matrices M, N such that
$$MAN = B.$$
Let
$$X = B_2 B_1^{-1}.$$
Then if
$$M = M_0 + M_1\lambda + \ldots + M_r\lambda^r,$$
where the M_i are matrices over K, and if
$$p = M_r\lambda^{r-1} + (M_{r-1} + XM_r)\lambda^{r-2} + \ldots + (M_1 + XM_2 + \ldots + X^{r-1}M_r),$$

and
$$P = M_0 + X M_1 + \ldots + X^r M_r,$$

then
$$M = (\lambda I_n - X) p + P = (\lambda I_n - B_2 B_1^{-1}) B_1 B_1^{-1} p + P,$$

that is
$$M = B P_1 + P,$$

where
$$P_1 = B_1^{-1} p.$$

Similarly, let
$$Y = B_1^{-1} B_2,$$

and write
$$N = N_0 + N_1 \lambda + \ldots + N_s \lambda^s,$$
$$q = N_s \lambda^{s-1} + (N_{s-1} + N_s Y) \lambda^{s-2} + \ldots + (N_1 + N_2 Y + \ldots + N_s Y^{s-1}),$$
$$Q = N_0 + N_1 Y + \ldots + N_s Y^s.$$

Then we have
$$N = q(\lambda I_n - Y) + Q$$
$$= Q_1 B + Q,$$

where
$$Q_1 = q B_1^{-1}.$$

Now
$$PAQ - B = (M - B P_1) A (N - Q_1 B) - B$$
$$= MAN - MAQ_1 B - B P_1 AN + B P_1 A Q_1 B - B$$
$$= B P_1 A Q_1 B - B N^{-1} Q_1 B - B P_1 M^{-1} B$$

(since $MAN = B$). Thus $PAQ - B = BRB$, where
$$R = P_1 A Q_1 - N^{-1} Q_1 - P_1 M^{-1},$$

and since M and N are regular λ-matrices, R is a λ-matrix. Suppose that R is not zero, say
$$R = R_0 + R_1 \lambda + \ldots + R_t \lambda^t \quad (R_t \neq 0, \ t \geqslant 0).$$

Then, from the above,
$$PAQ - B = BRB,$$

where the left-hand side is of degree 1 at most in λ, whilst the right-hand side is of degree
$$t + 2 \geqslant 2.$$

This contradiction shows that $R = 0$, and therefore
$$PAQ = B.$$

Since P, Q are independent of λ,
$$PA_1 Q = B_1, \quad PA_2 Q = B_2.$$

Since B_1 is not singular, P, Q are not singular, and the theorem is proved.

10. Miscellaneous theorems. We conclude this chapter with a number of results which will be needed later. Some of them require the use of theorems which are more appropriately dealt with in later chapters, and it will avoid repetition if we borrow these theorems without proof at the present stage.

If A is any $n \times n$ matrix over K, the λ-matrix

$$A - \lambda I_n$$

is called the *characteristic matrix* of A, and its determinant

$$f(\lambda) = \det(A - \lambda I_n)$$

is called the *characteristic function* of A. The roots of the *characteristic equation*

$$f(\lambda) = 0$$

are called the *latent roots of A*. Let us write

$$f(\lambda) = a_0 + a_1\lambda + \ldots + a_n\lambda^n.$$

Form the adjugate matrix of $A - \lambda I_n$. It is a λ-matrix whose elements are at most of degree $n-1$. We may therefore write it as

$$B_0 + B_1\lambda + \ldots + B_{n-1}\lambda^{n-1},$$

where the B_i are $n \times n$ matrices over K. Remembering that

$$(A - \lambda I_n) \text{ adjugate } (A - \lambda I_n) = \det(A - \lambda I_n)I_n,$$

we have the equation

$$(A - \lambda I_n)(B_0 + B_1\lambda + \ldots + B_{n-1}\lambda^{n-1}) = f(\lambda)I_n.$$

Equating like powers of λ on both sides of this equation, we have

$$AB_0 = a_0 I_n,$$
$$AB_1 - B_0 = a_1 I_n,$$
$$AB_2 - B_1 = a_2 I_n,$$
$$\cdot \qquad \cdot \qquad \cdot$$
$$-B_{n-1} = a_n I_n.$$

Premultiply these equations by I_n, A, A^2, ..., A^n respectively, and add. We obtain the matrix equation

$$0 = a_0 I_n + a_1 A + a_2 A^2 + \ldots + a_n A^n.$$

This result is usually stated in the form

THEOREM I. *A square matrix satisfies its own characteristic equation.*

We note that since the characteristic function

$$f(\lambda) = a_0 + a_1\lambda + \ldots + a_n\lambda^n = \det(A - \lambda I_n),$$

$$f(0) = a_0 = \det A.$$

Hence $\lambda = 0$ is a root of the characteristic equation if and only if A is singular.

We next introduce the idea of the *square root* of a matrix. Assuming the ground field K to be not only commutative but *algebraically closed*, so that every polynomial $\phi(x)$ in $K[x]$ is expressible as the product of linear factors, we shall prove the following theorem in the next chapter [III, §8, Th. II]:

If $\phi(x)$ is any polynomial in $K[x]$ such that $\phi(0) \neq 0$, then there exists a polynomial $g(x)$ such that $[g(x)]^r - x$ is divisible by $\phi(x)$, r being any given positive integer.

We use the case $r = 2$ of this theorem and take $\phi(x)$ to be the characteristic function $f(x)$ of a non-singular matrix A. Then we can find $g(x)$ such that

$$[g(x)]^2 - x = f(x)\,h(x).$$

Since $f(A) = 0$,

$$[g(A)]^2 - A = 0,$$

that is,

$$[g(A)]^2 = A.$$

Hence we have

THEOREM II. *If A is a non-singular matrix over an algebraically closed field K, there exists a matrix X such that*

$$X^2 = A.$$

Finally, we introduce the idea of the *minimum function* of a matrix A. If

$$\psi(\lambda) = \lambda^m + a_1\lambda^{m-1} + \ldots + a_m$$

is the polynomial of least degree for which

$$\psi(A) = 0,$$

we call $\psi(\lambda)$ the *minimum function* of the matrix A. Let the invariant factors of $A - \lambda I_n$ which are of degree > 0 be

$$E_{s+1}(\lambda), \ldots, E_n(\lambda).$$

We shall see in VIII, § 2, that there exists a matrix B, where

$$B = \begin{pmatrix} B_{s+1} & 0 & . & 0 \\ 0 & B_{s+2} & . & 0 \\ . & . & . & \\ 0 & . & . & B_n \end{pmatrix}$$

such that

(a) $B = P^{-1}AP$ for some non-singular P over K,

(b) $\det(B_i - \lambda I) = \pm E_i(\lambda)$ $(i = s+1, ..., n)$.

In fact, we need only take

$$B_i = \begin{pmatrix} 0 & 1 & 0 & . & 0 \\ 0 & 0 & 1 & . & 0 \\ . & . & . & . & . \\ 0 & 0 & 0 & . & 1 \\ -a_{ir_i} & . & . & . & -a_{i1} \end{pmatrix},$$

where $\qquad E_i(\lambda) = \lambda^{r_i} + a_{i1}\lambda^{r_i-1} + ... + a_{ir_i}.$

By Theorem I, $\qquad E_i(B_i) = 0.$

We observe that $E_i(\lambda)$ is the minimum function for the matrix B_i. To see this, we first note that when $r < r_i$ the rth power of B_i has the form

$$(B_i)^r = \begin{pmatrix} A & I_{r_i-r} \\ B & C \end{pmatrix},$$

where A is the zero $(r_i-r) \times r$ matrix, I_{r_i-r} is the unit matrix of r_i-r rows and columns, and B and C are, respectively, $r \times r$ and $r \times (r_i-r)$ matrices whose elements are polynomials in the a_{ij}. Now let

$$f(\lambda) = b_0 + b_1\lambda + ... + b_s\lambda^s \quad (b_s \neq 0)$$

be a polynomial of degree s over K, where $s < r_i$. Then it follows that $f(B_i)$ is a $r_i \times r_i$ matrix having the $(s+1)$th element in the first row equal to b_s. Hence $f(B_i)$ cannot be zero.

Again, if $g(\lambda)$ is any polynomial over K such that $g(B_i) = 0$, we can write

$$g(\lambda) = a(\lambda)E_i(\lambda) + b(\lambda),$$

where $b(\lambda)$ is of degree less than r_i. Then

$$b(B_i) = g(B_i) - a(B_i)E_i(B_i)$$
$$= 0,$$

and by the result just proved it follows that $b(\lambda) = 0$. Thus $g(\lambda)$ must have $E_i(\lambda)$ as a factor.

Now suppose that $F(\lambda)$ is any polynomial over K such that $F(A) = 0$. We have

$$F(B) = \begin{pmatrix} F(B_{s+1}) & 0 & . & 0 \\ 0 & F(B_{s+2}) & . & 0 \\ . & . & . & . \\ 0 & . & . & F(B_n) \end{pmatrix}$$

$$= F(P^{-1}AP) = P^{-1}F(A)\,P = 0,$$

and hence $\qquad F(B_i) = 0 \quad (i = s+1, \ldots, n).$

Thus $F(\lambda)$ must have $E_{s+1}(\lambda), E_{s+2}(\lambda), \ldots, E_n(\lambda)$ as factors, and conversely, if $F(\lambda)$ contains these polynomials as factors, $F(B) = 0$. Since $E_i(\lambda)$ is a factor of $E_j(\lambda)$ for $i < j$ we obtain

THEOREM III. *If A is an $n \times n$ matrix over K, and $A - \lambda I_n$ has the invariant factors $E_1(\lambda), \ldots, E_n(\lambda)$, $E_n(\lambda)$ is the minimum function of A, and a necessary and sufficient condition that a polynomial $f(\lambda)$ over K be such that $f(A)$ is zero is that $f(\lambda)$ has $E_n(\lambda)$ as a factor.*

CHAPTER III

CHAPTER III

ALGEBRAIC DEPENDENCE

IN this chapter it is assumed that all fields are commutative.

1. Simple algebraic extensions. In I, § 9, we discussed a method of extending a commutative field K by the adjunction of an indeterminate x. We now describe another method by which we can extend a commutative field K.

Let $f(x)$ be an irreducible polynomial of degree n in $K[x]$. We use $f(x)$ to define an equivalence relation in $K[x]$.

Two polynomials $a(x)$ and $b(x)$ of $K[x]$ are to be equivalent if

$$a(x) - b(x) = c(x) f(x),$$

where $c(x)$ is in $K[x]$. This relation is clearly reflexive, symmetric, and transitive, and it is therefore a proper equivalence relation [I, § 2]. The polynomials of $K[x]$ are divided into classes by this relation. We denote a class of equivalent polynomials by $\{a(x)\}$, where $a(x)$ is any member of the class.

If $a(x)$, $a'(x)$ are equivalent polynomials, and $b(x)$, $b'(x)$ are also equivalent,

$$a'(x) = a(x) + c(x) f(x),$$

and
$$b'(x) = b(x) + d(x) f(x).$$

Hence $\quad a'(x) + b'(x) = a(x) + b(x) + [c(x) + d(x)] f(x),$

and $\quad a'(x) b'(x) = a(x) b(x) + g(x) f(x),$

where $\quad g(x) = a(x) d(x) + b(x) c(x) + c(x) d(x) f(x).$

Hence we may define *addition* of classes of equivalent polynomials unambiguously by the equation

$$\{a(x)\} + \{b(x)\} = \{a(x) + b(x)\},$$

and *multiplication* by the equation

$$\{a(x)\} \{b(x)\} = \{a(x) b(x)\}.$$

It may be verified without difficulty that the classes form an Abelian group under addition, and that multiplication is associative, commutative, and distributive over addition. Hence the classes form a commutative ring with the given laws of composition. The zero of the ring is the class $\{0\}$, that is, the class of polynomials divisible by $f(x)$. There is also a unity, represented by $\{1\}$.

Now let $\{g(x)\}$ be any non-zero class. Then $g(x)$ is not divisible by $f(x)$. Since $f(x)$ is irreducible it follows that the highest common factor of $f(x)$ and $g(x)$ lies in K, and therefore polynomials $a(x)$, $b(x)$ can be found so that

$$a(x)\,g(x) + b(x)\,f(x) = 1.$$

We deduce that

$$\{a(x)\}\{g(x)\} = \{1\}.$$

Thus every non-zero element of the ring of equivalent classes of polynomials has an inverse. That is, the ring is a *field*, which we denote by K'.

If α, β are any elements of K,

$$\{\alpha\} = \{\beta\}$$

if and only if $\alpha - \beta$ is divisible by $f(x)$; that is, if and only if $\alpha = \beta$. Hence the classes $\{\alpha\}$ form a subfield of K' *isomorphic with* K. By I, § 2, Th. I, we deduce the existence of an extension K^* of K which is isomorphic with K'. The field K^* is uniquely defined to within an isomorphism in which the elements of K are self-corresponding.

Let ξ denote the element of K^* which corresponds to $\{x\}$ in K'. Then, if $g(x)$ is any polynomial of $K[x]$, $g(\xi)$ corresponds to $\{g(x)\}$. By the division algorithm we can write

$$g(x) = h(x)\,f(x) + g_1(x),$$

where $g_1(x)$ is a polynomial of degree less than n. If $g(x)$ itself is of degree less than n, we take $h(x) = 0$, $g(x) = g_1(x)$. Since

$$\{g(x)\} = \{g_1(x)\},$$

we have

$$g(\xi) = g_1(\xi).$$

It follows that any element η of K^* can be written in the form

$$\eta = \alpha_0 + \alpha_1\xi + \ldots + \alpha_{n-1}\xi^{n-1} \quad (\alpha_i \text{ in } K), \tag{1}$$

and, of course, the right-hand side of this equation, for any $\alpha_0, \ldots, \alpha_{n-1}$ in K, represents an element of K^*. Now the element $f(\xi)$ of K^* corresponds to the element $\{f(x)\}$ of K'. Since

$$\{f(x)\} = \{0\},$$
$$f(\xi) = 0.$$

Let $F(x)$ be any polynomial over K such that

$$F(\xi) = 0.$$

Then $\qquad\qquad \{F(x)\} = \{0\},$

and hence $F(x)$ is divisible by $f(x)$. $F(x)$ is therefore zero or of degree n at least, and it follows that the representation (1) of the elements of K^* is unique. Equation (1) thus gives a very convenient means of representing the elements of K^*. Using this representation we have

$$(\alpha_0 + \alpha_1\xi + \ldots + \alpha_{n-1}\xi^{n-1}) + (\beta_0 + \beta_1\xi + \ldots + \beta_{n-1}\xi^{n-1})$$
$$= (\alpha_0 + \beta_0) + (\alpha_1 + \beta_1)\xi + \ldots + (\alpha_{n-1} + \beta_{n-1})\xi^{n-1}.$$

To construct the product we have

$$(\alpha_0 + \alpha_1\xi + \ldots + \alpha_{n-1}\xi^{n-1})(\beta_0 + \beta_1\xi + \ldots + \beta_{n-1}\xi^{n-1})$$
$$= \alpha_0\beta_0 + (\alpha_0\beta_1 + \alpha_1\beta_0)\xi + \ldots + \alpha_{n-1}\beta_{n-1}\xi^{2n-2},$$

and we then use the relations

$$0 = \xi^r f(\xi) = \gamma_0 \xi^r + \gamma_1 \xi^{r+1} + \ldots + \gamma_n \xi^{n+r} \quad (r = n-2, n-3, \ldots, 0)$$

to express ξ^{2n-2} in terms of $\xi^{n-2}, \ldots, \xi^{2n-3}$, and then ξ^{2n-3} in terms of $\xi^{n-3}, \ldots, \xi^{2n-4}$, and finally to eliminate powers of ξ of degree higher than $n-1$ from the product.

A simple example will serve to show that for some fields K a true extension is constructed in this way. If K is the field of rational numbers, and

$$f(x) = x^2 - 2,$$

K^* is the field of numbers

$$a + b\sqrt{2},$$

where a and b are rational. K^* is not equal to K. If, on the other hand, K is the field of complex numbers, every polynomial of degree greater than one is reducible, and no proper extension of K can be constructed.

The method of extension described above is called *simple algebraic extension*.

2. Extensions of a commutative field. We now consider some general properties of extensions of a commutative field K, first defining *equivalent extensions*. Extensions $K_1, K_2, \ldots$ of K are said to be *equivalent* if they are isomorphic in such a way that those elements of $K_1, K_2, \ldots$ which lie in K are self-corresponding.

Let K^* be any extension of K, and let ξ be any element of K^*. We say that ξ is *algebraic over* K if there exists a non-zero polynomial $f(x)$ in $K[x]$ such that

$$f(\xi) = 0.$$

If ξ is not algebraic, it is *transcendental over* K.

Clearly, any element α of K is algebraic over K; for we merely have to take
$$f(x) = x - \alpha.$$

THEOREM I. *If ξ is algebraic over K, there exists an irreducible polynomial $f(x)$ in $K[x]$, unique save for a non-zero factor in K, such that*
$$f(\xi) = 0.$$

Since ξ is algebraic over K there exists a non-zero polynomial $g(x)$ in $K[x]$ such that
$$g(\xi) = 0.$$

Let
$$g(x) = g_1(x)\, g_2(x) \dots g_r(x)$$

represent the factorisation of $g(x)$ into irreducible factors. Then $g_i(\xi)$ is in K^*, and
$$g_1(\xi)\, g_2(\xi) \dots g_r(\xi) = g(\xi) = 0.$$

Since K^* is a field, and therefore has no divisors of zero, for some integer i $(1 \leqslant i \leqslant r)$ we have
$$g_i(\xi) = 0.$$

Take
$$f(x) = g_i(x).$$

If $h(x)$ is any irreducible polynomial such that
$$h(\xi) = 0,$$

then either
$$h(x) = \alpha f(x) \quad (\alpha \text{ in } K),$$

or $h(x)$ and $f(x)$ are relatively prime. In the latter case there exist polynomials $a(x)$ and $b(x)$ such that

$$a(x)\, f(x) + b(x)\, h(x) = 1.$$

But this gives us the equation

$$a(\xi)\, f(\xi) + b(\xi)\, h(\xi) = 1,$$

which, since the left-hand side is zero, is a contradiction. Hence $f(x)$ is uniquely defined, save for a non-zero factor in K. It is called the *characteristic polynomial of* ξ with respect to K.

Now let ξ denote any element of an extension K^* of K. We consider all the elements of K^* which can be obtained by performing the operations of addition, subtraction and multiplication (a finite number of times) on ξ and the elements of K. Such elements can be written

$$\alpha_0 + \alpha_1 \xi + \ldots + \alpha_r \xi^r \quad (\alpha_i \text{ in } K). \tag{1}$$

Clearly these elements form a commutative ring with unity, the unity being that of K. If η, ζ are two elements of this ring, the product $\eta\zeta$ is equal to the product of these elements regarded as elements of K^*, and therefore $\eta\zeta = 0$ only if either η or ζ is zero. The ring is therefore an integral domain. We denote it by $K[\xi]$, noting that $K[\xi] = K$ if and only if ξ is in K. Since $K[\xi]$ is an integral domain, it can be embedded in a field [I, §4]. We denote this quotient field by $K(\xi)$, and refer to it as *the field obtained by adjoining ξ to K*.

Case (i). Let ξ be algebraic over K, and let $f(x)$ be its characteristic polynomial, of degree n. If

$$g(\xi) = \alpha_0 + \alpha_1 \xi + \ldots + \alpha_r \xi^r,$$

we can write

$$g(x) = h(x)f(x) + g_1(x),$$

where $g_1(x)$ is of degree less than n. Then

$$g(\xi) = g_1(\xi),$$

and hence every element of $K[\xi]$ can be expressed in the form (1), where $r \leqslant n - 1$. This expression is unique, for if any element could be so expressed in two ways, there would exist a non-zero polynomial $g(x)$ of degree less than n such that

$$g(\xi) = 0,$$

and this would contradict Th. I.

It follows that the integral domain $K[\xi]$ is equivalent to the simple algebraic extension of K defined, as in §1, by $f(x)$. Hence, in particular, $K[\xi]$ is a field, and

$$K[\xi] = K(\xi).$$

As an important corollary we have

THEOREM II. *If ξ_1 and ξ_2 are two elements of an extension of K which are algebraic over K and have the same characteristic polynomial, then $K(\xi_1)$ and $K(\xi_2)$ are equivalent extensions of K.*

Case (ii). Now suppose that ξ is transcendental over K. Then

$$\alpha_0 + \alpha_1 \xi + \ldots + \alpha_r \xi^r = \beta_0 + \beta_1 \xi + \ldots + \beta_s \xi^s \quad (\alpha_r, \beta_s \neq 0),$$

if and only if $r = s$ and $\alpha_i = \beta_i$ $(i = 0, \ldots, r)$. It follows that $K[\xi]$ is equivalent to the integral domain $K[x]$, and therefore that $K(\xi)$ is equivalent to the field of rational functions of the indeterminate x over K. The field $K(\xi)$ is called a *transcendental extension* of K.

In either case it is clear that $K(\xi)$ is the smallest extension of K which contains ξ. There may, of course, be extensions of K which are proper subfields of $K(\xi)$, but these will not contain ξ. For instance, if ξ is transcendental over K,

$$K \subset K(\xi^2) \subset K(\xi).$$

The ideas introduced above can be extended by considering the smallest extension of K which contains a finite set $\xi_1, \ldots, \xi_n$ of elements of K^*. The elements of this extension are those elements of K^* which are obtained by applying the operations of addition, subtraction, multiplication and division (except by zero) to $\xi_1, \ldots, \xi_n$ and to the elements of K. The resulting field is denoted by $K(\xi_1, \ldots, \xi_n)$, and evidently does not depend on the order of the elements $\xi_1, \ldots, \xi_n$. We can define the field $K(\xi_1, \ldots, \xi_n)$ inductively as follows: $K(\xi_1, \ldots, \xi_r)$ is the field obtained by adjoining ξ_r to $K(\xi_1, \ldots, \xi_{r-1})$ $(r = 2, \ldots, n)$.

Some of the ξ_i may be algebraic over K, and we shall usually find it convenient to order the ξ_i in the set $\xi_1, \ldots, \xi_n$ to satisfy certain conditions. If each ξ_i is algebraic, there is no restriction on the order. If some of the ξ_i are transcendental over K, we take one of them as ξ_1. If $\xi_{i_2}, \ldots, \xi_{i_s}$ are transcendental over $K(\xi_1)$ (and hence transcendental over K), we take one as ξ_2, and continue thus. Eventually we can say that in $K(\xi_1, \ldots, \xi_n)$ the element ξ_1 is transcendental over K, the element ξ_s is transcendental over $K(\xi_1, \ldots, \xi_{s-1})$ $(s = 2, \ldots, r)$, and $\xi_{r+1}, \ldots, \xi_n$ are algebraic over $K(\xi_1, \ldots, \xi_r)$.

With this arrangement, $K(\xi_1, \ldots, \xi_r)$ is equivalent to the field of rational functions of $x_1, \ldots, x_r$ with coefficients in K [I, § 9]. We have proved this result when $r = 1$, and we now assume it is true for $r = s - 1$. Then $K(\xi_1, \ldots, \xi_{s-1})$ is equivalent to the field of rational functions $K(x_1, \ldots, x_{s-1})$. Now

$$K(\xi_1, \ldots, \xi_{s-1}, \xi_s) = K(\xi_1, \ldots, \xi_{s-1})(\xi_s),$$

and since ξ_s is transcendental over $K(\xi_1, \ldots, \xi_{s-1})$, $K(\xi_1, \ldots, \xi_{s-1})(\xi_s)$ is equivalent to $K(\xi_1, \ldots, \xi_{s-1})(x_s)$, and hence to

$$K(x_1, \ldots, x_{s-1})(x_s) = K(x_1, \ldots, x_s).$$

The elements $\xi_1, \dots, \xi_r$ are said to be *independent indeterminates* over K.

In this book we shall only be concerned with the extensions of a field K obtained by adjoining a finite number of elements $\xi_1, \dots, \xi_n$ to K.

3. Extensions of finite degree.

An extension K^* of K is said to be of finite degree if there exists a finite number of elements $\xi_1, \dots, \xi_n$ of K^* such that any element η of K^* is expressible in the form

$$\eta = \alpha_1 \xi_1 + \dots + \alpha_n \xi_n,$$

the $\alpha_1, \dots, \alpha_n$ lying in K. The elements $\xi_1, \dots, \xi_n$ are said to form *a basis for K^* over K*. This basis is a *minimal basis* if the equation

$$\alpha_1 \xi_1 + \dots + \alpha_n \xi_n = 0 \quad (\alpha_i \text{ in } K)$$

implies that $\quad\quad\quad \alpha_i = 0 \quad (i = 1, \dots, n).$

The elements of K^* clearly form a linear set

$$L(\xi_1, \dots, \xi_n)$$

over K [II, § 1], and therefore if K^* is of finite degree over K we deduce the existence of a minimal basis, the number of elements in the basis being the same for all minimal bases [II, § 1, Th. VI]. This number is called *the degree of the extension K^* of K*.

THEOREM I. *If K^* is an extension of K of finite degree n, every element of K^* is algebraic over K, and has a characteristic polynomial of degree not greater than n.*

Let $\xi_1, \dots, \xi_n$ be a minimal basis for K^* over K. Then, if η is any element of K^*, $\eta \xi_i$ is an element of K^* and

$$\eta \xi_i = \alpha_{i1} \xi_1 + \dots + \alpha_{in} \xi_n \quad (i = 1, \dots, n).$$

The linear equations

$$(\alpha_{11} - \eta) x_1 + \dots + \alpha_{1n} x_n = 0,$$
$$\dots\dots\dots\dots\dots\dots\dots\dots\dots$$
$$\alpha_{n1} x_1 + \dots + (\alpha_{nn} - \eta) x_n = 0,$$

have a solution in K^*, namely, $(\xi_1, \dots, \xi_n)$, which is not trivial. Hence

$$\begin{vmatrix} \alpha_{11} - \eta & \alpha_{12} & \cdot & \alpha_{1n} \\ \alpha_{21} & \alpha_{22} - \eta & \cdot & \alpha_{2n} \\ \cdot & \cdot & \cdot & \cdot \\ \alpha_{n1} & \alpha_{n2} & \cdot & \alpha_{nn} - \eta \end{vmatrix} = 0.$$

The polynomial

$$F(x) = \begin{vmatrix} \alpha_{11}-x & \alpha_{12} & \cdot & \alpha_{1n} \\ \alpha_{21} & \alpha_{22}-x & \cdot & \alpha_{2n} \\ \cdot & \cdot & \cdot & \cdot \\ \alpha_{n1} & \alpha_{n2} & \cdot & \alpha_{nn}-x \end{vmatrix}$$

is not zero, the term of highest degree being $(-1)^n x^n$. Since η satisfies the equation
$$F(\eta) = 0,$$

η is algebraic over K. Moreover, its characteristic polynomial is a factor of $F(x)$; hence its degree cannot exceed n.

An extension K^* of K in which every element is algebraic over K is called an *algebraic extension* of K. We have proved that *every extension of K of finite degree is algebraic*. We now prove

THEOREM II. *If the elements $\xi_1, ..., \xi_n$ of an extension K^* of K are algebraic over K, then $K(\xi_1, ..., \xi_n)$ is an algebraic extension of K.*

We first prove that any element η of $K(\xi_1, ..., \xi_n)$ can be expressed in the form
$$\eta = \sum_{i_1=0}^{r_1-1} \cdots \sum_{i_n=0}^{r_n-1} \alpha_{i_1 \ldots i_n} \xi_1^{i_1} \cdots \xi_n^{i_n},$$

the coefficients $\alpha_{i_1 \ldots i_n}$ lying in K, and $r_1, ..., r_n$ being integers which are independent of the element η. We prove this result by induction, assuming the truth of our statement for $K(\xi_1, ..., \xi_{n-1})$. Since ξ_n is algebraic over K, it is also algebraic over $K(\xi_1, ..., \xi_{n-1})$. Let r_n be the degree of its characteristic polynomial with respect to this field. Then, since $K(\xi_1, ..., \xi_n)$ is obtained by adjoining ξ_n to $K(\xi_1, ..., \xi_{n-1})$, any element η of $K(\xi_1, ..., \xi_n)$ can be written in the form
$$\eta = \theta_0 + \theta_1 \xi_n + ... + \theta_{r_n-1} \xi_n^{r_n-1},$$

the θ_i lying in $K(\xi_1, ..., \xi_{n-1})$. But by the hypothesis of induction we can write
$$\theta_i = \sum_{i_1=0}^{r_1-1} \cdots \sum_{i_{n-1}=0}^{r_{n-1}-1} \alpha_{i_1 \ldots i_{n-1} i} \xi_1^{i_1} \cdots \xi_{n-1}^{i_{n-1}} \quad (i = 0, ..., r_n-1),$$

where the integers $r_1, ..., r_{n-1}$ are independent of θ_i, and hence of η, and the coefficients $\alpha_{i_1 \ldots i_{n-1} i}$ lie in K. Hence
$$\eta = \sum_{i_1=0}^{r_1-1} \cdots \sum_{i_n=0}^{r_n-1} \alpha_{i_1 \ldots i_n} \xi_1^{i_1} \cdots \xi_n^{i_n}.$$

This proof is valid when $n = 1$ and therefore our result is proved.

It follows that the $r_1 r_2 \ldots r_n$ elements

$$\xi_1^{i_1} \ldots \xi_n^{i_n} \quad (i_1 = 0, \ldots, r_1 - 1; \ldots; i_n = 0, \ldots, r_n - 1)$$

form a basis for $K(\xi_1, \ldots, \xi_n)$. Hence, by Th. I, any element of $K(\xi_1, \ldots, \xi_n)$ is algebraic over K. By definition, therefore, $K(\xi_1, \ldots, \xi_n)$ is an algebraic extension of K, and the theorem is proved.

Suppose now that of the elements $\xi_1, \ldots, \xi_n$ the first r, $\xi_1, \ldots, \xi_r$, are independent indeterminates over K, but that $\xi_{r+1}, \ldots, \xi_n$ are algebraically dependent on $K(\xi_1, \ldots, \xi_r)$. Then $K(\xi_1, \ldots, \xi_n)$ *is an algebraic extension of* $K(\xi_1, \ldots, \xi_r)$. It is called an *algebraic function field*, and its elements are *algebraic functions* of the indeterminates $\xi_1, \ldots, \xi_r$.

THEOREM III. *If K^* is any extension of K, the elements of K^* which are algebraic over K form a field K', where*

$$K \subseteq K' \subseteq K^*.$$

If ξ and η are elements of K^* which are algebraic over K so is every element of $K(\xi, \eta)$, by the previous theorem. Hence, the elements $\xi - \eta$ and $\xi \eta$, lying in $K(\xi, \eta)$, are algebraic over K. It follows that the elements of K^* which are algebraic over K form an integral domain which contains K as a subring. Further, if ξ is algebraic over K, but not zero, ξ^{-1} lies in $K(\xi)$ and is therefore algebraic over K. Hence the set of algebraic elements of K^* form a field K'. Clearly $\qquad K \subseteq K' \subseteq K^*.$

THEOREM IV. *If K^* is any extension of K, and K' a subfield of K^* whose elements are algebraic over K, then any element of K^* which is algebraic over K' is also algebraic over K.*

We do not assume that K' contains K. Let ξ be any element of K^* which is algebraic over K', and let

$$x^n + \eta_1 x^{n-1} + \ldots + \eta_n \quad (\eta_i \text{ in } K')$$

be its characteristic polynomial with respect to K'. Consider the field $K(\eta_1, \ldots, \eta_n, \xi)$. Any element can be written as

$$\sum_{i=1}^{n} \zeta_i \xi^{i-1} \quad (\zeta_i \text{ in } K(\eta_1, \ldots, \eta_n)).$$

But for each i we can write

$$\zeta_i = \sum_{i_1=1}^{r_1} \ldots \sum_{i_n=1}^{r_n} \alpha_{i_1 \ldots i_n}^{i} \eta_1^{i_1 - 1} \ldots \eta_n^{i_n - 1} \quad (\alpha_{i_1 \ldots i_n}^{i} \text{ in } K),$$

and therefore $K(\eta_1, \ldots, \eta_n, \xi)$ has a finite basis over K, and hence, by Th. I, it is algebraic. It follows that ξ is algebraic over K.

We now introduce the notion of *algebraic dependence*. A set of elements $\xi_1, ..., \xi_r$ of an extension K^* of K is said to be *algebraically dependent over* K if there exists a non-zero polynomial $f(x_1, ..., x_r)$ in $K[x_1, ..., x_r]$ such that

$$f(\xi_1, ..., \xi_r) = 0.$$

If not dependent the elements are *algebraically independent over* K.

In the case $r = 1$, ξ_1 is algebraically dependent over K if and only if it is *algebraic* over K. A proof similar to that of §2, Th. I, enables us to show that if $\xi_1, ..., \xi_r$ are algebraically dependent over K there exists an *irreducible polynomial* $f(x_1, ..., x_r)$ such that

$$f(\xi_1, ..., \xi_r) = 0.$$

If $\xi_1, ..., \xi_r$ are algebraically independent, $\xi_1, ..., \xi_r$ are independent indeterminates over K, and therefore $K(\xi_1, ..., \xi_r)$ is the field of rational functions of the indeterminates $\xi_1, ..., \xi_r$.

We have already remarked that there exists in $K(\xi_1, ..., \xi_n)$ a set of indeterminates, which we may take as $\xi_1, ..., \xi_r$, which are algebraically independent over K, and which are such that any element of $K(\xi_1, ..., \xi_n)$ is algebraic over $K(\xi_1, ..., \xi_r)$. More generally, there may exist in any extension K^* of K a finite set of elements $\xi_1, ..., \xi_r$ which are algebraically independent over K, and such that any element η of K^* is algebraic over $K(\xi_1, ..., \xi_r)$. When this is the case we say that K^* has a *finite algebraic basis* with respect to K, and since $\xi_1, ..., \xi_r$ are algebraically independent over K, these elements are said to form a *minimal* algebraic basis.

Certain properties of extensions K^* of K with finite algebraic bases are similar to properties of linear sets of finite dimension [II, §1]. We now prove the generalised form of the Exchange Theorem.

THEOREM V. *If* $(\eta_1, ..., \eta_s)$ *is any algebraic basis for an extension* K^* *of* K, *and* $\zeta_1, ..., \zeta_t$ *are* t *algebraically independent elements of* K^*, *then* $t \leqslant s$, *and for a suitable rearrangement of* $\eta_1, ..., \eta_s$ *the set* $(\zeta_1, ..., \zeta_t, \eta_{t+1}, ..., \eta_s)$ *is a basis for* K^*.

We consider the case $t = 1$ first of all. Since ζ_1 is in K^*, it is algebraically dependent over $K(\eta_1, ..., \eta_s)$. Therefore there exists a non-zero polynomial $f(x_1, ..., x_{s+1})$ such that

$$f(\eta_1, ..., \eta_s, \zeta_1) = 0.$$

If $s = 0$, this implies that ζ_1 is algebraic over K, which is contrary to hypothesis. Hence $s \geqslant 1$.

Again, and for the same reason, one at least of the indeterminates $x_1, \ldots, x_s$ must be present in $f(x_1, \ldots, x_{s+1})$. We may suppose that the η_i are rearranged so that x_1 is present. Then it follows that η_1 is algebraically dependent over $K(\zeta_1, \eta_2, \ldots, \eta_s)$. By hypothesis, any element ξ of K^* is algebraically dependent over $K(\eta_1, \eta_2, \ldots, \eta_s)$. But we now know that $\eta_1, \eta_2, \ldots, \eta_s$ are algebraic over $K(\zeta_1, \eta_2, \ldots, \eta_s)$. Hence, by Th. IV, we deduce that ξ is algebraically dependent over $K(\zeta_1, \eta_2, \ldots, \eta_s)$. This proves the theorem when $t = 1$. We now proceed by induction on t.

It is clear from the definition of algebraic dependence that if $\zeta_1, \ldots, \zeta_t$ are algebraically independent over K, any subset is also algebraically independent. In particular, $\zeta_1, \ldots, \zeta_{t-1}$ are independent. Hence, if we assume that our theorem is true for $t-1$ elements ζ_i, we have the relation

$$t - 1 \leqslant s,$$

and we may suppose that the $\eta_1, \ldots, \eta_s$ are arranged so that the set

$$(\zeta_1, \ldots, \zeta_{t-1}, \eta_t, \ldots, \eta_s)$$

is an algebraic basis for K^* over K. Since ζ_t is in K^*, it is algebraic over $K(\zeta_1, \ldots, \zeta_{t-1}, \eta_t, \ldots, \eta_s)$. That is, there exists a non-zero polynomial $f(x_1, \ldots, x_{s+1})$ such that

$$f(\zeta_1, \ldots, \zeta_{t-1}, \eta_t, \ldots, \eta_s, \zeta_t) = 0.$$

If $t - 1 = s$, it would follow that $\zeta_1, \ldots, \zeta_t$ are algebraically dependent, contrary to hypothesis. Hence

$$t - 1 < s, \quad \text{that is} \quad t \leqslant s.$$

Again, one at least of the indeterminates $x_t, \ldots, x_s$ must be present in $f(x_1, \ldots, x_{s+1})$, otherwise $\zeta_1, \ldots, \zeta_t$ would be algebraically dependent over K. We may suppose that the η_i are rearranged so that x_t is present. Then it follows that η_t is algebraically dependent over

$$K(\zeta_1, \ldots, \zeta_{t-1}, \zeta_t, \eta_{t+1}, \ldots, \eta_s).$$

By hypothesis, any element ξ of K^* is algebraically dependent over $K(\zeta_1, \ldots, \zeta_{t-1}, \eta_t, \ldots, \eta_s)$. But we now know that $\zeta_1, \ldots, \zeta_{t-1}, \eta_t, \ldots, \eta_s$ are algebraic over $K(\zeta_1, \ldots, \zeta_t, \eta_{t+1}, \ldots, \eta_s)$. Hence, by Th. IV, we deduce that ξ is algebraically dependent over $K(\zeta_1, \ldots, \zeta_t, \eta_{t+1}, \ldots, \eta_s)$. Hence $(\zeta_1, \ldots, \zeta_t, \eta_{t+1}, \ldots, \eta_s)$ is an algebraic basis for K^*, and the theorem is proved.

We deduce from the first part of this theorem that any set of t elements, where $t > s$, must be algebraically dependent. Now suppose that the set $(\eta_1, ..., \eta_s)$ is a *minimal* basis for K^*, and let $(\zeta_1, ..., \zeta_{s'})$ be another minimal basis. Then

$$s' \leqslant s \quad \text{and} \quad s \leqslant s',$$

and therefore

$$s = s'.$$

Therefore *the number of elements in a minimal algebraic basis for K^* with respect to K is independent of the minimal basis chosen.* We call this number *the dimension of K^* with respect to K.*

THEOREM VI. *If $\xi_1, ..., \xi_r$ is a minimal algebraic basis for an extension K^* of K, and ζ is any element of K^*, there exists a non-zero irreducible polynomial $f(x_1, ..., x_{r+1})$ in $K[x_1, ..., x_{r+1}]$ such that*

$$f(\xi_1, ..., \xi_r, \zeta) = 0.$$

If $g(x_1, ..., x_{r+1})$ is any other polynomial such that

$$g(\xi_1, ..., \xi_r, \zeta) = 0,$$

then $g(x_1, ..., x_{r+1}) = f(x_1, ..., x_{r+1}) \, h(x_1, ..., x_{r+1}),$

where $h(x_1, ..., x_{r+1})$ is in $K[x_1, ..., x_{r+1}]$.

Since ζ is algebraic over $K(\xi_1, ..., \xi_r)$ there exists a non-zero irreducible polynomial $f(x_1, ..., x_{r+1})$ in $K[x_1, ..., x_{r+1}]$ such that

$$f(\xi_1, ..., \xi_r, \zeta) = 0.$$

Now let $g(x_1, ..., x_{r+1})$ be any polynomial such that

$$g(\xi_1, ..., \xi_r, \zeta) = 0.$$

Since $f(x_1, ..., x_{r+1})$, regarded as a polynomial in $K(x_1, ..., x_r)[x_{r+1}]$, is irreducible, $g(x_1, ..., x_{r+1})$, likewise regarded as a polynomial in $K(x_1, ..., x_r)[x_{r+1}]$, either contains $f(x_1, ..., x_{r+1})$ as a factor, or the two polynomials are relatively prime.

Case (i). Suppose that

$$g(x_1, ..., x_{r+1}) = f(x_1, ..., x_{r+1}) \frac{h(x_1, ..., x_{r+1})}{k(x_1, ..., x_r)}.$$

Then $k(x_1, ..., x_r) \, g(x_1, ..., x_{r+1}) = f(x_1, ..., x_{r+1}) \, h(x_1, ..., x_{r+1}).$

Since $K[x_1, ..., x_{r+1}]$ is a unique factorisation domain, and $f(x_1, ..., x_{r+1})$ is irreducible, and contains terms in x_{r+1}, the polynomial $k(x_1, ..., x_r)$ must be a factor of $h(x_1, ..., x_{r+1})$. Hence, after division by $k(x_1, ..., x_r)$,

$$g(x_1, ..., x_{r+1}) = f(x_1, ..., x_{r+1}) \, h'(x_1, ..., x_{r+1}).$$

Case (ii). If $f(x_1, ..., x_{r+1})$ and $g(x_1, ..., x_{r+1})$ are relatively prime as polynomials in $K(x_1, ..., x_r)[x_{r+1}]$, there exist elements $a(x_1, ..., x_{r+1})$ and $b(x_1, ..., x_{r+1})$ of $K(x_1, ..., x_r)[x_{r+1}]$ such that

$$a(x_1, ..., x_{r+1})f(x_1, ..., x_{r+1}) + b(x_1, ..., x_{r+1})g(x_1, ..., x_{r+1}) = 1.$$

Let
$$a(x_1, ..., x_{r+1}) = \frac{A(x_1, ..., x_{r+1})}{A_1(x_1, ..., x_r)},$$

and
$$b(x_1, ..., x_{r+1}) = \frac{B(x_1, ..., x_{r+1})}{B_1(x_1, ..., x_r)},$$

where $A(x_1, ..., x_{r+1})$ and $B(x_1, ..., x_{r+1})$ lie in $K[x_1, ..., x_{r+1}]$, and $A_1(x_1, ..., x_r)$ and $B_1(x_1, ..., x_r)$ lie in $K[x_1, ..., x_r]$. Then

$$B_1(x_1, ..., x_r) A(x_1, ..., x_{r+1})f(x_1, ..., x_{r+1})$$
$$+ A_1(x_1, ..., x_r) B(x_1, ..., x_{r+1}) g(x_1, ..., x_{r+1})$$
$$= A_1(x_1, ..., x_r) B_1(x_1, ..., x_r),$$

and therefore
$$A_1(\xi_1, ..., \xi_r) B_1(\xi_1, ..., \xi_r)$$
$$= B_1(\xi_1, ..., \xi_r) A(\xi_1, ..., \xi_r, \zeta)f(\xi_1, ..., \xi_r, \zeta)$$
$$+ A_1(\xi_1, ..., \xi_r) B(\xi_1, ..., \xi_r, \zeta) g(\xi_1, ..., \xi_r, \zeta)$$
$$= 0.$$

Hence $\xi_1, ..., \xi_r$ are algebraically dependent over K, contrary to hypothesis. The only possible case is therefore the first, and the theorem is therefore established.

4. Factorisation of polynomials. Let $f(x)$ be any irreducible polynomial in $K[x]$, and let us use it, as in § 1, to construct an algebraic extension $K(\xi)$ of K. Now consider $f(x)$ as a polynomial in $K(\xi)[x]$. By the Remainder Theorem [I, § 6],

$$f(x) = (x - \xi)f_1(x),$$

since $f(\xi) = 0$, $f_1(x)$ lying in $K(\xi)[x]$. Thus, when we extend K to $K(\xi)$, $f(x)$ becomes reducible. More generally, let $F(x)$ be any polynomial of degree n in $K[x]$, and suppose that

$$F(x) = F_1(x) F_2(x) \dots F_k(x),$$

where the factor $F_i(x)$ is irreducible and of degree $n_i > 0$. Then

$$\sum_1^k n_i = n.$$

If, for some i, $n_i > 1$, we can construct an algebraic extension of K in which $F_i(x)$ is reducible; that is, we can find an algebraic extension K' of K over which $F(x)$ has at least $k+1$ factors. Proceeding in this way, we reach a field K^*, which is an algebraic extension of K, over which $F(x)$ is equal to the product of n factors, each of the first degree. When a polynomial with coefficients in a given field can be expressed as the product of *linear* factors, it is said to be *completely reducible* over the field. Hence we have

THEOREM I. *Given any polynomial $f(x)$ in $K[x]$, there exists an algebraic extension of K over which $f(x)$ is completely reducible.*

This theorem takes the place in our present work of the 'Fundamental Theorem of Algebra', which asserts that when K is the field of complex numbers every polynomial in $K[x]$ is completely reducible over K.

A field K which is such that *every* polynomial in $K[x]$ is completely reducible over K is said to be *algebraically closed*. The field of complex numbers is one example of such a field. In later chapters we shall often begin by considering a field K which is algebraically closed. But we cannot restrict ourselves to such fields, for the adjunction of an indeterminate to K gives a field which is not algebraically closed. For instance, if K is the field of complex numbers, and x, y are indeterminates, $x^2 + y^2 - 1$, regarded as a polynomial in y, is irreducible over $K(x)$. We shall therefore investigate fields which are not algebraically closed, merely *stating* the important

THEOREM II. *Given any field K there exists an algebraic extension K^* of K which is algebraically closed. K^* is uniquely defined by K to within equivalent extensions.*

This field K^* is called the *algebraic closure* of K. We shall not use this theorem, and therefore omit the proof, which is difficult.

Let us return to the commutative field K in which the polynomial

$$F(x) = F_1(x) \dots F_k(x)$$

is of degree n, the $F_i(x)$ being irreducible polynomials in $K[x]$. Let K_1^* and K_2^* be any extensions of K over each of which $F(x)$ is completely reducible. If

$$F(x) = a \prod_{i=1}^{n} (x - \xi_i), \quad \text{and} \quad F(x) = a \prod_{i=1}^{n} (x - \eta_i)$$

are the respective factorisations of $F(x)$ in K_1^*, K_2^*, we examine the relation between the extensions $K(\xi_1, ..., \xi_n)$ and $K(\eta_1, ..., \eta_n)$. These fields are subfields of K_1^* and K_2^* respectively. Since we shall not go outside these subfields, we may suppose that

$$K_1^* = K(\xi_1, ..., \xi_n) \quad \text{and} \quad K_2^* = K(\eta_1, ..., \eta_n).$$

Then K_1^* and K_2^* are both algebraic extensions of K [§ 3, Th. II]. We prove that they are *equivalent* extensions of K.

The proof is by induction on n. If $n = 1$ there is nothing to prove, since $K_1^* = K = K_2^*$. We therefore assume that the theorem is true for polynomials $F(x)$ of degree less than n. If the polynomial we are considering has a linear factor $x - \alpha$ in $K[x]$,

$$K(\alpha, \xi_2, ..., \xi_n) = K(\xi_2, ..., \xi_n),$$

and the theorem follows by the induction hypothesis. We now assume that no irreducible factor $F_i(x)$ of $F(x)$ is of degree 1, so that none of $\xi_1, ..., \xi_n$ and $\eta_1, ..., \eta_n$ is in K. Since K_1^* is a field, $K_1^*[x]$ is a unique factorisation domain, and hence the factors of $F_1(x)$ are certain of the factors $x - \xi_i$. By renaming the factors, if necessary, we may assume that $x - \xi_1$ is a factor of $F_1(x)$, so that $F_1(\xi_1) = 0$. Similarly, we may suppose that $F_1(\eta_1) = 0$. By § 2, Th. II, the fields $K(\xi_1)$ and $K(\eta_1)$ are equivalent. It follows that the rings $K(\xi_1)[x]$ and $K(\eta_1)[x]$ are equivalent, so that if

$$F(x) = F_1^{(\xi_1)}(x) ... F_k^{(\xi_1)}(x)$$

is the factorisation of $F(x)$ in $K(\xi_1)[x]$, the polynomials $F_i^{(\xi_1)}(x)$ being irreducible polynomials with coefficients in $K(\xi_1)$, then also

$$F(x) = F_1^{(\eta_1)}(x) ... F_k^{(\eta_1)}(x)$$

is an equivalent factorisation of $F(x)$ in $K(\eta_1)[x]$, the polynomial $F_i^{(\eta_1)}(x)$ being the isomorph of $F_i^{(\xi_1)}(x)$. But $F(x)$ has now a linear factor $x - \xi_1$ in $K(\xi_1)[x]$, or $x - \eta_1$ in $K(\eta_1)[x]$, so that, by the induction hypothesis, we may assume that the extension obtained by adjoining $\xi_2, ..., \xi_n$ to $K(\xi_1)$ is isomorphic with the extension obtained by adjoining $\eta_2, ..., \eta_n$ to $K(\eta_1)$, the isomorphism being such that any element of $K(\xi_1)$ is the isomorph of the corresponding element of the equivalent field $K(\eta_1)$. Hence, $K(\xi_1, ..., \xi_n)$ and $K(\eta_1, ..., \eta_n)$ are equivalent extensions of K.

If $F(x)$ is any polynomial of degree n in $K[x]$, and, if over some extension of K

$$F(x) = a \prod_{i=1}^{n} (x - \xi_i),$$

the field $K(\xi_1, ..., \xi_n)$ is called a *root field* of $F(x)$. We have therefore proved

THEOREM III. *The root field of a polynomial $F(x)$ in $K[x]$ is uniquely defined to within equivalence over K.*

We may use these theorems to illustrate an important observation, namely that, given two extensions K_1 and K_2 of a field K, there may be no extension K^* of K which contains K_1 and K_2 as subfields. To see this, let $F(x)$ be an irreducible polynomial over K, of degree $n(n > 1)$, and take K_1 and K_2 to be equivalent, but not identical, root fields of $F(x)$ such that K_1 and K_2 intersect only in K. Suppose that $\xi_1, ..., \xi_n$ are the roots of $F(x)$ in K_1, and that $\eta_1, ..., \eta_n$ are its roots in K_2. Then $\xi_i \neq \eta_j$ for any choice of i, j. If K^* were a field containing both K_1 and K_2, we should have, over K^*,

$$F(x) = a \prod_{i=1}^{n} (x - \xi_i),$$

and
$$F(\eta_j) = 0.$$

Hence
$$\prod_{i=1}^{n} (\eta_j - \xi_i) = 0,$$

and therefore $\eta_j = \xi_k$ for some choice of k, contrary to hypothesis.

If $F(x)$ is any non-zero polynomial in $K[x]$, any element ξ in K, or in an extension of K, such that $F(\xi) = 0$, is called a *root* or *zero* of $F(x)$. We now prove

THEOREM IV. *A necessary and sufficient condition that two polynomials in $K[x]$ should have a common root is that their highest common factor should be of degree greater than zero.*

Let $F(x)$ and $G(x)$ be the polynomials, $d(x)$ their highest common factor. Then there exist polynomials $a(x), b(x), f(x), g(x)$, all in $K[x]$, such that

$$a(x)\,F(x) + b(x)\,G(x) = d(x), \tag{1}$$

and
$$F(x) = d(x)f(x), \quad G(x) = d(x)g(x). \tag{2}$$

Let K^* be an extension of K such that $F(x)$ and $G(x)$ are completely reducible in $K^*[x]$. Then $d(x)$ is also completely reducible. If ξ is a common root of $F(x)$ and $G(x)$ then, from (1), ξ is a root of $d(x)$, and if ξ is a root of $d(x)$ we see, from (2), that ξ is a root both of $F(x)$ and $G(x)$. This proves the theorem.

We note that the highest common factor of $F(x)$ and $G(x)$ can be found by operations in $K[x]$ [I, § 6], but the common root of $F(x)$

and $G(x)$, if there is one, may lie in some algebraic extension of K, defined by $d(x)$.

The theory of root fields is a large one, but most of it lies outside the scope of this book. We conclude this section with an account of the symmetric functions of the roots of a polynomial.

Let $x_1, \ldots, x_n$ be n independent indeterminates over K, and let

$$c_1 = x_1 + \ldots + x_n,$$
$$c_2 = x_1 x_2 + x_1 x_3 + \ldots + x_{n-1} x_n,$$
$$\cdot \qquad \cdot \qquad \cdot \qquad \cdot \qquad \cdot$$
$$c_n = x_1 \ldots x_n.$$

We call $c_1, c_2, \ldots, c_n$ *the elementary symmetric functions of* $x_1, \ldots, x_n$. They are evidently unchanged by the $n!$ permutations of the indeterminates $x_1, \ldots, x_n$. Any polynomial in $K[x_1, \ldots, x_n]$ is said to be a *symmetric integral function* of $x_1, \ldots, x_n$ if it is unaltered by the $n!$ permutations of $x_1, \ldots, x_n$. We prove that such a polynomial is expressible in terms of the elementary symmetric functions, or, more precisely, we prove

THEOREM V. *If $f(x_1, \ldots, x_n)$ is a symmetric integral function of* $x_1, \ldots, x_n$, *it lies in $K[c_1, \ldots, c_n]$.*

We define the *total degree* of an expression $x_1^{r_1} x_2^{r_2} \ldots x_n^{r_n}$ to be $\sum\limits_{i=1}^{n} r_i$, and the total degree of $f(x_1, \ldots, x_n)$ to be the maximum of the total degrees of its terms $x_1^{r_1} x_2^{r_2} \ldots x_n^{r_n}$ for which the coefficient $a_{r_1 r_2 \ldots r_n} \neq 0$. We prove the theorem by induction, first on n, then on the total degree of $f(x_1, \ldots, x_n)$.

In the case $n = 1$, $c_1 = x_1$, and hence $K[x_1] = K[c_1]$, and the theorem is trivial. On the other hand, if $f(x_1, \ldots, x_n)$ is of total degree 1,

$$f(x_1, \ldots, x_n) = a_1 x_1 + \ldots + a_n x_n + b.$$

Interchange x_i and x_j. Since $f(x_1, \ldots, x_n)$ is symmetric, we must have $a_i = a_j$. We deduce that

$$f(x_1, \ldots, x_n) = a(x_1 + \ldots + x_n) + b$$
$$= ac_1 + b.$$

It therefore lies in $K[c_1, \ldots, c_n]$. Having established our theorem when $n = 1$, we assume that it is true for symmetric integral functions of $x_1, \ldots, x_{n-1}$. It is true for symmetric integral functions of $x_1, \ldots, x_n$ of total degree 1; and so we assume it is true when the total degree is $k-1$, and prove it is true for the symmetric polynomial $f(x_1, ..., x_n)$ of total degree k.

Write
$$f(x_1, ..., x_n) = f_0 + f_1 x_n + ... + f_k x_n^k,$$

where $f_0, ..., f_k$ are in $K[x_1, ..., x_{n-1}]$. If we consider the permutations of $x_1, ..., x_n$ which leave x_n unchanged, $f(x_1, ..., x_n)$ is unchanged, and therefore $f_0, ..., f_k$ are unchanged by the permutations of $x_1, ..., x_{n-1}$. It follows that $f_0, ..., f_k$ are symmetric integral functions of $x_1, ..., x_{n-1}$. By the induction hypothesis each of these polynomials, and in particular f_0, is expressible in terms of the elementary symmetric functions of $x_1, ..., x_{n-1}$. Writing

$$d_0 = 1,$$
$$d_1 = x_1 + ... + x_{n-1},$$
$$d_2 = x_1 x_2 + x_1 x_3 + ... + x_{n-2} x_{n-1},$$
$$\cdot \quad \cdot \quad \cdot \quad \cdot \quad \cdot$$
$$d_{n-1} = x_1 x_2 ... x_{n-1},$$
$$d_n = 0,$$

we have
$$f_0 = \phi_0(d_1, ..., d_{n-1}),$$

and we note that
$$c_i = d_i + x_n d_{i-1} \quad (i = 1, ..., n). \tag{3}$$

Now
$$f(x_1, ..., x_n) = f_0 + x_n F(x_1, ..., x_n),$$

and, by (3),
$$\phi_0(c_1, ..., c_{n-1}) = \phi_0(d_1, ..., d_{n-1}) + x_n \Phi_0(x_1, ..., x_n).$$

Therefore
$$f(x_1, ..., x_n) - \phi_0(c_1, ..., c_{n-1}) = x_n[F(x_1, ..., x_n) - \Phi_0(x_1, ..., x_n)]. \tag{4}$$

The total degree of $\phi_0(c_1, ..., c_{n-1})$, regarded as polynomial in $x_1, ..., x_n$, is equal to that of $\phi_0(d_1, ..., d_{n-1})$, which is that of f_0. Hence, since this cannot exceed k, the total degree of the right-hand side of (4) cannot exceed k. Since the left-hand side of (4) is a symmetric integral function of $x_1, ..., x_n$, the right-hand side must contain, besides x_n, the factor $x_1 x_2 ... x_{n-1}$. We can therefore write

$$f(x_1, ..., x_n) - \phi_0(c_1, ..., c_{n-1}) = x_1 ... x_n G(x_1, ..., x_n)$$
$$= c_n G(x_1, ..., x_n),$$

where $G(x_1, ..., x_n)$ must be symmetric in $x_1, ..., x_n$, and is of total degree $\leqslant k - n$. By hypothesis, we can write

$$G(x_1, ..., x_n) = \psi(c_1, ..., c_n),$$

and finally

$$f(x_1, ..., x_n) = \phi_0(c_1, ..., c_{n-1}) + c_n \psi(c_1, ..., c_n),$$

and thus $f(x_1, ..., x_n)$ lies in $K[c_1, ..., c_n]$. This proves the theorem.

This theorem is mainly used to connect the coefficients of a polynomial with the roots of the polynomial. We adjoin $c_1, ..., c_n$ to K, obtaining a field K^* which is a subfield of $K(x_1, ..., x_n)$. We consider the polynomial in $K^*[x]$,

$$f(x) = x^n - c_1 x^{n-1} + c_2 x^{n-2} - ... + (-1)^n c_n.$$

In an extension of $K^*[x]$ this equation can be written as

$$f(x) = (x - x_1)(x - x_2) ... (x - x_n),$$

and Th. V can be regarded as a property of the root field of $f(x)$.

Again, consider the polynomial

$$F(x) = x^n - \nu_1 x^{n-1} + ... + (-1)^n \nu_n$$

in $K[x]$, and let $\xi_1, ..., \xi_n$ be its roots, in some extension K^* of K. Any element of the root field $K(\xi_1, ..., \xi_n)$ can be written as a polynomial in $\xi_1, ..., \xi_n$ with coefficients in K [§3, Th. II]. Let $a(\xi_1, ..., \xi_n)$ denote such a polynomial. It is said to be a *symmetric function of the roots* $\xi_1, ..., \xi_n$ if $a(x_1, ..., x_n)$ is a symmetric integral function of the indeterminates $x_1, ..., x_n$. By Th. V,

$$a(x_1, ..., x_n) = b(c_1, ..., c_n),$$

where $b(c_1, ..., c_n)$ is a polynomial with coefficients in K. Hence, by specialising $x_i \to \xi_i$ $(i = 1, ..., n)$, we find that

$$a(\xi_1, ..., \xi_n) = b(\nu_1, ..., \nu_n),$$

and we have proved

THEOREM VI. *If $F(x)$ is any polynomial in $K[x]$, any symmetric function of the roots of $F(x)$ lies in K.*

On the other hand, it may happen that $a(\xi_1, ..., \xi_n)$ is in K, although $a(x_1, ..., x_n)$ is not symmetric.

THEOREM VII. *If η is any element in the root field of $F(x)$, the characteristic polynomial of η over K is completely reducible in the root field.*

As above, let $\xi_1, ..., \xi_n$ be the roots of $F(x)$, and let us write

$$\eta = a(\xi_1, ..., \xi_n),$$

where $a(x_1, ..., x_n)$ lies in $K[x_1, ..., x_n]$. Now let

$$a^i(x_1, ..., x_n) \quad (i = 1, ..., n!)$$

denote the result of performing a permutation on the indeterminates $x_1, ..., x_n$ in $a(x_1, ..., x_n)$. Consider the polynomial

$$\prod_{i=1}^{n!} [x - a^i(x_1, ..., x_n)] = x^{n!} + b_1 x^{n!-1} + ... + b_{n!}.$$

The coefficients b_i are clearly symmetric integral functions of $x_1, ..., x_n$, and therefore if

$$\phi(x) = \prod_{i=1}^{n!} [x - a^i(\xi_1, ..., \xi_n)],$$

$\phi(x)$ lies in $K[x]$. But $\phi(\eta) = 0$, and therefore the characteristic polynomial of η is a factor of $\phi(x)$. Since $\phi(x)$ is completely reducible in the root field, so is the characteristic polynomial.

We conclude this section with

THEOREM VIII. *The elementary symmetric functions $c_1, ..., c_n$ of n independent indeterminates over K are themselves algebraically independent over K.*

Let the indeterminates be $x_1, ..., x_n$. If $n = 1$, $c_1 = x_1$, and the result is evident. We prove the theorem by induction on n, using the notation of Th. V. By hypothesis, then, $d_1, ..., d_{n-1}$ are algebraically independent over K. Now, if $c_1, ..., c_n$ are algebraically dependent, there is a relation

$$\phi(c_1, ..., c_n) = \phi_0 + \phi_1 c_n + ... + \phi_l c_n^l = 0,$$

where the ϕ_i lie in $K[c_1, ..., c_{n-1}]$, and are not all zero. Putting $x_n = 0$ in this identity, we find that

$$\phi(d_1, ..., d_{n-1}, 0) = \phi_0(c_1, ..., c_{n-1})_{x_n=0} = \phi_0(d_1, ..., d_{n-1})$$
$$= 0.$$

By hypothesis, $\phi_0(d_1, ..., d_{n-1}) = 0$ implies that ϕ_0 is identically zero. Hence, if $\phi(c_1, ..., c_n) = 0$, we have

$$\phi(c_1, ..., c_n) = c_n \psi(c_1, ..., c_n) = 0,$$

and therefore $\quad \psi(c_1, ..., c_n) = \phi_1 + ... + \phi_l c_n^{l-1} = 0.$

The theorem now follows. For we prove, in succession, that $\phi_1, \phi_2, ..., \phi_l$ are all identically zero.

5. Differentiation of polynomials. Let x be an indeterminate over K, and let

$$f(x) = \alpha_0 + \alpha_1 x + \alpha_2 x^2 + \ldots + \alpha_n x^n$$

be any polynomial in $K[x]$. Then, if h is any new indeterminate,

$$f(x+h) - f(x) = \alpha_0 - \alpha_0 + \alpha_1[(x+h) - x] + \ldots + \alpha_n[(x+h)^n - x^n]$$
$$= h\{\alpha_1 + \alpha_2[x+h+x] + \ldots + \alpha_n[(x+h)^{n-1}$$
$$+ x(x+h)^{n-2} + \ldots + x^{n-1}]\},$$

and therefore

$$\frac{f(x+h) - f(x)}{h} = f'(x) + hg(x, h),$$

where $g(x, h)$ is a polynomial in $K[x, h]$, and

$$f'(x) = \alpha_1 + 2\alpha_2 x + 3\alpha_3 x^2 + \ldots + n\alpha_n x^{n-1}.$$

The polynomial $f'(x)$ is called the *derivative* of $f(x)$ with respect to x, and is often written $\frac{d}{dx} f(x)$ or $\frac{df}{dx}$.

Let us consider in what circumstances $f'(x) = 0$. We must have

$$\alpha_1 = 0, \quad 2\alpha_2 = 0, \quad \ldots, \quad n\alpha_n = 0.$$

If K is without characteristic, this implies that

$$\alpha_1 = \alpha_2 = \ldots = \alpha_n = 0,$$

and therefore $f(x) = \alpha_0$, and so lies in K. Conversely, if $f(x)$ is in K we find that $f'(x) = 0$.

If K has characteristic p, the equation $f'(x) = 0$ implies that the coefficient $\alpha_i = 0$ only when i is not a multiple of p. In this case, then, $f(x)$ lies in $K[x^p]$. Conversely, if $f(x)$ is in $K[x^p]$, the derivative is zero. This difference between fields with and without characteristic has many important consequences, and will shortly lead us to impose the restriction that K be without characteristic.

Let us first note some formal consequences of the law of differentiation. If

$$g(x) = \beta_0 + \beta_1 x + \ldots + \beta_m x^m,$$

we see at once that

$$[f(x) + g(x)]' = (\alpha_1 + \beta_1) + 2(\alpha_2 + \beta_2) x + \ldots$$
$$= f'(x) + g'(x),$$

and that

$$[f(x)\,g(x)]'$$
$$= [\alpha_0\beta_0 + (\alpha_1\beta_0 + \alpha_0\beta_1)\,x + \ldots + (\alpha_r\beta_0 + \alpha_{r-1}\beta_1 + \ldots + \alpha_0\beta_r)\,x^r$$
$$+ \ldots + \alpha_n\beta_m x^{m+n}]'$$
$$= (\alpha_1\beta_0 + \alpha_0\beta_1) + \ldots + r(\alpha_r\beta_0 + \ldots + \alpha_0\beta_r)\,x^{r-1}$$
$$+ \ldots + (m+n)\,\alpha_n\beta_m x^{m+n-1}$$
$$= (\alpha_1 + 2\alpha_2 x + \ldots + n\alpha_n x^{n-1})\,(\beta_0 + \beta_1 x + \ldots + \beta_m x^m)$$
$$+ (\alpha_0 + \alpha_1 x + \ldots + \alpha_n x^n)\,(\beta_1 + 2\beta_2 x + \ldots + m\beta_m x^{m-1})$$
$$= f'(x)\,g(x) + f(x)\,g'(x).$$

As an immediate corollary, we have, for any positive integer r,

$$\{[f(x)]^r\}' = rf'(x)\,[f(x)]^{r-1}.$$

We extend the definition of a derivative to rational functions of x as follows.

If
$$y = \frac{f(x)}{g(x)},$$
so that
$$yg(x) = f(x),$$

we define y', formally, by the equation

$$f'(x) = y'g(x) + yg'(x),$$

and therefore we have the equation

$$y' = \frac{f'(x)}{g(x)} - \frac{f(x)\,g'(x)}{[g(x)]^2} = \frac{f'(x)\,g(x) - f(x)\,g'(x)}{[g(x)]^2}.$$

In the particular case in which $g(x)$ is a factor of $f(x)$, y is a polynomial $h(x)$, and we can verify that $y' = h'(x)$.

The operation of differentiation may be repeated any finite number of times. If $f^{(s)}(x)$ denotes the sth derivative of $f(x)$, the following results are immediate:

(i) $[f^{(r)}(x)]^{(s)} = f^{(r+s)}(x)$;

(ii) $[x^n]^{(r)} = n(n-1)\ldots(n-r+1)\,x^{n-r}$ $(r \leqslant n)$;

(iii) $f^{(r)}(x) = 0$

if $f(x)$ is a polynomial of degree less than r;

(iv) if K is of characteristic p, and $r \geqslant p$,

$$f^{(r)}(x) = 0.$$

This follows from (ii), since, if $r \geqslant p$, one at least of the integers $n, n-1, \ldots, n-r+1$ is a multiple of p.

(v) if K^* is an extension of K, and $f(x)$ is in $K[x]$, the derivative of $f(x)$ in $K^*[x]$ is equal to its derivative in $K[x]$.

If $f(x_1, \ldots, x_n)$ is a polynomial in $K[x_1, \ldots, x_n]$, we may consider it as a polynomial in $K[x_1, \ldots, x_{r-1}, x_{r+1}, \ldots, x_n][x_r]$, and so define its derivative with respect to x_r. We call this the *partial derivative* with respect to x_r, and write it

$$\frac{\partial}{\partial x_r} f(x_1, \ldots, x_r).$$

When $r = 1$,
$$\frac{\partial f}{\partial x_1} = \frac{df}{dx_1}.$$

Now

$$\frac{\partial}{\partial x_r} (ax_1^{m_1} \ldots x_r^{m_r} \ldots x_n^{m_n}) = m_r a x_1^{m_1} \ldots x_{r-1}^{m_{r-1}} x_r^{m_r-1} x_{r+1}^{m_{r+1}} \ldots x_n^{m_n},$$

and therefore, if $r \neq s$,

$$\frac{\partial^2}{\partial x_s \partial x_r} (ax_1^{m_1} \ldots x_n^{m_n}) = \frac{\partial}{\partial x_s} \left[\frac{\partial}{\partial x_r} (ax_1^{m_1} \ldots x_n^{m_n}) \right]$$

$$= m_r m_s a x_1^{m_1} \ldots x_{r-1}^{m_{r-1}} x_r^{m_r-1} \ldots x_{s-1}^{m_{s-1}} x_s^{m_s-1} \ldots x_n^{m_n}$$

$$= \frac{\partial^2}{\partial x_r \partial x_s} (ax_1^{m_1} \ldots x_n^{m_n}),$$

and this relation is obviously true when $r = s$. Similarly, we show that

$$\frac{\partial}{\partial x_r} \left(\frac{\partial^2}{\partial x_s \partial x_t} [ax_1^{m_1} \ldots x_n^{m_n}] \right) = \frac{\partial^2}{\partial x_r \partial x_s} \left(\frac{\partial}{\partial x_t} [ax_1^{m_1} \ldots x_n^{m_n}] \right),$$

and we can write either of these expressions as

$$\frac{\partial^3}{\partial x_r \partial x_s \partial x_t} [ax_1^{m_1} \ldots x_n^{m_n}].$$

Since the polynomial $f(x_1, \ldots, x_n)$ is a sum of terms like $ax_1^{m_1} \ldots x_n^{m_n}$, we obtain the commutative and associative laws

$$\frac{\partial^2}{\partial x_r \partial x_s} f(x_1, \ldots, x_n) = \frac{\partial^2}{\partial x_s \partial x_r} f(x_1, \ldots, x_n),$$

and
$$\frac{\partial}{\partial x_r} \left(\frac{\partial^2}{\partial x_s \partial x_t} f(x_1, \ldots, x_n) \right) = \frac{\partial^2}{\partial x_r \partial x_s} \left(\frac{\partial}{\partial x_t} f(x_1, \ldots, x_n) \right)$$

$$= \frac{\partial^3}{\partial x_r \partial x_s \partial x_t} f(x_1, \ldots, x_n).$$

Our next result is valid without restriction only when the field K is without characteristic. As a preliminary we note that the usual elementary proof of the multinomial theorem

$$(x_1 + \ldots + x_n)^r = \Sigma \frac{r!}{r_1! \ldots r_n!} x_1^{r_1} \ldots x_n^{r_n},$$

where the summation is over all ordered partitions $(r_1, \ldots, r_n)$ of r, is valid over any field K without characteristic.

Now let

$$\Delta_{yx}^r f(x_1, \ldots, x_n) = \Sigma \frac{r!}{r_1! \ldots r_n!} y_1^{r_1} \ldots y_n^{r_n} \frac{\partial^r f(x_1, \ldots, x_n)}{\partial x_1^{r_1} \ldots \partial x_n^{r_n}}.$$

We can write this symbolically as

$$\Delta_{yx}^r f(x_1, \ldots, x_n) = \left(y_1 \frac{\partial}{\partial x_1} + \ldots + y_n \frac{\partial}{\partial x_n} \right)^r f(x_1, \ldots, x_n).$$

We prove

TAYLOR'S THEOREM. *If $f(x_1, \ldots, x_n)$ is any polynomial in $K[x_1, \ldots, x_n]$ of total degree N, then*

$$f(x_1 + y_1, \ldots, x_n + y_n) = \sum_{r=0}^{N} \frac{1}{r!} \Delta_{yx}^r f(x_1, \ldots, x_n).$$

Let us first establish this theorem when $n = 1$. If

$$f(x) = \alpha_0 + \alpha_1 x + \ldots + \alpha_N x^N,$$

then $f(x+y) = \alpha_0 + \alpha_1(x+y) + \ldots + \alpha_N(x+y)^N$

$$= \alpha_0 + \alpha_1 x + \ldots + \alpha_N x^N$$
$$+ y[\alpha_1 + 2\alpha_2 x + \ldots + N\alpha_N x^{N-1}]$$
$$+ \frac{y^2}{2!}[2 \cdot 1\alpha_2 + 3 \cdot 2\alpha_3 x + \ldots + N(N-1)\alpha_N x^{N-2}]$$
$$+ \ldots$$
$$+ \frac{y^N}{N!} N! \alpha_N$$
$$= f(x) + \frac{1}{1!} y \frac{\partial f(x)}{\partial x} + \frac{1}{2!} y^2 \frac{\partial^2 f(x)}{\partial x^2} + \ldots + \frac{1}{N!} y^N \frac{\partial^N f(x)}{\partial x^N}$$
$$= \sum_{r=0}^{N} \frac{1}{r!} \Delta_{yx}^r f(x).$$

We now proceed by the method of induction, assuming that the result is true for any polynomial in less than n indeterminates. If

$$D_{yx}^r = \left(y_1\frac{\partial}{\partial x_1} + \cdots + y_{n-1}\frac{\partial}{\partial x_{n-1}}\right)^r,$$

we verify by direct calculation that

$$\Delta_{yx}^r f(x_1, \ldots, x_n) = \left(y_1\frac{\partial}{\partial x_1} + \cdots + y_{n-1}\frac{\partial}{\partial x_{n-1}} + y_n\frac{\partial}{\partial x_n}\right)^r f(x_1, \ldots, x_n)$$

$$= \sum_{s=0}^r \binom{r}{s} y_n^s \frac{\partial^s}{\partial x_n^s}[D_{yx}^{r-s}f(x_1, \ldots, x_n)].$$

Now, by the induction hypothesis,

$$f(x_1+y_1, \ldots, x_{n-1}+y_{n-1}, x_n+y_n) = \sum_{s=0}^N \frac{1}{s!}D_{yx}^s f(x_1, \ldots, x_{n-1}, x_n+y_n),$$

and, applying Taylor's Theorem for the case $n = 1$, we have

$$D_{yx}^s f(x_1, \ldots, x_{n-1}, x_n+y_n) = \sum_{t=0}^{N-s}\frac{1}{t!}y_n^t\frac{\partial^t}{\partial x_n^t}D_{yx}^s f(x_1, \ldots, x_n).$$

Therefore

$$f(x_1+y_1, \ldots, x_n+y_n) = \sum_{s=0}^N\frac{1}{s!}\sum_{t=0}^{N-s}\frac{1}{t!}y_n^t\frac{\partial^t}{\partial x_n^t}D_{yx}^s f(x_1, \ldots, x_n).$$

The summations on the right are over a lattice of points on the boundary of and within an isosceles right-angled triangle of side N. We may exhaust all the points of the lattice by considering those on lines parallel to the hypotenuse. In other words, put

$$s+t = r \quad (0 \leqslant t \leqslant r),$$

and let r vary from 0 to N. Then

$$f(x_1+y_1, \ldots, x_n+y_n) = \sum_{r=0}^N\sum_{t=0}^r\frac{1}{(r-t)!}\frac{1}{t!}y_n^t\frac{\partial^t}{\partial x_n^t}D_{yx}^{r-t}f(x_1, \ldots, x_n)$$

$$= \sum_{r=0}^N\frac{1}{r!}\sum_{t=0}^r\binom{r}{t}y_n^t\frac{\partial^t}{\partial x_n^t}D_{yx}^{r-t}f(x_1, \ldots, x_n)$$

$$= \sum_{r=0}^N\frac{1}{r!}\Delta_{yx}^r f(x_1, \ldots, x_n),$$

by the result stated above. This proves the theorem.

We now consider certain applications of the process of differentiation to the theory of the roots of a polynomial.

THEOREM I. *If $f(x)$ is any polynomial in $K[x]$ of degree n greater than zero, a necessary and sufficient condition that (in an extension K^* of K in which it is completely reducible) $f(x)$ should have less than n distinct roots is that the highest common factor of $f(x)$ and $f'(x)$ be of degree greater than zero, or else that $f'(x) = 0$.*

The latter case only arises in the case of a field of finite characteristic.

(i) The condition is necessary. Suppose that $f(x)$ is completely reducible in $K^*[x]$ and that

$$f(x) = a(x - \xi_1)^{m_1} \dots (x - \xi_r)^{m_r} \quad (m_i > 0),$$

where $\xi_1, \dots, \xi_r$ are distinct. Then

$$f'(x) = a \sum_{i=1}^{r} m_i (x - \xi_1)^{m_1} \dots (x - \xi_i)^{m_i - 1} \dots (x - \xi_r)^{m_r}.$$

If $m_1, \dots, m_s > 1$, $m_{s+1}, \dots, m_r = 1$, then

$$f'(x) = 0,$$

or else $\qquad\qquad (x - \xi_1)^{m_1 - 1} \dots (x - \xi_s)^{m_s - 1}$

is a common factor in $K^*[x]$ of $f(x)$ and $f'(x)$. Since $f(x)$ and $f'(x)$ are not relatively prime in $K^*[x]$, they cannot be relatively prime in $K[x]$ [I, § 6, Th. II].

(ii) The condition is sufficient. Consider, first, the case in which $f'(x)$ is zero. Then, as we saw above, p. 119, K must be of finite characteristic, say p, and $f(x)$ is in $K[x^p]$. Let

$$f(x) = \phi(x^p),$$

where $\phi(y)$ is in $K[y]$. There exists an extension K' of K such that $\phi(y)$ is completely reducible in $K'[y]$:

$$\phi(y) = a \prod_{i=1}^{r} (y + \eta_i) \quad (rp = n).$$

There also exists an extension K^* of K' containing elements $\xi_1, \dots, \xi_r$ such that

$$\xi_i^p = \eta_i \quad (i = 1, \dots, r).$$

Now, since K^* is of characteristic p, a simple application of the binomial theorem shows that

$$(x + \xi_i)^p = x^p + \xi_i^p = x^p + \eta_i.$$

Hence in $K^*[x]$,

$$f(x) = a \prod_{i=1}^{r} (x^p + \eta_i)$$

$$= a \left\{ \prod_{i=1}^{r} (x + \xi_i) \right\}^p.$$

Hence $f(x)$ is completely reducible in $K^*[x]$ and has only r distinct roots, $\xi_1, ..., \xi_r$.

Next, suppose that $f'(x)$ is not zero, and that $f(x)$ and $f'(x)$ have a common factor $g(x)$ of degree greater than zero. Since $f'(x)$ is of degree $n-1$, $g(x)$ is of degree $m < n$. We have

$$f(x) = g(x)\, h(x),$$

and hence $$f'(x) = g(x)\, h'(x) + g'(x)\, h(x).$$

Since $g(x)$ is a factor of $f'(x)$ it is a factor of $g'(x)\, h(x)$, or else this product is zero. Since $h(x)$ is not zero, the product can only vanish if $g'(x)$ is zero. The proof given above shows that $g(x)$ is then the pth power of a polynomial in some extension $K'[x]$ of $K[x]$, and hence in this extension $f(x)$ has a multiple factor. On the other hand, if $g'(x)$ is not zero and $g(x)$ is a factor of $g'(x)\, h(x)$, $g(x)$ and $h(x)$ must have a common factor, since $g'(x)$ is of lower degree than $g(x)$. Hence once again $f(x)$ contains a multiple factor. Hence in both cases we have, for a suitable extension K',

$$f(x) = \prod_i [f_i(x)]^{m_i},$$

where some $m_i > 1$. Making a further extension K^* of K' so that each $f_i(x)$ is completely reducible in $K^*[x]$, we obtain the required theorem.

We conclude this section with

THEOREM II. *If K is without characteristic, the roots of an irreducible polynomial $f(x)$ are all distinct.*

In the root field we may write

$$f(x) = a \prod_{i=1}^{n} (x - \xi_i),$$

and we must prove that $\xi_1, ..., \xi_n$ are all distinct. If they are not, the previous theorem tells us that $f(x)$ and $f'(x)$ have a common factor. Since $f'(x)$ is of lower degree than $f(x)$, and $f(x)$ is irreducible, there is no common factor. K being without characteristic, we have excluded the possibility of $f'(x)$ being identically zero.

6. Primitive elements of algebraic extensions. In § 3, Th. I, we saw that any extension of K of finite degree was an algebraic extension of K. On the other hand, we saw in § 1 that a simple algebraic extension of K is an extension of finite degree. We now strengthen this relationship between extensions of finite degree and simple algebraic extensions by proving

THEOREM I. *If K is a commutative field without characteristic, any extension K^* of K which is of finite degree is a simple algebraic extension.*

Since K^* is an extension of finite degree we can write

$$K^* = K(\tau_1, \ldots, \tau_n),$$

where $\tau_1, \ldots, \tau_n$ are algebraic over K. We prove the theorem by induction on n. When $n = 1$, $K(\tau_1)$ is the algebraic extension of K defined by the characteristic polynomial of τ_1 [§ 2, Th. I]. We therefore assume that the theorem is true for $K(\tau_1, \ldots, \tau_{n-1})$. By hypothesis, there exists an element ζ of $K(\tau_1, \ldots, \tau_{n-1})$ such that

$$K(\zeta) = K(\tau_1, \ldots, \tau_{n-1}).$$

We must show that $K(\zeta, \tau_n)$ is a simple algebraic extension of K. Thus we need only consider the case $n = 2$; that is, we need only prove the theorem for the field $K(\xi, \eta)$, and the theorem will then be proved by induction.

Let $f(x)$ and $g(x)$ be the characteristic polynomials of ξ and η with respect to K, and suppose that in the extension K' of K

$$f(x) = (x - \xi_1) \ldots (x - \xi_n), \quad g(x) = (x - \eta_1) \ldots (x - \eta_m),$$

where we may suppose that $\xi = \xi_1$ and $\eta = \eta_1$. The result we are trying to prove is trivial if either n or m is equal to 1, so we assume that $n > 1$, and $m > 1$.

Since K is without characteristic and $f(x)$, $g(x)$ are both irreducible, the roots $\xi_1, \ldots, \xi_n$ are distinct, and so are the roots $\eta_1, \ldots, \eta_m$ [§ 5, Th. II]. If $k \neq 1$, then $\eta_k \neq \eta$, and therefore the equation

$$\xi_i + x\eta_k = \xi + x\eta \tag{1}$$

has, for all values of i, a unique solution $x = c_{ik}$ in K'. The field K is without characteristic, and therefore contains an infinite number of distinct elements. We can therefore find in K an element c different from any of the solutions

$$c_{ik} \quad (i = 1, ..., n; \; k = 2, ..., m)$$

of the equation (1) which happen to be in K. For this value of c,

$$\xi_i + c\eta_k \neq \xi + c\eta \quad (i = 1, ..., n; \; k = 2, ..., m).$$

Let θ be the element in $K(\xi, \eta)$ defined by

$$\theta = \xi + c\eta.$$

Since θ is in $K(\xi, \eta)$, $K(\theta)$ lies in $K(\xi, \eta)$. We prove, conversely, that $K(\xi, \eta)$ lies in $K(\theta)$, and therefore that the two fields are the same.
     We know that
$$g(\eta) = 0,$$
and
$$f(\xi) = f(\theta - c\eta) = 0.$$
Writing
$$f(\theta - cx) = h(x),$$

the polynomial $h(x)$ lies in $K(\theta)[x]$. Also, the polynomials $h(x)$ and $g(x)$ have the common factor $x - \eta$ in $K'[x]$. This is also the *highest* common factor, for if $x - \eta_k$ $(k > 1)$ were a common factor,

$$h(\eta_k) = f(\theta - c\eta_k) = 0,$$

and for some value of i we should have

$$\theta - c\eta_k = \xi_i,$$
and therefore
$$\theta = \xi_i + c\eta_k,$$

contrary to the definition of c. The polynomials $g(x)$, $h(x)$ of $K(\theta)[x]$ therefore have $x - \eta$ as their highest common factor in $K'[x]$. Their highest common factor in $K(\theta)[x]$ is therefore

$$ax + b = a(x - \eta) \quad (a \text{ and } b \text{ in } K(\theta)).$$

It follows that η is in $K(\theta)$. But

$$\xi = \theta - c\eta,$$

and therefore ξ is also in $K(\theta)$. Hence $K(\xi, \eta)$ is in $K(\theta)$, and the theorem follows.
     An element ξ of an extension K^* of K is called a *primitive element* of K if $K^* = K(\xi)$. Any extension of finite degree of a field without characteristic therefore contains primitive elements.

7. Differentiation of algebraic functions. In §5 we defined the partial derivatives of a polynomial in $K[x_1, ..., x_n]$ with respect to $x_1, ..., x_n$. *Assuming that the ground field K is without characteristic* we now show how to extend the definition so that we can define the partial derivatives of an algebraic function η of $x_1, ..., x_n$. We shall then obtain an important criterion for the algebraic independence of a given set of elements of a given function field.

Let K^* be an algebraic extension of $K[x_1, ..., x_n]$, and let η be any element of it. As in §3, η is said to be an *algebraic function* of the indeterminates $x_1, ..., x_n$. By §3, Th. VI, there exists an irreducible polynomial $f(x_1, ..., x_n, y)$, unique save for a non-zero factor in K, such that

$$f(x_1, ..., x_n, \eta) = 0.$$

Any polynomial $g(x_1, ..., x_n, y)$ such that

$$g(x_1, ..., x_n, \eta) = 0$$

contains $f(x_1, ..., x_n, y)$ as a factor. Now, $x_1, ..., x_n$ are algebraically independent over K. The polynomial $f(x_1, ..., x_n, y)$ therefore contains y, and, since K is without characteristic,

$$\frac{\partial}{\partial y} f(x_1, ..., x_n, y) \neq 0.$$

We write

$$\frac{\partial}{\partial \eta} f(x_1, ..., x_n, \eta)$$

for the result of replacing y by η in $\frac{\partial}{\partial y} f(x_1, ..., x_n, y)$. This latter polynomial cannot contain $f(x_1, ..., x_n, y)$ as a factor, and therefore

$$\frac{\partial}{\partial \eta} f(x_1, ..., x_n, \eta) \neq 0.$$

With these preliminaries, we define the partial derivatives $\partial \eta / \partial x_i$ by means of the equations

$$\frac{\partial}{\partial \eta} f(x_1, ..., x_n, \eta) \frac{\partial \eta}{\partial x_i} + \frac{\partial}{\partial x_i} f(x_1, ..., x_n, \eta) = 0 \quad (i = 1, ..., n).$$

We note that if $F(x_1, ..., x_n, y)$ is any polynomial such that

$$F(x_1, ..., x_n, \eta) = 0,$$

then $\qquad F(x_1, ..., x_n, y) = G(x_1, ..., x_n, y) f(x_1, ..., x_n, y),$

and therefore

$$\frac{\partial}{\partial y} F(x_1, ..., x_n, y) \frac{\partial \eta}{\partial x_i} + \frac{\partial}{\partial x_i} F(x_1, ..., x_n, y)$$

$$= f(x_1, ..., x_n, y) \left[\frac{\partial}{\partial y} G(x_1, ..., x_n, y) \frac{\partial \eta}{\partial x_i} + \frac{\partial}{\partial x_i} G(x_1, ..., x_n, y) \right]$$

$$+ G(x_1, ..., x_n, y) \left[\frac{\partial}{\partial y} f(x_1, ..., x_n, y) \frac{\partial \eta}{\partial x_i} + \frac{\partial}{\partial x_i} f(x_1, ..., x_n, y) \right].$$

It follows that

$$\frac{\partial}{\partial \eta} F(x_1, ..., x_n, \eta) \frac{\partial \eta}{\partial x_i} + \frac{\partial}{\partial x_i} F(x_1, ..., x_n, \eta) = 0.$$

In the particular case in which η lies in $K(x_1, ..., x_n)$, our definition of $\partial \eta / \partial x_i$ coincides with that given in § 5. For if

$$\eta = \frac{g(x_1, ..., x_n)}{h(x_1, ..., x_n)},$$

where both $g(x_1, ..., x_n)$ and $h(x_1, ..., x_n)$ are polynomials without common factor, the characteristic polynomial of η is

$$f(x_1, ..., x_n, y) = h(x_1, ..., x_n) y - g(x_1, ..., x_n),$$

and our present definition leads to

$$\frac{\partial \eta}{\partial x_i} = \left[h(x_1, ..., x_n) \frac{\partial}{\partial x_i} g(x_1, ..., x_n) - g(x_1, ..., x_n) \frac{\partial}{\partial x_i} h(x_1, ..., x_n) \right]$$
$$\times [h(x_1, ..., x_n)]^{-2}.$$

Since the dimension of K^* is n, a minimal basis is formed by any n algebraically independent elements of K^*. Let $\xi_1, ..., \xi_n$ be n such elements. Then, by § 3, Th. VI, there exists a unique irreducible polynomial $F(x_1, ..., x_n, y)$ such that

$$F(\xi_1, ..., \xi_n, \eta) = 0.$$

As above, we show that

$$\frac{\partial}{\partial \eta} F(\xi_1, ..., \xi_n, \eta) \neq 0,$$

and define $\partial \eta / \partial \xi_i$ by the equations

$$\frac{\partial}{\partial \eta} F(\xi_1, ..., \xi_n, \eta) \frac{\partial \eta}{\partial \xi_i} + \frac{\partial}{\partial \xi_i} F(\xi_1, ..., \xi_n, \eta) = 0.$$

We wish to establish a relation between the partial derivatives $\partial \eta / \partial x_i$ and $\partial \eta / \partial \xi_i$, but we must first prove a lemma.

HP I

Let $\xi_1, ..., \xi_r$ be r elements of an algebraic extension of a field K without characteristic, and let $f_i(x)$ be the characteristic polynomial of ξ_i with respect to K. We prove that

If $F(x_1, ..., x_r)$ is any polynomial in $K[x_1, ..., x_r]$ such that
$$F(\xi_1, ..., \xi_r) = 0,$$
then there exist polynomials $A(x_1, ..., x_r)$, $B_i(x_1, ..., x_r)$ in $K[x_1, ..., x_r]$, where $A(\xi_1, ..., \xi_r) \neq 0$, such that
$$A(x_1, ..., x_r) F(x_1, ..., x_r) = \sum_{i=1}^{r} B_i(x_1, ..., x_r) f_i(x_i).$$

This result has been proved already when $r = 1$, being implicit in § 2, Th. I, and we proceed by induction, assuming its truth when $r = s - 1$. In place of K, we consider the field $K(\xi_s)$, which is a simple algebraic extension of K. Over this new field the characteristic polynomials $f_i(x)$ $(i = 1, ..., s-1)$ of $\xi_1, ..., \xi_{s-1}$ may be reducible. But since $K(\xi_s)$, with K, is without characteristic, only one irreducible factor of each characteristic polynomial $f_i(x)$ can become zero for the specialisation $x \to \xi_i$. We write
$$f_i(x) = \phi_i(\xi_s, x) \, \psi_i(\xi_s, x),$$
where $\phi_i(x_s, x)$ and $\psi_i(x_s, x)$ are polynomials in $K[x_s, x]$, $\phi_i(\xi_s, x)$ is irreducible in $K(\xi_s)[x]$, and
$$\phi_i(\xi_s, \xi_i) = 0, \quad \psi_i(\xi_s, \xi_i) \neq 0 \quad (i = 1, ..., s-1).$$
By hypothesis, there exist polynomials
$$a(x_1, ..., x_{s-1}, \xi_s) \quad \text{and} \quad b_i(x_1, ..., x_{s-1}, \xi_s)$$
in $K(\xi_s)[x_1, ..., x_{s-1}]$ such that $a(\xi_1, ..., \xi_{s-1}, \xi_s) \neq 0$, and
$$a(x_1, ..., x_{s-1}, \xi_s) F(x_1, ..., x_{s-1}, \xi_s) = \sum_{i=1}^{s-1} b_i(x_1, ..., x_{s-1}, \xi_s) \phi_i(\xi_s, x_i). \quad (1)$$

Since $K(\xi_s)$ is a simple algebraic extension of K we may assume [§ 1, (1)] that $a(x_1, ..., x_s)$ and $b_i(x_1, ..., x_s)$ are in $K[x_1, ..., x_s]$. Now multiply (1) by appropriate factors, so that each term $\phi_i(\xi_s, x_i)$ is replaced by $f_i(x_i)$. Then (1) becomes
$$\left\{ \prod_{i=1}^{s-1} \psi_i(\xi_s, x_i) \right\} a(x_1, ..., x_{s-1}, \xi_s) F(x_1, ..., x_{s-1}, \xi_s)$$
$$= \sum_{i=1}^{s-1} B_i(x_1, ..., x_{s-1}, \xi_s) f_i(x_i), \quad (2)$$
where
$$B_i(x_1, ..., x_{s-1}, \xi_s) = b_i(x_1, ..., x_{s-1}, \xi_s) \prod_j \psi_j(\xi_s, x_j)$$
$$(j = 1, ..., i-1, i+1, ..., s-1).$$

If we write

$$A(x_1, ..., x_s) = a(x_1, ..., x_s) \prod_{i=1}^{s-1} \psi_i(x_s, x_i),$$

we have

$$A(\xi_1, ..., \xi_s) = a(\xi_1, ..., \xi_s) \prod_{i=1}^{s-1} \psi_i(\xi_s, \xi_i) \neq 0.$$

Now, the polynomial

$$A(x_1, ..., x_s) F(x_1, ..., x_{s-1}, x_s) - \sum_{i=1}^{s-1} B_i(x_1, ..., x_s) f_i(x_i) \qquad (3)$$

vanishes (by (2)) for the specialisation

$$x_s \to \xi_s.$$

This must be true for the coefficient of each power-product in $x_1, ..., x_{s-1}$. Hence, the coefficient of each power-product must be of the form $\theta(x_s) f_s(x_s)$. Therefore the polynomial (3) must be equal to $B_s(x_1, ..., x_s) f_s(x_s)$, where $B_s(x_1, ..., x_s)$ lies in $K[x_1, ..., x_s]$. Therefore

$$A(x_1, ..., x_s) F(x_1, ..., x_s) = \sum_{i=1}^{s} B_i(x_1, ..., x_s) f_i(x_i),$$

and our lemma is proved.

Now let $\eta_1, ..., \eta_n$ be n elements of an algebraic extension K^* of $K(x_1, ..., x_n)$ which are algebraically independent over K, and let ζ be any other element of K^*. By §3, Th. VI, there exist unique irreducible polynomials $f(x_1, ..., x_n, z)$, $g(y_1, ..., y_n, z)$ such that

$$f(x_1, ..., x_n, \zeta) = 0 \quad \text{and} \quad g(\eta_1, ..., \eta_n, \zeta) = 0,$$

and also unique irreducible polynomials $f_i(x_1, ..., x_n, y_i)$ such that

$$f_i(x_1, ..., x_n, \eta_i) = 0 \quad (i = 1, ..., n).$$

In the lemma proved above, take the field $K(x_1, ..., x_n)$ in place of K, and the field K^* in place of the extension field of K. Then we can find polynomials

$$A(x, y, z) = A(x_1, ..., x_n, y_1, ..., y_n, z),$$
$$B_i(x, y, z) = B_i(x_1, ..., x_n, y_1, ..., y_n, z),$$
$$C(x, y, z) = C(x_1, ..., x_n, y_1, ..., y_n, z)$$

such that

$$A(x, y, z) g(y_1, ..., y_n, z)$$
$$= \sum_{i=1}^{n} B_i(x, y, z) f_i(x_1, ..., x_n, y_i) + C(x, y, z) f(x_1, ..., x_n, z),$$

where

$$A(x, \eta, \zeta) \neq 0.$$

Differentiating this equation with respect to x_i, y_j, z, and substituting η_j for y_j, ζ for z, we obtain the equations

$$0 = \sum_{t=1}^{n} B_t(x, \eta, \zeta) \frac{\partial}{\partial x_i} f_t(x, \eta_t) + C(x, \eta, \zeta) \frac{\partial}{\partial x_i} f(x, \zeta), \tag{4}$$

$$A(x, \eta, \zeta) \frac{\partial}{\partial \eta_j} g(\eta, \zeta) = B_j(x, \eta, \zeta) \frac{\partial}{\partial \eta_j} f_j(x, \eta_j), \tag{5}$$

$$A(x, \eta, \zeta) \frac{\partial}{\partial \zeta} g(\eta, \zeta) = C(x, \eta, \zeta) \frac{\partial}{\partial \zeta} f(x, \zeta). \tag{6}$$

Since $A(x, \eta, \zeta) \neq 0$ and $\frac{\partial}{\partial \zeta} g(\eta, \zeta) \neq 0$, it follows that $C(x, \eta, \zeta) \neq 0$.

We know already that $\frac{\partial}{\partial \zeta} f(x, \zeta) \neq 0$. Now, since $f(x, \zeta) = 0$,

$$\frac{\partial \zeta}{\partial x_i} = -\frac{\partial}{\partial x_i} f(x, \zeta) \Big/ \frac{\partial}{\partial \zeta} f(x, \zeta)$$

$$= \sum_{t=1}^{n} B_t(x, \eta, \zeta) \frac{\partial}{\partial x_i} f_t(x, \eta_t) \Big/ C(x, \eta, \zeta) \frac{\partial}{\partial \zeta} f(x, \zeta)$$

$$= \sum_{t=1}^{n} B_t(x, \eta, \zeta) \frac{\partial}{\partial x_i} f_t(x, \eta_t) \Big/ A(x, \eta, \zeta) \frac{\partial}{\partial \zeta} g(\eta, \zeta)$$

$$= \sum_{t=1}^{n} \left[\frac{\partial}{\partial \eta_t} g(\eta, \zeta) \Big/ \frac{\partial}{\partial \zeta} g(\eta, \zeta) \right] \left[\frac{\partial}{\partial x_i} f_t(x, \eta_t) \Big/ \frac{\partial}{\partial \eta_t} f_t(x, \eta_t) \right],$$

using (4), (6), and (5) respectively. But this last expression is

$$\sum_{t=1}^{n} \frac{\partial \zeta}{\partial \eta_t} \frac{\partial \eta_t}{\partial x_i}.$$

Hence we have proved

THEOREM I. *If $\eta_1, \ldots, \eta_n$ is any minimal basis for an algebraic extension K^* of $K(x_1, \ldots, x_n)$, and ζ is any element of K^*, then*

$$\frac{\partial \zeta}{\partial x_i} = \sum_{j=1}^{n} \frac{\partial \zeta}{\partial \eta_j} \frac{\partial \eta_j}{\partial x_i}.$$

Since the particular basis $x_1, \ldots, x_n$ for K^* has no special significance, this theorem gives a rule for determining the partial derivatives of ζ with respect to any base $\eta_1, ..., \eta_n$ when they are known for any other base $x_1, ..., x_n$. In particular

$$\frac{\partial x_i}{\partial x_j} = \delta_{ij} = \sum_{k=1}^{n} \frac{\partial x_i}{\partial \eta_k} \frac{\partial \eta_k}{\partial x_j}.$$

Hence we have a

Corollary. The matrices

$$\left(\frac{\partial x_i}{\partial \eta_j}\right) \quad and \quad \left(\frac{\partial \eta_i}{\partial x_j}\right)$$

are inverses of one another.

The partial derivatives $\dfrac{\partial \zeta}{\partial \eta_i}$ $(i = 1, ..., n)$ are defined only when the minimal basis $\eta_1, ..., \eta_n$ is given. If $\eta_1, ..., \eta_r$ are *any* elements of K^* and ζ is any other element of K^* algebraically dependent on them, the irreducible polynomial $f(y_1, ..., y_r, z)$ such that

$$f(\eta, \zeta) = f(\eta_1, ..., \eta_r, \zeta) = 0$$

may not be unique. If $\dfrac{\partial f}{\partial \zeta} = \left[\dfrac{\partial}{\partial z} f(y, z)\right]_{\substack{y_i = \eta_i \\ z = \zeta}}$ is not zero, and if we define $\dfrac{\partial \zeta}{\partial \eta_i}$ formally by the equation

$$\frac{\partial}{\partial \zeta} f(\eta, \zeta) \frac{\partial \zeta}{\partial \eta_i} + \frac{\partial}{\partial \eta_i} f(\eta, \zeta) = 0,$$

the proof of Th. I, which does not make use of the fact that $\eta_1, ..., \eta_n$ are algebraically independent, shows that

$$\frac{\partial \zeta}{\partial x_i} = \sum_{j=1}^{r} \frac{\partial \zeta}{\partial \eta_j} \frac{\partial \eta_j}{\partial x_i}.$$

This result has some importance in practical problems.

Now let $x_1, ..., x_n$ be any minimal basis for an algebraic function field, and let $\eta_1, ..., \eta_r$ be r elements of the function field. The $r \times n$ matrix

$$\left(\frac{\partial \eta_i}{\partial x_j}\right)$$

is called the *Jacobian matrix* of the functions $\eta_1, ..., \eta_r$ with respect to $x_1, ..., x_n$. When $r = n$ the determinant of the Jacobian matrix is called, simply, the *Jacobian* of $\eta_1, ..., \eta_n$ with respect to $x_1, ..., x_n$, and is denoted by

$$\frac{\partial(\eta_1, ..., \eta_n)}{\partial(x_1, ..., x_n)}.$$

THEOREM II. *If $(x_1, \ldots, x_n)$ is a minimal basis for an algebraic function field K^*, and $\eta_1, \ldots, \eta_n$ are n elements of K^*, a necessary and sufficient condition for $\eta_1, \ldots, \eta_n$ to be algebraically independent is*

$$\frac{\partial(\eta_1, \ldots, \eta_n)}{\partial(x_1, \ldots, x_n)} \neq 0.$$

(i) Suppose that $\eta_1, \ldots, \eta_n$ are algebraically dependent. Let $f(y_1, \ldots, y_n)$ be a non-zero polynomial such that

$$f(\eta_1, \ldots, \eta_n) = 0.$$

At least one of the $\eta_1, \ldots, \eta_n$ is algebraically dependent on the rest. After rearrangement, let this be η_n. Then we may assume that $f(\eta_1, \ldots, \eta_{n-1}, y_n)$ is a non-zero irreducible polynomial in

$$K[\eta_1, \ldots, \eta_{n-1}][y_n],$$

and since $K(\eta_1, \ldots, \eta_{n-1})$ is without characteristic,

$$\frac{\partial}{\partial \eta_n} f(\eta_1, \ldots, \eta_{n-1}, \eta_n) \neq 0.$$

Also, $f(\eta_1, \ldots, \eta_{n-1}, \eta_n)$ is the zero of K^*, and therefore

$$\frac{\partial}{\partial x_i} f(\eta_1, \ldots, \eta_n) = 0 \quad (i = 1, \ldots, n).$$

But

$$\sum_{j=1}^{n} \frac{\partial f}{\partial \eta_j} \frac{\partial \eta_j}{\partial x_i} = \frac{\partial f}{\partial x_i} = 0 \quad (i = 1, \ldots, n),$$

and, since not all $\partial f/\partial \eta_j$ are zero, it follows that

$$\det\left(\frac{\partial \eta_i}{\partial x_j}\right) = \frac{\partial(\eta_1, \ldots, \eta_n)}{\partial(x_1, \ldots, x_n)} = 0.$$

(ii) Now suppose that $\eta_1, \ldots, \eta_n$ are algebraically independent. Then we may take them to be a minimal basis for K^*, and $\partial x_i/\partial \eta_j$ is uniquely defined. By the corollary to Th. I,

$$\frac{\partial(\eta_1, \ldots, \eta_n)}{\partial(x_1, \ldots, x_n)} \frac{\partial(x_1, \ldots, x_n)}{\partial(\eta_1, \ldots, \eta_n)} = 1,$$

and therefore

$$\frac{\partial(\eta_1, \ldots, \eta_n)}{\partial(x_1, \ldots, x_n)} \neq 0.$$

More generally, we can prove

THEOREM III. *If $(x_1, ..., x_n)$ is a minimal basis for an algebraic function field K^*, and $\eta_1, ..., \eta_r$ are r elements of K^*, a necessary and sufficient condition that $\eta_1, ..., \eta_r$ be algebraically independent is that the Jacobian matrix of $\eta_1, ..., \eta_r$ with respect to $x_1, ..., x_n$ be of rank r.*

Suppose that the Jacobian matrix is of rank r. By II, § 3, Th. IV, this matrix can be augmented to a regular $n \times n$ matrix, the elements in the part added being

$$\delta_{i_\rho j} \quad (\rho = r+1, ..., n; j = 1, ..., n),$$

where $(i_{r+1}, ..., i_n)$ is a derangement of the set $(r+1, ..., n)$. Hence, by the above theorem, the elements

$$\eta_1, ..., \eta_r, \quad x_{i_{r+1}}, ..., x_{i_n}$$

are algebraically independent. Therefore the subset $\eta_1, ..., \eta_r$ is a set of algebraically independent elements.

To prove that the condition is necessary, we assume that $\eta_1, ..., \eta_r$ are algebraically independent. Then $r \leqslant n$, and by the Exchange Theorem for algebraic dependence [§ 3, Th. V], we can find $n - r$ of the x's, say

$$\eta_\rho = x_{i_\rho} \quad (\rho = r+1, ..., n),$$

such that the set $(\eta_1, ..., \eta_n)$ is a minimal basis for K^*. Then

$$\frac{\partial(\eta_1, ..., \eta_n)}{\partial(x_1, ..., x_n)} \neq 0,$$

and the rows of the matrix

$$\left(\frac{\partial \eta_i}{\partial x_j}\right)$$

must be linearly independent. In particular, the first r rows are linearly independent, and the rank of the Jacobian matrix of $\eta_1, ..., \eta_r$ with respect to $x_1, ..., x_n$ is r. This completes the proof.

Finally, we note the following theorem, which is an immediate consequence of the results proved in Th. I:

THEOREM IV. *If $(x_1, ..., x_n)$, $(y_1, ..., y_n)$, $(z_1, ..., z_n)$ are three minimal bases of an algebraic function field K^*, the Jacobians satisfy the relations*

$$\frac{\partial(z_1, ..., z_n)}{\partial(x_1, ..., x_n)} = \frac{\partial(z_1, ..., z_n)}{\partial(y_1, ..., y_n)} \frac{\partial(y_1, ..., y_n)}{\partial(x_1, ..., x_n)},$$

$$\frac{\partial(y_1, ..., y_n)}{\partial(x_1, ..., x_n)} \frac{\partial(x_1, ..., x_n)}{\partial(y_1, ..., y_n)} = 1.$$

8. Some useful theorems. We conclude this chapter with the proof of some theorems which are of use in later chapters.

THEOREM I. *If K is any commutative field containing an infinite number of elements, and if*

$$\phi_i(x_1, \ldots, x_n) \quad (i = 1, \ldots, r)$$

are r non-zero polynomials in $K[x_1, \ldots, x_n]$, there exist elements $c_1, \ldots, c_n$ in K such that

$$\phi_i(c_1, \ldots, c_n) \neq 0 \quad (i = 1, \ldots, r).$$

We need only consider the case $r = 1$, for if

$$\psi(x_1, \ldots, x_n) = \prod_{i=1}^{r} \phi_i(x_1, \ldots, x_n),$$

then
$$\psi(c_1, \ldots, c_n) \neq 0$$

implies
$$\phi_i(c_1, \ldots, c_n) \neq 0 \quad (i = 1, \ldots, r).$$

We prove the theorem for a single polynomial $\phi(x_1, \ldots, x_n)$ by induction on n. If $n = 1$, let $\phi(x_1)$ be of degree m $(m \geqslant 0)$, that is,

$$\phi(x_1) = d_0 x_1^m + d_1 x_1^{m-1} + \ldots + d_m \quad (d_0 \neq 0).$$

By § 4, there is an extension K^* of K in which $\phi(x_1)$ is completely reducible That is,

$$\phi(x_1) = d_0(x_1 - \xi_1) \ldots (x_1 - \xi_m),$$

where $\xi_1, \ldots, \xi_m$ are uniquely determined elements in K^*. Since $K \subseteq K^*$, and K contains an infinite number of elements, there is an element c_1 in K not equal to any one of the set $\xi_1, \ldots, \xi_m$. Hence

$$\phi(c_1) = d_0(c_1 - \xi_1) \ldots (c_1 - \xi_m) \neq 0,$$

since $c_1 \neq \xi_i$, and there are no divisors of zero.

We now assume that the theorem is true when $n - 1$ indeterminates are adjoined to K. Let

$$\phi(x_1, \ldots, x_n)$$
$$= \phi_0(x_1, \ldots, x_{n-1}) x_n^m + \phi_1(x_1, \ldots, x_{n-1}) x_n^{m-1} + \ldots + \phi_m(x_1, \ldots, x_{n-1})$$

be a non-zero polynomial in $K[x_1, \ldots, x_n]$. We may suppose that $\phi_0(x_1, \ldots, x_{n-1}) \neq 0$. By hypothesis we can therefore find elements $c_1, \ldots, c_{n-1}$ of K such that $\phi_0(c_1, \ldots, c_{n-1}) \neq 0$. Now apply the proof for the case $n = 1$ to the polynomial $\phi(c_1, \ldots, c_{n-1}, x_n)$, and the result follows.

Corollary. The theorem is true if K is any commutative field without characteristic. For K then contains the field of rational numbers, and therefore has an infinite number of elements.

THEOREM II. *If K is a commutative field without characteristic which is algebraically closed, $\phi(x)$ any polynomial in $K[x]$ such that $\phi(0) \neq 0$, and if r is a given positive integer, then there exists a polynomial $f(x)$ such that $[f(x)]^r - x$ is divisible by $\phi(x)$.*

Since K is algebraically closed we can write

$$\phi(x) = a \prod_{i=1}^{k} (x - \xi_i)^{s_i} \quad (\xi_i \text{ in } K),$$

where $\xi_1, \ldots, \xi_k$ are assumed to be distinct. Let polynomials $g_1(x), \ldots, g_k(x)$ be defined by the equations

$$g_i(x) = \xi_i^{1/r} \left[1 + \frac{1}{r\xi_i}(x - \xi_i) + \frac{1-r}{r^2\xi_i^2 2!}(x - \xi_i)^2 \right.$$
$$\left. + \ldots + \frac{(1-r)(1-2r)\ldots(1-\overline{s_i-2}r)}{r^{s_i-1}\xi_i^{s_i-1}(s_i-1)!}(x - \xi_i)^{s_i-1} \right],$$

where $\xi_i^{1/r}$ denotes an element of K such that $(\xi_i^{1/r})^r = \xi_i$. Such elements exist, since K is algebraically closed. By direct calculation it may be seen that $[g_i(x)]^r - x$ is divisible by $(x - \xi_i)^{s_i}$. Now write

$$\phi(x) = (x - \xi_i)^{s_i} \phi_i(x),$$

so that $\phi_i(x)$ does not contain $x - \xi_i$ as a factor. By the division algorithm, there exists a pair of polynomials $a_i(x), b_i(x)$ such that

$$a_i(x)\phi_i(x) + b_i(x)(x - \xi_i)^{s_i} = 1.$$

Then, using this identity,

$$\frac{g_i(x)}{\phi(x)} = \frac{g_i(x)a_i(x)\phi_i(x)}{\phi(x)} + \frac{g_i(x)b_i(x)(x - \xi_i)^{s_i}}{\phi(x)}$$
$$= \frac{g_i(x)a_i(x)}{(x - \xi_i)^{s_i}} + \frac{g_i(x)b_i(x)}{\phi_i(x)}.$$

We may write

$$\frac{g_i(x)a_i(x)}{(x - \xi_i)^{s_i}} = h_i(x) + \frac{A_i(x)}{(x - \xi_i)^{s_i}},$$

$A_i(x)$ being a polynomial of degree less than s_i, and then

$$\frac{g_i(x)b_i(x)}{\phi_i(x)} = -h_i(x) + \frac{B_i(x)}{\phi_i(x)}.$$

Hence $\qquad g_i(x) = A_i(x)\phi_i(x) + B_i(x)(x-\xi_i)^{s_i},$

and since $[g_i(x)]^r - x$ contains $(x-\xi_i)^{s_i}$ as a factor, it follows that $[A_i(x)\phi_i(x)]^r - x$ contains $(x-\xi_i)^{s_i}$ as a factor. Now let

$$f(x) = \sum_{i=1}^{k} A_i(x)\phi_i(x).$$

Since $A_j(x)\phi_j(x)$ contains $(x-\xi_i)^{s_i}$ as a factor for all $j \neq i$, and $[A_i(x)\phi_i(x)]^r - x$ contains $(x-\xi_i)^{s_i}$ as a factor, it follows that $[f(x)]^r - x$ contains $(x-\xi_i)^{s_i}$ as a factor. By symmetry, this holds for all values of i from 1 to k, and therefore $[f(x)]^r - x$ contains $\prod_{1}^{k} (x-\xi_i)^{s_i}$ as a factor. But a is in K, and not zero. Therefore $[f(x)]^r - x$ contains $\phi(x)$ as a factor. This proves the theorem.

It will be noted that the degree of $f(x)$ is less than that of $\phi(x)$. But $f(x)$ is not uniquely defined by the requirements of the theorem. We could, for instance, take

$$f(x) = \sum_{i=1}^{k} \epsilon_i A_i(x)\phi_i(x) + \psi(x)\phi(x),$$

where $\epsilon_1, \ldots, \epsilon_k$ are k elements of K such that $\epsilon_i^r = 1$, and $\psi(x)$ is any polynomial.

CHAPTER IV

ALGEBRAIC EQUATIONS

1. Introduction. In this chapter we shall be dealing with polynomials in several indeterminates, with coefficients in a field K. This field will be assumed to be commutative, and to contain an infinite number of elements.

Let $f(x_1, \ldots, x_n)$, $g(x_1, \ldots, x_n), \ldots$ be a set of polynomials in $K[x_1, \ldots, x_n]$. A set of elements $(\xi_1, \ldots, \xi_n)$ of an extension K^* of the ground field K is called *a solution* of the equations

$$\left. \begin{aligned} f(x_1, \ldots, x_n) &= 0, \\ g(x_1, \ldots, x_n) &= 0, \\ \cdot \quad \cdot \quad \cdot \end{aligned} \right\} \qquad (1)$$

if

$$\left. \begin{aligned} f(\xi_1, \ldots, \xi_n) &= 0, \\ g(\xi_1, \ldots, \xi_n) &= 0, \\ \cdot \quad \cdot \quad \cdot \end{aligned} \right\}$$

It will be observed that $x_1, \ldots, x_n$ in (1) are not indeterminates, but *unknowns*, otherwise (1) would imply that $f(x_1, \ldots, x_n), \ldots$ were zero polynomials. Strictly speaking, we should use a different symbol for an unknown, but it will save a multiplication of our symbols if we use the same letters for unknowns and indeterminates. There will be no confusion provided that we observe the following conventions: if $f(x_1, \ldots, x_n)$ is written alone, it is a polynomial in the indeterminates $x_1, \ldots, x_n$; if we write

$$f(x_1, \ldots, x_n) = 0$$

the $x_1, \ldots, x_n$ are unknowns; and if we wish to express the fact that the polynomial $f(x_1, \ldots, x_n)$ is the zero polynomial, that is, that $f(x_1, \ldots, x_n)$ is *identically zero*, we shall write

$$f(x_1, \ldots, x_n) \equiv 0.$$

The main purpose of this chapter is to find criteria for the existence of a solution of a given set of equations. While we shall often discover solutions in a field K^* which is a transcendental extension of K, our reasoning will show that if a set of equations with coefficients in a field K has a solution, the set necessarily has a solution in an *algebraic* extension of K.

We shall be much concerned with *homogeneous* equations. The equations (1) are homogeneous equations if all the polynomials $f(x_1, ..., x_n)$, $g(x_1, ..., x_n)$, ... appearing in the equations are homogeneous. The polynomial $f(x_1, ..., x_n)$ is homogeneous of degree r if, for an indeterminate λ,

$$f(\lambda x_1, ..., \lambda x_n) \equiv \lambda^r f(x_1, ..., x_n).$$

All terms in $f(x_1, ..., x_n)$ then have the same total degree r. A homogeneous polynomial is usually called a *form*.

If $(\xi_1, ..., \xi_n)$ is any solution of a set of homogeneous equations, so is $(\lambda \xi_1, ..., \lambda \xi_n)$, where λ lies in any extension of K. Thus $(0, ..., 0)$ is always a solution, but we shall regard this as the trivial solution. We shall find it convenient to consider two solutions $(\xi_1, ..., \xi_n)$, $(\eta_1, ..., \eta_n)$ which are non-trivial as *equivalent solutions* if there exists a μ such that

$$\xi_i = \mu \eta_i \quad (i = 1, ..., n).$$

Any non-trivial solution of a set of homogeneous equations will be identified with all equivalent solutions.

So far we have said nothing about the *number* of equations in a given set, and have not even assumed the set to be enumerable. We shall be concerned with the number of equations in our next section. We remark here that there are two ideals associated with a given set of equations. First, in the non-homogeneous case, let $h(x_1, ..., x_n)$, $k(x_1, ..., x_n)$ be two polynomials which vanish for every solution $(\xi_1, ..., \xi_n)$ of (1). Then

$$h(\xi_1, ..., \xi_n) = k(\xi_1, ..., \xi_n) = 0.$$

But if $a(x_1, ..., x_n)$ is any polynomial in $K[x_1, ..., x_n]$, the equations

$$h(x_1, ..., x_n) - k(x_1, ..., x_n) = 0 \quad \text{and} \quad a(x_1, ..., x_n) h(x_1, ..., x_n) = 0$$

are satisfied by $(\xi_1, ..., \xi_n)$, since

$$h(\xi_1, ..., \xi_n) - k(\xi_1, ..., \xi_n) = 0, \quad \text{and} \quad a(\xi_1, ..., \xi_n) h(\xi_1, ..., \xi_n) = 0.$$

Therefore the polynomials $h(x_1, ..., x_n)$, $k(x_1, ..., x_n)$, ... form an ideal [I, § 2]. Now consider the case in which the equations (1) are homogeneous. Let us write

$$h(x_1, ..., x_n) \equiv h_0(x_1, ..., x_n) + h_1(x_1, ..., x_n) + ... + h_r(x_1, ..., x_n),$$

where $h_i(x_1, ..., x_n)$ is homogeneous of degree i in $x_1, ..., x_n$. Since the set (1) is a set of *homogeneous* equations, if $(\xi_1, ..., \xi_n)$ satisfies $h(x_1, ..., x_n) = 0$, so does $(\lambda\xi_1, ..., \lambda\xi_n)$. That is,

$$h_0(\xi_1, ..., \xi_n) + \lambda h_1(\xi_1, ..., \xi_n) + ... + \lambda^r h_r(\xi_1, ..., \xi_n) = 0.$$

Since λ may be taken as an indeterminate over $K(\xi_1, ..., \xi_n)$ it follows that

$$h_0(\xi_1, ..., \xi_n) = h_1(\xi_1, ..., \xi_n) = ... = h_r(\xi_1, ..., \xi_n) = 0.$$

Therefore *every polynomial of the ideal is a sum of homogeneous polynomials, each of which belongs to the ideal.*

Again, suppose that we may write the equations (1) in the form

$$f_1(x_1, ..., x_n) = 0,$$
$$f_2(x_1, ..., x_n) = 0,$$
$$\cdot \qquad \cdot \qquad \cdot$$

Consider the polynomials

$$\sum_i a_i(x_1, ..., x_n)f_i(x_1, ..., x_n),$$

where the $a_i(x_1, ..., x_n)$ are in $K[x_1, ..., x_n]$, and the various summations are all over a finite number of values of i. It is clear that these polynomials form an ideal. Also, every polynomial of this ideal vanishes for every solution of the equations (1), and therefore belongs to the first ideal. In the case in which (1) consists of homogeneous equations we may write

$$a_i(x_1, ..., x_n) \equiv a_{0i}(x_1, ..., x_n) + ... + a_{r_i\,i}(x_1, ..., x_n),$$

where $a_{ji}(x_1, ..., x_n)$ is homogeneous of degree j, and hence

$$\sum a_i(x_1, ..., x_n)f_i(x_1, ..., x_n) = \sum_j \sum_i a_{ji}(x_1, ..., x_n)f_i(x_1, ..., x_n),$$

where each term in the summation is homogeneous and belongs to the ideal.

The two ideals we have associated with the set of equations (1) do not necessarily coincide. To take a very simple example, let the set (1) be simply

$$x_1^2 = 0.$$

Then the polynomial x_1 lies in the first ideal, but not in the second.

2. Hilbert's basis theorem. We now show that in considering sets of equations, homogeneous or not, it is sufficient to confine ourselves to sets containing a *finite* number of equations. We first consider non-homogeneous equations, and then deduce the result for homogeneous equations.

THEOREM I. *In any non-vacuous ideal i in $K[x_1, ..., x_n]$ there exists a finite number of polynomials $g_j(x_1, ..., x_n)$ $(j = 1, ..., r)$ such that any polynomial $F(x_1, ..., x_n)$ in i can be written in the form*

$$F(x_1, ..., x_n) \equiv \sum_{i=1}^{r} a_i(x_1, ..., x_n) g_i(x_1, ..., x_n),$$

where the $a_i(x_1, ..., x_n)$ are in $K[x_1, ..., x_n]$.

Such a set of polynomials $g_i(x_1, ..., x_n)$ is said to form *a basis for the ideal i.* It is evident, conversely, that if the $g_i(x_1, ..., x_n)$ are in i, and the $a_i(x_1, ..., x_n)$ in $K[x_1, ..., x_n]$, then $F(x_1, ..., x_n)$ is in i.

We prove the theorem by induction on n. If $n = 0$, the result is trivial. In this case $K[x_1, ..., x_n] = K$. If i contains only the zero of K there is nothing to prove. If i contains a non-zero element α of K it contains any other element β of K, since $\beta = (\beta \alpha^{-1}) \alpha$. Hence, to prove the theorem, we need only take $g_1 = \alpha$.

Now suppose that the theorem has been proved for ideals in $K[x_1, ..., x_{n-1}]$. We write the elements of i in $K[x_1, ..., x_n]$ as polynomials in x_n, with coefficients in $K[x_1, ..., x_{n-1}]$. We consider the coefficients of the highest powers of x_n in the various polynomials, that is, the *leading terms* of each polynomial. We write

$$F(x_1, ..., x_n) \equiv f_1(x_1, ..., x_{n-1}) x_n^{\alpha} + f_2(x_1, ..., x_{n-1}) x_n^{\alpha-1} + ...,$$

and prove that the polynomials $f_1(x_1, ..., x_{n-1})$ form an ideal in $K[x_1, ..., x_{n-1}]$. To prove this, let

$$G(x_1, ..., x_n) \equiv g_1(x_1, ..., x_{n-1}) x_n^{\beta} + g_2(x_1, ..., x_{n-1}) x_n^{\beta-1} + ...$$

be another polynomial in i, and suppose that $\alpha \geqslant \beta$. Then

$$F(x_1, ..., x_n) - x_n^{\alpha-\beta} G(x_1, ..., x_n)$$
$$\equiv [f_1(x_1, ..., x_{n-1}) - g_1(x_1, ..., x_{n-1})] x_n^{\alpha} + ...$$

is a polynomial in i with leading coefficient

$$f_1(x_1, ..., x_{n-1}) - g_1(x_1, ..., x_{n-1}).$$

Also, if $a(x_1, \ldots, x_{n-1})$ is any element of $K[x_1, \ldots, x_{n-1}]$, then

$$a(x_1, \ldots, x_{n-1})\, F(x_1, \ldots, x_n) \equiv a(x_1, \ldots, x_{n-1}) f_1(x_1, \ldots, x_{n-1})\, x_n^\alpha + \ldots$$

is a polynomial in i whose leading coefficient is

$$a(x_1, \ldots, x_{n-1}) f_1(x_1, \ldots, x_{n-1}).$$

Hence, from the definition of an ideal, we deduce that the leading coefficients of polynomials in i, together with zero, form an ideal in $K[x_1, \ldots, x_{n-1}]$. By hypothesis, there exists in this ideal j a finite set of polynomials

$$\phi_i(x_1, \ldots, x_{n-1}) \quad (i = 1, \ldots, r_0),$$

such that any element of j can be written as the sum

$$\sum_{i=1}^{r_0} a_i(x_1, \ldots, x_{n-1})\, \phi_i(x_1, \ldots, x_{n-1}),$$

where the $a_i(x_1, \ldots, x_{n-1})$ are elements of $K[x_1, \ldots, x_{n-1}]$. Since $\phi_i(x_1, \ldots, x_{n-1})$ is in j, there is a polynomial $g_i(x_1, \ldots, x_n)$ of i which, considered as a polynomial in x_n, has $\phi_i(x_1, \ldots, x_{n-1})$ for its leading coefficient. Select polynomials $g_i(x_1, \ldots, x_n)$ corresponding to the r_0 values of i considered, and let N_i be the degree of $g_i(x_1, \ldots, x_n)$ in x_n. Let

$$N = \max(N_1, \ldots, N_{r_0}).$$

Then if $$F(x_1, \ldots, x_n) \equiv f(x_1, \ldots, x_{n-1})\, x_n^\alpha + \ldots$$

is any element of i, of degree $\alpha \geqslant N$, we can write

$$f(x_1, \ldots, x_{n-1}) \equiv \sum_{i=1}^{r_0} a_i(x_1, \ldots, x_{n-1})\, \phi_i(x_1, \ldots, x_{n-1}),$$

and $$F(x_1, \ldots, x_n) - \sum_{i=1}^{r_0} a_i(x_1, \ldots, x_{n-1})\, x_n^{\alpha - N_i} g_i(x_1, \ldots, x_n)$$

is a polynomial in i of degree less than α. Repeating this argument at most $\alpha - N$ further times, we show that there exist polynomials $b_i(x_1, \ldots, x_n)$ such that

$$F(x_1, \ldots, x_n) - \sum_{i=1}^{r_0} b_i(x_1, \ldots, x_n)\, g_i(x_1, \ldots, x_n) \equiv h(x_1, \ldots, x_n)$$

is a polynomial in i of degree less than N.

We therefore consider the polynomials in i of degree less than N

in x_n. We show that the coefficients of x_n^{N-1} in these polynomials form an ideal j_1 in $K[x_1, ..., x_{n-1}]$. Let

$$h(x_1, ..., x_n) \equiv h_1(x_1, ..., x_{n-1}) x_n^{N-1} + ...,$$

and $\qquad k(x_1, ..., x_n) \equiv k_1(x_1, ..., x_{n-1}) x_n^{N-1} + ...$

Then

$$h(x_1, ..., x_n) - k(x_1, ..., x_n)$$
$$\equiv [h_1(x_1, ..., x_{n-1}) - k_1(x_1, ..., x_{n-1})] x_n^{N-1} + ...,$$

and

$$a(x_1, ..., x_{n-1}) h(x_1, ..., x_n)$$
$$\equiv a(x_1, ..., x_{n-1}) h_1(x_1, ..., x_{n-1}) x_n^{N-1} + ...$$

are polynomials in i of degree less than N, and their leading coefficients are

$$h_1(x_1, ..., x_{n-1}) - k_1(x_1, ..., x_{n-1}), \quad a(x_1, ..., x_{n-1}) h_1(x_1, ..., x_{n-1}),$$

where $a(x_1, ..., x_{n-1})$ is an element of $K[x_1, ..., x_{n-1}]$. The leading coefficients therefore form an ideal j_1, which, by hypothesis, has a basis

$$\phi_{r_0+1}(x_1, ..., x_{n-1}), \quad ..., \quad \phi_{r_1}(x_1, ..., x_{n-1}).$$

If the polynomials of degree $N-1$ whose leading coefficients are these $\phi_{r_0+i}(x_1, ..., x_{n-1})$ are

$$g_{r_0+i}(x_1, ..., x_n) \equiv \phi_{r_0+i}(x_1, ..., x_{n-1}) x_n^{N-1} + ...,$$

we can write any element of i of degree $N-1$ in the form

$$h(x_1, ..., x_n) \equiv h_1(x_1, ..., x_{n-1}) x_n^{N-1} + ...$$
$$\equiv \sum_{i=1}^{r_1-r_0} a_{r_0+i}(x_1, ..., x_{n-1}) \phi_{r_0+i}(x_1, ..., x_{n-1}) x_n^{N-1} + ...,$$

and therefore

$$h(x_1, ..., x_n) - \sum_{i=1}^{r_1-r_0} a_{r_0+i}(x_1, ..., x_{n-1}) g_{r_0+i}(x_1, ..., x_n)$$

is an element of i of degree $N-2$ at most. Repeating this process $N-2$ times at most, we obtain a finite number of polynomials $g_i(x_1, ..., x_n)$ ($i = 1, ..., s$) in i such that for suitable $a_i(x_1, ..., x_n)$ in $K[x_1, ..., x_n]$ we find that

$$F(x_1, ..., x_n) - \sum_{i=1}^{s} a_i(x_1, ..., x_n) g_i(x_1, ..., x_n)$$

is a polynomial of degree zero, and a further application of the hypothesis of induction shows that

$$F(x_1, ..., x_n) \equiv \sum_{i=1}^{r} a_i(x_1, ..., x_n) g_i(x_1, ..., x_n).$$

This proves Hilbert's basis theorem.

Now suppose that we are given an enumerable sequence of equations
$$f_j(x_1, ..., x_n) = 0 \quad (j = 1, 2, ...). \tag{1}$$
We have seen that the polynomials
$$\Sigma a_j(x_1, ..., x_n) f_j(x_1, ..., x_n),$$
where the summation is over a finite number of values of j, form an ideal i. This has a finite basis consisting, say, of polynomials
$$g_k(x_1, ..., x_n) \quad (k = 1, ..., r).$$
Since each of these polynomials lies in i,
$$g_k(x_1, ..., x_n) \equiv \Sigma a_{kj}(x_1, ..., x_n) f_j(x_1, ..., x_n),$$
where the summation is over a finite number of values of j. There exists, therefore, a finite number s such that
$$g_k(x_1, ..., x_n) \equiv \sum_{j=1}^{s} a_{kj}(x_1, ..., x_n) f_j(x_1, ..., x_n) \quad (k = 1, ..., r).$$
Now, any polynomial of the sequence (1), say $f_l(x_1, ..., x_n)$, is expressible in terms of the $g_k(x_1, ..., x_n)$; that is,
$$f_l(x_1, ..., x_n) \equiv \sum_{k=1}^{r} b_{lk}(x_1, ..., x_n) g_k(x_1, ..., x_n)$$
$$\equiv \sum_{j=1}^{s} c_{lj}(x_1, ..., x_n) f_j(x_1, ..., x_n), \tag{2}$$
where
$$c_{lj}(x_1, ..., x_n) \equiv \sum_{k=1}^{r} b_{lk}(x_1, ..., x_n) a_{kj}(x_1, ..., x_n).$$

From (2) we see that in the sequence of equations (1) we may consider only the first s of them, the remaining polynomials $f_j(x_1, ..., x_n)$ belonging to the ideal defined by the first s, and vanishing at all common zeros of these s polynomials.

The argument given above holds whether the set (1) is homogeneous or non-homogeneous.

Another application of the basis theorem is to the ideal defined by polynomials which vanish for every solution of a given set of equations. Let
$$g_j(x_1, ..., x_n) \quad (i = 1, ..., r)$$
be a basis for this ideal. Then
$$g_j(x_1, ..., x_n) = 0 \quad (i = 1, ..., r) \tag{3}$$
is satisfied by all the solutions of the given set of equations. If
$$f(x_1, ..., x_n) = 0$$

is any equation of the set, $f(x_1, ..., x_n)$ is in the ideal we are considering, and therefore

$$f(x_1, ..., x_n) \equiv \sum_{j=1}^{r} a_j(x_1, ..., x_n)\, g_j(x_1, ..., x_n).$$

Hence every solution of the set (3) is a solution of the set of equations considered. The two sets of solutions therefore coincide, and we may replace the set of equations by the finite set (3).

If the given set of equations is homogeneous we can replace it by a finite set of *homogeneous* equations. For we saw in § 1 that if we write

$$g_j(x_1, ..., x_n) \equiv g_{0j}(x_1, ..., x_n) + ... + g_{n_j j}(x_1, ..., x_n),$$

where $g_{ij}(x_1, ..., x_n)$ is homogeneous and of degree i, the homogeneous polynomials (or *forms*) $g_{ij}(x_1, ..., x_n)$ belong to the ideal. Hence, the set of homogeneous equations can be replaced by the finite set of homogeneous equations

$$g_{ij}(x_1, ..., x_n) = 0 \quad (i = 1, ..., n_j;\, j = 1, ..., r).$$

3. The resultant of two binary forms. The results of the previous section enable us to confine our study of systems of algebraic equations to finite systems. We proceed to investigate the conditions that a system of equations may have a solution.

While we are ultimately concerned with equations whose coefficients lie in the given ground field K, it is essential to consider, as part of our method, equations with coefficients which may belong to an extension K' (possibly transcendental) of K. If the coefficients of the various equations in the system are $\alpha, \beta, ..., \delta$, the elements of K' obtained by applying the operations of addition and multiplication to $\alpha, \beta, ..., \delta$ and to the elements of K lie in an integral domain which is a subring of K'. We call this subring of K' *the ring of the coefficients*, and its quotient field is *the field of the coefficients*.

An extreme case is that in which the coefficients are all independent indeterminates over K. The ring of the coefficients is then $K[\alpha, \beta, ..., \delta]$, while the field of the coefficients is $K(\alpha, \beta, ..., \delta)$, the field of *rational functions* of these indeterminates. The system of equations will be called *a system with indeterminate coefficients* in this case.

The idea of the specialisation of polynomials has been described in I, § 5. Let
$$f_i(x_1, ..., x_n) = 0 \quad (i = 1, ..., s) \tag{1}$$
be a set of equations with indeterminate coefficients. We obtain a

set of polynomials in the coefficients (that is, elements in the ring of coefficients) which has the following property: a necessary and sufficient condition that the set of s equations

$$f_i^*(x_1, ..., x_n) = 0 \quad (i = 1, ..., s) \tag{2}$$

obtained from (1) by the specialisations

$$f_i(x_1, ..., x_n) \rightarrow f_i^*(x_1, ..., x_n)$$

should have a solution is that the corresponding specialisations of the set of polynomials all vanish.

As a first step in our reasoning, and as an illustration of the method, we consider the case of a pair of homogeneous equations in two unknowns,

$$f(x_0, x_1) = 0, \quad g(x_0, x_1) = 0.$$

In the case of a single non-homogeneous equation

$$f(x) = 0$$

it has already been shown [III, §4] that there is an algebraic extension of the field of coefficients in which $f(x)$ is completely reducible, so that

$$f(x) \equiv a(x - \alpha_1) \dots (x - \alpha_m).$$

If K^* is any other extension of the field of coefficients in which $f(x)$ is completely reducible, and if

$$f(x) \equiv a(x - \xi_1) \dots (x - \xi_m),$$

we know that $K(\xi_1, ..., \xi_m)$ and $K(\alpha_1, ..., \alpha_m)$ are equivalent extensions of K, in which ξ_i and α_i correspond if the factors are suitably arranged. For our present purpose we need not distinguish between ξ_i and α_i. Hence we can say that the *only* solutions of $f(x) = 0$ are $\alpha_1, ..., \alpha_m$.

If $f(x_0, x_1)$ is a form, that is, a homogeneous polynomial of degree m, we can write

$$f(x_0, x_1) \equiv a(\beta_1 x_1 - \alpha_1 x_0) \dots (\beta_m x_1 - \alpha_m x_0)$$

in some algebraic extension of the field of coefficients, and the only solutions, in the homogeneous sense, of $f(x_0, x_1) = 0$ are

$$(\beta_1, \alpha_1), \quad ..., \quad (\beta_m, \alpha_m).$$

Now consider a pair of forms in x_0, x_1 (usually called *binary* forms) in which all the coefficients are indeterminates over K:

$$f(x_0, x_1) \equiv a_0 x_1^m + a_1 x_1^{m-1} x_0 + \ldots + a_m x_0^m, \\ g(x_0, x_1) \equiv b_0 x_1^n + b_1 x_1^{n-1} x_0 + \ldots + b_n x_0^n. \tag{3}$$

Then

$$a_0 x_1^{m+n-1} + \ldots + a_m x_1^{n-1} x_0^m \qquad\qquad \equiv x_1^{n-1} f(x_0, x_1),$$
$$a_0 x_1^{m+n-2} x_0 + \ldots + a_m x_1^{n-2} x_0^{m+1} \qquad \equiv x_1^{n-2} x_0 f(x_0, x_1),$$
$$\cdot \qquad \cdot \qquad \cdot \qquad \cdot \qquad \cdot \qquad \cdot \qquad \cdot$$
$$a_0 x_1^m x_0^{n-1} + \ldots + a_m x_0^{m+n-1} \equiv x_0^{n-1} f(x_0, x_1),$$
$$b_0 x_1^{m+n-1} + \ldots + b_n x_1^{m-1} x_0^n \qquad\qquad \equiv x_1^{m-1} g(x_0, x_1),$$
$$b_0 x_1^{m+n-2} x_0 + \ldots + b_n x_1^{m-2} x_0^{n+1} \qquad \equiv x_1^{m-2} x_0 g(x_0, x_1),$$
$$\cdot \qquad \cdot \qquad \cdot \qquad \cdot \qquad \cdot \qquad \cdot \qquad \cdot$$
$$b_0 x_1^n x_0^{m-1} + \ldots + b_n x_0^{m+n-1} \equiv x_0^{m-1} g(x_0, x_1).$$

If R is the determinant of the square matrix

$$\left. \begin{pmatrix} a_0 & a_1 & \cdot & \cdot & \cdot & a_m & \cdot & \cdot \\ 0 & a_0 & a_1 & \cdot & \cdot & \cdot & a_m & \cdot \\ \cdot & \cdot & \cdot & \cdot & \cdot & \cdot & \cdot & \cdot \\ \cdot & \cdot & \cdot & a_0 & a_1 & \cdot & \cdot & a_m \\ b_0 & b_1 & \cdot & \cdot & b_n & \cdot & \cdot & \cdot \\ 0 & b_0 & b_1 & \cdot & \cdot & b_n & \cdot & \cdot \\ \cdot & \cdot & \cdot & \cdot & \cdot & \cdot & \cdot & \cdot \\ \cdot & \cdot & \cdot & b_0 & b_1 & \cdot & \cdot & b_n \end{pmatrix} \begin{array}{l} \left.\vphantom{\begin{matrix}a\\a\\a\\a\end{matrix}}\right\} n \text{ rows} \\ \\ \left.\vphantom{\begin{matrix}a\\a\\a\\a\end{matrix}}\right\} m \text{ rows} \end{array} \right. \tag{4}$$

the multiplication of these $m + n$ equations in order by the corresponding cofactors of the successive elements in a column of the matrix (4) gives us the identity

$$R x_1^r x_0^s \equiv A_{rs}(x_0, x_1) f(x_0, x_1) + B_{rs}(x_0, x_1) g(x_0, x_1), \tag{5}$$

where $A_{rs}(x_0, x_1)$ and $B_{rs}(x_0, x_1)$ are forms of degrees $n-1$ and $m-1$ respectively whose coefficients are in the ring $K[a_0, \ldots, a_m, b_0, \ldots, b_n]$. There is one such equation for each pair of values of r, s such that $r + s = m + n - 1$. In particular,

$$R x_0^{m+n-1} \equiv A(x_0, x_1) f(x_0, x_1) + B(x_0, x_1) g(x_0, x_1), \tag{6}$$

when $r = 0$, $s = m + n - 1$.

Now consider any specialisation in $K'[x_0, x_1]$ of the forms (3), where K' is any extension of K. If, for this specialisation, R is not zero, the specialised equations

$$f(x_0, x_1) = 0, \quad g(x_0, x_1) = 0$$

can have no solution. Suppose, indeed, that they have the solution (c_0, c_1), in which c_0, say, is not zero. From (6) we have the equation

$$Rc_0^{m+n-1} = A(c_0, c_1)f(c_0, c_1) + B(c_0, c_1)g(c_0, c_1)$$
$$= 0,$$

which is a contradiction.

Suppose, on the other hand, that for some specialisation of the forms (3) the determinant R is zero. The rows of the matrix (4), considered as vectors, are then linearly dependent. Hence we can find elements

$$d_0, d_1, \ldots, d_{n-1}, \, c_0, c_1, \ldots, c_{m-1}$$

in K', not all zero, such that

$$d_0 u_0 + d_1 u_1 + \ldots + d_{n-1} u_{n-1} - c_0 v_0 - c_1 v_1 - \ldots - c_{m-1} v_{m-1} = 0,$$

where the vectors $u_0, \ldots, u_{n-1}, v_0, \ldots, v_{m-1}$ are the row-vectors of the matrix (4). We therefore have the set of equations

$$\left.\begin{array}{l} d_0 a_0 - c_0 b_0 \qquad\quad = 0, \\ d_0 a_1 + d_1 a_0 - c_0 b_1 - c_1 b_0 = 0, \\ \qquad\quad \cdot \qquad \cdot \qquad \cdot \\ d_{n-1} a_m - c_{m-1} b_n \qquad = 0. \end{array}\right\} \qquad (7)$$

If
$$d(x_0, x_1) \equiv d_0 x_1^{n-1} + \ldots + d_{n-1} x_0^{n-1},$$

and
$$c(x_0, x_1) \equiv c_0 x_1^{m-1} + \ldots + c_{m-1} x_0^{m-1},$$

the equations (7) express the fact that

$$d(x_0, x_1)f(x_0, x_1) \equiv c(x_0, x_1)g(x_0, x_1), \qquad (8)$$

being merely the equations which express the equality on both sides of (8) of the coefficients of $x_1^{m+n-1}, \ldots, x_0^{m+n-1}$.

Now resolve both sides of (8) into irreducible factors in $K'[x_0, x_1]$. By the unique factorisation theorem [I, § 7], any irreducible factor on one side must also appear on the other. Since $d(x_0, x_1)$ is of degree $n-1$, at most, one of the factors of $g(x_0, x_1)$ must be a factor of $f(x_0, x_1)$. Hence if $R = 0, f(x_0, x_1)$ and $g(x_0, x_1)$ have a common factor of degree greater than zero. Any solution of the equation obtained by equating this common factor to zero is a solution of the equations

$$f(x_0, x_1) = 0, \quad g(x_0, x_1) = 0.$$

The common factor can be found in $K'[x_0, x_1]$ by the division algorithm. The common solution of the two equations is in an algebraic extension of K'.

Calling R the *resultant* of the two binary forms (or equations), we have proved

THEOREM I. *A necessary and sufficient condition that two homogeneous equations with coefficients in a field K' have a common solution is that their resultant vanishes. The common solution, when it exists, lies in an algebraic extension of K'.*

We may use this result to obtain a theorem for two *polynomials* in $K'[x]$. Let

$$f(x) \equiv a_0 x^m + \ldots + a_m,$$
$$g(x) \equiv b_0 x^n + \ldots + b_n.$$

Make these polynomials homogeneous by introducing a new indeterminate y; we obtain the forms

$$f(x, y) \equiv a_0 x^m + \ldots + a_m y^m,$$
$$g(x, y) \equiv b_0 x^n + \ldots + b_n y^n.$$

Let R be the resultant of these two forms. If $R \neq 0$, the equations

$$f(x) = 0, \quad g(x) = 0 \tag{9}$$

cannot have a solution. For if they had a solution $x = c$, the homogeneous equations

$$f(x, y) = 0, \quad g(x, y) = 0$$

would have the solution $(c, 1)$.

If $R = 0$, the homogeneous equations have a solution. Let this be (c, d). If $d \neq 0$, this solution is equivalent to $(cd^{-1}, 1)$, and $x = cd^{-1}$ is a solution of (9). But this reasoning fails if $d = 0$. In this case substitution in $f(x, y)$ and $g(x, y)$ shows that $a_0 = 0$, $b_0 = 0$. The determinantal expression for R makes it evident that if $a_0 = b_0 = 0$, then $R = 0$. Hence we have

THEOREM II. *A necessary condition for the existence of a solution of two non-homogeneous equations is $R = 0$. It is not a sufficient condition unless we impose the additional condition that the leading coefficients of the equations are not both zero.*

We deduce from (6) that the resultant of two polynomials $f(x)$ and $g(x)$ can always be expressed in the form

$$R \equiv A(x)f(x) + B(x)g(x), \qquad (10)$$

where both $A(x)$ and $B(x)$ are polynomials in x with coefficients in the ring of coefficients of $f(x)$ and $g(x)$.

We conclude this section by indicating how an alternative approach to the foregoing argument can be extended to give a set of conditions to be satisfied when the binary forms $f(x_0, x_1)$ and $g(x_0, x_1)$ in (3) have a common factor which is at least of degree t. If this is the case,

$$f(x_0, x_1) \equiv f_1(x_0, x_1)\, d(x_0, x_1),$$

and
$$g(x_0, x_1) \equiv g_1(x_0, x_1)\, d(x_0, x_1),$$

where
$$f_1(x_0, x_1) \equiv d_0 x_1^{m-t} + \ldots + d_{m-t} x_0^{m-t},$$
$$g_1(x_0, x_1) \equiv c_0 x_1^{n-t} + \ldots + c_{n-t} x_0^{n-t}.$$

Since
$$g_1(x_0, x_1) f(x_0, x_1) \equiv f_1(x_0, x_1) g(x_0, x_1),$$

we have the equations

$$\left. \begin{aligned} c_0 a_0 - d_0 b_0 \quad\quad &= 0, \\ c_0 a_1 + c_1 a_0 - d_0 b_1 - d_1 b_0 &= 0, \\ \cdot \quad \cdot \quad \cdot \quad \cdot \quad &\\ c_{n-t} a_m - d_{m-t} b_n &= 0. \end{aligned} \right\} \qquad (11)$$

Hence the rows of the $(m + n - 2t + 2) \times (m + n - t + 1)$ matrix

$$\begin{pmatrix} a_0 & a_1 & \cdot & \cdot & a_m & \cdot & \cdot & 0 \\ 0 & a_0 & a_1 & \cdot & \cdot & a_m & \cdot & 0 \\ \cdot & \cdot & \cdot & \cdot & \cdot & \cdot & \cdot & \cdot \\ \cdot & \cdot & \cdot & a_0 & a_1 & \cdot & \cdot & a_m \\ b_0 & b_1 & \cdot & \cdot & b_n & \cdot & \cdot & \cdot \\ 0 & b_0 & b_1 & \cdot & \cdot & b_n & \cdot & \cdot \\ \cdot & \cdot & \cdot & \cdot & \cdot & \cdot & \cdot & \cdot \\ \cdot & \cdot & \cdot & b_0 & b_1 & \cdot & \cdot & b_n \end{pmatrix} \begin{matrix} \left. \begin{matrix} \\ \\ \\ \end{matrix} \right\} \begin{matrix} n-t+1 \\ \text{rows} \end{matrix} \\ \left. \begin{matrix} \\ \\ \\ \end{matrix} \right\} \begin{matrix} m-t+1 \\ \text{rows} \end{matrix} \end{matrix} \qquad (12)$$

are linearly dependent. Its rank is therefore not greater than $m + n - 2t + 1$. Conversely, if the rank of this matrix is less than $m + n - 2t + 2$, the rows are linearly dependent, and we can find elements $d_0, \ldots, d_{m-t},\ c_0, \ldots, c_{n-t}$, not all zero, in the field of the coefficients such that (11) is true. Defining $f_1(x_0, x_1)$ and $g_1(x_0, x_1)$ as above, it follows that

$$g_1(x_0, x_1) f(x_0, x_1) \equiv f_1(x_0, x_1) g(x_0, x_1),$$

and from the unique factorisation theorem we deduce that $f(x_0, x_1)$ and $g(x_0, x_1)$ have a common factor which is of degree t at least. Hence

THEOREM III. *A necessary and sufficient condition that $f(x_0, x_1)$ and $g(x_0, x_1)$ have in common a factor of degree t at least is that all the determinants of $m + n - 2t + 2$ rows and columns in (12) should be zero.*

4. Some properties of the resultant. Let $\alpha_1, ..., \alpha_m$, $\beta_1, ..., \beta_n$ be $m + n$ indeterminates over the ground field K, and let $c_1, ..., c_m$, $d_1, ..., d_n$ be the elementary symmetric functions of these two sets. That is, let

$$c_1 = \alpha_1 + ... + \alpha_m, \qquad d_1 = \beta_1 + ... + \beta_n,$$
$$c_2 = \alpha_1 \alpha_2 + ... + \alpha_{m-1} \alpha_m, \qquad d_2 = \beta_1 \beta_2 + ... + \beta_{n-1} \beta_n,$$
$$\cdot \qquad \cdot$$
$$c_m = \alpha_1 \alpha_2 ... \alpha_m, \qquad d_n = \beta_1 \beta_2 ... \beta_n.$$

Let a_0, b_0 be two further indeterminates, and write

$$a_i = (-1)^i a_0 c_i \quad (i = 1, ..., m),$$
$$b_i = (-1)^i b_0 d_i \quad (i = 1, ..., n).$$

If $\qquad f(x) \equiv a_0 x^m + a_1 x^{m-1} + ... + a_m,$

and $\qquad g(x) \equiv b_0 x^n + b_1 x^{n-1} + ... + b_n,$

then $\qquad f(x) \equiv a_0(x^m - c_1 x^{m-1} + c_2 x^{m-2} + ... + (-1)^m c_m)$

$$\equiv a_0 \prod_{i=1}^{m} (x - \alpha_i),$$

and $\qquad g(x) \equiv b_0 \prod_{j=1}^{n} (x - \beta_j).$

Let R be the resultant of $f(x)$ and $g(x)$. Then R is an element of $K[a_0, ..., a_m, b_0, ..., b_n]$, and we express this by writing

$$R = R(a_0, ..., a_m, b_0, ..., b_n).$$

The determinantal expression for the resultant shows that it is homogeneous, of degree n, in $a_0, ..., a_m$, and homogeneous, of degree

m, in $b_0, \ldots, b_n$. For every term in R contains one and only one element from every row, and one and only one element from every column of the determinant. The principal diagonal of the determinant gives the term $a_0^n b_n^m$ as one term in R. We may write, by the above remark,

$$R(a_0, \ldots, a_m, b_0, \ldots, b_n) = a_0^n b_0^m R(1, -c_1, \ldots, \pm c_m, 1, -d_1, \ldots, \pm d_n).$$

Now, $R(1, -c_1, \ldots, \pm c_m, 1, -d_1, \ldots, \pm d_n)$ is an element of

$$K[\alpha_1, \ldots, \alpha_m, \beta_1, \ldots, \beta_n],$$

and may therefore be regarded as a polynomial in α_i, with coefficients in $K[\alpha_1, \ldots, \alpha_{i-1}, \alpha_{i+1}, \ldots, \alpha_m, \beta_1, \ldots, \beta_n]$. This polynomial vanishes for each of the specialisations

$$\alpha_i \to \beta_j \quad (j = 1, \ldots, n),$$

since $f(x)$ and $g(x)$ then have a common factor. Hence, since the $\beta_1, \ldots, \beta_n$ are all distinct, a factor of the polynomial is

$$(\alpha_i - \beta_1) \ldots (\alpha_i - \beta_n).$$

This is true for each value of i, and therefore

$$R(1, -c_1, \ldots, \pm c_m, 1, -d_1, \ldots, \pm d_n),$$

regarded as a polynomial in $K[\alpha_1, \ldots, \alpha_m, \beta_1, \ldots, \beta_n]$, contains

$$S' = \prod_{i=1}^{m} \prod_{j=1}^{n} (\alpha_i - \beta_j)$$

as a factor; or $R(a_0, \ldots, a_m, b_0, \ldots, b_n)$ contains

$$S = a_0^n b_0^m \prod_{i=1}^{m} \prod_{j=1}^{n} (\alpha_i - \beta_j) \tag{1}$$

as a factor. But

$$g(\alpha_i) = b_0 \prod_{j=1}^{n} (\alpha_i - \beta_j),$$

and therefore

$$\prod_{i=1}^{m} g(\alpha_i) = b_0^m \prod_{i=1}^{m} \prod_{j=1}^{n} (\alpha_i - \beta_j),$$

that is,

$$S = a_0^n \prod_{i=1}^{m} g(\alpha_i). \tag{2}$$

Similarly

$$S = (-1)^{mn} b_0^m \prod_{j=1}^{n} f(\beta_j), \tag{3}$$

since

$$f(x) = a_0 \prod_{i=1}^{m} (x - \alpha_i) = (-1)^m a_0 \prod_{i=1}^{m} (\alpha_i - x).$$

Now (2) can be expanded as a homogeneous polynomial of degree m in the coefficients $b_0, ..., b_n$ of $g(x)$. The coefficient of each term is $a_0^n \times$ (a symmetric function of $\alpha_1, ..., \alpha_m$). Hence [III, § 4, Th. V] S is a form of degree m in $b_0, ..., b_n$, with coefficients which are polynomials in $a_0, c_1, ..., c_m$. We deduce from (3) that S can also be expressed as a form of degree n in $a_0, ..., a_m$ with coefficients which are polynomials in $b_0, d_1, ..., d_n$. Comparing these two results, we see that S is an element of $K[a_0, ..., a_m, b_0, ..., b_n]$ which is homogeneous of degree n in $a_0, ..., a_m$, and homogeneous of degree m in $b_0, ..., b_n$. It also follows from (2) that one term in S is $a_0^n b_n^m$.

We have already noted that

$$R(a_0, -a_0 c_1, ..., \pm a_0 c_m, b_0, -b_0 d_1, ..., \pm b_0 d_n),$$

regarded as a polynomial in $a_0, b_0, \alpha_1, ..., \alpha_m, \beta_1, ..., \beta_n$, contains S as a factor. That is,

$$R(a_0, -a_0 c_1, ..., \pm a_0 c_m, b_0, -b_0 d_1, ..., \pm b_0 d_n) = ST,$$

where T is a polynomial in $a_0, b_0, \alpha_1, ..., \alpha_m, \beta_1, ..., \beta_n$ which must be symmetric in $\alpha_1, ..., \alpha_m$ and in $\beta_1, ..., \beta_n$. Hence T can be expressed as a polynomial in $a_0, b_0, c_1, ..., c_m, d_1, ..., d_n$. By comparing degrees on each side and remembering [III, § 4, Th. VIII] that $a_0, b_0, c_1, ..., c_m, d_1, ..., d_n$ are algebraically independent over K, we see that T is in K. Hence, expressing S as a polynomial in $a_0, ..., a_m, b_0, ..., b_n$, we have a relation

$$R(a_0, a_1, ..., a_m, b_0, ..., b_n) = ST$$

between the a_i and b_j which must be an identity. By considering the coefficient of $a_0^n b_n^m$ on each side we find that $T = 1$. Hence

$$R = a_0^n \prod_{i=1}^m g(\alpha_i) = (-1)^{mn} b_0^m \prod_{j=1}^n f(\beta_j) = a_0^n b_0^m \prod_{i=1}^m \prod_{j=1}^n (\alpha_i - \beta_j). \quad (4)$$

Now consider any specialisation

$$a_i \to \lambda_i, \quad b_j \to \mu_j$$

of the coefficients of $f(x)$ and $g(x)$, and let the roots of the specialised polynomials be $\xi_1, ..., \xi_m, \eta_1, ..., \eta_n$. Then, since the specialisations

$$\alpha_i \to \xi_i, \quad \beta_j \to \eta_j, \quad a_0 \to \lambda_0, \quad b_0 \to \mu_0$$

imply the specialisations

$$a_i \to \lambda_i, \quad b_j \to \mu_j,$$

we obtain the equation

$$R(\lambda_0, ..., \lambda_m, \mu_0, ..., \mu_n) = \lambda_0^n \mu_0^m \prod_{i=1}^m \prod_{j=1}^n (\xi_i - \eta_j).$$

We show next that R is *isobaric* in the a_i and b_j, of *weight mn*. In other words, if $ca_0^{i_0} a_1^{i_1} \ldots a_m^{i_m} b_0^{j_0} \ldots b_n^{j_n}$ is any term of

$$R(a_0, \ldots, a_m, b_0, \ldots, b_n),$$

then

$$\sum_0^m r i_r + \sum_0^n s j_s = mn.$$

To prove this, consider the expressions for R given in (4). If in these we substitute $\alpha_i' = \lambda \alpha_i$, $\beta_j' = \lambda \beta_j$, where λ is an indeterminate, we obtain

$$\bar{R} = a_0^n b_0^m \prod_i \prod_j (\alpha_i' - \beta_j') = \lambda^{mn} a_0^n b_0^m \prod_i \prod_j (\alpha_i - \beta_j),$$

that is,

$$\bar{R} = \lambda^{mn} R,$$

where $\bar{R}$ is the resultant of the polynomials

$$\bar{f}(x) = a_0 \prod_i (x - \alpha_i') = a_0 \prod_i (x - \lambda \alpha_i),$$

$$\bar{g}(x) = b_0 \prod_j (x - \beta_j') = b_0 \prod_j (x - \lambda \beta_j).$$

But these polynomials may also be written in the form

$$\bar{f}(x) \equiv a_0 x^m + \lambda a_1 x^{m-1} + \lambda^2 a_2 x^{m-2} + \ldots + \lambda^m a_m,$$

$$\bar{g}(x) \equiv b_0 x^n + \lambda b_1 x^{n-1} + \lambda^2 b_2 x^{n-2} + \ldots + \lambda^n b_n,$$

so that

$$\bar{R} = R(a_0, \lambda a_1, \ldots, \lambda^m a_m, b_0, \lambda b_1, \ldots, \lambda^n b_n)$$
$$= \lambda^{mn} R(a_0, \ldots, a_m, b_0, \ldots, b_n).$$

This proves the theorem.

In later applications we shall need to consider the case in which the coefficients a_i, b_j are forms in an integral domain $K[\xi_1, \ldots, \xi_s]$, obtained by adjoining the indeterminates $\xi_1, \ldots, \xi_s$ to K. We suppose that the degree of a_i is $h + i$, where h is constant, and that the degree of b_j is $k + j$, where k is constant. Since R is homogeneous, of degree n, in the a_i, and homogeneous, of degree m, in the b_j, the degree of a term

$$ca_0^{i_0} \ldots a_m^{i_m} b_0^{j_0} \ldots b_n^{j_n}$$

in R is

$$\sum_{t=0}^m (h+t) i_t + \sum_{t=0}^n (k+t) j_t$$

$$= h \sum_{t=0}^m i_t + k \sum_{t=0}^n j_t + \sum_{t=0}^m t i_t + \sum_{t=0}^n t j_t$$

$$= hn + km + mn,$$

R being isobaric, of weight mn. Hence R is a form in $K[\xi_1, \ldots, \xi_s]$ of degree $nh + mk + mn$.

5. The resultant of a system of binary equations. We consider the system of r homogeneous equations

$$f_i(x_0, x_1) = 0 \quad (i = 1, \ldots, r), \tag{1}$$

and suppose, in the first place, that the coefficients are independent indeterminates over K. Let $f_i(x_0, x_1)$ be of degree m_i, and let $m = \max[m_1, \ldots, m_r]$. Then if

$$\left.\begin{array}{l} \phi_i(x_0, x_1) \equiv a_i x_0^{m-m_i} f_i(x_0, x_1), \\ \phi_{r+i}(x_0, x_1) \equiv b_i x_1^{m-m_i} f_i(x_0, x_1), \end{array}\right\} \quad (i = 1, \ldots, r),$$

where the a_i, b_i are new indeterminates, we consider the auxiliary system of equations

$$\phi_i(x_0, x_1) = 0 \quad (i = 1, \ldots, 2r). \tag{2}$$

Clearly if, for any specialisation of the coefficients in an extension K' of K, the system (1) has a solution, so has the system (2). Conversely, if the system (2) has the solution (c, d), so that

$$\left.\begin{array}{l} a_i c^{m-m_i} f_i(c, d) = 0, \\ b_i d^{m-m_i} f_i(c, d) = 0, \end{array}\right\} \quad (i = 1, \ldots, r),$$

then, since a_i, b_i are not zero, and c, d are not both zero, it follows that

$$f_i(c, d) = 0 \quad (i = 1, \ldots, r),$$

and therefore the system (1) has a solution. Thus, in order to find conditions for a solution of (1) when the coefficients are specialised in K', we merely need to find the conditions for a solution of (2) under the same specialisations. We do this by combining the system (2) into two equations.

Let $u_1, \ldots, u_{2r}, v_1, \ldots, v_{2r}$ be $4r$ further indeterminates, and let

$$\Phi(x_0, x_1) \equiv \sum_1^{2r} u_i \phi_i(x_0, x_1),$$

$$\Psi(x_0, x_1) \equiv \sum_1^{2r} v_i \phi_i(x_0, x_1).$$

If $R(u, v)$ is the resultant of this pair of binary forms $\Phi(x_0, x_1)$ and $\Psi(x_0, x_1)$, we first note that $R(u, v)$ is a polynomial in $u_1, \ldots, u_{2r}, v_1, \ldots, v_{2r}$. The coefficient of

$$u_1^{i_1} \ldots u_{2r}^{i_{2r}} v_1^{j_1} \ldots v_{2r}^{j_{2r}}$$

is evidently of the form

$$D_s = d_s a_1^{i_1+j_1} \ldots a_r^{i_r+j_r} b_1^{i_{r+1}+j_{r+1}} \ldots b_r^{i_{2r}+j_{2r}},$$

where d_s is a polynomial in the coefficients of the original forms

$f_i(x_0, x_1)$. These polynomials $d_1, \ldots, d_N$ constitute a *resultant system* of the set of homogeneous equations (1).

If, for any specialisation of the coefficients, the system (1) has a solution, so has the system (2), and hence also the pair of equations

$$\Phi(x_0, x_1) = 0, \quad \Psi(x_0, x_1) = 0.$$

Then $R(u, v) = 0$. This implies that every coefficient D_s vanishes, and therefore, since the a_i, b_j are indeterminates,

$$d_1 = 0, \quad \ldots, \quad d_N = 0.$$

Conversely, if each d_s vanishes, the forms

$$\Phi(x_0, x_1), \quad \Psi(x_0, x_1)$$

have a common factor. This can be determined by the division algorithm [I, § 6], and it is therefore an element of

$$K'(a_i, b_j, u_s, v_l) [x_0, x_1].$$

We may assume that the common factor is in $K'[a_i, b_j, u_s, v_l] [x_0, x_1]$ and is not divisible by an element of $K'[a_i, b_j, u_s, v_l]$. Now, $\Phi(x_0, x_1)$ does not contain $v_1, \ldots, v_{2r}$, so that this common factor does not contain any v_j, and $\Psi(x_0, x_1)$ does not contain $u_1, \ldots, u_{2r}$, and so the common factor is independent of the u_i. Hence every common factor of $\Phi(x_0, x_1)$ and $\Psi(x_0, x_1)$ is independent of u_i, v_j, and must therefore be a common factor of the forms

$$\phi_i(x_0, x_1) \quad (i = 1, \ldots, 2r).$$

The system (2), and hence the system (1), therefore has a solution.

From § 3, (5), we may write

$$R(u, v) x_0^r x_1^s \equiv a_{rs}(x_0, x_1) \Phi(x_0, x_1) + b_{rs}(x_0, x_1) \Psi(x_0, x_1), \qquad (3)$$

where $r + s = 2m - 1$, and $a_{rs}(x_0, x_1)$, $b_{rs}(x_0, x_1)$ are forms in x_0, x_1 whose coefficients are polynomials in the coefficients of $\Phi(x_0, x_1)$ and $\Psi(x_0, x_1)$. Remembering that $\Phi(x_0, x_1)$ and $\Psi(x_0, x_1)$ are linear expressions in the $\phi_i(x_0, x_1)$, and how these are obtained from the original forms $f_i(x_0, x_1)$, we obtain, on equating like powers of u_i, v_j, a_s, b_l on both sides of (3),

$$d_i x_0^r x_1^s \equiv \sum_{j=1}^{r} b_{rs, ij}(x_0, x_1) f_j(x_0, x_1). \qquad (4)$$

As in the case of two forms, we can deduce from these results others applicable to a system of r equations in one unknown. As before, we make the equations homogeneous, and construct the resultant system. Then we show that for specialised coefficients the members of the resultant system vanish if the given equations have a common solution, but that if the resultant system vanishes the equations either have a common solution, or the leading coefficient in each of the equations vanishes. We have proved the following result:

Given r polynomials $f_1(x), \ldots, f_r(x)$ in one indeterminate with indeterminate coefficients there exists a set $d_1, \ldots, d_N$ of polynomials in the coefficients with the property that for specialisations of the coefficients the conditions $d_1 = 0, \ldots, d_N = 0$ are necessary and sufficient to ensure that (i) *the equations $f_1(x) = 0, \ldots, f_r(x) = 0$ are soluble in some extension field; or* (ii) *the leading coefficients in $f_1(x), \ldots, f_r(x)$ all vanish. Moreover, if the equations have a solution, they have a solution in an algebraic extension of the field of coefficients.*

From (4) above we derive important expressions for $d_1, \ldots, d_N$. Putting $s = 0$, we find that

$$d_i \equiv \sum_{j=1}^{r} b_{ij}(x) f_j(x). \tag{5}$$

Finally, we extend the result proved at the end of §4 for two forms $f(x_0, x_1)$, $g(x_0, x_1)$ whose coefficients are themselves forms in $K[\xi_1, \ldots, \xi_s]$. We consider r forms

$$f_i(x_0, x_1) \quad (i = 1, \ldots, r),$$

and suppose that the coefficient of $x_1^i x_0^j$ in $f_k(x_0, x_1)$ is a form in $K[\xi_0, \ldots, \xi_s]$ of degree $h_k + j$. If $h = \max[h_1, \ldots, h_r]$, then in the preparatory stage of finding a resultant system for the $f_i(x_0, x_1)$ we choose a_i, b_i to be forms in $\xi_1, \ldots, \xi_s$, with indeterminate coefficients, of degrees $h - h_i + m - m_i$ and $h - h_i$ respectively. At this stage our forms are

$$\phi_i(x_0, x_1) \equiv a_i x_0^{m-m_i} f_i(x_0, x_1),$$
$$\phi_{r+i}(x_0, x_1) \equiv b_i x_1^{m-m_i} f_i(x_0, x_1).$$

The coefficient of $x_1^{i+m-m_k} x_0^j$ in $\phi_k(x_0, x_1)$ is a form of degree $h + j$ in $\xi_1, \ldots, \xi_s$. Hence we may apply the result of §4 to

$$\Phi(x_0, x_1) \equiv \sum_{1}^{2r} u_k \phi_k(x_0, x_1),$$

and

$$\Psi(x_0, x_1) \equiv \sum_{1}^{2r} v_k \phi_k(x_0, x_1).$$

The coefficient of $u_1^{i_1} \dots u_{2r}^{i_{2r}} v_1^{j_1} \dots v_{2r}^{j_{2r}}$ in $R(u, v)$, which is

$$D_t = d_t a_1^{i_1 + j_1} \dots a_r^{i_r + j_r} b_1^{i_{r+1} + j_{r+1}} \dots b_r^{i_{2r} + j_{2r}}$$

is therefore a form of degree $2mh + m^2$ in $\xi_1, \dots, \xi_s$. Since the a_i, b_j are forms in $\xi_1, \dots, \xi_s$, it follows that *the d_t are forms in $\xi_1, \dots, \xi_s$.*

6. The resultant system for a set of homogeneous equations in several unknowns.

We now consider r homogeneous equations in $n+1$ unknowns

$$f_i(x_0, \dots, x_n) = 0 \quad (i = 1, \dots, r), \tag{1}$$

again beginning with the case in which all the coefficients are indeterminates. Let ξ_0, ξ_1 be two further indeterminates, and write

$$\left. \begin{array}{l} x_i = \xi_0 x_i', \\ x_n = \xi_1 \end{array} \right\} \quad (i = 0, \dots, n-1).$$

We then obtain from (1) a set of equations, homogeneous in ξ_0, ξ_1,

$$f_i(\xi_0 x_0', \dots, \xi_0 x_{n-1}', \xi_1) = 0 \quad (i = 1, \dots, r). \tag{2}$$

The coefficient of $\xi_1^k \xi_0^j$ in $f_i(\xi_0 x_0', \dots, \xi_0 x_{n-1}', \xi_1)$ is a form in $x_0', \dots, x_{n-1}'$ of degree j. If we construct the resultant system of the equations (2), using the result of the preceding section, we obtain a set of forms in $x_0', \dots, x_{n-1}'$,

$$d_i(x_0', \dots, x_{n-1}') \quad (i = 1, \dots, N),$$

whose coefficients are in the ring of coefficients of (1), with the following properties:

(i) $$d_i \xi_0^{\rho_i} \equiv \sum_j a_{ij}(\xi_0, \xi_1) f_j(\xi_0 x_0', \dots, \xi_0 x_{n-1}', \xi_1)$$

for a suitable integer ρ_i, where the $a_{ij}(\xi_0, \xi_1)$ are forms in ξ_0, ξ_1 with coefficients in the ring which contains $x_0', \dots, x_{n-1}'$, K, and the coefficients of the equations (1);

(ii) if for the specialisations $(\bar{x}_0, \dots, \bar{x}_{n-1})$ of $(x_0', \dots, x_{n-1}')$,

$$d_i(\bar{x}_0, \dots, \bar{x}_{n-1}) = 0 \quad (i = 1, \dots, N),$$

the specialised equations (2) have a solution, and conversely. This result remains true for any specialisation of the coefficients of (1), the coefficients of the forms $d_i(x_0', \dots, x_{n-1}')$ being specialised to correspond to the specialisation of (1).

Now, if the equations (2) have the solutions (c, d) for the specialisations $(\bar{x}_0, \dots, \bar{x}_{n-1})$ of $(x_0', \dots, x_{n-1}')$, evidently $(c\bar{x}_0, \dots, c\bar{x}_{n-1}, d)$ is a solution of the set (1). Conversely, suppose that the set (1) has the solution $(\bar{x}_0, ..., \bar{x}_n)$. If $\bar{x}_0, ..., \bar{x}_{n-1}$ are not all zero, the set (2) has the solution $(1, \bar{x}_n)$ for the specialisation $(\bar{x}_0, ..., \bar{x}_{n-1})$ of $(x'_0, ..., x'_{n-1})$. If, on the other hand, $\bar{x}_0 = ... = \bar{x}_{n-1} = 0$, $\bar{x}_n \neq 0$, the equations (2) have the solution $(0, \bar{x}_n)$ for any specialisation of $x'_0, ..., x'_{n-1}$. Hence, in this case,

$$d_i(x'_0, ..., x'_{n-1}) \equiv 0 \quad (i = 1, ..., N).$$

We see then that a necessary and sufficient condition that the equations (1) have a solution is that the equations

$$d_i(x'_0, ..., x'_{n-1}) = 0 \quad (i = 1, ..., N)$$

have a solution. Since these are homogeneous equations, and $x_i = \xi_0 x'_i$, this is simply the condition that the equations

$$d_i(x_0, ..., x_{n-1}) = 0 \quad (i = 1, ..., N) \tag{3}$$

have a solution. We see that if the equations (3) have a solution which is algebraic over the field of coefficients, so has the system (1).

As a final preparatory step towards our first theorem, consider the reverse transformation connecting x_i with x'_i,

$$\left. \begin{array}{l} x'_i = x_i \xi_0^{-1}, \\ \xi_1 = x_n \end{array} \right\} \quad (i = 0, ..., n-1),$$

and its effect on the identity

$$d_i \xi_0^{\rho_i} \equiv \sum_j a_{ij}(\xi_0, \xi_1) f_j(\xi_0 x'_0, ..., \xi_0 x'_{n-1}, \xi_1).$$

This becomes

$$d_i(x_0 \xi_0^{-1}, ..., x_{n-1} \xi_0^{-1}) \, \xi_0^{\rho_i} \equiv \sum_j \frac{b_{ij}(x_0, ..., x_n)}{\xi_0^{m_{ij}}} f_j(x_0, ..., x_n),$$

where $b_{ij}(x_0, ..., x_n)$ is a form in $x_0, ..., x_n$; the coefficients are polynomials in ξ_0. On multiplying by a suitable power of ξ_0 we obtain the equation

$$d_i(x_0, ..., x_{n-1}) \, \xi_0^m \equiv \sum \xi_0^{n_{ij}} b_{ij}(x_0, ..., x_n) f_j(x_0, ..., x_n),$$

and on equating like powers of ξ_0 we have, finally,

$$d_i(x_0, ..., x_{n-1}) \equiv \sum_j c_{ij}(x_0, ..., x_n) f_j(x_0, ..., x_n). \tag{4}$$

We are now in a position to prove

THEOREM I. *Let*

$$f_i(x_0, ..., x_n) = 0 \quad (i = 1, ..., r) \tag{1}$$

be a set of homogeneous equations with indeterminate coefficients, and let

$$\bar{f}_i(x_0, ..., x_n) = 0 \quad (i = 1, ..., r) \tag{5}$$

be the equations obtained from (1) *by a given specialisation of the coefficients in* (1). *Then there exists a finite set of polynomials in the coefficients of* (1), $d_1, ..., d_k$, *with the properties*

(i) $$d_i x_0^m \equiv \sum_{j=0}^{r} a_{ij}(x_0, ..., x_n) f_j(x_0, ..., x_n)$$

for some value of m, the coefficients of $a_{ij}(x_0, ..., x_n)$ being in the ring of coefficients of (1); *and*

(ii) *a necessary and sufficient condition that the equations* (5) *have a solution in an algebraic extension of the ring of coefficients is that the specialisations of the polynomials d_i arising from the given specialisations of the coefficients should be zero.*

We have proved this theorem when $n = 1$ [§ 5] and we now proceed by induction. Beginning with the set of equations (1), we construct the set of forms $d_i(x_0, ..., x_{n-1})$ which satisfy (4) and have the property that the equations (3) have a solution if and only if the equations (1) have a solution. This property remains true for any specialisation of the coefficients.

Now consider a set of N homogeneous equations

$$D_i(x_0, ..., x_{n-1}) = 0 \quad (i = 1, ..., N) \tag{6}$$

with indeterminate coefficients, $D_i(x_0, ..., x_{n-1})$ being of the same degree as $d_i(x_0, ..., x_{n-1})$. Applying the hypothesis of induction to (6), we construct the set $E_i\,(i = 1, ..., k)$, of polynomials in the coefficients which are such that

$$E_i x_0^m \equiv \sum A_{ij}(x_0, ..., x_{n-1}) D_j(x_0, ..., x_{n-1}) \quad (i = 1, ..., k),$$

and which also have the property that a necessary and sufficient condition that any specialisation of (6) should have a solution is that the corresponding specialisations of the E_i should vanish.

We can specialise the coefficients of (6) in two stages. First we specialise the coefficients of (6) so that $D_i(x_0, ..., x_{n-1})$ becomes $d_i(x_0, ..., x_{n-1})$, and then we specialise the coefficients of $d_i(x_0, ... x_{n-1})$ by the specialisation which leads from (1) to (5). The first specialisation induces a specialisation

$$E_i \to d_i \quad (i = 1, ..., k)$$

of E_i, and we have

$$d_i x_0^m \equiv \sum a_{ij}(x_0, ..., x_{n-1}) d_j(x_0, ..., x_{n-1})$$
$$\equiv \sum\sum a_{ij} c_{jk} f_k(x_0, ..., x_n) \tag{7}$$

by (4), where $\sum a_{ij} c_{jk}$ is a form in $x_0, ..., x_n$, with coefficients in the ring of coefficients of (1).

When we make the further specialisation which leads from (1) to (5) we induce a further specialisation of the d_i. The vanishing of these is a necessary and sufficient condition for the existence of a solution of the specialised forms of (3) in an algebraic extension of the field of coefficients; that is, in an algebraic extension of the field of coefficients of (5). This, in turn, is a necessary and sufficient condition for the existence of a solution of (5) in an algebraic extension of the field of coefficients. Our result is therefore proved.

Moreover, if the set (5) has any solution, it follows from (7) that the d_i are all zero, and hence that the set (5) has a solution in an algebraic extension of the field of coefficients of (5).

7. Non-homogeneous equations in several unknowns. We now consider how we may apply a process similar to that of § 6 to test for the existence of a solution of a set of non-homogeneous equations
$$g_i(x_1, \ldots, x_n) = 0 \quad (i = 1, \ldots, r), \tag{1}$$
having coefficients in the ground field K. It will be recalled that the condition given in § 5 for the case $n = 1$ was necessary, but was only sufficient if we imposed the restriction that the actual degrees of the equations were equal to the assigned degrees. We make a similar restriction in the present case, but even when this is made we may not be able to proceed in the obvious manner. For, let the polynomial $g_i(x_1, \ldots, x_n)$ be of degree m_i, and let it be of degree m_i' when regarded as a polynomial in x_n with coefficients in $K[x_1, \ldots, x_{n-1}]$. Write
$$g_i(x_1, \ldots, x_n) \equiv a_i(x_1, \ldots, x_{n-1}) x_n^{m_i'} + b_i(a_1, \ldots, x_{n-1}) x_n^{m_i'-1} + \ldots. \tag{2}$$
$a_i(x_1, \ldots, x_{n-1})$ is a polynomial in $K[x_1, \ldots, x_{n-1}]$ of degree $m_i - m_i'$. Our restriction implies that it is not zero. When we apply the results of § 5 to (1), regarded as equations in x_n, we obtain a set of polynomials
$$h_i(x_1, \ldots, x_{n-1}) \quad (i = 1, \ldots, s)$$
having the properties

(i) $h_i(x_1, \ldots, x_{n-1}) \equiv \sum\limits_{j=1}^{r} a_{ij}(x_1, \ldots, x_n) g_j(a_1, \ldots, x_n) \quad (i = 1, \ldots, s)$;

(ii) necessary conditions that the equations
$$g_i(\bar{x}_1, \ldots, \bar{x}_{n-1}, x_n) = 0 \quad (i = 1, \ldots, r) \tag{3}$$
(where $\bar{x}_i$ is a specialisation of x_i) have a solution are
$$h_i(\bar{x}_1, \ldots, \bar{x}_{n-1}) = 0 \quad (i = 1, \ldots, s);$$

(iii) if $\qquad h_i(\bar{x}_1, ..., \bar{x}_{n-1}) = 0 \quad (i = 1, ..., s),$

then, either the equations (3) have a solution, or else

$$a_i(\bar{x}_1, ..., \bar{x}_{n-1}) = 0 \quad (i = 1, ..., r).$$

In order to remove this last possibility we proceed as follows. Let $u_1, ..., u_{n-1}$ be $n-1$ independent indeterminates, and write

$$y_i = x_i - u_i x_n \quad (i = 1, ..., n-1),$$
$$y_n = x_n.$$

Then we have $\qquad g_i(x_1, ..., x_n) \equiv G_i(y_1, ..., y_n),$

where $G_i(y_1, ..., y_n)$ is a polynomial with coefficients in $K[u_1, ..., u_{n-1}]$ of degree m_i in $y_1, ..., y_n$. In this polynomial $y_n^{m_i}$ appears with coefficient $g_i^*(u_1, ..., u_{n-1}, 1)$, where $g_i^*(x_1, ..., x_n)$ is the set of terms in $g_i(x_1, ..., x_n)$ which are of degree m_i. We apply the results of §5 to the equations
$$G_i(y_1, ..., y_n) = 0 \quad (i = 1, ..., r), \tag{4}$$

regarded as equations in y_n. We then obtain polynomials

$$H_i(y_1, ..., y_{n-1})$$

with coefficients in $K[u_1, ..., u_{n-1}]$, such that

(i) $H_i(y_1, ..., y_{n-1}) \equiv \sum_{j=1}^{r} A_{ij}(y_1, ..., y_n) G_j(y_1, ..., y_n) \quad (i = 1, ..., s);$

(ii) necessary and sufficient conditions for the existence of a solution of the equations

$$G_i(\bar{y}_1, ..., \bar{y}_{n-1}, y_n) = 0 \quad (i = 1, ..., r),$$
are $\qquad H_i(\bar{y}_1, ..., \bar{y}_{n-1}) = 0 \quad (i = 1, ..., s).$

In this case the possibility (iii) does not arise since

$$a_i(\bar{y}_1, ..., \bar{y}_{n-1}) \equiv g_i^*(u_1, ..., u_{n-1}, 1),$$

which is a non-zero element of $K[u_1, ..., u_{n-1}]$.

There exist [III, §8, Th. I] specialisations $\bar{u}_1, ..., \bar{u}_{n-1}$ of $u_1, ..., u_{n-1}$ such that

$$g_i^*(\bar{u}_1, ..., \bar{u}_{n-1}, 1) \neq 0 \quad (i = 1, ..., r),$$

and the results just stated hold when $u_1, ..., u_{n-1}$ are specialised to $\bar{u}_1, ..., \bar{u}_{n-1}$. In what follows we assume that these specialisations have been made.

Any solution $(x'_1, \ldots, x'_n)$ of the equations (1) leads to a solution $(x'_1 - \bar{u}_1 x'_n, \ldots, x'_n)$ of (4) and hence to a solution

$$(x'_1 - \bar{u}_1 x'_n, \ldots, x'_{n-1} - \bar{u}_{n-1} x'_n)$$

of
$$H_i(y_1, \ldots, y_{n-1}) = 0 \quad (i = 1, \ldots, s). \tag{5}$$

Conversely, any solution $(y'_1, \ldots, y'_{n-1})$ of (5) implies the existence of a solution y'_n of the equations (4) obtained by specialising $y_1, \ldots, y_{n-1}$ to $y'_1, \ldots, y'_{n-1}$; and the solution $(y'_1, \ldots, y'_n)$ of (4) implies the solution $(y'_1 + \bar{u}_1 y'_n, \ldots, y'_{n-1} + \bar{u}_{n-1} y'_n, y'_n)$ of (1).

Thus we have shown how to find a set of equations (4) in $n-1$ unknowns, the existence of a solution of which is a necessary and sufficient condition for the existence of a solution of the equation (1) in n unknowns. Repeating this process n times we can determine whether a given set of equations (1) has a solution.

THEOREM I. *If the equations*

$$g_i(x_1, \ldots, x_n) = 0 \quad (i = 1, \ldots, r) \tag{1}$$

have no common solution, there exist polynomials $A_i(x_1, \ldots, x_n)$ *such that*

$$\sum_{i=1}^{r} A_i(x_1, \ldots, x_n)\, g_i(x_1, \ldots, x_n) \equiv 1.$$

We have already [§ 5, (5)] proved this result in the case $n = 1$, so we proceed by induction. To this end, we assume the truth of the result for equations in $n-1$ unknowns, in particular for the equations (5) above. Since equations (1) have no solution, neither have (5) and therefore there exist polynomials $B_i(y_1, \ldots, y_{n-1})$ such that

$$1 \equiv \sum_{i=1}^{s} B_i(y_1, \ldots, y_{n-1})\, H_i(y_1, \ldots, y_{n-1}).$$

Using the property found above of the polynomials $H_i(y_1, \ldots, y_{n-1})$ we have

$$1 \equiv \sum_{i=1}^{s} B_i(y_1, \ldots, y_{n-1}) \sum_{j=1}^{r} A_{ij}(y_1, \ldots, y_n)\, G_j(y_1, \ldots, y_n)$$

$$\equiv \sum_{j=1}^{r} C_j(y_1, \ldots, y_n)\, G_j(y_1, \ldots, y_n),$$

where $C_j(y_1, \ldots, y_n) \equiv \sum_{i=1}^{s} B_i(y_1, \ldots, y_{n-1})\, A_{ij}(y_1, \ldots, y_n).$

Replacing y_i by $x_i - \bar{u}_i x_n$ $(i = 1, \ldots, n-1)$ and y_n by x_n we have

$$1 \equiv \sum_{i=1}^{r} A_i(x_1, \ldots, x_n)\, g_i(x_1, \ldots, x_n),$$

where $A_i(x_1, \ldots, x_n) \equiv C_i(x_1 - \bar{u}_1 x_n, \ldots, x_n).$

This important result will be used in the next section. Apart from this application we shall not have occasion to consider other properties of non-homogeneous equations, and we do not pursue the topic further.

8. Hilbert's zero-theorem. Let

$$f_i(x_1, ..., x_n) = 0 \quad (i = 1, ..., r) \tag{1}$$

be any set of non-homogeneous equations with coefficients in K, and let $g(x_1, ..., x_n)$ be a non-zero polynomial which is such that

$$g(\xi_1, ..., \xi_n) = 0$$

for every solution $\xi_1, ..., \xi_n$ of (1) which is algebraic over the ground field. We prove Hilbert's zero-theorem:

THEOREM I. *There exist polynomials $a_i(x_1, ..., x_n)$ and an integer s such that*

$$[g(x_1, ..., x_n)]^s \equiv \sum_{i=1}^{r} a_i(x_1, ..., x_n) f_i(x_1, ..., x_n).$$

Let z be any new indeterminate. Consider the equations (1) together with the additional equation

$$zg(x_1, ..., x_n) - 1 = 0 \tag{2}$$

as equations in $K[x_1, ..., x_n, z]$. This new set of equations has no solution in any algebraic extension of K, since for any such solution the left-hand side of (2) is -1. There can be no solution in *any* extension of K, since this would involve the vanishing of the resultant system, and hence lead to a solution in an algebraic extension of K. Hence [§7, Th. I] there exist polynomials

$$A_i(x_1, ..., x_n, z), \quad B(x_1, ..., x_n, z)$$

in $K[x_1, ..., x_n, z]$ such that

$$1 \equiv \sum_{i=1}^{r} A_i(x_1, ..., x_n, z) f_i(x_1, ..., x_n)$$
$$+ B(x_1, ..., x_n, z) [zg(x_1, ..., x_n) - 1].$$

This identity remains true when we replace z by $[g(x_1, ..., x_n)]^{-1}$. Hence

$$1 \equiv \sum_{i=1}^{r} A_i(x_1, ..., x_n, g^{-1}) f_i(x_1, ..., x_n),$$

and multiplying both sides by a suitable power of $g(x_1, ..., x_n)$ we have the required result:

$$[g(x_1, ..., x_n)]^s \equiv \sum_{i=1}^{r} a_i(x_1, ..., x_n) f_i(x_1, ..., x_n), \tag{3}$$

the $a_i(x_1, ..., x_n)$ lying in $K[x_1, ..., x_n]$.

From this we deduce immediately that if (1) is a system of homogeneous equations, and $g(x_1, ..., x_n)$ is a form of degree m which is satisfied by all non-trivial solutions of (1) in an algebraic extension of K, then a relation (3) holds, the $a_i(x_1, ..., x_n)$ being homogeneous and of degree $ms - m_i$, where m_i is the degree of $f_i(x_1, ..., x_n)$.

9.   The resultant ideal.   The procedure we followed in obtaining the resultant system of a set of homogeneous equations was not symmetric in the indeterminates $x_0, ..., x_n$. We eliminated these in a definite order, and a different order of elimination may well lead to a different resultant system. Also, the *number* of forms which appear in the resultant system has not been indicated. We show here that a *single* resultant suffices for $n+1$ forms in $n+1$ variables, whereas for any number of forms less than $n+1$ no condition for solubility in a suitable extension of the ground field is necessary. The method is based on the consideration of *resultant-forms*.

Let the set of homogeneous equations considered be

$$f_i(x_0, ..., x_n) = 0 \quad (i = 1, ..., r),$$

where $$f_i(x_0, ..., x_n) \equiv a_i x_0^{m_i} + ... + \omega_i x_n^{m_i} \quad (i = 1, ..., r),$$

all coefficients being indeterminates. In § 6 we have already encountered polynomials $d_1, ..., d_N$ in the coefficients of the forms f_i with the properties expressed by the identities

$$d_i x_k^\tau \equiv \sum_{j=1}^r A_j(x_0, ..., x_n) f_j(x_0, ..., x_n)$$

for a suitable τ and a suitable k, the A_j being polynomials in $x_0, ..., x_n$ with coefficients in the ring of coefficients. We use this property to define resultant-forms.

Any polynomial $T(a_1, ..., a_r, ..., \omega_1, ..., \omega_r)$ in $K[a_1, ..., \omega_r]$ for which there is a relation

$$Tx_k^\tau \equiv \sum_1^r A_j(x_0, ..., x_n) f_j(x_0, ..., x_n) \tag{1}$$

for a suitable τ and a suitable k, the A_j being polynomials in $x_0, ..., x_n$ with coefficients in $K[a_1, ..., \omega_r]$, is called a *resultant-form*. The polynomials $d_1, ..., d_N$ of § 6 are all resultant-forms. We may give another definition of resultant-forms. Write

$$f_i \equiv a_i x_0^{m_i} + ... + \omega_i x_n^{m_i} \equiv f_i^* + \omega_i x_n^{m_i}.$$

Then if we substitute
$$\omega_i = -f_i^*/x_n^{m_i} \qquad (2)$$

in (1), the f_i all vanish, and therefore
$$x_k^\tau T\left(a_1, \ldots, a_r, \ldots, -\frac{f_1^*}{x_n^{m_1}}, \ldots, -\frac{f_r^*}{x_n^{m_r}}\right) \equiv 0. \qquad (3)$$

Conversely, if for any polynomial $T(a_1, \ldots, a_r, \ldots, \omega_1, \ldots, \omega_r)$ the relation (3) holds, we have

$$T(a_1, \ldots, a_r, \ldots, \omega_1, \ldots, \omega_r)$$
$$\equiv T\left(a_1, \ldots, a_r, \ldots, -\frac{f_1^*}{x_n^{m_1}} + \omega_1 + \frac{f_1^*}{x_n^{m_1}}, \ldots, -\frac{f_r^*}{x_n^{m_r}} + \omega_r + \frac{f_r^*}{x_n^{m_r}}\right)$$
$$\equiv T\left(a_1, \ldots, a_r, \ldots, -\frac{f_1^*}{x_n^{m_1}}, \ldots, -\frac{f_r^*}{x_n^{m_r}}\right)$$
$$+ \Sigma\left(\omega_i + \frac{f_i^*}{x_n^{m_i}}\right) A_i\left(a_1, \ldots, a_r, \ldots, -\frac{f_1^*}{x_n^{m_1}}, \ldots, -\frac{f_r^*}{x_n^{m_r}}\right),$$

on expanding the polynomial $T(a_1, \ldots, a_r, \ldots, \omega_1, \ldots, \omega_r)$ in ascending powers of $\omega_i + (f_i^*/x_n^{m_i})$. Multiplying this last equation by a suitable power of x_n, and using (3), we find
$$x_n^\sigma T(a_1, \ldots, \omega_r) \equiv \sum_1^r B_i(x_0, \ldots, x_n) f_i(x_0, \ldots, x_n).$$

Hence T is a resultant-form. From (1) we can deduce (3), and from (3) arrive back at (1), but with x_n instead of x_k. Since the suffix n plays no special part in this process, we see that from (3) we may deduce (1), k being any one of the numbers $0, 1, \ldots, n$.

The resultant-forms can be used as a resultant system for the set of homogeneous equations
$$f_i(x_0, \ldots, x_n) = 0 \quad (i = 1, \ldots, r). \qquad (4)$$

For if, after specialisation of the coefficients, there is a non-trivial solution, and we substitute this in (1), the right-hand side vanishes, and since not all x_i are zero, $T = 0$, T being any resultant-form. On the other hand, if all resultant-forms vanish for a given specialisation of the coefficients of (4), those resultant-forms $d_1, \ldots, d_N$ which belong to the resultant system of (4) also vanish, and the set of equations has a non-trivial solution. As we shall see immediately, the resultant-forms constitute an ideal in the ring of polynomials $K[a_1, \ldots, \omega_r]$. If we can find a basis for this ideal [cf. §2], this same basis will serve as a resultant system for the equations (4).

If $S(a_1, ..., \omega_r)$ and $T(a_1, ..., \omega_r)$ are two resultant-forms, and $R(a_1, ..., \omega_r)$ is any element of $K[a_1, ..., \omega_r]$, then since

$$S\left(a_1, ..., -\frac{f_r^*}{x_n^{m_r}}\right) - T\left(a_1, ..., -\frac{f_r^*}{x_n^{m_r}}\right) \equiv 0,$$

and

$$R\left(a_1, ..., -\frac{f_r^*}{x_n^{m_r}}\right) S\left(a_1, ..., -\frac{f_r^*}{x_n^{m_r}}\right) \equiv 0,$$

it follows that

$$S(a_1, ..., \omega_r) - T(a_1, ..., \omega_r) \quad \text{and} \quad R(a_1, ..., \omega_r) S(a_1, ..., \omega_r)$$

are resultant-forms. Hence resultant-forms constitute an ideal in $K[a_1, ..., \omega_r]$. We call this the *resultant ideal*.

If the product of two elements of $K[a_1, ..., \omega_r]$ lies in this ideal, one of the elements must lie in the ideal. For if $R(a_1, ..., \omega_r)$, $U(a_1, ..., \omega_r)$ are the elements, we have

$$R\left(a_1, ..., -\frac{f_r^*}{x_n^{m_r}}\right) U\left(a_1, ..., -\frac{f_r^*}{x_n^{m_r}}\right) \equiv 0.$$

One of the factors on the left must vanish, and therefore one of the polynomials must be a resultant-form. An ideal with this property is called a prime ideal. We now prove

THEOREM I. *If the number r of forms f_i is less than $n+1$, there are no resultant-forms different from zero.*

If T is a non-zero resultant-form,

$$T\left(a_1, ..., a_r, ..., -\frac{f_1^*}{x_n^{m_1}}, ..., -\frac{f_r^*}{x_n^{m_r}}\right) \equiv 0, \tag{5}$$

but

$$T(a_1, ..., a_r, ..., \omega_1, ..., \omega_r) \not\equiv 0. \tag{6}$$

We show that a relation of this type continues to hold even when the coefficients $a_1, ..., \omega_r$ are no longer indeterminates, but specialisations $\bar{a}_1, ..., \bar{\omega}_r$ in K. Consider, first of all, the specialisation $a_1 \rightarrow \bar{a}_1$. It may happen that

$$T(\bar{a}_1, ..., a_r, ..., \omega_1, ..., \omega_r) \equiv 0.$$

If this is so,

$$T(a_1, ..., a_r, ..., \omega_1, ..., \omega_r) \equiv (a_1 - \bar{a}_1)^s T^*(a_1, ..., \omega_r)$$

for some integer s, where

$$T^*(\bar{a}_1, ..., a_r, ..., \omega_1, ..., \omega_r) \not\equiv 0.$$

Since
$$(a_1 - \bar{a}_1)^s \, T^*\!\left(a_1, \ldots, a_r, \ldots, -\frac{f_1^*}{x_n^{m_1}}, \ldots, -\frac{f_r^*}{x_n^{m_r}}\right) \equiv 0,$$

it follows that
$$T^*\!\left(a_1, \ldots, a_r, \ldots, -\frac{f_r^*}{x_n^{m_r}}\right) \equiv 0,$$

and so $T^*(\bar{a}_1, \ldots, a_r, \omega_1, \ldots, \omega_r)$ is a non-zero resultant-form. Specialising each of the indeterminates present in turn, we find at each stage a non-zero polynomial which vanishes when the substitution (2) is made; that is, a resultant-form. Hence, finally, we obtain a non-zero resultant-form when
$$a_1 \to \bar{a}_1, \quad \ldots, \quad \omega_r \to \bar{\omega}_r,$$

provided that we began with a non-zero resultant-form before any indeterminates were specialised.

Now, since $r < n+1$, we may specialise $a_1, \ldots, \omega_r$ so that $f_i \to \bar{f}_i$, where
$$\bar{f}_i = x_{i-1}^{m_i} + x_n^{m_i} \quad (i = 1, \ldots, r).$$

The existence of a non-zero resultant-form before the specialisation involves the existence of a non-zero polynomial
$$T(\omega_1, \ldots, \omega_r)$$

such that
$$T\!\left(-\frac{x_0^{m_0}}{x_n^{m_0}}, \ldots, -\frac{x_{r-1}^{m_r}}{x_n^{m_r}}\right) \equiv 0.$$

But $x_0, \ldots, x_{r-1}, x_n$ are independent indeterminates, and we are therefore led to a contradiction. This proves the theorem.

It follows that the resultant system of $r(r < n+1)$ homogeneous equations in $n+1$ unknowns vanishes identically, and therefore that the equations always have a solution in some algebraic extension of the ground field.

THEOREM II. *There is a non-zero resultant-form for $n+1$ equations in $n+1$ unknowns.*

There must be one, at least. For if not, $n+1$ homogeneous equations always have a solution, for any specialisation of the coefficients. But there is an evident specialisation for which the equations become
$$x_i^{m_i} = 0 \quad (i = 0, \ldots, n),$$

and these equations have no non-trivial solution. Our assumption is therefore false, and there is at least one non-zero resultant-form.

The argument of the previous theorem shows us that when $r = n + 1$ there can be no non-zero resultant-form which is independent of ω_{n+1}. Assumption of the contrary hypothesis leads to an algebraic equation connecting $x_0, \ldots, x_n$.

Hence if we choose, from the ideal of all resultant-forms in $K[a_1, \ldots, \omega_{n+1}]$, a polynomial whose degree in ω_{n+1} is the least possible, this degree is not zero. If this polynomial is reducible, one of its irreducible factors must belong to the ideal, which is prime, and this factor must also be of the minimum possible degree in ω_{n+1}. We call this resultant-form R, and prove

THEOREM III. *Every resultant-form is divisible by* R.

Let
$$R \equiv A\omega_{n+1}^{\lambda} + \ldots,$$

when arranged in descending powers of ω_{n+1}, and let

$$S \equiv B\omega_{n+1}^{\mu} + \ldots$$

be any member of the ideal, similarly arranged. Since $\mu \geqslant \lambda$,

$$AS - B\omega_{n+1}^{\mu-\lambda}R \equiv T$$

is another member of the ideal, with a lower degree in ω_{n+1} than S. Repeating this process, using T instead of S for the next stage, we finally arrive at a polynomial

$$T^* \equiv A^k S - QR$$

in the ideal which is of lower degree than R. This must be a zero polynomial, and therefore

$$A^k S \equiv QR,$$

showing that $A^k S$ is divisible by R. Since R is irreducible and cannot divide A, which is independent of ω_{n+1}, R divides S. This proves the theorem.

This resultant-form R is therefore a basis for the ideal of resultant-forms in $K[a_1, \ldots, \omega_{n+1}]$. A necessary and sufficient condition for the $n + 1$ homogeneous equations

$$f_i(x_0, \ldots, x_n) = 0 \quad (i = 1, \ldots, n+1)$$

to have a non-trivial solution is given by the vanishing of R. We call R the *resultant* of the system.

10.   The u-resultant of a system of equations.   Suppose that we know that a system of homogeneous equations over K

$$f_i(x_0, ..., x_n) = 0 \quad (i = 1, ..., r) \tag{1}$$

has a finite number of solutions. Let these be

$$(\xi_0^{(j)}, ..., \xi_n^{(j)}) \quad (j = 1, ..., s),$$

in some extension of K.

To the equations (1) we add the equation with indeterminate coefficients

$$f_{r+1} \equiv u_0 x_0 + ... + u_n x_n = 0. \tag{2}$$

Since the u_i are indeterminates,

$$\sum_{i=0}^{n} u_i \xi_i^{(j)} \neq 0 \quad (j = 1, ..., s),$$

and therefore the resultant-forms of equations (1), (2), of which (1) are specialised, do not all vanish. These resultant-forms are polynomials in $u_0, ..., u_n$. If one such is $T(u)$,

$$T(u) x_n^\tau \equiv \sum_{i=1}^{r+1} A_i(x_0, ..., x_n, u) f_i(x_0, ..., x_n). \tag{3}$$

Now the f_i, if they contain $u_0, ..., u_n$, are homogeneous in these indeterminates. If we equate sums of terms of equal degree in the u's on each side of (3), we obtain equations similar to (3), but the $T(u)$ are now homogeneous in $u_0, ..., u_n$. These $T(u)$ are still resultant-forms, satisfying equations of type (3), and we therefore need only consider resultant-forms which are homogeneous in $u_0, ..., u_n$.

Let
$$b_1(u), ..., b_l(u) \tag{4}$$

be a basis for the resultant-forms of equations (1), (2). We may assume that each $b_i(u)$ is homogeneous in the u's, and is also of degree greater than zero, since all resultant-forms of the set (1) vanish. The set of forms (4) serves as a resultant system for the $r + 1$ equations given by (1) and (2).

This resultant system vanishes for the specialisations

$$u_i \rightarrow \overline{u}_i \quad (i = 0, ..., n),$$

if and only if a solution of the equations (1) satisfies (2); that is, if and only if

$$\overline{f}_{(j)} \equiv \overline{u}_0 \xi_0^{(j)} + ... + \overline{u}_n \xi_n^{(j)} = 0,$$

for some value of j. In other words, the common zeros of the forms (4), considered as forms in the set $u_0, ..., u_n$, are precisely the zeros of the product

$$G(u) \equiv \prod_{j=1}^{s} f_{(j)} \equiv \prod_{1}^{s} (u_0 \xi_0^{(j)} + ... + u_n \xi_n^{(j)})$$

in a suitable extension ring of $K[u]$.

It follows by Hilbert's zero-theorem that on the one hand

$$[b_i(u)]^{\tau_i} \equiv A_i(u) \, G(u) \quad (i = 1, ..., t), \tag{5}$$

and on the other that

$$[G(u)]^\sigma \equiv \sum_{i=1}^{t} a_i(u) \, b_i(u). \tag{6}$$

Now, the $f_{(j)}$ are linear forms in $u_0, ..., u_n$, and therefore irreducible. From (5) the $b_i(u)$, and therefore their highest common factor $D(u)$, can be divided by the linear factors $f_{(j)}$. But (6) can also be written

$$[G(u)]^\sigma \equiv B(u) \, D(u),$$

from which it follows that $D(u)$ contains no other linear factors but these $f_{(j)}$. We deduce therefore that

$$D(u) \equiv \prod_{j=1}^{s} (u_0 \xi_0^{(j)} + ... + u_n \xi_n^{(j)})^{\sigma_j} \quad (\sigma_j \geqslant 1).$$

Since $D(u)$ is the highest common factor of the forms (4) which are a basis for the resultant-forms of equations (1), (2), $D(u)$ divides *all* resultant-forms, and, in particular, $D(u)$ divides every member of any resultant system of the $r+1$ equations (1) and (2). We have proved

THEOREM I. *The linear forms $f_{(j)}$ which determine the solutions of equations* (1) *are found by the resolution into factors, in a suitable extension field, of the form $D(u)$. This form $D(u)$ is the highest common factor of the resultant-forms of $f_1, ..., f_r, f_{r+1}$, and is called the u-resultant of $f_1, ..., f_r$.*

If the set of equations (1) has an *infinite* number of solutions, we may extend the notion of the u-resultant. We consider the equations (1) together with the set of linear equations with indeterminate coefficients

$$f_{r+i} \equiv \sum_{j=0}^{n} u_{ij} x_j = 0 \quad (i = 1, ..., s). \tag{7}$$

If s is large enough, the sets of equations (1) and (7) have no common solutions. For if we take $s = n+1$, the set (7) taken by itself has no solution.

Choose s to be the smallest integer such that (1) and (7) have no common solution. Consider the resultant-forms of these equations. Generalising our previous argument, we see that the only resultant-forms we need consider are those homogeneous in each set of indeterminates

$$u_i = (u_{i0}, ..., u_{in}) \quad (i = 1, ..., s).$$

If for the specialisations

$$u_{sj} \to \bar{u}_{sj} \quad (j = 0, ..., n)$$

the equations (1) and (7) have a solution $(\xi_0, ..., \xi_n)$, all resultant-forms $T(u_1, ..., u_s)$ vanish for this specialisation. That is,

$$T(u_1, ..., u_{s-1}, \bar{u}_s) \equiv 0.$$

Reasoning as above, we see that

$$\sum_{i=0}^{n} u_{si} \xi_i$$

is a factor of $T(u_1, ..., u_s)$. If $D(u_1, ..., u_s)$ is the highest common factor of all resultant-forms, the factor (7) divides $D(u_1, ..., u_s)$.

But since this highest common factor, regarded as a form in $u_{s0}, ..., u_{sn}$ has only a finite number of linear factors in any extension field, *the equations*

$$f_i = 0 \quad (i = 1, ..., r+s-1) \tag{8}$$

have only a finite number of solutions.

The u_s-resultant of (8) is $D(u_1, ..., u_s)$. It may also be called the u-resultant of equations (1). In a case which will be considered in vol. II, in which the equations (1) define an irreducible variety, this generalised u-resultant is of considerable importance.

BOOK II
PROJECTIVE SPACE

CHAPTER V

PROJECTIVE SPACE: ALGEBRAIC DEFINITION

1. Introduction. It has been customary to follow two distinct and alternative lines of approach in defining a projective space of n dimensions. One is purely algebraic, and the other is based on the so-called 'propositions of incidence'. We propose to consider both methods of approach, devoting this chapter to the algebraic approach, and the next to the synthetic method. One of our main objects will be to compare the two methods in considerable detail. For this reason we shall begin by defining a more general space than that with which we shall ultimately be concerned. We shall impose new conditions only when we have examined their significance in some detail.

Our first action in defining a projective space algebraically is to select the ground field K. Initially we shall impose no restrictions on K. It may be non-commutative, and of finite characteristic. When K is non-commutative we shall be led to consider another field $\bar{K}$, which bears to K a relation similar to isomorphism, but differing in one respect. To define this relation, which we call *skew-isomorphism*, in general terms, let S denote a set of elements in one-to-one correspondence with the elements of K, a and $\bar{a}$ denoting corresponding elements of K and S respectively. We *define* addition and multiplication in the set by the rules

$$\bar{a}+\bar{b} = \overline{a+b}, \quad \bar{a}\bar{b} = (\overline{ba}).$$

It is easily proved that the elements of S, with these laws of composition, form a field, which we denote by $\bar{K}$. This field $\bar{K}$ is *isomorphic* with K, the reversal of the order of the factors in the product being, simply, a change of notation for the product of two elements $\bar{a}$ and $\bar{b}$ in $\bar{K}$. But we shall find it convenient to distinguish between an isomorphism between two fields K and $\bar{K}$ in which ab corresponds to $\overline{ab}$, and one in which ab corresponds to $\overline{ba}$. We shall refer to the first case simply as *isomorphism*, and to the second as *skew-isomorphism*.[*] In the case of a commutative field, of course, there is no difference between isomorphism and skew-isomorphism.

2.   Projective number space.

A set $(\alpha_0, ..., \alpha_n)$ of $n+1$ elements of the ground field K will be called an $(n+1)$-tuple if not all the elements $\alpha_0, ..., \alpha_n$ are zero. Two $(n+1)$-tuples $(\alpha_0, ..., \alpha_n), (\beta_0, ..., \beta_n)$ are said to be *right-hand equivalent* if there exists an element λ of K such that

$$\alpha_i = \beta_i \lambda \quad (i = 0, ..., n),$$

and *left-hand equivalent* if there exists an element μ of K such that

$$\alpha_i = \mu \beta_i \quad (i = 0, ..., n).$$

Clearly, when the two $(n+1)$-tuples are right-hand equivalent, λ cannot be zero, since, otherwise, each α_i would be zero. Similarly, if they are left-hand equivalent, μ cannot be zero. Right-hand (left-hand) equivalence is clearly reflexive, symmetric and transitive.

A set of right-hand equivalent $(n+1)$-tuples is called a *point of right-hand projective number space of dimension n over K*. The aggregate of such points is called a *projective number space of dimension n over K*. This is denoted by $PN_n^r(K)$. If left-hand equivalence is used in place of right-hand equivalence we obtain a *left-hand projective number space of dimension n over K*, denoted by $PN_n^l(K)$. If K is commutative, $PN_n^l(K) = PN_n^r(K)$.

If K is not commutative, and $\bar{K}$ is skew-isomorphic to K, two $(n+1)$-tuples $(\bar{\alpha}_0, ..., \bar{\alpha}_n), (\bar{\beta}_0, ..., \bar{\beta}_n)$ over $\bar{K}$ are right-hand (left-hand) equivalent if and only if the corresponding $(n+1)$-tuples $(\alpha_0, ..., \alpha_n), (\beta_0, ..., \beta_n)$ are left-hand (right-hand) equivalent. Hence, in an obvious sense, $PN_n^l(\bar{K})$ and $PN_n^r(K)$ are similar spaces, and $PN_n^l(K)$ and $PN_n^r(\bar{K})$ are also similar. For this reason it will be sufficient to develop the properties of $PN_n^r(K)$, those of $PN_n^l(K)$ being read off from those of $PN_n^r(\bar{K})$.

Let $A = (\alpha_{ij})$ be any regular $(n+1) \times (n+1)$ matrix whose elements are in K, and consider the equations

$$y_i = \sum_{j=0}^{n} \alpha_{ij} x_j \quad (i = 0, ..., n), \tag{1}$$

---

[*] van der Waerden uses the term *inverse-isomorphism*.

and also the equivalent equations

$$x_i = \sum_{j=0}^{n} \beta_{ij} y_j \quad (i = 0, \dots, n), \tag{2}$$

where $B = (\beta_{ij})$ is the inverse of A. If $(x_0 \lambda, \dots, x_n \lambda)$ is a set of right-hand equivalent $(n+1)$-tuples, the equations (1) transform these $(n+1)$-tuples into the set $(y_0 \lambda, \dots, y_n \lambda)$ of equivalent $(n+1)$-tuples; that is, the equations (1) transform a point of right-hand projective number space into a point of right-hand projective number space. By virtue of (2) this correspondence is one-to-one.

A set of equations (1), which we shall usually write in matrix form as

$$y = Ax, \tag{3}$$

determines a *projective transformation* of $PN_n^r(K)$ into itself.

To each regular $(n+1) \times (n+1)$ matrix A over K there corresponds a projective transformation (1). Let A_1 and A_2 be two regular matrices, defining the transformations

$$y = A_1 x, \tag{1_1}$$

$$y = A_2 x. \tag{1_2}$$

We operate on a point x with (1_1), and follow with (1_2). The point x becomes $y = A_1 x$, and y is transformed into $z = A_2 y = A_2 A_1 x$; and so the relation between x and z is

$$z = A_2 A_1 x.$$

Since [II, §3] $A_2 A_1$ is regular, the *product* of the two projective transformations of $PN_n^r(K)$ given by (1_1) and (1_2) is a projective transformation of $PN_n^r(K)$, and hence we have

THEOREM I. *The projective transformations of $PN_n^r(K)$ into itself form a group.*

Projective transformations of $PN_n^l(K)$ can be defined in a similar way. It should be noted that the equation of the transformation corresponding to the matrix A is now

$$y = xA, \tag{4}$$

where x and y are now $1 \times (n+1)$ matrices.

Let K^* be an extension of K. The points of $PN_n^r(K)$ are a subset of the points of $PN_n^r(K^*)$. The projective transformations of $PN_n^r(K^*)$ correspond to the regular $(n+1) \times (n+1)$ matrices over

K^*, and a subset of these are matrices over K. The projective transformations corresponding to the matrices of this subset form a subgroup of the group of projective transformations of $PN_n^r(K^*)$, and under the transformations of this subgroup the points of $PN_n^r(K)$ are transformed into points of $PN_n^r(K)$. We say that $PN_n^r(K^*)$ is the *extension* of $PN_n^r(K)$ corresponding to the extension K^* of K. Similarly, the group of projective transformations of $PN_n^r(K^*)$ is an extension of the group of projective transformations of $PN_n^r(K)$.

3.   Projective space of n dimensions.

Let S be a set of elements which can be put in one-to-one correspondence with the points of $PN_n^r(K)$, and let T denote a correspondence such that if A is any element of S, and B any point of $PN_n^r(K)$, there corresponds to A a unique point $T(A)$ of $PN_n^r(K)$, and to B a unique element $T^{-1}(B)$ of S. Then to each element A of S there corresponds a set of equivalent $(n+1)$-tuples $(\alpha_0\lambda, ..., \alpha_n\lambda)$, where $T(A)$ is $(\alpha_0, ..., \alpha_n)$. Any $(n+1)$-tuple of this set is called *a set of coordinates of A*.

Now consider a projective transformation in $PN_n^r(K)$. If this takes the point $T(A)$ of $PN_n^r(K)$, which corresponds to the element A of S, into $T'(A)$, the correspondence between the elements A of S and the points $T'(A)$ of $PN_n^r(K)$ is one-to-one, and thus a new coordinate system is defined in S. Indeed, a coordinate system is defined for each projective transformation of $PN_n^r(K)$. The various coordinate systems obtained in this way will be called *allowable coordinate systems in S*. From the group properties of projective transformations, discussed in § 2, it is clear that the same set of allowable coordinate systems in S is defined if the initial correspondence T between S and $PN_n^r(K)$ is replaced by any other correspondence T' which gives an allowable coordinate system.

The set S, with the set of allowable coordinate systems, is called a *right-hand projective space of n dimensions over K*, and the elements of S are called the *points* of this space. The space may be denoted by $P_n^r(K)$, but various other notations will be used. In the case in which K is commutative, and there is no doubt about the ground field, the symbols $[n]$, S_n, S_n' will be used to denote a projective space of n dimensions, the notation S_n being particularly useful when a number of projective spaces have to be considered simultaneously.

If $(x_0, ..., x_n)$ is a set of coordinates of a point P in $P_n^r(K)$ in a given allowable coordinate system, the coordinates $(y_0, ..., y_n)$ of this point in another allowable coordinate system are given by the equations

$$y_i = \sum_{j=0}^{n} \alpha_{ij} x_j \quad (i = 0, \ldots, n),$$

where $A = (\alpha_{ij})$ is a regular $(n+1) \times (n+1)$ matrix over K. The equations for transformation of coordinates in $P_n^r(K)$ can therefore be written, in matrix notation, as

$$y = Ax,$$

and there is one such transformation for each regular $(n+1) \times (n+1)$ matrix over K.

We consider how $P_n^r(K)$ can be extended when the field K is replaced by an extension K^*. In § 2 we saw how to extend $PN_n^r(K)$. We now embed the set S in a set S^* which can be put in one-to-one correspondence with the points of $PN_n^r(K^*)$ in such a way that the elements of S^* which lie in S correspond to points of $PN_n^r(K^*)$ which are in $PN_n^r(K)$. This is clearly possible; a set such as S^* can be formed by the elements of S and the points of $PN_n^r(K^*)$ which are not in $PN_n^r(K)$. Using the given correspondence between S^* and $PN_n^r(K^*)$, and the projective transformations of $PN_n^r(K^*)$, we construct a projective space of n dimensions $P_n^r(K^*)$ whose points are the elements of S^* in which $P_n^r(K)$ is embedded. Amongst the allowable coordinate systems of $P_n^r(K^*)$ there is a subset which induces the allowable coordinate systems of $P_n^r(K)$.

In later chapters we often have to replace a field K by an extension K^*. When this is done we shall assume that $P_n^r(K)$ has been extended to $P_n^r(K^*)$, as above. The effect of this is to add new points to $P_n^r(K)$, and to extend the group of allowable transformations.

Let us suppose that we have a coordinate system in $P_n^r(K^*)$ in which the points of $P_n^r(K)$ can be given coordinates in K. Consider the coordinates $(\alpha_0^*, \ldots, \alpha_n^*)$ of a point R in $P_n^r(K^*)$.

(i) If, for some λ^* in K^*,

$$\alpha_i^* \lambda^* \quad (i = 0, \ldots, n)$$

is in K, the point R is in $P_n^r(K)$, and is sometimes called a *rational point* of $P_n^r(K)$.

(ii) If, for some value of λ^*, each $\alpha_i^* \lambda^*$ is algebraic over K, R is called an *algebraic point* of $P_n^r(K)$.

(iii) If, however, for all λ^* in K^*, at least one $\alpha_i^* \lambda^*$ is transcendental over K, R is said to be a *transcendental point* of $P_n^r(K)$.

This completes our description of a right-hand projective space $P_n^r(K)$. The method of construction of a left-hand projective space $P_n^l(K)$ is now evident, and the reader can immediately read off the relations between $P_n^l(K)$ and $P_n^r(\bar{K})$, where $\bar{K}$ is skew-isomorphic to K.

4. Linear dependence in $P_n^r(K)$.

Consider $k+1$ points

$$A^0, \dots, A^k$$

in $P_n^r(K)$, and let

$$(\alpha_0^i, \dots, \alpha_n^i) \quad (i = 0, \dots, k)$$

be their coordinates in an allowable coordinate system. We say that the points $A^0, \dots, A^k$ are *linearly dependent* in $P_n^r(K)$ if there exist elements $\lambda_0, \dots, \lambda_k$ of K, not all zero, such that

$$\sum_{j=0}^{k} \alpha_i^j \lambda_j = 0 \quad (i = 0, \dots, n). \tag{1}$$

In order that linear dependence may be considered as a property of the points $A^0, \dots, A^k$, it must be shown to be independent of the coordinates selected for $A^0, \dots, A^k$ in the chosen coordinate system, and also to be independent of the allowable coordinate system.

To prove the first result, let $(\beta_0^i, \dots, \beta_n^i)$ be other coordinates for A^i in the given allowable coordinate system. Then

$$\beta_j^i = \alpha_j^i \mu_i,$$

where μ_i is some non-zero element of K. From (1) we deduce that

$$\sum_{j=0}^{k} \beta_i^j (\mu_j^{-1} \lambda_j) = 0 \quad (i = 0, \dots, n).$$

Hence, if a relation of type (1) holds for one choice of the coordinates in a given allowable coordinate system, a relation of this type also holds for any other choice in the given coordinate system.

Now consider any allowable transformation of coordinates given by

$$y = Cx, \tag{2}$$

where $C = (\gamma_{ij})$ is a regular $(n+1) \times (n+1)$ matrix over K. In the new coordinate system the coordinates of A^i can be taken as $(\beta_0^i, \dots, \beta_n^i)$, where

$$\beta_j^i = \sum_{\rho=0}^{n} \gamma_{j\rho} \alpha_\rho^i.$$

Then

$$\sum_{i=0}^{k} \beta_j^i \lambda_i = \sum_{i=0}^{k} \sum_{\rho=0}^{n} \gamma_{j\rho} \alpha_\rho^i \lambda_i = 0,$$

from (1). Hence, again, if a condition such as (1) holds in one allowable coordinate system, a similar condition holds in any other allowable coordinate system. Thus the linear dependence of points in $P_n^r(K)$ is a property of the points, and does not depend on the allowable coordinate system.

Recalling the properties of the linear dependence of vectors derived in Chapter II, we have the following alternative statements of the conditions for the linear dependence of the points $A^0, ..., A^k$.

(i) *If* $(\alpha_0^i, ..., \alpha_n^i)$ $(i = 0, ..., k)$ *are the coordinates of* $A^0, ..., A^k$ *in a given allowable coordinate system, a necessary and sufficient condition that* $A^0, ..., A^k$ *be linearly dependent is that the* $k + 1$ *right-hand vectors*

$$(\alpha_0^i, ..., \alpha_n^i) \quad (i = 0, ..., k)$$

be linearly dependent.

(ii) *A necessary and sufficient condition that* $A^0, ..., A^k$ *be linearly independent is that the matrix*

$$\begin{pmatrix} \alpha_0^0 & \alpha_0^1 & \cdot & \alpha_0^k \\ \alpha_1^0 & \alpha_1^1 & \cdot & \alpha_1^k \\ \cdot & \cdot & \cdot & \cdot \\ \alpha_n^0 & \alpha_n^1 & \cdot & \alpha_n^k \end{pmatrix}$$

be of rank $k + 1$.

An immediate corollary is

THEOREM I. *Any* m *points of* $P_n^r(K)$, *where* $m > n + 1$, *are linearly dependent.*

We can introduce a useful symbolic notation if we assume that the symbol A^i for a point represents a particular $(n + 1)$-tuple in the class of equivalent $(n + 1)$-tuples which give the coordinates of A^i in a given allowable system. The transformation (2) then defines a particular set of coordinates for each A^i in the new coordinate system, and this set will also be denoted by A^i. When we use the symbol A^i for a point in this way, we extend our notation by multiplying A^i, on the right, by a non-zero element of K, so that if $A^i = (\alpha_0, ..., \alpha_n)$, then $A^i \lambda = (\alpha_0 \lambda, ..., \alpha_n \lambda)$, and the symbols A^i and $A^i \lambda$ represent the same point. The equation (1) can then be written as

$$\sum_{i=0}^{k} A^i \lambda_i = 0,$$

and this relation does not depend on the allowable coordinate system used.

Any point A such that
$$A\mu = \sum_{i=0}^{k} A^i \mu_i,$$
for some non-zero μ in K, is said to be *linearly dependent* on $A^0, \ldots, A^k$. If $k = n$, and in a given allowable system of coordinates we take

$$A^i = (\delta_{i0}, \delta_{i1}, \ldots, \delta_{ii}, \ldots, \delta_{in}) \quad (i = 0, \ldots, n)$$
$$= (0, \ 0, \ldots, 1, \ldots, 0),$$

we obtain $n+1$ linearly independent points. Since any point
$$A = (\alpha_0, \ldots, \alpha_n)$$
can be written as
$$A = \sum_{i=0}^{n} A^i \alpha_i,$$

every point in $P_n^r(K)$ is linearly dependent on these $n+1$ points. They are said to form the *simplex of reference* for the given coordinate system.

The properties of the linear dependence of points can now be read off from the properties of the linear dependence of vectors [II, §1]. It will not be necessary to give proofs in detail, since these can be deduced at once from the corresponding proofs for vectors. The main results are as follows. In the first, A^i has the symbolic meaning just defined.

THEOREM II. *If $A^0, \ldots, A^k$ are linearly independent, and if*
$$A\lambda = \sum_{i=0}^{k} A^i \lambda_i$$
is linearly dependent on them, the $(k+1)$-tuple $(\lambda_0, \ldots, \lambda_k)$ is uniquely determined to within the class of equivalent $(k+1)$-tuples.

THEOREM III. *If $B^0, \ldots, B^h$ are linearly dependent on $A^0, \ldots, A^k$, and P is linearly dependent on $B^0, \ldots, B^h$, then P is linearly dependent on $A^0, \ldots, A^k$.*

THEOREM IV. *In any finite set of points $A^0, \ldots, A^k$ we can find a linearly independent subset $A^{i_0}, \ldots, A^{i_h}$ such that any point linearly dependent on $A^0, \ldots, A^k$ is linearly dependent on $A^{i_0}, \ldots, A^{i_h}$.*

THEOREM V. *If $B^0, \ldots, B^h$ are $h+1$ linearly independent points, each of which is linearly dependent on $A^0, \ldots, A^k$, then $h \leqslant k$, and we can find $k-h$ points $A^{i_{h+1}}, \ldots, A^{i_k}$ in the latter set such that every point linearly dependent on $A^0, \ldots, A^k$ is linearly dependent on $B^0, \ldots, B^h$, $A^{i_{h+1}}, \ldots, A^{i_k}$.* (*Exchange Theorem.*)

If $A^0, \ldots, A^k$ are $k+1$ linearly independent points of $P_n^r(K)$, the aggregate of points of $P_n^r(K)$ which are linearly dependent on them constitute *a linear space of k dimensions*. We shall call a linear space of 1 dimension a *line*, and a linear space of 2 dimensions a *plane*. From the first part of the Exchange Theorem we deduce that any $h+1$ points of a linear space of k dimensions, where $h > k$, are necessarily linearly dependent. On the other hand, there exists at least one set of $k+1$ independent points, $A^0, \ldots, A^k$. If $B^0, \ldots, B^k$ is any other set of $k+1$ linearly independent points of the space, the second part of the Exchange Theorem tells us that the linear space determined by $B^0, \ldots, B^k$ is the same as that determined by $A^0, \ldots, A^k$.

Any set of $k+1$ linearly independent points of a linear space of k dimensions is called a *basis* for that space.

We use the above results to show that *a linear space of k dimensions is a $P_k^r(K)$*. Let $A^0, \ldots, A^k$ be any basis for the linear space. Then any point Q of the space is given by an equation

$$Q = \sum_{i=0}^{k} A^i \lambda_i,$$

where the $(k+1)$-tuple $(\lambda_0, \ldots, \lambda_k)$ is uniquely determined by the point Q, to within right-hand equivalence. This establishes a one-to-one correspondence between the points of the linear space and those of $PN_k^r(K)$. Now consider what happens if $B^0, \ldots, B^k$ is any other basis for the linear space. We have

$$B^i = \sum_{j=0}^{k} A^j \beta_{ji}, \quad \text{and} \quad A^i = \sum_{j=0}^{k} B^j \alpha_{ji}.$$

Hence

$$A^i = \sum_{j=0}^{k} \sum_{h=0}^{k} A^h \beta_{hj} \alpha_{ji}.$$

But this must be an identity, since $A^0, \ldots, A^k$ are linearly independent. The matrices

$$B = (\beta_{ij}), \quad A = (\alpha_{ij})$$

are therefore inverse matrices. It follows that A and B are both regular.

Now, if $Q = \sum_0^k A^i \lambda_i$, we also have

$$Q = \sum_0^k \sum_0^k B^j \alpha_{ji} \lambda_i = \sum_0^k B^j \mu_j,$$

where

$$\mu_j = \sum_0^k \alpha_{ji} \lambda_i, \tag{3}$$

and therefore the change of basis from $A^0, ..., A^k$ to $B^0, ..., B^k$ results in the projective transformation (3) in $PN_k^r(K)$. Conversely, any projective transformation in $PN_k^r(K)$ corresponds to a change of basis in the linear space. Thus a linear space of k dimensions is a $P_k^r(K)$, each allowable coordinate system corresponding to a choice of basis in the linear space.

From Th. III we deduce at once that if S_h is a linear space of h dimensions determined by a basis $B^0, ..., B^h$, and if each B^i lies in a linear space S_k, then every point of S_h lies in S_k. That is, S_h *lies in* S_k. We write this

$$S_h \subseteq S_k.$$

It is evident that if $S_a \subseteq S_b$, and $S_b \subseteq S_c$, then $S_a \subseteq S_c$. Also, if $S_a \subseteq S_b$ and $S_b \subseteq S_a$, then $S_a = S_b$.

From Th. IV we deduce that any $k+1$ points lie in an S_h $(h \leqslant k)$ and that $h < k$ if and only if the points are linearly dependent.

Again, let S_p and S_q be two linear spaces in $P_n^r(K)$, and suppose that $P^0, ..., P^p$ is a basis for S_p, and $Q^0, ..., Q^q$ a basis for S_q. If the $p+q+2$ points $P^0, ..., P^p, Q^0, ..., Q^q$, are linearly dependent, so that

$$\sum_0^p P^i \lambda_i + \sum_0^q Q^i \mu_i = 0,$$

we deduce that S_p and S_q have a point in common. For neither $\sum_0^p P^i \lambda_i = 0$, nor $\sum_0^q Q^i \mu_i = 0$, since $P^0, ..., P^p$ are linearly independent, and so are $Q^0, ..., Q^q$. Hence $\sum_0^p P^i \lambda_i$ is a point in S_p which, since it can be written as $-\sum_0^q Q^i \mu_i$, is linearly dependent on $Q^0, ..., Q^q$, and therefore lies in S_q.

Finally, we note the trivial fact that if P and Q are distinct (that is, linearly independent) points of $P_n^r(K)$ the point which is represented symbolically by $P + Q$ is necessarily distinct from both P and Q; hence, since any S_1 contains at least two points, any S_1 contains at least *three* points, and we may sum up the results established in this section as follows:

In $P_n^r(K)$ there are linear spaces of dimensions $0, 1, 2, ..., n$, a space of 0 dimensions being a point. Between any two such spaces S_h and S_k there may exist a relation of one 'lying in' the other, say $S_h \subseteq S_k$. This relation satisfies the conditions

I.   If $S_h \subseteq S_k$, and $S_k \subseteq S_h$ then $S_k = S_h$.

II. If $S_p \subseteq S_q$ and $S_q \subseteq S_r$, then $S_p \subseteq S_r$.

A set of $p+1$ points is linearly dependent if there exists a linear space S_q containing them, where $q < p$.

III. Every S_1 contains at least three distinct points.

IV. Given $p+1$ linearly independent points there exists at least one S_p containing them.

V. In any S_p there exists at least one set of $p+1$ linearly independent points.

VI. If $P^0, ..., P^p$ are $p+1$ linearly independent points which lie in an S_q, any S_p containing them lies in S_q.

VII. If S_p and S_q are any two linear spaces of dimension p and q, and $P^0, ..., P^p$ are $p+1$ independent points of S_p and $Q^0, ..., Q^q$ are $q+1$ independent points of S_q, then if the $p+q+2$ points $P^0, ..., P^p, Q^0, ..., Q^q$ are linearly dependent there exists at least one point R which lies in S_p and in S_q.

VIII. There exists at least one set of $n+1$ linearly independent points, but any set of m points, where $m > n+1$, is linearly dependent.

We have, indeed, proved a great deal more, but it is desirable at this stage to emphasise that a right-hand projective space satisfies these propositions, which we call the *Propositions of Incidence*. In the next chapter we shall begin by taking an aggregate of undefined elements, which we shall call linear spaces of dimensions $0, 1, 2, ...$. We shall postulate the existence of a relation $\subseteq$ between certain of these spaces, and assume that this relation satisfies I and II above. The statement which follows II is then taken as a *definition* of linear dependence. We shall then impose the further conditions III–VIII, noting that it is only in VIII that the number n appears. It will be our main object in Chapter VI to show that these linear spaces of dimensions $0, 1, 2, ...$ can necessarily be represented as the linear spaces of a $P_n^r(K)$, for a suitably chosen K. This will follow directly from the above postulates if $n > 2$. If $n = 2$ a further postulate will be necessary. The case $n = 1$ is without interest.

For a left-hand space $P_n^l(K)$ a theory of linear dependence, similar to that developed for $P_n^r(K)$, may be stated. If

$$A^i = (\alpha_0^i, ..., \alpha_n^i) \quad (i = 0, ..., k)$$

are $k+1$ points, the points linearly dependent on them are the points

$$\sum_0^k \lambda_i A^i = \left(\sum_0^k \lambda_i \alpha_0^i, ..., \sum_0^k \lambda_i \alpha_n^i \right),$$

and the theorems proved earlier in this section can be proved for

$P_n^l(K)$, with the necessary formal alterations. In particular, we arrive at the same propositions of incidence, and we shall therefore be able to prove that, with the necessary reservations if $n \leqslant 2$, these propositions serve to define a left-hand projective space. This implies that a left-hand projective space may be regarded as a right-hand projective space, and conversely.

The explanation of this fact will be found in our method of constructing a projective space from the propositions of incidence. We shall have to construct a field, and we shall see that there are two ways of doing this, leading to two fields which are skew-isomorphic. Now, if $\overline{K}$ is skew-isomorphic to K, there is a one-to-one correspondence between the points of $P_n^r(\overline{K})$ and those of $P_n^l(K)$, and a one-to-one correspondence between their allowable coordinate systems. Choosing corresponding allowable coordinate systems in $P_n^l(K)$ and $P_n^r(\overline{K})$, the points

$$(\alpha_0^i, \ldots, \alpha_n^i) \quad \text{and} \quad (\overline{\alpha}_0^i, \ldots, \overline{\alpha}_n^i)$$

correspond. The point

$$(\Sigma\lambda_i\alpha_0^i, \ldots, \Sigma\lambda_i\alpha_n^i)$$

of $P_n^l(K)$ corresponds to the point

$$(\Sigma\overline{\alpha}_0^i\overline{\lambda}_i, \ldots, \Sigma\overline{\alpha}_n^i\overline{\lambda}_i)$$

of $P_n^r(\overline{K})$. Hence, the points of $P_n^l(K)$ which are linearly dependent on a given set of m points of $P_n^l(K)$ correspond to the points of $P_n^r(\overline{K})$ linearly dependent on the m corresponding points. Indeed, corresponding to any property of spaces $S_a, S_b, \ldots$ in $P_n^l(K)$ which remains unchanged under any allowable projective transformation in $P_n^l(K)$ there is a property of spaces $\overline{S}_a, \overline{S}_b, \ldots$ in $P_n^r(\overline{K})$ which remains unchanged under any allowable projective transformation in $P_n^r(\overline{K})$. We say that the two spaces are *projectively identical*.

5.   **Equations of linear spaces. Duality.**   We consider a right-hand projective space $P_n^r(K)$, and a left-hand projective space $P_n^l(K)$. In each of these we fix, quite arbitrarily, an allowable coordinate system, but, having done this, we regard the two as *associated*. We now show how we can proceed to associate with each allowable coordinate system in $P_n^r(K)$ a unique allowable coordinate system in $P_n^l(K)$.

If the transformation from the selected coordinate system in $P_n^r(K)$ to the new coordinate system is

$$y = Ax,$$

the transformation from the selected coordinate system in $P_n^l(K)$ to the coordinate system which we associate with the new system in $P_n^r(K)$ is taken to be

$$y' = x'A^{-1}$$

(where x' and y' are, of course, $1 \times (n+1)$ matrices).

It can be verified at once that this association of allowable co-ordinate systems in the two spaces is one-to-one, and is determined by the above rule when the selected coordinate systems are any pair of associated systems.

Now consider a linear space S_k in $P_n^r(K)$. Let $A^0, ..., A^k$ be a basis for this space, where

$$A^i = (\alpha_0^i, ..., \alpha_n^i)$$

are the coordinates of A^i in a given allowable system. Consider the equations

$$\sum_{j=0}^{n} x_j \alpha_j^i = 0 \quad (i = 0, ..., k). \tag{1}$$

Since the $(n+1) \times (k+1)$ matrix (α_j^i) is of rank $k+1$ [§ 4, (ii)], the solutions of the homogeneous equations (1) form a left-hand vector manifold of dimension $n-k$ [II, § 6]. Let the non-zero vectors of this manifold be taken as the coordinates of the points of a linear space in the associated coordinate system in $P_n^l(K)$. Its dimension will be $n-k-1$. We denote the space by Σ_{n-k-1}. If

$$(u_0^i, ..., u_n^i) \quad (i = 1, ..., n-k)$$

is a basis for Σ_{n-k-1}, the $(n-k) \times (n+1)$ matrix (u_j^i) is of rank $n-k$, and from (1),

$$\sum_{j=0}^{n} u_j^i \alpha_j^h = 0 \quad (i = 1, ..., n-k; h = 0, ..., k). \tag{2}$$

But, since (u_j^i) is of rank $n-k$, the equations

$$\sum_{j=0}^{n} u_j^i x_j = 0 \quad (i = 1, ..., n-k) \tag{3}$$

are satisfied by vectors of a right-hand vector manifold of dimension $k+1$. The non-zero vectors of this manifold are the coordinates of points of a linear space of dimension k in $P_n^r(K)$. By (2) above, this space contains $A^0, ..., A^k$, and therefore coincides with S_k. Thus S_k determines Σ_{n-k-1}, and conversely Σ_{n-k-1} determines S_k.

We now show that this association does not depend on the particular associated pair of coordinate systems in $P_n^r(K)$ and $P_n^l(K)$ of which we have made use.

To see this, we first note that the relation between S_k and Σ_{n-k-1} can be expressed as follows: the equation

$$\sum_{i=0}^{n} u_i x_i = 0$$

is satisfied for every point $(u_0, ..., u_n)$ of Σ_{n-k-1}, for all choices of $(x_0, ..., x_n)$ in S_k, and conversely. Now, if we perform the transformation of coordinates

$$y = Ax$$

in $P_n^r(K)$, and the associated transformation

$$v = uA^{-1}$$

in $P_n^l(K)$, then (noting that u, v are both $1 \times (n+1)$ matrices)

$$\sum_0^n v_i y_i = vy = uA^{-1}Ax = ux = \sum_0^n u_i x_i = 0.$$

Hence the property characterising the relation between S_k and Σ_{n-k-1} remains unchanged in the new associated pair of coordinate systems.

The spaces S_k and Σ_{n-k-1} are said to be *dual* spaces.

If we take any $n-k$ points of Σ_{n-k-1} which form a basis for this space, and which have the coordinates

$$(u_0^i, ..., u_n^i) \quad (i = 1, ..., n-k)$$

in an allowable coordinate system in $P_n^l(K)$, then the points of S_k in $P_n^r(K)$ satisfy the equations

$$\sum_{j=0}^{n} u_j^i x_j = 0 \quad (i = 1, ..., n-k) \tag{3}$$

in the associated coordinate system. We may call (3) *the equations of S_k.*

Given *any* set of equations

$$\sum_0^n u_j^i x_j = 0 \quad (i = 1, 2, ...), \tag{4}$$

we may consider the space in $P_n^l(K)$ linearly dependent on

$$(u_0^i, ..., u_n^i) \quad (i = 1, 2, ...).$$

If this is a Σ_{n-k-1}, the solutions of (4) are the points of the dual S_k, and the equations therefore determine this S_k. In algebraic language, *if the matrix of coefficients of a set of linear homogeneous equations* (4) *is of rank* $n-k$, *these equations determine a unique* S_k.

Now consider two linear spaces S_p and S_q in $P_n^r(K)$ with respective equations

$$\sum_0^n u_j^i x_j = 0 \quad (i = 1, ..., n-p),$$

and

$$\sum_0^n v_j^i x_j = 0 \quad (i = 1, ..., n-q).$$

Suppose that the $(2n-p-q) \times (n+1)$ matrix

$$\begin{pmatrix} u \\ v \end{pmatrix} \qquad (u = (u_{ij}),\, v = (v_{ij})) \tag{5}$$

is of rank $n-k$. Then the two sets of equations, taken together, determine an S_k. Each point of S_k lies in S_p and in S_q, and each point common to S_p and S_q must lie in S_k. We call S_k the *intersection* of S_p and S_q, and have proved

THEOREM I. *The intersection of two linear spaces is a linear space.*

If the matrix (5) is of rank $n-k$, the $2n-p-q$ points

$$\begin{aligned} (u_0^i, ..., u_n^i) \quad (i = 1, ..., n-p), \\ (v_0^i, ..., v_n^i) \quad (i = 1, ..., n-q) \end{aligned} \tag{6}$$

in $P_n^l(K)$ are linearly dependent on $n-k$ of them, and therefore the duals Σ_{n-p-1} and Σ_{n-q-1} of S_p and S_q lie in a Σ_{n-k-1}, which is the dual of S_k. Moreover, there is no smaller space containing both Σ_{n-p-1} and Σ_{n-q-1}. For any space containing both of these spaces must contain the $2n-p-q$ points (6), of which $n-k$ are linearly independent. Calling the smallest linear space which contains two linear spaces their *join*, we have

THEOREM II. *The dual of the intersection of two linear spaces is the join of their duals* (*and conversely*).

As a corollary we deduce that

If $S_p \supseteq S_q$, *then* $\Sigma_{n-p-1} \subseteq \Sigma_{n-q-1}$.

We now find a relation between the dimensions of the intersection S_k and the join S_r of two linear spaces S_p and S_q. Let $A^0, ..., A^k$ be a basis for the intersection. By the Exchange Theorem we can find bases $P^0, ..., P^p$ for S_p, and $Q^0, ..., Q^q$ for S_q such that

$$P^i = A^i = Q^i \quad (i = 0, ..., k).$$

Then clearly, any space containing $P^0, ..., P^p, Q^{k+1}, ..., Q^q$ contains S_p and S_q, and therefore S_r, their join. Therefore

$$r \leqslant p+q-k.$$

A similar argument applies to the duals Σ_{n-p-1}, Σ_{n-q-1} and their join, which, by Th. II is Σ_{n-k-1}. Hence

$$n-k-1 \leqslant (n-p-1)+(n-q-1)-(n-r-1),$$

that is, $$r \geqslant p+q-k.$$

It follows that $$k+r = p+q.$$

Hence we have

THEOREM III. *If S_p and S_q meet in S_k, their join is a linear space of dimension $p+q-k$.*

This theorem remains true when S_p and S_q have no intersection, provided that we then put $k = -1$.

We have established a correspondence between $P_n^r(K)$ and $P_n^l(K)$ in which an S_k of the former corresponds to a Σ_{n-k-1} of the latter, and intersections and joins correspond to joins and intersections respectively. If we establish any theorem for $P_n^r(K)$ which is based only on properties of linear spaces, their intersections and joins, this correspondence enables us to state forthwith a theorem for $P_n^l(K)$, without further proof. For historical reasons this relation between theorems for $P_n^r(K)$ and for $P_n^l(K)$ is called the *Principle of Duality for projective space.*

If $\overline{K}$ is a field skew-isomorphic to K, there is a correspondence between $P_n^l(K)$ and $P_n^r(\overline{K})$ in which a linear space of k dimensions corresponds to a linear space of k dimensions, and intersections and joins correspond to intersections and joins respectively. Hence, by the Principle of Duality, if we have any theorem in $P_n^r(K)$ which concerns linear spaces $S_a, S_b, \ldots$, their intersections and joins, we obtain a corresponding theorem in $P_n^r(\overline{K})$ concerning linear spaces $S_{n-a-1}, S_{n-b-1}, \ldots$, their joins and intersections. If K is a commutative field we can take $K = \overline{K}$, and the dual theorem is therefore true in $P_n^r(K)$. Again, if the original theorem is true for *all* ground fields K, it is true in particular for $P_n^r(\overline{K})$, and therefore the dual theorem is true in $P_n^r(K)$.

This last case is the most usual one. The theorems we shall prove will be either

(i) true for all ground fields K,

or (ii) true for commutative ground fields K,

or (iii) true for all ground fields with a given characteristic,

or (iv) true for all commutative and algebraically closed fields.

It will be noted that if K belongs to one of these classes, the skew-isomorphic field $\bar{K}$ belongs to the same class. Hence, every theorem which we shall prove in $P_n^r(K)$ will have a dual in $P_n^r(K)$.

6. Desargues' Theorem. In this section we consider the celebrated Theorem of Desargues which deals with two triangles in perspective in $P_n^r(K)$. In order to avoid needless repetition in the next chapter, we shall prove the theorem and its converse as consequences of the propositions of incidence [§ 4]. We notice here some immediate deductions from the propositions of incidence, which we shall use in this section. A more complete treatment will be found at the beginning of the next chapter.

Every S_1 (or line) contains at least three distinct points. Two distinct points determine one line. Any S_2 (or plane) contains three linearly independent points. If a line l is determined by the points P^0, P^1, and a line m is determined by the points Q^0, Q^1, and the points P^0, P^1, Q^0, Q^1 are linearly dependent, that is, the lines are coplanar, there is at least one point R on both lines. If P is any point in a plane π, at least three distinct lines can be drawn through P; for if P, Q, R is a set of linearly independent points in π, the line QR contains at least one point different from Q and R. Let this be S. Then PQ, PR, PS are three distinct lines through P. To complete the deductions from the propositions of incidence for a plane we show that if A, B, U are three distinct collinear points in π, we can draw lines a, b, u through A, B, U respectively which lie in π, are distinct from the line AU, and do not all pass through one point. For there is at least one point X in π such that X, A, U are linearly independent. The line XU contains a point Y distinct from X and U. The lines $a = AX$, $b = BY$, $u = UX$ satisfy the conditions.

The theorems we shall use in S_3 are: a line meets a plane in one point, or it lies in the plane; two planes in S_3 meet in a line; at least three distinct planes pass through a given line.

We now return to the consideration of Desargues' Theorem.

In order that we may avoid the consideration of a large number of special cases it will be useful to use the terms *collinear* and *concurrent* in the following sense: three points are *collinear* if there is at least one line containing them (if the points coincide there may be more than one line); three lines are *concurrent* if there is at least one point lying on all three of them. We shall use the word *triangle*, or the term *proper triangle*, to denote a triad of points which are not collinear.

Two triangles ABC, $A'B'C'$ are said to be *in perspective from O* if there exists a point O such that OAA', OBB' and OCC' are each collinear triads. We note that O need not be unique as, for example, when $A = A'$, and $B = B'$. With these definitions Desargues' Theorem is

THEOREM I. *If two triangles ABC, $A'B'C'$ are in perspective there exists a line l passing through a point common to BC and $B'C'$, a point common to CA and $C'A'$, and a point common to AB and $A'B'$.*

The converse theorem is

THEOREM II. *If ABC, $A'B'C'$ are two triangles such that there is a line l passing through a point common to BC and $B'C'$, a point common to CA and $C'A'$, and a point common to AB and $A'B'$, then the triangles are in perspective.*

We remark that in both theorems the whole configuration lies in a linear space of either two or three dimensions. (Since A, B, C, are not collinear the space cannot be of less than two dimensions.) For in Converse I there must be three lines a, b, c through O containing, respectively, AA', BB', CC'. On these lines take three points P, Q, R different from O. Then the set O, P, Q, R determines an S_r ($r \leqslant 3$) which contains O, P, Q, R and therefore O, A, A', B, B', C, C', and hence the whole configuration. The line l of the theorem lies in this S_r. We also note that if $r = 3$ the two planes determined by A, B, C and A', B', C' are necessarily distinct, except in the trivial case $A = A'$, $B = B'$, $C = C'$.

In Theorem II the triangles ABC, $A'B'C'$ each determine a plane. Let these be π and π'. The line l of the theorem meets BC, CA and AB, and, since A, B, C are not collinear, at least two of these intersections are distinct. Hence l has at least two points in π, and therefore lies in π. Similarly l lies in π'. The planes π, π' having at least a line in common, their join is an S_r ($r \leqslant 3$). The point O must lie in this S_r, except in the trivial case $A = A'$, $B = B'$, $C = C'$.

We may therefore confine ourselves to the two cases (i) $r = 3$ and (ii) $r = 2$. In case (i) the planes π and π' determined by A, B, C and A', B', C' are distinct, in case (ii) they are not.

Theorem I, Case (i). The lines a, b, c containing OAA', OBB', OCC' are distinct, otherwise they would all lie in a plane. Hence any two of them determine a plane. The points B, C, B', C' all lie in the plane determined by b and c. Therefore BC and $B'C'$ have at least one point P in common. Similarly there is a point Q common to CA

and $C'A'$, and a point R common to AB and $A'B'$. These three points P, Q, R all lie in π and π'. Now, π and π', being planes in S_3, meet in a line, and this is a line l satisfying the theorem. This line l is unique. Indeed, if there existed a line l' different from l satisfying the conditions of the theorem, l' could not lie both in π and in π'. Suppose it did not lie in π. Then it would meet π in a point common to BC, CA, AB, which is impossible, since A, B, C are not collinear.

Theorem II, Case (i). The line l must be the intersection of π and π'. Since BC and $B'C'$ have a point in common, B, B', C, C' are linearly dependent, and hence BB' and CC' have at least one point in common. If they have more than one point in common the four points are collinear, and must therefore lie on the intersection l of π and π'. In this latter case A and A' cannot lie on l. Since AB and $A'B'$ meet, we must have $B = B'$. Similarly $C = C'$, and therefore the triangles have two pairs of corresponding vertices coinciding. When two pairs of corresponding vertices of the triangles ABC, $A'B'C'$ coincide, the triangles are clearly in perspective from any point on the join of the other two vertices.

The case in which just one pair of corresponding vertices, say A and A', coincide is also easily disposed of. Then BB' and CC' meet, but do not coincide, and their intersection O is a point from which the two triangles are in perspective.

Finally, we have the case where no two corresponding vertices coincide, and therefore the lines AA', BB', CC' are each uniquely defined, and each has a single point in common with each of the other two. Let O be the point common to BB' and CC'. If O does not lie on AA', the points O, A, A' determine a plane containing AA', BB' and CC', and therefore $\pi = \pi'$, contrary to hypothesis. Therefore AA' passes through O, and the triangles ABC, $A'B'C'$ are in perspective from O.

We now turn to Case (ii), *when the two triangles lie in a plane*. It is desirable to deal, first of all, with certain special cases which may arise.

Theorem I. If all three pairs, A and A', B and B', C and C' coincide, the theorem is trivial. If two coincide, say $B = B'$ and $C = C'$, the line BC satisfies the theorem. If only one pair coincide, say $A = A'$, the line joining this to any point common to BC and $B'C'$ (there is at least one) satisfies the theorem. Again, if the lines BC, $B'C'$ coincide without any pairs of corresponding vertices coinciding, BC and $B'C'$ are the only pair of corresponding sides which coincide. Hence AB intersects $A'B'$ in just one point R, CA intersects $C'A'$ in just one point Q, and the line QR satisfies the theorem.

Next, suppose that the corresponding vertices A, A'; B, B'; C, C' are distinct, but that O coincides with at least one of the vertices, say A. Then $B'C'$ satisfies all the requirements of the theorem. This is also true if a non-corresponding vertex, B' say, coincides with A and with O.

Finally, if two vertices, say B and C', coincide, but not in O, the lines BC, $B'C'$ must coincide, and we are back at a case already examined.

There only remains the case in which the seven points A, B, C, A', B', C', O are all distinct, and corresponding sides, such as BC, $B'C'$ are also distinct. We call this *the general case*. We now consider the various special cases which may arise in proving Theorem II.

Theorem II. We consider the possibility of the pairs A, A'; B, B'; C, C' coinciding. If all three pairs coincide, the theorem is trivial. If two pairs coincide, say $B = B'$, $C = C'$, $A \neq A'$, the triangles are in perspective from any point on AA'. If only one pair coincide, say $A = A'$, $B \neq B'$, $C \neq C'$, the triangles are in perspective from the point (any point) common to BB' and CC'. Again, if two corresponding sides coincide, say $BC = B'C'$, the triangles are in perspective from a point on this line collinear with A and A'.

Next, suppose that l coincides with BC. Then $C'A'$ must pass through C, and $B'A'$ must pass through B. The triangles are therefore in perspective from A'. Finally, if two non-corresponding sides coincide, say $BC = C'A'$, but not in l, we must have $C = C'$, and we return to a case considered above.

The only remaining case to be considered in proving this theorem is therefore the *general case* in which the seven lines BC, CA, AB, $B'C'$, $C'A'$, $A'B'$, l are all distinct, and the pairs of points A, A'; B, B'; C, C' are also distinct.

We note that all the special cases considered above illustrate the two theorems, the proofs following directly from the propositions of incidence. We now prove the two theorems in the general case *on the assumption that $n > 2$*, that is, that there exists a point not in the plane $\pi = \pi'$.

Theorem I (general case). Since there exists a point not in π, there exists a line λ through O which is not in π. Take two distinct points V and V' on λ, distinct from O. The lines VV', AA' meet in O, and therefore lie in a plane. They do not coincide, because $VV' = \lambda$ does not lie in π. Hence $VA, V'A'$ have a unique point $A*$ in common. Since $A \neq A'$ (for we are in the general case) and VA is not in π, $A*$ is not in π. Nor is it on λ, since this would imply $A = O$ or $A' = O$. Similarly VB, $V'B'$ have a unique point $B*$ in common, and VC, $V'C'$ have a unique point $C*$ in common. The points $A*$, $B*$, $C*$ do not lie in π, and they are distinct from V and V'. If $A*$, $B*$, $C*$ were linearly dependent, the points V, $A*$, $B*$, $C*$ would lie in a plane which would be distinct from π. But this plane would contain A, B, C, and these would therefore be collinear points, contrary to hypothesis.

Hence ABC, $A*B*C*$ are two triangles in perspective from V. Therefore BC passes through the point P common to $B*C*$ and π, CA passes through the point Q common to $C*A*$ and π, and AB passes through the point R common to $A*B*$ and π.

Similarly $A'B'C'$ and $A*B*C*$ are in perspective from V', and we deduce in the same way that $B'C'$, $C'A'$ and $A'B'$ pass through P, Q, R respectively. But P, Q, R are on the intersection l of π with the plane of $A*B*C*$. This line l therefore satisfies the requirements of the theorem.

Theorem II (general case). Through l draw a plane π' distinct from π. P, Q, R are the intersections of BC, CA, AB respectively with l. If $Q = R$, then we must have $A = A'$, which is not the case (since we are dealing with the general case). Hence P, Q, R are all different, and we can draw through them three lines in π' to form a triangle $A*B*C*$. By the converse of the three-dimensional Desargues' Theorem, ABC and $A*B*C*$ are in perspective from some point V, and similarly $A'B'C'$ and $A*B*C*$ are in perspective from some point V'. If $V = V'$ we should also have $V = V' = A* = B* = C*$, whereas the points $A*$, $B*$, $C*$ are constructed so as to be distinct. Again, neither V nor V' lies in π, for if either did, we should have $\pi' = \pi$. The line VV' is therefore uniquely determined, and meets π in one point O. Since VA and $V'A'$ meet in $A*$, VV' and AA' meet in O. Similarly BB' and CC' pass through O.

Thus we have proved Desargues' Theorem and its converse, using only the propositions of incidence, except in the *general* case in two dimensions. We then had to make the additional assumption that the plane is contained in a space of higher dimension. This additional assumption can easily be justified for a space defined over a field K by the method of § 2, and we shall give a simple algebraic proof of

Desargues' Theorem in this case. But we first remark that *assuming* Desargues' Theorem in the plane, *the converse follows without any additional assumption.* We need only consider the general case.

Let BC, $B'C'$ meet in P, CA, $C'A'$ in Q, and AB, $A'B'$ in R. In the general case neither $BB'R$ nor $CC'Q$ can be collinear triads. We consider the two triangles $BB'R$, $CC'Q$, and we see that they are in perspective from P. Now, $B'R$ and $C'Q$ meet only in A', and RB and QC meet only in A. Hence, by Desargues' Theorem in the plane, BB' and CC' meet on AA'. That is, the triangles ABC, $A'B'C'$ are in perspective.

We conclude this section with a simple algebraic proof of Theorem I which is valid as long as O is distinct from the vertices of at least one of the triangles. Let this triangle be ABC. We use the symbolic notation introduced in § 4.

Since A' is on OA, and is assumed to be distinct from A, we may choose the multipliers of A', B', C' so that

$$A' = O + A\alpha,$$

and similarly

$$B' = O + B\beta,$$

and

$$C' = O + C\gamma,$$

where α, β, γ are in K. Then

$$P = B' - C' = B\beta - C\gamma$$

is a point on $B'C'$ and on BC.

Similarly,

$$Q = C' - A' = C\gamma - A\alpha$$

is on $C'A'$ and on CA, and

$$R = A' - B' = A\alpha - B\beta$$

is on $A'B'$ and on AB. But

$$P + Q + R = 0.$$

Therefore P, Q, R are collinear. This proves the theorem.

7. Some fundamental constructions.

We now discuss some constructions which are of fundamental importance in the next chapter. They are valid in any $P_n^r(K)$ for which $n \geqslant 2$.

Let O and U be any two distinct points in $P_n^r(K)$. We suppose that the multipliers of these points are fixed, and we define a point E, which is distinct from O and U, by the equation $E = O + U$.

Let A, B be two points of OU which are both distinct from U. We may suppose that their multipliers are chosen so that

$$A = O + U\alpha, \quad B = O + U\beta.$$

We propose to show how to obtain the points

$$O + U(\alpha + \beta), \quad O + U\alpha\beta$$

by geometrical construction. In each case the construction will be given in *italics*, and the justification for the construction will follow.

I. *A construction for* $O + U(\alpha + \beta)$. *In any plane through the line OU draw three lines a, b, u through A, B, U, respectively. These lines are distinct from OU and do not all pass through one point. Let M be the intersection of u and a, B' the intersection of u and b, A' the intersection of OB' and a, and L the intersection of UA' and b. The intersection P of LM and OU is the point* $O + U(\alpha + \beta)$. [See Plate I.]

By Proposition of Incidence V, if π is any plane through the line OU there exists a point X in π which is independent of O and U. The point $Y = U + X$ is different from X, and does not lie on OU or on AX. Hence the lines AX, BY, UX are three lines through A, B, U in π which are each distinct from OU, and do not all pass through one point. Hence the first part of the construction, the selection of the lines a, b, u, is possible.* The points M, B' are uniquely defined. So also is the point A'. For if OB' intersected a in more than one point, we should have $OB' = AM = a$. Then A, M, O, B' would be collinear, that is, MB' would contain O, and we should have $u = OU$, contrary to hypothesis. Similarly, the point L is uniquely defined. The points L, M can only coincide if both are at the intersection of a and b. But M is on u, and u does not pass through the intersection of a and b. Hence the line LM is uniquely defined. This line cannot coincide with OU, for M would then coincide with A, and we should have $u = OU$. The intersection P of LM and OU is therefore a unique point. We now show that $P = O + U(\alpha + \beta)$.

This is evident when one or both of the points A, B coincides with O, and we may therefore confine our attention to the case represented by the first two figures. In these cases A' is easily

---

* This was proved in § 6, using only the propositions of incidence. Here we merely *select* the point Y on UX.

PLATE I

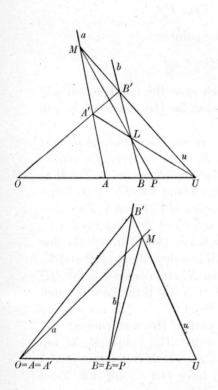

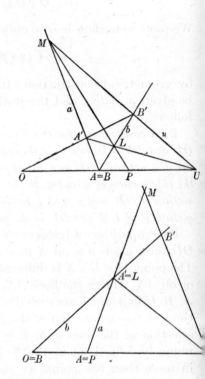

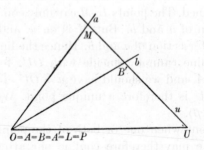

shown to be distinct from A and M. Hence, in writing the equation

$$M\lambda + A'\mu + A\nu = 0$$

which expresses the collinearity of M, A', A, the multipliers λ and ν are different from zero, and we may choose the multipliers of A and M so that

$$M = A + A'\mu = O + U\alpha + A'\mu.$$

Hence $M - U\alpha = O + A'\mu$ is on MU and on OA', and is therefore the point B'. We define the symbol for B' by the equation

$$B' = O + A'\mu.$$

Now $B' - B = O + A'\mu - O - U\beta = A'\mu - U\beta$, and therefore the point L, which is on $A'U$ and $B'B$ has the symbol

$$A'\mu - U\beta = B' - B.$$

Hence
$$M - L = A + A'\mu - A'\mu + U\beta = A + U\beta = O + U(\alpha + \beta)$$

is the symbol of a point on LM and on OU. This point is P, and we have therefore proved that $P = O + U(\alpha + \beta)$.

  II. *A construction for* $O + U\alpha\beta$. *In any plane through the line* OEU *draw three lines* a, b, u *through* A, B, U, *respectively. These lines are distinct from* OU *and do not all pass through one point. Let* P *be the intersection of* u *and* a, Y *the intersection of* u *and* b, X *the intersection of* EY *and* a, Q *the intersection of* OX *and* b. *Then* PQ *meets* OU *in the point* $R = O + U\alpha\beta$.

  By definition $E = O + U$, and it is therefore different from O and U. As above, the selection of the lines a, b, u is possible. The points P, Y are distinct, and neither lies on OU. The intersection X of EY and a is unique. For otherwise $EY = a$, and Y would coincide with the intersection of a and b. But Y is on u, and a, b, u are not concurrent. Again, X is distinct from O, since X is on EY, which does not coincide with OU, Y not lying on OU. Hence OX is defined. The point Q, the intersection of OX and b, is unique. For otherwise $OX = b$ and we should have, in the first place, $B = O$. If $B \neq O$, we have a contradiction. If $B = O$, and $OX = b$, we can still obtain a contradiction. For X and Y would lie on b, and since XY cuts OU in E, and b is distinct from OU, we should have $E = B = O$, contrary to hypothesis. Hence Q is unique. If P coincides with Q, it can only be at the intersection of a and b. Since P is on u, this would contradict the fact that a, b, u are not concurrent. Hence the line PQ is defined, and since P is not on OU the line PQ meets OU in a unique point R. We now prove that $R = O + U\alpha\beta$.

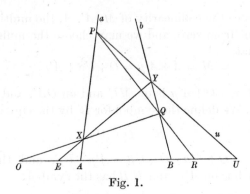

Fig. 1.

[Plate II shows the possible special cases.]

The proof is again trivial in the cases in which A or B coincides with O or E, and it will simplify matters if we confine ourselves to the cases in which A and B are different from O or E. When A is not at E the points P, A and X are all different. In the first place P is on u and not at U, hence it is not on OU, and therefore cannot coincide with A. If $P = X$, then E, P, Y are collinear. But PY is u which does not contain E, and we have a contradiction. Finally, since X is on a and on EY, it can only coincide with A when $A = E$, which is contrary to our hypothesis. Hence in the relation

$$P\lambda + A\mu + X\nu = 0$$

which expresses the collinearity of P, A, X, the multipliers λ, μ, ν are all different from zero.

Now if B is not at O, β is not zero, and it follows that we can choose the multipliers of P and X so that

$$P = A\beta + X.$$

Then
$$P + U(1-\alpha)\beta = (O + U\alpha)\beta + U(1-\alpha)\beta + X$$
$$= (O + U)\beta + X$$
$$= E\beta + X;$$

it follows that this is the symbol of a point on PU and on EX. Hence we may write

$$Y = (O + U)\beta + X.$$

PLATE II

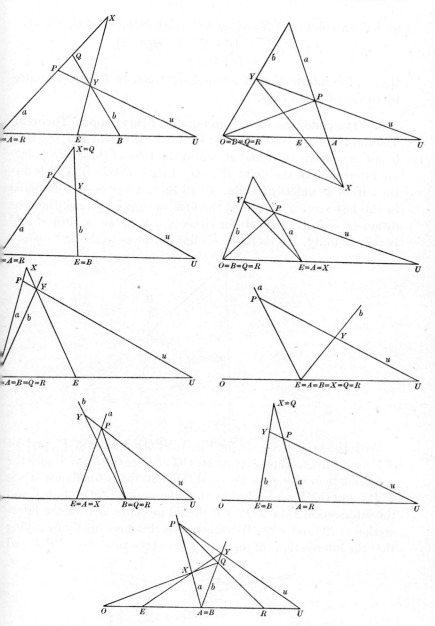

Then
$$Y - B = (O+U)\beta + X - O - U\beta$$
$$= X + O(\beta - 1);$$

we have a point on YB and on XO which is therefore Q. Finally,
$$P - Q = A\beta + X - X - O(\beta - 1)$$
$$= O + U\alpha\beta;$$

that is, the intersection of PQ and OU, namely R, is represented by the symbol $O + U\alpha\beta$.

8.   The condition for a commutative field; Pappus' Theorem.
The construction given in the last section for the point $R = O + U\alpha\beta$ is not symmetric in A and B, and if the roles of these two points are interchanged, the point $R' = O + U\beta\alpha$ is obtained. This is distinct from R, unless $\beta\alpha = \alpha\beta$. In all the various cases considered in the last section, except in the first or 'general' case, the condition $\alpha\beta = \beta\alpha$ is satisfied; for either $\alpha = \beta$, or one or both of α, β is zero or unity. We therefore confine ourselves to the first case.

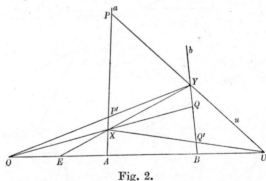

Fig. 2.

With the same figure as for Fig. 1, let OY meet a in P', and let XU meet b in Q'. Then $P'Q'$ meets OU in $R' = O + U\beta\alpha$. Hence the condition that $\alpha\beta = \beta\alpha$ is the condition that the two collinear triads $P'PX$ and $QQ'Y$ are such that the intersection O of $P'Y$, QX and the intersection U of XQ', YP should be collinear with the intersection of PQ and $P'Q'$. We can express this more briefly by saying that the intersections of the *cross-joins* of the two triads $PP'X$ and

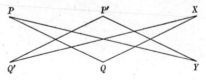

$Q'QY$ are collinear.

We consider this theorem by itself, altering the notation. Let l, l' be two coplanar lines, and let ABC and $A'B'C'$ be two triads of points on l, l' respectively. Let P, Q, R denote the intersections of their cross-joins BC', $B'C$; CA', $C'A$; AB', $A'B$.

It can at once be verified that if the three points of either triad are not distinct the points P, Q, R, as long as they are determinate, are collinear. On the other hand, if one or more of the points P, Q, R is indeterminate, there is at least one line containing a point P common to BC' and $B'C$, a point Q common to CA' and $C'A$, and a point R common to AB' and $A'B$. The theorem can also be proved at once when any one of the six points A, B, C, A', B', C' coincides with O, the intersection of l and l'. We notice further that if P, Q, R are not distinct, A, B, C, A', B', C' cannot all be distinct and distinct from O. If, for instance, $Q = R$, and $A \neq A'$, we must have $B = C$, $B' = C'$, in which case P is indeterminate, or $A = B = C$, with $P = Q = R = A$.

If ABC, $A'B'C'$ are two triads of points on two coplanar lines l and l' and the intersections of the cross-joins are collinear, we say that *Pappus' Theorem is satisfied*. We have seen that Pappus' Theorem is always satisfied in the case when either triad contains a pair of coincident points, or a point coinciding with the intersection O of l and l', and we need only consider the theorem when none of these special cases arises.

We can *prove* Pappus' Theorem for the case in which the lines AA', BB', CC' have a point in common. We apply Desargues' Theorem to the triangles $A'BC$, $AB'C'$. We deduce that the points O, Q, R are collinear. Similarly, by considering the triangles $AB'C$ and $A'BC'$ we deduce that P, O, R are collinear. By hypothesis these are triads of distinct points. It follows that P, Q, R, O are collinear.

On the other hand, if the ground field K is not commutative Pappus' Theorem cannot be true for all pairs of triads. For there must exist a pair of elements α, β in K such that $\alpha\beta \neq \beta\alpha$. We perform the construction (Fig. 2) given above for $R = O + U\alpha\beta$ and $R' = O + U\beta\alpha$. As we saw above, if Pappus' Theorem is true for the triads $PP'X$, $Q'QY$, then $R = R'$ and therefore $\alpha\beta = \beta\alpha$, contrary to hypothesis. We conclude that if Pappus' Theorem is universally true in $P_n^r(K)$, then K is a commutative field.

We now show, conversely, that if the ground field K is commutative, Pappus' Theorem is universally true in $P_n^r(K)$. This can be done by showing that any two triads can be taken as $PP'X$, $Q'QY$ for a suitable Fig. 2, but the following proof is simpler. As explained above, we need only consider the case in which A, B, C, A', B', C' are all distinct, and distinct from the intersection O of l and l'. We denote the intersections of the cross-joins by P, Q, R.

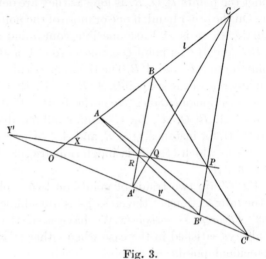

Fig. 3.

Then, since the special cases are excluded, P, Q, R are all distinct. If QR passes through O, the converse of Desargues' Theorem shows that the triads $A'BC$, $AB'C'$ are in perspective. Hence, as above, Pappus' Theorem holds for the triads ABC, $A'B'C'$. We assume then that QR does not pass through O, and cuts l in X, l' in Y'. It can be immediately verified that since A, B, C are distinct, and since also A', B', C' are distinct, the point X is distinct from points of the first triad, and Y' is distinct from points of the second triad. We may therefore choose the multipliers of O, X, Y' so that

$$A = O + X, \quad B' = O + Y'.$$

Since R is on AB' and on XY',

$$R = A - B' = X - Y'.$$

Now, if $\qquad B = O + X\beta, \quad A' = O + Y'\alpha',$

$A'B$ meets XY' in $X\beta - Y'\alpha'$. Since this is the point R, we must have $\alpha' = \beta$.

Again, if
$$C = O + X\gamma, \quad C' = O + Y'\gamma',$$

CA' meets XY' in $Q = X\gamma - Y'\alpha'$. But $C'A$ meets XY' in $X - Y'\gamma'$. Since this is the point Q, we must have $\gamma'\gamma = \alpha'$.

Now consider the intersection P of BC' and $B'C$. The line BC' meets XY' in the point $X\alpha' - Y'\gamma'$, and $B'C$ meets XY' in the point $X\gamma - Y'$. The point P is on XY', that is, Pappus' Theorem is true, if and only if
$$X\alpha' - Y'\gamma' = (X\gamma - Y')\gamma',$$

that is, if and only if
$$\gamma\gamma' = \alpha' = \gamma'\gamma.$$

But this is always the case, since K is commutative. Hence we have proved

THEOREM I. *A necessary and sufficient condition that Pappus' Theorem be universally true in $P_n^r(K)$ is that K be commutative.*

There are, of course, other geometrical theorems equivalent to the condition that K be commutative. But since Pappus' Theorem is one of the simplest of these, and since it is traditionally taken as the geometric equivalent of the assumption of commutativity, we take it as our geometric criterion.

9. Some finite geometries. The constructions given in §7 were possible because we were able to draw a sufficient number of distinct lines through a given point to make the various intersections determinate. If the ground field K contains an infinite number of elements, we can draw as many distinct lines through a given point O as we please. For in any plane through O there exist two points, X, Y such that O, X, Y are linearly independent. The lines joining O to $X + Y\alpha$, where α ranges over K, are infinite in number, and we can always select from these a finite number which satisfy our requirements.

If K is a finite field containing k elements (including 0 and 1) the line XY contains the k points $X + Y\alpha$ (α in K) and also the point Y. Through O we can therefore draw exactly $k+1$ lines ($k \geqslant 2$); that is we can draw at least *three* distinct lines through O in the given plane. As we saw in §7 this is a sufficient number to make the constructions given there determinate.

The plane through O contains at least seven points, namely
$$O, \ X, \ Y, \ O+X, \ O+Y, \ X+Y, \ O+X+Y.$$

If K is the field of integers reduced *modulo* 2, in which case K

contains only the elements 0, 1, these seven points are the only points in the plane. Then, since

$$O + X + X + Y + O + Y = 2(O + X + Y) = 0,$$

the three points $O + X$, $X + Y$, $O + Y$ are collinear. We shall return to this finite geometry of seven points in the next chapter.

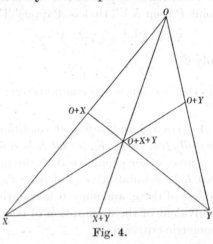
Fig. 4.

The number of points in $P_n^r(K)$, where K is the field containing only the elements 0, 1, is $2^{n+1} - 1$. For in a given allowable coordinate system these are the points $(\alpha_0, ..., \alpha_n)$, where each α_i takes the values 0, 1 independently, only the case in which every α_i is zero being excluded. The number of points in $P_n^l(K)$ is the same, since $P_n^r(K) = P_n^l(K)$.

In the same way we can show that if K is the field of integers reduced *modulo* p, so that K contains only the elements

$$0, 1, ..., p-1,$$

the number of points in $P_n^r(K) = P_n^l(K)$ is

$$\frac{p^{n+1} - 1}{p - 1}.$$

10. *r*-way spaces. Many generalisations of $P_n^r(K)$ are possible. Only one will be used in this work. The ground field K is here taken to be commutative.

We consider r projective number spaces

$$PN_{n_i}(K) \quad (i = 1, ..., r),$$

and suppose that

$$(x_0^i, ..., x_{n_i}^i) \quad (i = 1, ..., r)$$

are the coordinates in allowable coordinate systems of points in these r spaces. Now consider an ordered association of these points

$$x = (x_0^1, \ldots, x_{n_1}^1, x_0^2, \ldots, x_{n_2}^2, \ldots, x_0^r, \ldots, x_{n_r}^r).$$

These are called the *points* of the *r-way* projective number space $PN_{n_1 \ldots n_r}(K)$.

An allowable transformation of $PN_{n_1 \ldots n_r}(K)$ is defined to correspond to a projective transformation of $PN_{n_1}(K)$, a projective transformation of $PN_{n_2}(K), \ldots$, a projective transformation of $PN_{n_r}(K)$.

We consider a set S of elements which can be put in one-to-one correspondence with the points of $PN_{n_1 \ldots n_r}(K)$. This correspondence establishes a coordinate system in S. The allowable transformations of $PN_{n_1 \ldots n_r}(K)$ lead to new correspondences, and hence to new coordinate systems in S. The elements of S, taken together with these allowable coordinate systems, constitute the points of *r-way projective space* $P_{n_1 \ldots n_r}(K)$. In fact $P_{n_1 \ldots n_r}(K)$ is simply an aggregate in one-to-one correspondence with all the sets of points $(A_1, \ldots, A_r)$, where $A_1, \ldots, A_r$ are arbitrary points of $P_{n_1}(K), \ldots, P_{n_r}(K)$, the coordinate systems being obtained by associating allowable coordinate systems in each of these spaces.

CHAPTER VI

PROJECTIVE SPACE: SYNTHETIC DEFINITION

1. Propositions of incidence. In Chapter V we defined a projective space of n dimensions over a field K, and derived [V, § 4] certain theorems which we called the Propositions of Incidence. The object of this chapter is to consider to what extent these propositions characterise a projective space.

We begin by postulating the existence of certain objects which we call linear spaces of $0, 1, 2, \ldots$ dimensions (or *points*, *lines*, *planes*, ...) and a relation which may exist between a linear space S_p of p dimensions and a linear space S_q of q dimensions. If this relation connects S_p and S_q, we say that S_p *lies in* S_q, and write

$$S_p \subseteq S_q.$$

This relation is also written

$$S_q \supseteq S_p,$$

and is then read 'S_q *contains* S_p'.

If $P_0, \ldots, P_p$ are any $p+1$ points we say that they are *linearly dependent* if there is a linear space S_q of q dimensions such that

$$P_i \subseteq S_q \quad (i = 0, \ldots, p),$$

where $q < p$. Otherwise the points are said to be *linearly independent*.

We now postulate the following properties for the incidence relation $\subseteq$ [cf. V, § 4].

I. If $S_h \subseteq S_k$ and $S_k \subseteq S_h$ then $S_k = S_h$.

II. If $S_p \subseteq S_q$ and $S_q \subseteq S_r$, then $S_p \subseteq S_r$.

III. Every line contains at least three distinct points.

IV. Given any $p+1$ linearly independent points, there is at least one linear space of p dimensions which contains them.

V. Any linear space of p dimensions contains at least one set of $p+1$ linearly independent points.

VI. If $P_0, \ldots, P_p$ are $p+1$ linearly independent points which lie in an S_q, any S_p containing them is contained in S_q.

---

* This chapter is almost completely independent of the rest of the book, and may be omitted at a first reading.

VII. If $P_0, \ldots, P_p$ are $p+1$ linearly independent points of an S_p, and $Q_0, \ldots, Q_q$ are $q+1$ linearly independent points of an S_q, and if the $p+q+2$ points $P_0, \ldots, P_p, Q_0, \ldots, Q_q$ are linearly dependent, there exists at least one point R which lies both in S_p and in S_q.

VIII. There exists a finite integer $n \geqslant 1$ such that there is at least one set of $n+1$ linearly independent points, but any set of m points, where $m > n+1$, is linearly dependent.

That these are a set of consistent postulates is proved by the example of a projective space, defined in the previous chapter.

We now draw certain conclusions about the relation $\subseteq$, about linear dependence, and, later on, about the intersections of linear spaces.

(1) Each linear space S_h lies in itself. For by V, S_h contains $h+1$ linearly independent points. By VI, any S_h' containing these points lies in S_h. Choose $S_h' = S_h$, and the result follows.

(2) If $S_p \subseteq S_q$, then $p \leqslant q$. For by V there is a set of $p+1$ linearly independent points lying in S_p. By II these lie in S_q. If $q < p$, these points would be linearly dependent. Hence $p \leqslant q$.

(3) If $S_p \subseteq S_p'$, then $S_p = S_p'$. For if $P_0, \ldots, P_p$ are $p+1$ linearly independent points of S_p, by II they are $p+1$ linearly independent points of S_p'. Hence, by VI, $S_p' \subseteq S_p$, and therefore, by I, $S_p = S_p'$.

Corollary. The S_p containing $p+1$ linearly independent points is unique, and any set of $p+1$ independent points of an S_p serves to determine it.

We shall call any set of $p+1$ linearly independent points in an S_p a *basis* for the S_p.

(4) Let $P_0, \ldots, P_p$ be $p+1$ independent points, and suppose that $P_0, \ldots, P_s$ is a linearly dependent subset. Then $P_0, \ldots, P_s$ lie in some S_t, where $t < s$. Let $Q_0, \ldots, Q_t$ be a basis for S_t, and consider the $q+1 = p-s+t+1$ points $Q_0, \ldots, Q_t, P_{s+1}, \ldots, P_p$. If these are linearly independent they determine an S_q. In any case, they lie in an S_r, where $r \leqslant q < p$. Now, S_r contains $Q_0, \ldots, Q_t$ and hence, by VI, S_t. Therefore, by II, S_r contains $P_0, \ldots, P_s$. Also, S_r contains $P_{s+1}, \ldots, P_p$. Hence $P_0, \ldots, P_p$ are contained in S_r $(r < p)$ and are therefore linearly dependent. From this contradiction we deduce that *any subset of a linearly independent set of points is necessarily a linearly independent set.*

Corollary. The points of a linearly independent set are all distinct.

(5) Let $P_0, ..., P_p$ be a basis for S_p; $Q_0, ..., Q_q$ a basis for S_q. If S_p and S_q have no common point it follows from VII that $P_0, ..., P_p$, $Q_0, ..., Q_q$ are linearly independent. Suppose that S_p and S_q have at least one point in common. Considering the set of common points there exists an integer r $(0 \leqslant r \leqslant n)$ such that there is at least one set $A_0, ..., A_r$ of $r+1$ linearly independent points common to S_p and S_q, but any set of m points $(m > r+1)$ common to S_p and S_q must be linearly dependent. Now, $A_0, ..., A_r$ determine an S_r. Since $A_i \subseteq S_p$ $(i = 0, ..., r)$, it follows from VI that $S_r \subseteq S_p$. Similarly $S_r \subseteq S_q$. Hence $r \leqslant \min(p, q)$. Also, if the point R lies in S_r, $R \subseteq S_r \subseteq S_p$, and therefore, by II, $R \subseteq S_p$. Similarly $R \subseteq S_q$. On the other hand, if the point B lies in S_p and in S_q, the points $A_0, ..., A_r$, B are linearly dependent, and therefore lie in an S_t $(t \leqslant r)$. Since $A_i \subseteq S_t$ $(i = 0, ..., r)$, $S_r \subseteq S_t$ and therefore $r \leqslant t$. Hence $r = t$ and $S_r = S_t$. Therefore *the points common to S_p and S_q are all the points of a linear space S_r*. If now S_t is any space lying both in S_p and in S_q, and $C_0, ..., C_t$ is a basis for S_t, then the points of this basis lie in S_p and in S_q and therefore in S_r. Hence S_t lies in S_r.

(6) With the notation of (5) we prove the converse of VII, that if S_p and S_q have at least one point (and therefore all the points of an S_r) in common, the $p+q+2$ points $P_0, ..., P_p$, $Q_0, ..., Q_q$ are linearly dependent. If $p > r$ there exists a point in S_p which is not in S_r. Otherwise $S_p \subseteq S_r$, and hence $p \leqslant r$. Let B_{r+1} be a point which is in S_p but not in S_r. Then $A_0, ..., A_r$, B_{r+1} must be linearly independent. Otherwise we could show, as above, that B_{r+1} is in S_r. Hence $A_0, ..., A_r$, B_{r+1} determine an S_{r+1} in S_p. If $p > r+1$ we can, similarly, find another point in S_p, B_{r+2}, say, such that $A_0, ..., A_r$, B_{r+1}, B_{r+2} are linearly independent. If we continue in this way we obtain a basis $A_0, ..., A_r$, $B_{r+1}, ..., B_p$ for S_p whose first $r+1$ points are a basis for S_r. In the same way we can construct a basis $A_0, ..., A_r$, $C_{r+1}, ..., C_q$ for S_q. If the points $A_0, ..., A_r$, $B_{r+1}, ..., B_p$, $C_{r+1}, ..., C_q$ are linearly independent, they determine a linear space of $p+q-r$ dimensions. In any case they determine an S_t $(t \leqslant p+q-r)$. Since S_t contains $A_0, ..., A_r$, $B_{r+1}, ..., B_p$, it contains S_p, and therefore, by II, $P_0, ..., P_p$. Similarly it contains $Q_0, ..., Q_q$. Hence the set $P_0, ..., P_p$, $Q_0, ..., Q_q$ lies in S_t $(t \leqslant p+q-r < p+q+1)$ and is therefore linearly dependent.

(7) We now prove that in fact the points $A_0, ..., A_r$, $B_{r+1}, ..., B_p$, $C_{r+1}, ..., C_q$ are linearly independent. For, let us suppose that they are linearly dependent. By construction, $A_0, ..., A_r, B_{r+1}, ..., B_p$

are linearly independent and determine S_p. Also, $C_{r+1}, ..., C_q$ is a subset of a linearly independent set. By (4) above this subset is a linearly independent set, and it therefore determines an S_{q-r-1}. By VII, S_p and S_{q-r-1} have a point, R, say, in common. Since $C_i \subseteq S_q$ $(i = r+1, ..., q)$, $S_{q-r-1} \subseteq S_q$, and therefore R lies in S_q and in S_p. Hence, by (5) above, it is in S_r. Since S_r and S_{q-r-1} have the point R in common, the points $A_0, ..., A_r$, $C_{r+1}, ..., C_q$ must be linearly dependent, by (6) above. This contradiction proves that $A_0, ..., A_r$, $B_{r+1}, ..., B_p$, $C_{r+1}, ..., C_q$ are linearly independent. These points therefore determine an S_{p+q-r}, the result still holding, as at the beginning of (5) above, if S_p and S_q have no point in common, provided that we put $r = -1$. Clearly $S_p \subseteq S_{p+q-r}$, and $S_q \subseteq S_{p+q-r}$. On the other hand, if S_k is any linear space such that $S_p \subseteq S_k$, and also $S_q \subseteq S_k$, then $A_0, ..., A_r$, $B_{r+1}, ..., B_p$, $C_{r+1}, ..., C_q$ are all in S_k. Therefore $S_{p+q-r} \subseteq S_k$. Finally then, S_{p+q-r} is contained in every linear space which contains both S_p and S_q. If we call this space the *join* of S_p and S_q, the space S_r being called the *intersection* of S_p and S_q, we have proved

THEOREM I. *The dimension r of the intersection of two linear spaces S_p and S_q is connected with the dimension t of their join by the relation*

$$r + t = p + q.$$

We know, by VIII, that there exists a set of $n+1$ linearly independent points. Let these be $A_0, ..., A_n$. They define an S_n. If R is *any* other point, then, again by VIII, $A_0, ..., A_n$, R are linearly dependent, and therefore lie in an S_m $(m \leqslant n)$. Since $A_i \subseteq S_m$ $(i = 0, ..., n)$, it follows that $S_n \subseteq S_m$ and therefore, by (1) above, $n \leqslant m$. Hence $S_m = S_n$, and all points (and similarly all lines, planes, ...) lie in S_n. The complete configuration of points, lines, planes, ... lying in S_n is said to form *an incidence space of n dimensions*.

A set of $n+1$ linearly independent points in S_n is called a *simplex*. Let $A_0, ..., A_n$ be a simplex. The points $A_0, ..., A_{i-1}, A_{i+1}, ..., A_n$ are linearly independent, and determine an S_{n-1} (or *prime*) Σ^i, which we call a *face* of the simplex.

For the sake of later applications [§ 6] we now prove that there is a point E which does not lie in any face of the simplex $A_0, ..., A_n$. We prove this by induction on n. If $n = 1$, the result is simply Postulate III. We therefore suppose that we have proved the theorem for a space of $n-1$ dimensions, in particular for Σ^0, the face of the simplex which does not contain A_0. Let $E_{12\ldots n}$ be a point of Σ^0 which does not lie in any face of the simplex $A_1, \ldots, A_n$ of that space. Since any point common to Σ^0 and Σ^i $(i > 0)$ lies in a face of this simplex, $E_{12\ldots n}$ does not lie in any Σ^i $(i > 0)$. Since A_0 is not in Σ^0, the points A_0 and $E_{12\ldots n}$ must be linearly independent. They determine, in consequence, a line l_0. This line cannot lie in Σ^0, since A_0 is not in Σ^0; nor in Σ^i $(i = 1, \ldots, n)$, since $E_{12\ldots n}$ does not lie in Σ^i. The line meets Σ^i $(i = 0, \ldots, n)$ in unique points, namely, in the points $E_{12\ldots n}$, $A_0, \ldots, A_0$. Now, l_0 contains at least one point E distinct from A_0 and $E_{12\ldots n}$, and this point satisfies our requirements.

Now let $i_0, \ldots, i_n$ be any derangement of the integers $0, \ldots, n$, and consider the points $A_{i_{k+1}}, \ldots, A_{i_n}$ $(k \geqslant 0)$. These are linearly independent. If, therefore, the set $A_{i_{k+1}}, \ldots, A_{i_n}$, E was linearly dependent, E would lie in the space determined by $A_{i_{k+1}}, \ldots, A_{i_n}$, and therefore in Σ^{i_0}. This is contrary to hypothesis. The $n - k + 1$ points considered therefore determine an S_{n-k}. Now, $A_{i_0}, \ldots, A_{i_k}$ determine an S_k, and since the join of S_k and S_{n-k} is the whole space S_n, the spaces S_k and S_{n-k} have just one point in common. We denote this by $E_{i_0 \ldots i_k}$. The points $E_{i_0 \ldots i_k}$, $A_{i_{k+1}}, \ldots, A_{i_n}$ are linearly independent.

If $E_{i_0 \ldots i_k}$ lay in any of the faces of the simplex $A_{i_0}, \ldots, A_{i_k}$ of S_k, say in that face determined by $A_{i_1}, \ldots, A_{i_k}$, S_{n-k} would lie in the space determined by $A_{i_1}, \ldots, A_{i_k}$, $A_{i_{k+1}}, \ldots, A_{i_n}$, that is, in Σ^{i_0}. Hence Σ^{i_0} would contain E, and this contradiction proves that $E_{i_0 \ldots i_k}$ does not lie in any of the $(k-1)$-spaces determined by the points $A_{i_0}, \ldots, A_{i_{j-1}}, A_{i_{j+1}}, \ldots, A_{i_k}$.

We obtain in this way $2^{n+1} - 1$ points $E_{i_0 \ldots i_k}$, including $E_i = A_i$ and $E_{0 \ldots n} = E$. It should be noted that any incidence space of n dimensions contains such a set of points, at least, and that they are all distinct.

Let us now consider the space S_k determined by $A_{i_0}, \ldots, A_{i_k}$. In this space let us use the point $E_{i_0 \ldots i_k}$, which does not lie in any of the faces of the simplex $A_{i_0} \ldots, A_{i_k}$, to construct points $E'_{j_0 \ldots j_s}$, where $j_0, \ldots, j_s$ is a subset of $i_0, \ldots, i_k$. Arrange $i_0, \ldots, i_k$ so that $(j_0, \ldots, j_s) = (i_0, \ldots, i_s)$. Then $E'_{j_0 \ldots j_s}$ is the intersection of the space determined by $A_{i_0}, \ldots, A_{i_s}$ with that determined by $E_{i_0 \ldots i_k}, A_{i_{s+1}}, \ldots, A_{i_k}$. But this last space is the intersection of the space determined by $A_{i_0}, \ldots, A_{i_k}$, or S_k, and the space determined by $E, A_{i_{s+1}}, \ldots, A_{i_n}$. It follows that $E'_{j_0 \ldots j_s} = E_{j_0 \ldots j_s}$, so that no new points are obtained in this way.

We shall always assume that $n > 1$ in subsequent sections, the case $n = 1$ being of little interest. Indeed all that we can deduce from the propositions of incidence when $n = 1$ is that there are at least three points, and that two points are linearly independent if and only if they are distinct.

2. Desargues' Theorem. This theorem is fundamental for the development of this chapter. Since the proof of both Theorem and converse given in V, § 6 was based only on the propositions of incidence, except in the case $n = 2$, we may state the theorems without further proof for the case $n > 2$.

THEOREM I. *If ABC and A'B'C' are two triangles in perspective there exists a line l passing through a point common to BC and B'C', a point common to CA and C'A' and a point common to AB and A'B'.*

THEOREM II. *If ABC and A'B'C' are two triangles such that there is a line l passing through a point common to BC and B'C', a point common to CA and C'A' and a point common to AB and A'B', the triangles are in perspective.*

We shall refer to these theorems as Desargues' Theorem and its converse.

The theorems were only proved from the propositions of incidence in the case $n = 2$ for a number of special cases. The connection between the algebraic proof given in V, § 6 and the propositions of incidence is necessarily not very clear at present. But we have no *a priori* reasons for thinking that the case $n = 2$ is *not* a consequence of the propositions of incidence. However, we now show, by means of a counter-example, that when $n = 2$ *the theorems cannot be deduced from the propositions of incidence.* In fact, we construct an aggregate of points and lines which satisfy the propositions of incidence in the case $n = 2$, but for which Desargues' Theorem is not true. This construction is due to F. R. Moulton.

As a preliminary, we consider a Euclidean plane referred to rectangular Cartesian coordinates (x, y), and in it a certain set of loci, which we call L-loci. An L-locus is defined by the equation

$$y = m f(y, m) (x - a),$$

where m, a are real numbers, and $f(y, m)$ is defined as follows:

(i) if $m \leqslant 0$, $f(y, m) = 1$;

(ii) if $m > 0$, $f(y, m) = 1$,   when $y < 0$,

                           $f(y, m) = \tfrac{1}{2}$,   when $y \geqslant 0$.

We also include the case $m = \infty$, the line $x = a$ being an L-locus, and $m = 0$, $a = \infty$, the line $y = b$ being an L-locus.

It is clear that an L-locus is completely determined by that part of it which lies in the region $y \geqslant 0$, or by that part which lies in $y \leqslant 0$. Moreover, if an L-locus has $m > 0$ (and is therefore not a line), the line joining any two points of it has positive slope. Bearing these facts in mind, it is easily seen that there is an L-locus joining any two points A, B, of the plane, and that it is uniquely determined by these points. In fact, if A and B both lie in $y \geqslant 0$ the upper half of the L-locus is the upper half-line through A and B; and this determines the L-locus uniquely. A similar result holds if A and B both lie in $y \leqslant 0$. Suppose now that A lies in the region $y > 0$, and B in $y < 0$. If the line AB has negative slope, the unique L-locus containing A and B is the line AB. If, finally, AB has positive slope, let A be (x_1, y_1), and let A' be the point $(x_1, 2y_1)$. Let $A'B$ meet $y = 0$ in M. Then the L-locus containing A and B is necessarily that determined by the half-line MA.

We show now that any two distinct L-loci

$$y = m f(y, m)\,(x - a), \quad y = n f(y, n)\,(x - b)$$

$(m \neq n)$ have a unique point in common. This is evident if both m, n are negative, or, by the above remarks, if one of m, n is negative. If both m, n are positive, and we solve the equations

$$y = m(x - a), \quad y = n(x - b),$$

we find that

$$y = mn(b - a)/(n - m);$$

and solving the equations

$$y' = \tfrac{1}{2} m(x' - a), \quad y' = \tfrac{1}{2} n(x' - b),$$

we find that

$$y' = \tfrac{1}{2} mn(b - a)/(n - m).$$

Thus y gives the intersection of the L-loci if $(b - a)/(n - m)$ is negative, and y' if this ratio is positive. This proves the result, and we deduce again that one and only one L-locus joins any two points.

If $m = n$ the L-loci do not meet, unless they coincide. They are then said to be *parallel*.

The process by which we pass from a Euclidean plane to a projective plane by the introduction of elements at infinity is well known. In this projective plane Desargues' Theorem is, of course, true. We can now follow a similar process to arrive at a set of elements for which our postulates (with $n = 2$) are satisfied, but Desargues' Theorem is not true. To distinguish the points and lines of this space from those of the original Euclidean plane, we shall call them Points and Lines. The points of the Euclidean plane are Points. Corresponding to each set of parallel L-loci we postulate a further Point (at infinity) which is regarded as a Point of each locus of the set. The Lines are the L-loci of the Euclidean plane together with one other element, the Line at infinity, which contains all the Points at infinity. It is now a simple exercise to verify that the Plane which contains these Points and Lines, and the Points and Lines themselves satisfy the Propositions of Incidence of p. 208.

In this Plane we now construct a configuration which violates Desargues' Theorem. The construction involves certain points and lines in the Euclidean plane which are treated as Points and Lines. It is important to observe the difference between points and lines on the one hand, and Points and Lines on the other. The justification of the assertions concerning the elementary geometry involved may be left to the reader.

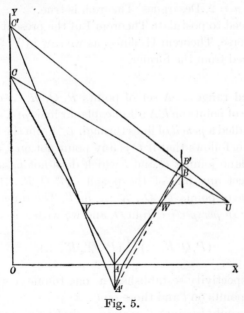

Fig. 5.

We construct two triads ABC, $A'B'C'$ for which the lines AA', BB', CC' are all parallel to OY, C and C' lying on OY, for simplicity, A on OX, and the intersections of corresponding sides lying on a line UVW parallel to OX in the upper half of the plane. We also suppose that the slopes of BC, $B'C'$, $C'A'$, CA are negative, while those of AB, $A'B'$ are positive. Then the Lines AA', BB', CC' are parallel, and therefore concurrent, the Lines BC, $B'C'$ intersect in U, the Lines CA, $C'A'$ in V. The Line AB is the same as the half-line AB (since A is on OX), and passes through W, whereas if A' is on the opposite side of OX to B', as in the diagram, the line $A'B'$ passes through W, and therefore the Line $A'B'$ cannot pass through W. Hence ABC, $A'B'C'$ are two triads in perspective whose corresponding sides do not intersect in the points of a Line, and Desargues' Theorem does not follow from the Propositions of Incidence when $n = 2$. An even simpler example than the above shows (as we should expect) that the converse of Desargues' Theorem is also not necessarily true in an incidence S_2.

Geometries in which Desargues' Theorem is not true have been the subject of numerous researches, but since they cannot be identified with the geometry of Chapter V we are not concerned with them here. We add to our postulates

VIIIa. If $n = 2$, Desargues' Theorem is true.

We only need to postulate Theorem I of the present section, and not the converse, Theorem II, since, as we saw in V, § 6, the latter can be deduced from the former.

3. Related ranges. A set of points P, Q, R, ... on a line l is called a *range* of points on l. A set of coplanar lines $p, q, r, ...$ through a point L is called a *pencil* of lines through L. From the Propositions of Incidence it follows that if O is any point not on l, and l' is any line in the plane joining O and l which does not pass through O, l' will intersect any line of the pencil $O(P, Q, R, ...)$ in a point, giving a range of points P', Q', R', ... on l'. The ranges on l and l' are said to be *in perspective* from O, and we write

$$(P, Q, R, ...) \; \frac{O}{\wedge} \; (P', Q', R', ...).$$

Such a perspectivity establishes a one-to-one correspondence between the points on l and those on l'.

If l contains only k points, l' contains only k points, and every line in the plane contains exactly k points. Through O there pass exactly k lines, and through every point in the plane there pass exactly k lines lying in the plane. By Postulate III, $k \geqslant 3$. We shall see that there are geometries in which a plane contains only a finite number of points, and our methods must be devised to take account of these *finite* geometries, especially when $k = 3$. The Propositions of Incidence assure us of the existence of 7 points in a plane in this case, and there are finite geometries in which a plane contains exactly 7 points [V, § 9].

Returning to our perspectivities, suppose that another perspectivity has been established between the points of l' and those of a line l'', the vertex being O'. The line l'' must cut l', but need not lie in the plane joining O to l, which we write $O(l)$. We describe the perspectivities thus:

$$(P, Q, R, \ldots) \underset{\wedge}{O} (P', Q', R', \ldots) \underset{\wedge}{O'} (P'', Q'', R'', \ldots).$$

A one-to-one correspondence, which is not necessarily a perspectivity, is set up between the ranges on l and l'', and we say that these ranges are *projectively*, or *homographically*, *related*, or simply that they are *related ranges*. We write

$$(P, Q, R, \ldots) \overline{\wedge} (P'', Q'', R'', \ldots)$$

in this case.

The process may be continued, and we say that two ranges are related if they can be put into a one-to-one correspondence by means of a finite chain of perspectivities. It is clear that in a perspectivity distinct points are projected into distinct points. Hence, if two ranges are related, distinct points in one range correspond to distinct points in the other range.

An important problem in the theory of related ranges is to determine when two given ranges, which are in a one-to-one correspondence, are related by a series of perspectivities. The following theorem is a first step towards an answer. We shall use the term *projectivity* for *series of perspectivities*.

THEOREM I. *Given two triplets of distinct points P_1, Q_1, R_1 and P_3, Q_3, R_3 lying, respectively, on two distinct lines l_1 and l_3, there is a projectivity which assigns P_1, Q_1, R_1 to P_3, Q_3, R_3 respectively.*

Since P_1, Q_1, R_1 are distinct, and l_1 is distinct from l_3, at most one of these points lies on l_3. Similarly, at most one of the points P_3, Q_3, R_3 lies on l_1. Hence we can always choose one pair of points which are not required to correspond in the projectivity, say P_1 and Q_3, neither of which lies on both l_1 and l_3. Let $P_1 Q_3$ be the line l_2.

The join Q_1Q_3 is distinct from l_1 and l_2. On it take a point O_1 which is not on either of these lines, and let O_1R_1 meet l_2 in R_2 (O_1 and R_1 lie in the plane $O_1(l_2)$). Since l_3 and l_2 meet, P_1P_3 and R_2R_3 meet. Indeed, their intersection is unique, since $P_3 \neq R_3$, and P_1P_3 has a single point in common with l_3. Let this intersection be O_2. (It is not necessarily distinct from O_1.) Then

$$(P_1, Q_1, R_1) \overset{O_1}{\overline{\wedge}} (P_1, Q_3, R_2) \overset{O_2}{\overline{\wedge}} (P_3, Q_3, R_3).$$

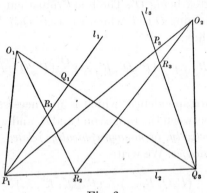

Fig. 6.

An immediate corollary is that a projectivity which is the result of three perspectivities, at most, can be set up between two ranges on the *same* line, so that three distinct, arbitrarily chosen points correspond to three distinct, arbitrarily chosen points.

It may be thought that the projectivity established between l_1 and l_3 is a special one, because it is the result of only two perspectivities. This is not the case, for we now prove

THEOREM II. *If a range of points on a line l_1 is related by a chain of m perspectivities to a range of points on a line $l_{m+1} \neq l_1$, this projectivity is equivalent to at most two perspectivities.*

Two preliminary theorems are necessary. Consider a sequence of two perspectivities between the lines l_1 and l_2, and l_2 and l_3. We shall call l_2 the *intermediary line* for the projectivity between l_1 and l_3. l_1 and l_2 must intersect: let them meet in the point L_{12}, and let l_2, l_3 intersect in the point L_{23}; the points L_{12} and L_{23} may or may not coincide. If they do, we have

THEOREM III. *If l_1, l_2, l_3 are concurrent and $l_1 \neq l_3$ the sequence of two perspectivities between the points of l_1 and l_3 is equivalent to a single perspectivity.*

Let

$$(P_1, Q_1, R_1, \ldots) \underset{\wedge}{\overset{O_{12}}{\quad}} (P_2, Q_2, R_2, \ldots),$$

and

$$(P_2, Q_2, R_2, \ldots) \underset{\wedge}{\overset{O_{23}}{\quad}} (P_3, Q_3, R_3, \ldots).$$

There is nothing to prove if $O_{12} = O_{23}$, so we may suppose that $O_{12} \neq O_{23}$. We consider the triads $P_1 P_2 P_3$, $Q_1 Q_2 Q_3$, and we see that

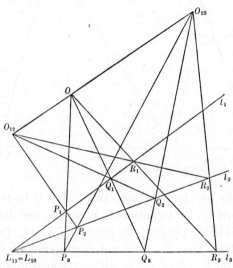

Fig. 7.

these are in perspective from $L_{12} = L_{23}$. If both triads are proper triangles we are necessarily in the general case of Desargues' Theorem, and the sides $P_1 P_3, Q_1 Q_3$ intersect on the join $O_{12} O_{23}$ of the two centres of perspective at a point O, say. Thus $Q_1 Q_3$, and similarly $R_1 R_3$, passes through O, the intersection of $O_{12} O_{23}$ with $P_1 P_3$. Thus

$$(P_1, Q_1, R_1 \ldots) \underset{\wedge}{\overset{O}{\quad}} (P_3, Q_3, R_3 \ldots).$$

If the points P_1, P_2, P_3 are collinear, which is the case when P_1 lies on $O_{12} O_{23}$, the point O may be taken at the intersection of $Q_1 Q_3$ with $O_{12} O_{23} = P_1 P_2 P_3$. If both sets of points P_1, P_2, P_3 and Q_1, Q_2, Q_3 are collinear then we must have $O_{12} = O_{23}$.

If, on the other hand, $L_{12} \neq L_{23}$, we have

THEOREM IV. *In the sequence of two perspectivities between the points of l_1 and l_3, the intermediary line may be replaced by any other* *line l_2^* which joins a pair of points on l_1 and l_3 which are neither corresponding nor coincident.*

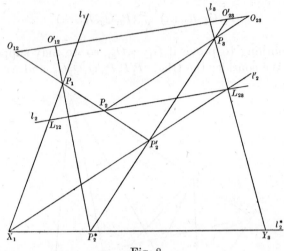

Fig. 8.

We apply the previous theorem twice. Let l_2^* be the line joining X_1 of l_1 to Y_3 of l_3. By hypothesis, X_1 and Y_3 are distinct, and do not correspond in the projectivity between l_1 and l_3. Let us suppose, in the first place, that X_1 does not correspond to L_{23}, the intersection of l_2 and l_3. Since L_{23} is self-corresponding in the perspectivity, centre O_{23}, between l_2 and l_3, we deduce that $X_1 L_{23}$ does not pass through O_{12}. We take the line $X_1 L_{23}$ as l_2'. It satisfies the requirements of our theorem, since X_1 and L_{23} are not corresponding points.

We can project the range $(P_2, ...)$ on l_2 from O_{12} into the range $(P_2', ...)$ on l_2'. For l_2' lies in the plane $L_{23}(l_1) = O_{12}(l_1)$. By a sequence of two perspectivities, vertices O_{12} and O_{23}, we have set up a projectivity between the ranges $(P_2', ...)$ on l_2' and $(P_3, ...)$ on l_3, and the lines, l_2', l_2, l_3 are concurrent. By the previous theorem there is a point O_{23}' on $O_{12} O_{23}$ such that

$$(P_1, ...) \underset{\wedge}{\overset{O_{12}}{}} (P_2', ...) \underset{\wedge}{\overset{O_{23}'}{}} (P_3, ...).$$

Similarly, since X_1 and Y_3 are not corresponding points, and X_1 is self-corresponding in the perspectivity, centre O_{12}, between l_1 and l_2', the line $X_1 Y_3 = l_2^*$ does not pass through O_{23}'. If we now project the range $(P_2', \ldots)$ on l_2' into the range $(P_2^*, \ldots)$ on l_2^* from the point O_{23}', then again, by the previous theorem, since l_2^*, l_2', l_1 are concurrent, there exists a point O_{12}' on $O_{12}O_{23}'$ and therefore on $O_{12}O_{23}$, such that

$$(P_1, \ldots) \overset{O_{12}'}{\overline{\wedge}} (P_2^*, \ldots) \overset{O_{23}'}{\overline{\wedge}} (P_3, \ldots).$$

The line l_2^* therefore satisfies the requirements of our theorem, and may be used instead of l_2 as an intermediary line.

If X_1 corresponds to L_{23}, the argument fails. If L_{12} does *not* correspond to Y_3 we can prove the theorem, as above, by taking $L_{12}Y_3$ in place of l_2' as the first intermediary line used in our argument. There remains the case in which X_1 corresponds to L_{23}, and L_{12} corresponds to Y_3. We consider this case.

On l_1 there exists at least one other point besides L_{12} and X_1. Let T_1 be such a point. If l_3 meets l_1, and T_1 is the point of intersection, the point T_3 of l_3 which corresponds to T_1 is different from T_1, unless the join $O_{12}O_{23}$ of the centres of perspective passes through T_1. Suppose that $O_{12}O_{23}$ passes through T_1, and that $T_1 = T_3$. There are two possibilities:

(i) There is a point Z_3 on l_3 distinct from T_3, L_{23}, Y_3. We can pass from the intermediary line l_2 to the intermediary line l_2^* by taking as intermediary lines, in order

$$L_{12}L_{23}, \quad L_{12}Z_3, \quad Z_3X_1, \quad X_1Y_3,$$

none of which joins corresponding points, or passes through the intersection of l_1 and l_3.

(ii) Every line contains only three points. Then the ranges on l_1 and l_3 are in perspective from the intersection of X_1L_{23} and Y_3L_{12}, and this point is $O_{12} = O_{23}$. The case in which $O_{12} = O_{23}$ is, of course, trivial.

Finally, if l_1 and l_3 meet, and T_3 and T_1 are different, or if l_1 and l_3 do not meet, and T_3 corresponds to T_1, we replace Z_3 by T_3 in the proof of (i), above. This concludes the proof of Theorem IV.

We are now in a position to complete the proof of Theorem II. In order to do this we first consider the case of four lines l_1, l_2, l_3, l_4, with ranges $(P_1, \ldots), (P_2, \ldots), (P_3, \ldots), (P_4, \ldots)$ on them, and suppose that

$$(P_1, \ldots) \overset{O_{12}}{\overline{\wedge}} (P_2, \ldots), \quad (P_2, \ldots) \overset{O_{23}}{\overline{\wedge}} (P_3, \ldots), \quad (P_3, \ldots) \overset{O_{34}}{\overline{\wedge}} (P_4, \ldots).$$

By the definition of perspective, l_1 and l_2 are distinct intersecting lines, and similarly for l_2 and l_3, and for l_3 and l_4; but other coincidences of the lines l_1, l_2, l_3, l_4 consistent with these restrictions are permissible, and must be taken into account.

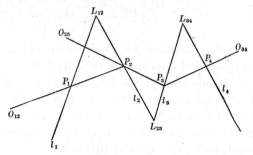

Fig. 9.

We first prove that if l_1 and l_4 are distinct lines we can pass from the range $(P_1, \ldots)$ to the range $(P_4, \ldots)$ by two perspectivities. We first observe that in the case in which each line of the configuration contains only three points the result follows by the argument used to prove Theorem I. Indeed, the ranges on l_1 and l_4 each consist of three points and are in one-to-one correspondence. Using the argument adopted to prove Theorem I it follows at once that we can pass from the range on l_1 to the range on l_4 by two perspectivities.

In proving the result generally we may now confine ourselves to the case in which each line of the configuration contains at least four distinct points. We first consider the cases which arise when the lines l_1, l_2, l_3, l_4 have certain special mutual relationships.

(i) l_1, l_2, l_3 distinct but concurrent. By Theorem III, we can pass from $(P_1, \ldots)$ to $(P_3, \ldots)$ by one perspectivity, and the result follows at once.

(ii) l_2, l_3, l_4 distinct but concurrent. This case follows in exactly the same way as (i).

(iii) $l_1 = l_3$, l_4 not through $L_{12} = L_{23}$. Then there is a line l_3^* through L_{12}, different from l_3, which meets l_4 in a point different from a possible intersection of l_2 and l_4 and from the point of l_4 which corresponds to L_{12} on l_2. By Theorem IV we may replace l_3 by l_3^* and then apply (ii).

(iv) $l_2 = l_4$, l_1 not through $L_{23} = L_{34}$. This case follows as in (iii).

(v) $l_1 = l_3$, $l_2 = l_4$. Let m be any line through $L_{12} = L_{23} = L_{34}$ different from $l_1 = l_3$ and from $l_2 = l_4$. From a point V_1 in the plane of l_1 and m we project the range $(P_1, \ldots)$ on l_1 into the range $(P, \ldots)$ on m. Then

$$(P, \ldots) \underset{\wedge}{\overset{V_1}{}} (P_1, \ldots) \underset{\wedge}{\overset{O_{12}}{}} (P_2, \ldots) \underset{\wedge}{\overset{O_{23}}{}} (P_3, \ldots) \underset{\wedge}{\overset{O_{34}}{}} (P_4, \ldots).$$

Using Theorem III, we obtain, in turn,

$$(P, \ldots) \underset{\wedge}{\overset{V_i}{}} (P_i, \ldots) \quad (i = 1, 2, 3, 4)$$

for suitably chosen points V_2, V_3, V_4. Hence we have

$$(P_1, \ldots) \underset{\wedge}{\overset{V_1}{}} (P, \ldots) \underset{\wedge}{\overset{V_4}{}} (P_4, \ldots),$$

and indeed, by another application of Theorem III, we see that the ranges on l_1 and l_4 are in perspective in this case.

The cases considered above deal with all the cases in which l_1, l_2, l_3 are concurrent, or l_2, l_3, l_4 are concurrent. The remaining cases are first, the general case illustrated in Fig. 9, and the cases in which l_1, l_2, l_4 are concurrent (but all different) or l_1, l_3, l_4 are concurrent (but all different). These last possibilities cannot occur simultaneously, otherwise we should be in a case already considered. We need only consider the case in which l_1, l_2, l_4 are not concurrent (whether l_1, l_3, l_4 are concurrent or not), since the case in which l_1, l_2, l_4 are concurrent and l_1, l_3, l_4 are not concurrent is obtained by interchanging the roles of l_2 and l_3. Our argument, of course, includes the general case.

Since l_1, l_2, l_4 are not concurrent we may replace l_3 by a line l_3^* joining L_{12} to a point of l_4 not on l_2, nor corresponding, in the range on l_4, to L_{12} regarded as a point of l_2. We then have l_1, l_2, l_3^* concurrent, and may apply (i). This completes our proof of Theorem II in the case $m = 3$.

Now consider m perspectivities, that is, the general case of Theorem II. The case in which each line has only three points can be dealt with as when $m = 3$, and may be omitted. If, in the sequence of lines

$$l_1, l_2, l_3, \ldots, l_{m+1} \quad (m > 2),$$

we can find a line l_i which is different from l_{i+3} we can apply the case $m = 3$ to reduce the number of perspectivities. We proceed in this way until either we reach the case of two perspectivities, or else

$$l_i = l_{i+3} \quad (i = 1, \ldots, m-2).$$

In this case $m > 3$ since we have assumed $l_1 \neq l_{m+1}$. Then l_1, l_2, l_3 are distinct lines. We can, by Theorem IV, replace l_2 by a different line l_2^* without altering any other l_i. Then, since $l_2^* \neq l_5$ we can apply the result for $m = 3$ to shorten the sequence of perspectivities. Thus in all cases we can reduce the number of perspectivities to *two* and our theorem is proved.

Corollary. A one-to-one projective correspondence between two ranges on the same straight line can be obtained as the result of at most three perspectivities.

4.   Harmonic conjugates.   On a line l take two distinct points A and B. If C is any point of l we construct a new point D on l as follows.

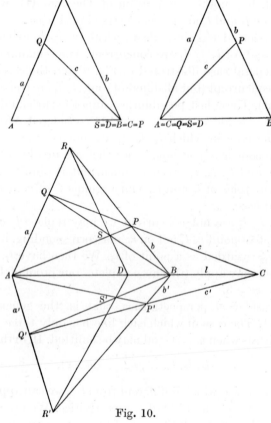

Fig. 10.

In a plane π through l take three lines a, b, c passing respectively through A, B, C, each distinct from l and not all meeting in one point. Since at least three distinct lines pass through every point in π, it is possible to choose a, b, c to satisfy these conditions. Let b and c meet in P, c and a in Q, and let a meet b in the point R. Then A cannot coincide with P, nor B with Q. Since A, B, P, Q are coplanar points, and not collinear, AP and BQ meet in a point. Let this be S. Then S must be distinct from R, since B is distinct from A. The line RS has a unique intersection D with l. This is the point we seek.

It is immediately verified that if $C = B$ then $D = B$, and if $C = A$, then $D = A$. In these cases the construction of D does not depend on the particular set of lines a, b, c chosen. We prove now that if C is distinct from A and B the point D is independent of the coplanar set of lines a, b, c chosen: in other words, *D is determined only by the ordered triad A, B, C.*

We first examine the case in which there are only three points A, B, C on l. Then D must coincide with one of these points. If $D = A$, then R, S, Q, A must be collinear, and hence $Q = S$ or $Q = A$. If $Q = S$, then $R = P$, and a, b, c are concurrent, contrary to hypothesis; if $Q = A$, then $C = A$, which is again contrary to hypothesis. Similarly we cannot have $D = B$, and so the only remaining possibility is $D = C$. Hence in this case too, the position of D does not depend on the particular choice of A, B, C.

We may now confine ourselves to the case in which l (and hence every line) contains at least four points, and through any point there pass at least four lines which lie in any given plane through the point. We consider any plane π' (not necessarily distinct from π) through l, and in it we draw three lines a', b', c' through A, B, C respectively, these lines being distinct from l and not concurrent. We repeat the construction given above, denoting the points corresponding to P, Q, R, S by P', Q', R', S'. Let $R'S'$ meet l in D'.

Consider, first of all, the case in which the lines a, a'; b, b'; c, c' are all distinct. Corresponding sides of the triangles PQR, $P'Q'R'$ intersect in A, B, C, which are collinear. Hence, by the converse of Desargues' Theorem, these triangles are in perspective. If $P = P'$, then $b = b'$, and $c = c'$, contrary to hypothesis; for similar reasons $Q \neq Q'$, $R \neq R'$. Thus the lines PP', QQ', RR' are determinate, and they have a point O in common. If two of these lines coincide, say $QQ' = RR'$, then $QR = Q'R'$, that is, $a = a'$, which is contrary to hypothesis. Therefore O is determined by any two of the three lines.

Again, corresponding sides of the triangles PQS, $P'Q'S'$ intersect in B, A, C, and therefore these triangles are in perspective. Hence S, S' and O, the intersection of PP' and QQ', are collinear. The triangles QRS, $Q'R'S'$ are therefore in perspective from O. Let us assume, first of all, that $SQ \neq S'Q'$. Since SQ meets $S'Q'$ in B, and QR meets $Q'R'$ in A, Desargues' Theorem shows that RS and $R'S'$ have a point in common on $BA = l$. Since RS meets l only in D, and $R'S'$ meets it only in D' it follows that $D = D'$.

If $SQ = S'Q'$, but $SP \neq S'P'$ we may use the triangles PRS, $P'R'S'$ in place of QRS, $Q'R'S'$ and prove that $D = D'$. If $SQ = S'Q'$ and $SP = S'P'$ then $S = S'$ and QQ', PP' meet in S. Since PQR, $P'Q'R'$ are in perspective, RR' goes through $S = S'$. Hence $RS = R'S'$ meets l in the same point D.

This proof may break down if the lines a, a'; b, b'; and c, c' are not all distinct. For instance, if $c = c'$, the triangles PQR, $P'Q'R'$ are in perspective from the intersection of RR' with c, and PQS, $P'Q'S'$ are in perspective from the intersection of SS' with c, but since $PP' = QQ'$ we cannot deduce from these facts that QRS, $Q'R'S'$ are in perspective. We must therefore modify our proof.

We note that if $c = c'$ the planes π, π' coincide. We show that if the lines a, a'; b, b'; c, c' are not all distinct there exists at least one other set of lines a^*, b^*, c^* through A, B, C satisfying the requirements of the construction, such that a, a^*; b, b^*; c, c^*, and a', a^*; b', b^*; c', c^* are distinct sets of lines. The case in which $c = c'$ is typical. Since through each point of l there pass at least four distinct lines of π we can find lines a^* and b^* through A and B respectively distinct from l, a, a' and l, b, b' respectively. Let b^* meet a^* in R^*. Since $c = c'$, there is at least one line c^* in π which passes through C and is distinct from $c = c'$, l and CR^*. The lines a^*, b^*, c^* satisfy our requirements. We use them to construct a point D^*. By the proof given above $D = D^*$ and similarly $D' = D^*$. It follows once more that $D = D'$.

This unique point D is called *the harmonic conjugate of C with respect to A and B*, and is denoted by

$$D = (A, B)/C.$$

It is clear from the construction that

$$D = (B, A)/C.$$

We now prove that

$$C = (A, B)/D = (B, A)/D.$$

To construct the harmonic conjugate of D with respect to A and B we draw three lines AQR, BSQ, DSR through A, B, D respectively to form a triangle QSR. Then BR and AS intersect in P, and QP meets l in the harmonic conjugate of D with respect to A and B (or B and A). This is the point C, so that the result is proved.

We saw in §3, Th. I, that a projectivity can be established between the points A, B, C, and the points A', B', C', these being two triplets of distinct collinear points. We now prove that such a projectivity makes $(A, B)/C$ correspond to $(A', B')/C'$.

If in fact $C = A$ or $C = B$ then we must have $C' = A'$ or $C' = B'$, and in these cases the result is evident. We therefore suppose that A, B, C (and therefore A', B', C') are distinct. Since a projectivity is the result of a finite number of perspectivities, we need only consider ranges A, B, C, A', B', C' on distinct lines l, l', which are in perspective.

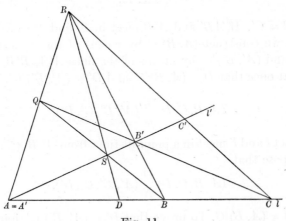

Fig. 11.

(i) $A = A'$. Let the ranges be in perspective from R. To construct $D = (A, B)/C$ we draw the lines AR, BB', CB' through A, B, C, respectively, to form the triangle $B'QR$. Since AB', BQ meet in S, RS meets l in the required point D. To construct $D' = (A', B')/C'$, we draw through A', B', C' the lines $A'QR$, $B'QC$ and $C'CR$ respectively to form the triangle CRQ. Since $A'C$ and $B'R$ meet in B, BQ meets l' in D'. Therefore $D' = S$. Hence (A, B, C, D) and (A', B', C', D') are in perspective from R.

(ii) $B = B'$. This case follows at once from (i) since

$$(A, B)/C = (B, A)/C.$$

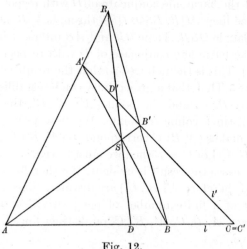

Fig. 12.

(iii) $C = C'$. If AB' and $A'B$ meet in S, and RS meets l in D, l' in D', we construct $(A, B)/C$ by means of the lines AA', BB', $CA'B'$, and $(A', B')/C'$ by means of the lines $A'A$, $B'B$, CAB. It follows at once that $D = (A, B)/C$, and $D' = (A', B')/C'$. Hence

$$(A, B, C, D) \underset{\wedge}{\overset{R}{}} (A', B', C', D').$$

(iv) Let l and l' meet in a point distinct from A, B, C, A', B', C', and suppose that

$$(A, B, C, D) \underset{\wedge}{\overset{O}{}} (A', B', C', D'),$$

where $D = (A, B)/C$. To prove that $D' = (A', B')/C'$, join CA' and let this line meet ODD' in D_1, and OBB' in B_1. Since

$$(A, B, C, D) \underset{\wedge}{\overset{O}{}} (A', B_1, C, D_1),$$

and $D = (A, B)/C$, it follows from (iii) that $D_1 = (A', B_1)/C$, and since

$$(A', B_1, C, D_1) \underset{\wedge}{\overset{O}{}} (A', B', C', D'),$$

it follows from (i) that $D' = (A', B')/C'$.

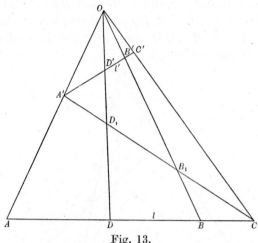

Fig. 13.

These results are usually stated in the following form:

THEOREM I. *Harmonic conjugacy is projectively invariant.*

An important corollary is

THEOREM II. *If there exist three distinct points A, B, C such that $C = (A, B)/C$, then, given any three points A', B', C', with $A' \neq B'$, we have $C' = (A', B')/C'$.*

This is evident if $C' = A'$ or $C' = B'$. If C' is distinct from A' and B', there is a projectivity which takes A', B', C' into A, B, C. By Theorem I this takes $(A', B')/C'$ into $(A, B)/C$. Since, by hypothesis, this last point coincides with C, we must have

$$C' = (A', B')/C'.$$

When this happens we shall say that we are in *the special case*.

For the purpose of completing the relationship between the pairs A, B and C, D, we find it convenient to define $(A, B)/C$ when $A = B$. The definition varies with the circumstances. If we are in the special case we allow any point of the line to be $D = (A, A)/C$. If we are not in the special case we define $(A, A)/C$ to be A when $C \neq A$, and to be any point of the line when $C = A$.

We now prove that if $D = (A, B)/C$, then $A = (C, D)/B$. It may be seen at once that this follows from the definition of harmonic conjugacy, with the above convention, if the points A, B, C, D are not all distinct. We need only consider the case, therefore, in which A, B, C, D are four distinct points on l.

With the notation of Fig. 10 let PD meet RA in Q', and QD meet RB in P'. The lines RD, AP, BQ pass through S, so that the sides of the triangles RAB, DPQ must intersect in collinear points. Therefore $P'Q'$ passes through C.

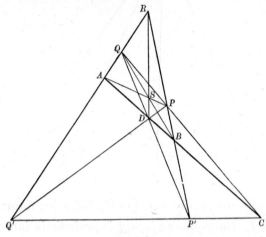

Fig. 14.

To construct $(C, D)/B$ we draw the lines DP', CP and BPP' through D, C and B, forming the triangle $PP'Q$. The lines DP and CP' meet in Q', and QQ' meets l in the required point, which is therefore A. To sum up, we have proved

THEOREM III. *The harmonic relation is symmetric in A, B and in C, D and also in the pairs (A, B) and (C, D).*

We may now describe (A, B) and (C, D) as harmonically conjugate *pairs*. The harmonic property is not of much interest in the special case, but it is of fundamental importance in all other cases.

If we are not in the special case we cannot extend § 3, Th. I and find a projectivity which relates *four* distinct points A, B, C, D of one range to four distinct points A', B', C', D' of another. For if $D = (A, B)/C$, but $D' \neq (A', B')/C'$, the existence of such a projectivity would contradict Theorem I.

Finally, if (A, B), (C, D) are harmonically conjugate, and O is any point not on the line $ABCD$, consider the lines $a = OA, b = OB$, $c = OC, d = OD$. If l' is any line in the plane of these lines which does not pass through O, and cuts these lines in A', B', C', D' respectively, then

$$(A, B, C, D) \; \underset{\wedge}{\overset{O}{}} \; (A', B', C', D'),$$

and so (A', B') are harmonically conjugate with respect to (C', D'). We express this property of the pencil of lines a, b, c, d by saying that (a, b) are harmonically conjugate with respect to (c, d).

5. Two projectively invariant constructions.

We re-examine the constructions already given in V, § 7, and prove that they are projectively invariant. Their importance lies in the fact that they can be used to construct a field by which we shall introduce co-ordinates into the incidence space [§§ 7, 8].

On a line l take three distinct points O, E, U. Let A, B be two points of l, each distinct from U.

Construction I. In a plane π through l draw three lines a, b, u through A, B, U, respectively. These lines are to be distinct from l and must not all pass through one point. Let P be the intersection of u and a, Q the intersection of u and b, R the intersection of OQ and a, S the intersection of UR and b. Then PS intersects l in a definite point T.

After justifying this construction we shall show that T depends on O, U, A, B only, and not on the construction lines a, b, u. The first part of the construction, the selection of the three lines a, b, u, is possible because, as we have already seen [§ 3], at least three distinct lines pass through every point in π. The point Q cannot coincide with O, and so the line OQ is defined. The point R is unique, since even when $A = O$, $P \neq Q$. Since R is on a, $R \neq U$, and therefore UR is determined. The points P and S are distinct, and their join is distinct from l, since u does not go through the intersection of a and b, and does not coincide with l. Hence PS meets l in a definite point T, and since PS is distinct from u, $T \neq U$.

The 'general' case is illustrated by Plate III, (i). We first show, however, that T is independent of the construction lines a, b, u in the following special cases, in which the points O, A, B are not all distinct (the numbering refers to the diagrams in Plate III):

(ii) $A = B \neq O$. We see that $T = (A, U)/O$, performing the usual construction for the harmonic conjugate, using only lines of the figure.

(iii) $O = A$. Evidently $T = B$.

(iv) $O = B$. Here $T = A$.

(v) $A = B = O$. We see that $T = O$.

If in a projectivity the points O, A, B, U become the points O', A', B', U', the point T becomes the point T' in the above special cases, since coincident points become coincident points, and harmonic conjugates become harmonic conjugates. In these cases, then, the constructions are projectively invariant.

We now suppose that O, A, B, U are distinct. We prove that P, Q, R, S are distinct points, no three of which are collinear. By construction, P and Q are distinct points. Also $OQ \neq b$, and Q does not lie on a. Hence R is not on b, and, in particular, $R \neq Q$. If $R = P$ then we should have $QR = QP$; but QR meets l in O, and QP meets l in U. Since $O \neq U$, it follows that $R \neq P$. Again, since $U \neq A$, $UP \neq UR$, and since $U \neq B$ the points Q, S are distinct. Finally, R is not on b, and therefore $S \neq R$. We conclude that P, Q, R, S are distinct points, no three of which are collinear.

If R were on l, R would be A, and OQ would be l; that is, Q would lie on l, contrary to our construction. Similarly, if S were on l, S would be B, and R would lie on l, which we have seen is not the case. Hence none of the points P, Q, R, S lies on l. These facts will help to clarify certain points in subsequent proofs.

We must show that if π' is any plane through l (which may coincide with π) and a', b', u' are lines of π' through A, B, U respectively, all distinct from l and not concurrent, then the construction given above, with a, b, u replaced by a', b', u' respectively, leads to a point T' which coincides with T.

Case (i). $\pi \neq \pi'$. By the converse of Desargues' Theorem the triangles PQR, $P'Q'R'$ are in perspective, corresponding sides intersecting at the collinear points O, A, U. Similarly, the triangles SQR, $S'Q'R'$ are in perspective. Hence there is a point common to the lines PP', QQ', RR', SS', so that the triangles SPQ, $S'P'Q'$ are in perspective. Hence SP meets $S'P'$ on the line UB; that is, $T = T'$.

Case (ii). $\pi = \pi'$. If the configuration lies in a space of dimension $n > 2$, then the uniqueness of the point T is at once established by a double application of (i); the two constructions in $\pi = \pi'$ are compared with a construction in a plane through l distinct from $\pi = \pi'$. But if $n = 2$, we must proceed differently. We first establish the uniqueness of T for the cases, three in number, in which two and only two of the coincidences $a = a'$, $b = b'$, $u = u'$ occur. Having done this, we observe that there are at least three lines in π distinct from l through each of the points A, B, U, for l has been assumed to contain at least four distinct points O, A, B, U. The reader may now easily verify that we can pass from construction lines a, b, u to construction lines a', b', u' by a series of steps in each of which only

PLATE III

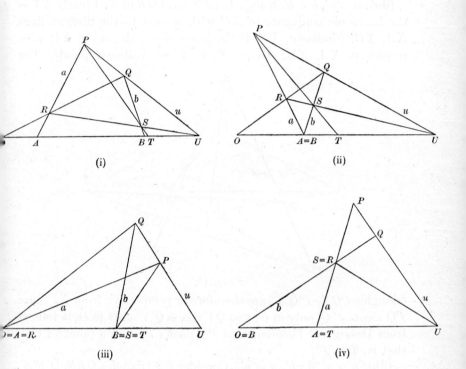

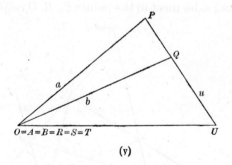

one of these lines is altered. Thus we have only to consider the three following special cases (ii a), (ii b), (ii c).

(ii a). $a = a'$, $b = b'$, $u \neq u'$. Let PS meet QR in Y. Clearly XY is the harmonic conjugate of XU with respect to the distinct lines XA, XB. Similarly, XY' is the harmonic conjugate of XU with respect to XA, XB. Hence X, Y, Y' are collinear points. The

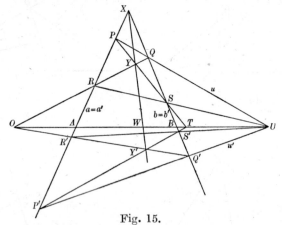

Fig. 15.

triangles PQY, $P'Q'Y'$ are therefore in perspective from X. Since PQ meets $P'Q'$ only in U, and QY meets $Q'Y'$ only in O, it follows from Desargues' Theorem that PY meets $P'Y'$ in a point of OU; that is, $T = T'$.

(ii b). $a = a'$, $b \neq b'$, $u = u'$. Consider the triangles QRS, $Q'R'S'$. Corresponding sides meet in the points U, B, O respectively. Hence

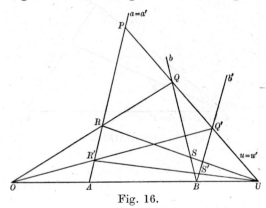

Fig. 16.

the triangles are in perspective. But QQ' meets RR' in the one point P. Therefore P, S, S' are collinear, and hence $T = T'$.

(iic). $a \neq a'$, $b = b'$, $u = u'$. The triangles PRS, $P'R'S'$ are in perspective from Q. Since PR meets $P'R'$ only at A, and RS meets

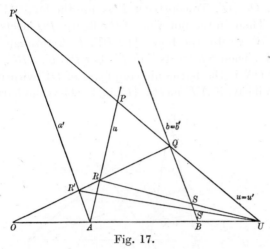

Fig. 17.

$R'S'$ only at U (if $S = S'$, $R = R'$, since $O \neq U$, and then $a = a'$), it follows from Desargues' Theorem that PS meets $P'S'$ on AU. That is, $T = T'$.

The three special cases having been examined, the uniqueness of T is now completely established.

We now proceed to establish the projective invariance of the point T; that is, we shall prove that if there is a projective correspondence between l and l' such that

$$(A, B, U, O, ...) \; \overline{\wedge} \; (A', B', U', O', ...),$$

and if T' is the point obtained by applying Construction I to A', B', U', O', then

$$(A, B, U, O, T, ...) \; \overline{\wedge} \; (A', B', U', O', T', ...).$$

We need only prove the invariance of the construction in question under a perspectivity.

If $n \geqslant 3$, and the ranges on l and l' are in perspective from V, there are planes π, π' through l, l' respectively which do not contain V. We perform Construction I on l in π, and project the configuration in π from V on to π'. The projected figure gives Construction I on l', and therefore the projective invariance of T is proved.

If $n = 2$ we must use other arguments. As we have already noted, we need only consider the case in which A, B, O, U are all distinct.

We suppose that A, B, O, U and A', B', O', U' are two ranges on lines l, l' respectively, which are in perspective from V.

Case (i). $O = O'$. To construct T we use the lines AV, BV, UB' for a, b, u. Then, in the notation of the figure, PQ meets l in T. To construct T' we use the lines $AV, BV, U'B$ through A', B', U' respectively. Then SR meets l' in T'. Let $PB'U, SBU'$ meet in X. Evidently OX is the harmonic conjugate of OV with respect to l and l'. Similarly, if $A'U$ meets AU' in Y, OY is the harmonic con-

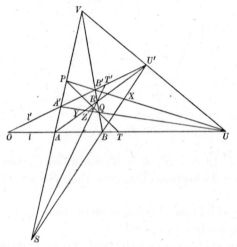

Fig. 18.

jugate of OV with respect to l and l'. Hence, O, X, Y are collinear points, and XY meets BB' in $(B, B')/V$. Projecting from X, we see that XY meets AA' in $(P, S)/V$, and, projecting from Y, it meets BB' in $(Q, R)/V$. Hence, the intersection Z of PQ, SR is on XY. Now, the corresponding sides of the triangles $T'U'R, TUQ$ meet at Y, Z, O respectively, and therefore, by the converse of Desargues' Theorem TT' passes through V, the intersection of UU', QR.

Case (ii). $U = U'$. To construct T we use the lines AV, BV, l' for a, b, u respectively. If OB' meets AV in R and UR meets BV in S, then $A'S$ meets l in T. To construct T' we use the lines AV, BV, l. If $O'B$ meets AV in R', and UR' meets BV in S', then AS' meets l' in T'. Let $B'R$ meet $A'S$ in X, and BR' meet AS' in X'. Then VX is the harmonic conjugate of VU with respect to VA, VB, and so is VX'. Hence V, X, X' are collinear. Similarly, if BR' meets $B'R$ at L, and AS' meets $A'S$ at M, we see that UL and UM are both harmonic conjugates of UV with respect to UO, UO'. Hence U, L, M are collinear. Now consider the triangles OXT, $O'X'T'$.

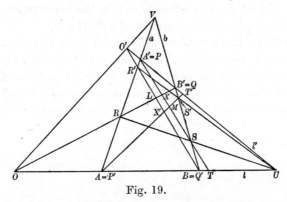

Fig. 19.

Corresponding sides intersect at the collinear points M, U, L. The triangles are therefore in perspective. But OO' and XX' meet only in V. Therefore T, T', V are collinear.

Case (iii). The intersection of l and l' is distinct from O and U. Join $O'U$, and let this line cut VA, VB in A^*, B^*. Using O', A^*, B^*, U, we construct T^*. By Case (ii) above TT^* passes through V,

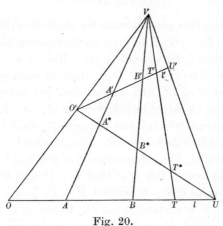

Fig. 20.

and by Case (i) above T^*T' passes through V. Hence TT' passes through V, and the proof of the projective invariance of Construction I is complete.

We shall return to a study of this construction later. We note here that given O and U the point T is determined by A and B *independently of the order in which they are taken*; that is, T is *symmetric* in A and B. For, having already shown that T is invariant, we may use the line USR as u, and although this interchanges the parts played by A and B, we evidently obtain the same point T in the only case we need examine, namely $A \neq O$, $B \neq O$.

Construction II. In a plane π through l draw three lines a, b, u through A, B, U respectively. These lines are to be distinct from l and must not pass through one point. Let P be the intersection of u and a, Q the intersection of u and b, R the intersection of EQ and a, S the intersection of OR and b. Then PS intersects l in a definite point T.

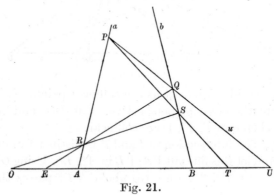

Fig. 21.

After justifying this construction we shall show that T depends on the points A, B, U, O, E, but not on the construction lines a, b, u. As in Construction I, we can select three lines a, b, u to satisfy the given conditions. The points P, Q are distinct, and neither lies on l. The intersection R of EQ and a is unique. For otherwise $EQ = a$, and Q would coincide with the intersection of a and b, so that a, b, u would be concurrent, which is not the case. Again R is distinct from O, since R is on EQ, which does not coincide with l, Q not lying on l. Hence OR is defined. The intersection S of OR and b is unique. For if not, we should have $OR = b$, so that $B = O$, and since Q lies on b, we should also have $QR = b$, so that $E = B$. But we cannot have $E = B = O$, for E is distinct from O. Hence S is unique, and it does not coincide with P, because P does not lie on b. The line PS is therefore determinate, and since P does not lie on l, PS has a unique intersection T with l. Finally, $T \neq U$. For if $T = U$, $S = Q$, and $QR = SR$, and therefore $O = E$, which is contrary to hypothesis.

To show that T is independent of the plane π and of the construction lines a, b, u, we first consider a number of cases in which A, B, U, O, E are not all distinct. These are illustrated in Plate IV.

PLATE IV

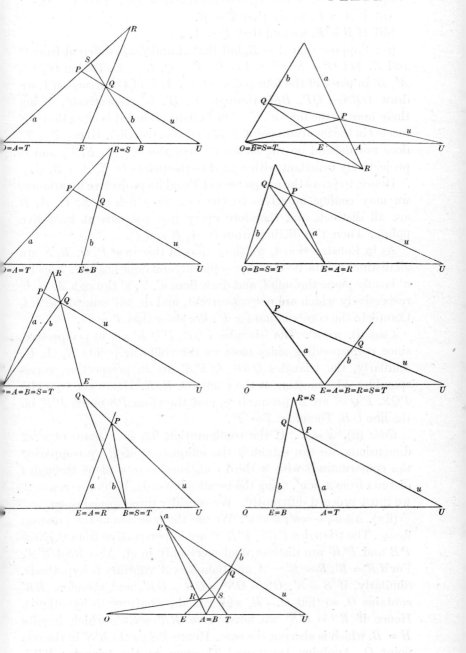

(i) If $A = O$, or $B = O$, the construction shows that $T = O$.

(ii) If $A = E$, we see that $T = B$.

(iii) If $B = E$, we find that $T = A$.

(iv) Suppose that $A = B$, but that A and B are different from O and E. Let $O' = E$, $U' = A = B$, $A' = O$, $B' = U$. Taking O', U', A', B' in place of the four points O, U, A, B of Construction I, we draw ORS, UQP, BSQ through A', B', U' respectively. Using these lines as the lines a', b', u' of Construction I it is clear that PS meets l in the invariant point T' of that construction. Hence $T = T'$ does not depend on the choice of lines through A, B, U, and is projectively invariant with regard to the points O, E, $A = B$, U.

Hence, to prove the uniqueness of T and its projective invariance, we may confine ourselves to the case in which O, E, U, A, B are all distinct, and therefore every line contains at least five points. Then T is distinct from O, A, B and U.

As in Construction I, we show that in this case P, Q, R, S are all distinct points, no three are collinear, and none lies on l. Now let π' be any plane through l, and draw lines a', b'', u' through A, B, U respectively which are not concurrent, and do not coincide with l. Complete the construction for T'. We show that $T = T'$.

Case (i). $\pi \neq \pi'$. The triangles PQR, $P'Q'R'$ are in perspective, since corresponding sides meet at the collinear points E, A, U. Similarly, the triangles QRS, $Q'R'S'$ are in perspective, corresponding sides meeting at the points O, B, E. Hence the triangles PQS, $P'Q'S'$ are in perspective, and therefore PS meets $P'S'$ on the line UB. Therefore $T = T'$.

Case (ii). $\pi = \pi'$. If the configuration lies in a space of $n > 2$ dimensions, we can establish the uniqueness of T by comparing the constructions with a third construction in a plane through l distinct from $\pi = \pi'$, using the result of Case (i). If, however, $n = 2$, we must proceed differently. We consider three special cases.

(ii$a$). $a \neq a'$, $b = b'$, $u = u'$. We use the notation of the previous figure. The triangles PRS, $P'R'S'$ are in perspective from Q. Now PR and $P'R'$ are distinct, and meet only in A. Also $RS \neq R'S'$. For if $R = R'$, $R = R' = A$, and then $E = A$, contrary to hypothesis. Similarly, if $S = S'$, $OS = OS' = OR = OR'$, and therefore RR' contains O, so that $O = E$, which is also contrary to hypothesis. Hence if $RS = R'S'$ we must have $RR' = SS'$, which implies $E = B$, which is also not the case. Hence RS meets $R'S'$ in the one point O. Applying Desargues' Theorem to the triangles PRS,

$P'R'S'$, we see then that PS meets $P'S'$ on OA. That is, $T = T'$.

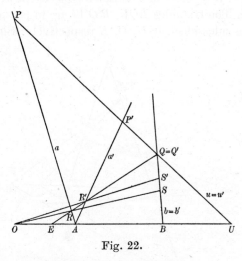

Fig. 22.

(iib). $a = a'$, $b \neq b'$, $u = u'$. Since $b \neq b'$, $Q \neq Q'$, and therefore $R \neq R'$. Also, $RR' = a \neq u = QQ'$. Now, QR meets $Q'R'$ at E, RS

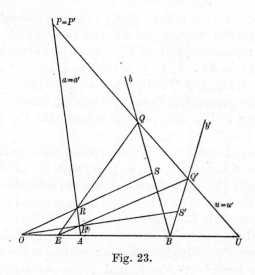

Fig. 23.

meets $R'S'$ at O, and QS meets $Q'S'$ only at B. Hence the triangles QRS, $Q'R'S'$ are in perspective. But QQ' and RR' meet only in P. Therefore P, S, S' are collinear points, and so $T = T'$.

(iic). $a = a'$, $b = b'$, $u \neq u'$. Let a, b meet in X, let PS, RQ meet in Y, and $P'S'$, $R'Q'$ meet in Y'. Let RS meet u in V, and let $R'S'$ meet u' in V'. The triangles RQV, $R'Q'V'$ are in perspective, since corresponding sides meet at U, O, E respectively. Since RR' and

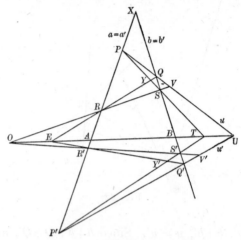

Fig. 24.

QQ' meet only in X, it follows that VV' passes through X. Now, XY is the harmonic conjugate of XV with respect to XA, XB, and XY' is the harmonic conjugate of XV' with respect to the same pair of lines. Since $XV = XV'$, X, Y, Y' are collinear points. Now consider the triangles PYQ, $P'Y'Q'$. By what we have just proved, these triangles are in perspective from X. Since PQ meets $P'Q'$ only at U, and YQ meets $Y'Q'$ only at E, it follows that PY meets $P'Y'$ on l. Hence $T = T'$.

Having proved that $T = T'$ in these special cases, we can proceed, as in the case of Construction I, to prove that $T = T'$ for any two constructions in the one plane which use the same distinct points O, E, U, A, B. Since at least four lines distinct from l pass through each of the points A, B, U we can pass from the first construction to the second by a series of alterations of one of the lines a, b, u. At each change T remains invariant, since we have one of the three special cases considered above, and finally we reach the lines a', b', u' of the second construction.

We now prove that if there is a projective correspondence such that

$$(O, E, U, A, B, ...) \ \overline{\wedge} \ (O', E', U', A', B', ...)$$

and if T'' is the point obtained by applying Construction II to the points O', E', U', A', B', then

$$(O, E, U, A, B, T) \barwedge (O', E', U', A', B', T').$$

We need only consider the case when the two ranges are in perspective from a vertex V. We may suppose that O, E, U, A, B are all distinct, the cases in which A, B coincide with O or E, or $A = B$ having already been considered. We suppose in the first instance that

(i) $O = O'$. To construct T and T'' we use the lines VAA', VBB' first as a, b, then as a', b'. Let EA' meet VB in P. We take UP as u,

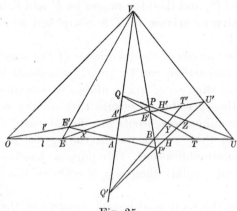

Fig. 25.

meeting a in Q, and QB' then meets l in T. Let $E'A$ meet VB in P'. We take $U'P'$ as u', meeting a' in Q', and then $Q'B$ meets l' in T'. Let EA' meet $E'A$ in X, BT'' meet $B'T$ in Y, and let PQ meet $P'Q'$ in Z. Finally, denote the intersections of PQ and l', and of $P'Q'$ and l, by H' and H respectively.

Consider the triangles $A'PH'$, $AP'H$. Since corresponding sides intersect at Z, O, X respectively we can deduce that HH' passes through V if we prove that Z, O, X are collinear. But this follows at once from the fact that the triangles EPU, $E'P'U'$ are in perspective from V, since corresponding sides of these triangles intersect at Z, O, X respectively. The triangles $H'QB'$, $HQ'B$ are now seen to be in perspective, vertex V. Since corresponding sides intersect at Y, O, Z it follows that O, X, Y, Z are collinear. It is clear that OX is the harmonic conjugate of OV with respect to l and l'. If TT'' meets BB' in K, the harmonic conjugate of OK with respect to l and l' is OY, which coincides with OX. Hence $OK = OV$, and therefore TT' passes through V.

(ii) Now let $U = U'$. This case can be deduced from the one just proved by observing that if we rename the points O, E, U, A, B by writing
$$(\bar{O}, \bar{E}, \bar{U}, \bar{A}, \bar{B}) = (U, E, O, B, A),$$
and construct $\bar{T}$ from the points $\bar{O}, \bar{E}, \bar{U}, \bar{A}, \bar{B}$, we have $\bar{T} = T$. Thus the projective invariance of T when $U = U'$ is covered by the previous case.

Finally, let the lines l, l' meet in a point distinct from O and U. If l^* is the line $O'U$ we proceed in two stages, first considering the ranges on l and l^*, and then the ranges on l^* and l', and the proof of the projective invariance of T is completed as in the case of Construction I.

The preceding proofs of the invariance of the points T obtained by the two constructions can be greatly simplified when $n = 2$ if we may assume that every line contains an unlimited number of points. It is then possible to ensure that all the required intersections in the uniqueness proofs are determinate. Alternatively, the assumption that we are not in the *special case* mentioned in §4 leads to simplifications. Our purpose has been to provide proofs which are valid when $n = 2$ without the use of these assumptions.

We conclude this section with some remarks on the various constructions we have discussed. It will be observed that in the 'general' cases of Constructions I and II a set of four coplanar points P, Q, R, S enters, with the property that no three of the points are collinear. These points form a *quadrangle* with three pairs of opposite sides: PQ, RS; PS, QR; PR, QS. The respective intersections Z, X, Y of these pairs of opposite sides are the *diagonal points* of the quadrangle, and the joins of the diagonal points are the *diagonals*.

If we apply the usual construction for $(R, S)/Z$ we see that this point is the intersection of RS and XY. Hence X, Y, Z are collinear if and only if we are in the *special case*.

Let l be any line in the plane which is distinct from the sides of the quadrangle. It meets the sides in six points which form three pairs, each pair corresponding to a pair of opposite sides. We can select a set of three points from the six, one belonging to each pair, in eight possible ways. These triads fall into pairs, two paired triads making up the whole set of six points. The sides of the quadrangle to which a given triad belongs either form a triangle or are concurrent. In the first case we say the triad is a *triangle* triad; in the second case we say it is a *point* triad. Thus, in the figure, A, B, C is a triangle triad, A', B', C' a point triad. If a given triad is a triangle triad (point triad) the triad with which it is paired is a point triad (triangle triad). If two triads have one point in common they are of like type; if they have two points in common they are of opposite type.

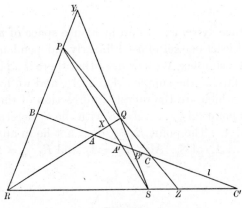

Fig. 26.

It may, of course, happen that the pairs are not all distinct. Suppose, for instance, that $C = C'$ $(= Z)$. Then A, B, C may be regarded as both a triangle and a point-triad, and so may A', B', C; but A, A', C and B, B', C, which also have one point in common, may be regarded as each consisting of two triangle triads.

Our Constructions I and II are, essentially, constructions for completing our *quadrangular* set of six points, given five of them. In I, one pair consists of the point U counted twice, and another is the pair A, B. The construction is then simply a method for determining the third pair of the quadrangular set, given one of its points, namely O. The fact that triangle triads are point triads, and conversely, explains why the construction for the point T is symmetric in A and B. In II, the given points are paired as (O, U) and (A, B), and we are given one member E of the third pair. The problem is then to construct T so that E, B, U *is a point-triad*.

If we denote the quadrangular set of points which occurs in II by

$$Q(OEA, UTB),$$

where OEA is a point triad, UTB a triangle triad, and O and U, E and T, A and B are respectively the intersections with the line of the set of the pairs of opposite sides of the quadrangle $PQRS$, we have proved that

The property of being a quadrangular set $Q(OEA, UTB)$ is invariant under any projectivity.

6. Reference systems. In an incidence space of n dimensions there exists at least one set of $n+1$ linearly independent points. We call such a set a simplex. We saw in § 1 that there is a point E which is not in any face of the simplex $A_0, ..., A_n$, and we found $2^{n+1}-1$ points $E_{i_0...i_k}$ which are the unique intersection of the S_{n-k} determined by the points $A_{i_{k+1}}, ..., A_{i_n}, E$ with the S_k determined by the points $A_{i_0}, ..., A_{i_k}$. The point $E_{i_0...i_k}$ does not lie in any face of the simplex $A_{i_0}, ..., A_{i_k}$ of S_k. Also, $E_i = A_i$, and $E_{0...n} = E$.

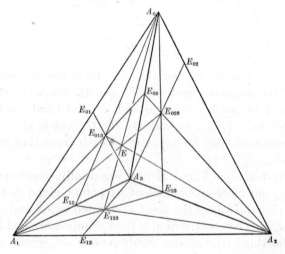

Fig. 27.

We now construct a further set of $\frac{1}{2}n(n+1)$ points F_{ij} $(i, j = 0, ..., n; i \neq j)$. Since A_i and A_j are distinct, and E_{ij} is distinct from each of these points, the harmonic conjugate of E_{ij} with respect to A_i and A_j is uniquely determined. It is always different from A_i

and A_j, and coincides with E_{ij} if and only if we are in the *special case* mentioned in §4. We denote this harmonic conjugate by $F_{ij} = F_{ji}$.

To construct F_{ij} consider the plane $A_i A_j A_k$ through $A_i A_j$, and in this draw $A_i E_{jk}$, $A_j A_k$, $E_{ij} A_k$ through A_i, A_j, E_{ij} respectively. These lines form the triangle $A_k E_{ijk} E_{jk}$. Since $A_i A_k$ and $A_j E_{ijk}$ meet in E_{ik}, it follows that $E_{ik} E_{jk}$ passes through $(A_i A_j)/E_{ij}$, that is, through F_{ij}. This is true for all values of k.

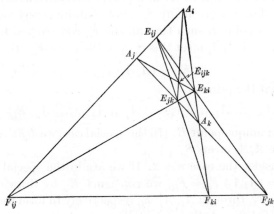

Fig. 28.

Suppose, first, that we are not in the special case. Then E_{ij}, E_{jk}, E_{ki} are not collinear. The triangles $A_i A_j A_k$, $E_{jk} E_{ki} E_{ij}$ are in perspective from E_{ijk}. Hence the intersections of corresponding sides are collinear; that is, F_{jk}, F_{ki}, F_{ij} are collinear. If we are in the special case, E_{ij}, E_{jk}, E_{ki} are collinear, and so $F_{ij} = E_{ij}$, $F_{jk} = E_{jk}$ and $F_{ki} = E_{ki}$ are again collinear.

We now prove that the $\frac{1}{2}n(n+1)$ points F_{ij} all lie in an S_{n-1}. This result has just been proved when $n = 2$, and we prove the theorem by induction on n. We suppose that the theorem is true for the configuration in Σ^0, the face opposite the vertex A_0. That is, we assume that the points F_{ij} $(i, j = 1, ..., n)$ lie in an S_{n-2}. If all the points F_{0i} lie in this S_{n-2} the result is evident. Suppose that F_{01} is not in this S_{n-2}. Then F_{01} and S_{n-2} determine a prime, S_{n-1} say. Consider the point F_{0i}. Since the points F_{0i}, F_{01}, F_{1i} are collinear, and F_{01}, F_{1i} are in S_{n-1} and are distinct, the point F_{0i} lies in S_{n-1} also, and the theorem is proved.

It is easily seen that the points F_{ij} cannot all lie in an S_k ($k < n-1$). For if they do, and A_0 is a vertex of the simplex which does not lie in this S_k, the vertex A_0 and S_k determine an S_{k+1}. This S_{k+1} contains A_0 and F_{0i}, which is distinct from A_0. Hence S_{k+1} contains the line $A_0 A_i$, and in particular it contains A_i. Therefore S_{k+1} $(k+1 < n)$ contains the set $A_0, ..., A_n$, contradicting our assumption that these points are linearly independent. The above results still hold in the special case.

The points $E_{i_0 ... i_k}$ were constructed by means of the vertices $A_0, ..., A_n$ and the point E. We now prove, as a converse to the above result, that if we are given any S_{n-1} not containing any vertices A_i, we can find a point E such that all the F_{ij} constructed from E lie in this S_{n-1}. Let $A_i A_j$ meet this S_{n-1} in the point F_{ij}. If

$$E_{ij} = (A_i A_j)/F_{ij},$$

we show that the primes

$$A_0, ..., A_{i-1}, A_{i+1}, ..., A_{j-1}, A_{j+1}, ..., A_n, E_{ij}$$

all meet in a unique point E. (In the special case we *define* E_{ij} as the point where $A_i A_j$ meets S_{n-1}.)

First consider the case $n = 2$. If we are in the special case, for which $E_{ij} = (A_i A_j)/F_{ij} = F_{ij}$, we construct E_{ij} by drawing $A_i A_k$, $A_j A_k$, $F_{ij} F_{jk} F_{ki}$ through A_i, A_j, F_{ij} respectively to form the triangle $A_k F_{ki} F_{jk}$. If $A_i F_{kj}$, $A_j F_{ki}$ meet in E_{ijk} then $A_k E_{ijk}$ passes through $(A_i A_j)/F_{ij} = E_{ij}$. Since $F_{ki} = E_{ki}$, $F_{kj} = E_{kj}$, E_{ijk} clearly satisfies the requirements of our theorem. If we are not in the special case, $E_{ij} \neq F_{ij}$, and we have

$$A_k = (E_{ik} F_{ik})/A_i, \quad A_k = (E_{jk} F_{jk})/A_j.$$

Hence it follows that the lines $A_i A_j$, $E_{ik} E_{jk}$, $F_{ik} F_{jk}$ are concurrent, that is, $E_{ik} E_{jk}$ passes through F_{ij}. Consider the triangles $A_i A_j A_k$, $E_{jk} E_{ki} E_{ij}$. Corresponding sides meet in the collinear points F_{jk}, F_{ki}, F_{ij}. Hence, by the converse of Desargues' Theorem the triangles are in perspective from a point E_{ijk}, and this point satisfies the requirements of the theorem. It is easily verified that if E_{ijk} lay on any side of the triangle $A_i A_j A_k$, the line $F_{jk} F_{ki} F_{ij}$ would contain a vertex of the triangle, contrary to hypothesis.

We now suppose that the theorem is true for each face Σ^i and construct the points $E_{0...i-1 i+1...n}$. If $i \neq j$, the lines $A_j E_{0...i-1 i+1...n}$ and $A_i E_{0...j-1 j+1...n}$ have the point $E_{0...i-1 i+1...j-1 j+1...n}$ in common. Hence the lines $A_i E_{0...i-1 i+1...n}$ and $A_j E_{0...j-1 j+1...n}$ intersect. This is true for all values of i and j. Since all these lines cannot lie in a plane they must all pass through a point E. This point does not lie in any of the Σ^i, and from E and the vertices $A_0, ..., A_n$ we return to the points F_{ij}, if we carry out the constructions given at the beginning of the section.

The configuration discussed above will be called a *system of reference* in the space.

We have seen [§ 3, Th. I] that a projectivity can be established between two ranges on lines l, l' so that three distinct assigned points on l correspond to three distinct assigned points on l'. We also saw, later on, that this theorem cannot be extended to any four pairs of corresponding points. But we do not know, as yet, whether the projectivity is *uniquely* determined by the assignment of three pairs of corresponding points.

We may therefore establish a correspondence between ranges on any two lines $A_i A_j$ and $A_h A_k$ of our reference system so that A_i, A_j, E_{ij} correspond to A_h, A_k, E_{hk} respectively. We wish to do this, however, in such a way that if $A_i A_j$, $A_h A_k$ and $A_l A_m$ are three lines between which such correspondences are established, and P_{ij} corresponds to P_{hk}, and also P_{hk} corresponds to P_{lm}, then P_{ij} also corresponds to P_{lm} (P_{ij}, P_{hk}, P_{lm} being, of course, points on $A_i A_j$, $A_h A_k$ and $A_l A_m$ respectively). We do this as follows.

Let T^i_{jk} denote the operation of projecting $A_i A_j$ into $A_i A_k$ from the vertex F_{jk}, which is E_{jk} in the special case. The result of following the projection T^i_{jk} by the projection T^i_{kl} or by the projection T^k_{il} will be denoted by $T^i_{jk} T^i_{kl}$, or by $T^i_{jk} T^k_{il}$, respectively. We note that $T^i_{jk} T^a_{bc}$ is not defined unless

$$(i, k) = (a, b) \quad \text{or} \quad (i, k) = (b, a).$$

Since the operation $T^i_{jk} T^i_{kj}$ consists of projecting $A_i A_j$ into $A_i A_k$ and back again, we write $T^i_{jk} T^i_{kj} = 1$, where, as is usual, 1 denotes the identical transformation.

Now, we can pass from the points (A_i, A_j, E_{ij}) to the points (A_h, A_k, E_{hk}) by a series of projections T^a_{bc}, and we wish to show that *the correspondence between the ranges does not depend on the series of projections chosen*. We first consider the transformation between points on $A_i A_j$ given by

(i) $T^i_{jk} T^k_{ij} T^i_{ki} = H_{ij}$. Let P_{ij} be any point on $A_i A_j$, and let $F_{jk} P_{ij}$ meet $A_i A_k$ in P_{ki}; let $F_{ij} P_{ki}$ meet $A_j A_k$ in P_{jk}; and let $F_{ik} P_{jk}$ meet $A_i A_j$ in P'_{ij}. H_{ij} is a transformation of the points of $A_i A_j$ into points of $A_i A_j$, and we see at once that $H_{ij} A_i = A_j$, and $H_{ij} A_j = A_i$; also $H_{ij} E_{ij} = E_{ij}$ and $H_{ij} F_{ij} = F_{ij}$. We now consider the case of any other point P_{ij} of $A_i A_j$. It is verified at once that $P_{ij}, P_{ki}, P_{jk}, P'_{ij}$ are then all distinct.

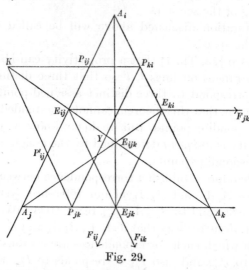

Fig. 29.

Let $P_{ki} P_{ij}$ meet $P_{jk} P'_{ij}$ in K. We first prove that $A_k K$ passes through E_{ij}. We may construct the harmonic conjugate of F_{ij} with respect to A_i, A_j by taking the lines $A_i A_k$, $A_j A_k$, $F_{ij} P_{ki} P_{jk}$ through A_i, A_j, F_{ij}. It follows that $A_i P_{jk}$ and $A_j P_{ki}$ meet on the line joining A_k to $(A_i, A_j)/F_{ij}$, that is, to E_{ij}. Now consider the triangles $A_i A_j A_k$ and $P_{jk} P_{ki} K$ (which are proper triangles, even in the special case). Corresponding sides meet in F_{jk}, F_{ki}, F_{ij}, and hence, by the converse of Desargues' Theorem, $A_i P_{jk}$ and $A_j P_{ki}$ meet on $A_k K$, which is therefore the same as $A_k E_{ij}$.

The triangles $E_{ik} E_{jk} A_k$ and $P'_{ij} P_{ij} K$ are in perspective, since corresponding sides intersect in the collinear points F_{jk}, F_{ki}, F_{ij}. Hence $E_{ik} P'_{ij}$ and $E_{jk} P_{ij}$ meet on $K A_k = E_{ij} A_k$. Also, the triangles $E_{ik} E_{jk} A_k$ and $P_{ij} P'_{ij} K$ are in perspective, since corresponding sides meet in P_{jk}, P_{ki}, F_{ij}, and hence $E_{ik} P_{ij}$ meets $E_{jk} P'_{ij}$ on $K A_k = E_{ij} A_k$. From these results we deduce a simple construction for the transformation H_{ij}: let the join of P_{ij} to E_{jk} meet $A_k E_{ij}$ in Q; then $E_{ik} Q$ meets A_{ij} in P'_{ij}. We also deduce the following properties of H_{ij}:

$$(a) \quad H_{ij} = H_{ji};$$
$$(b) \quad (H_{ij})^2 = 1.$$

Further, we have

$$T^i_{jk} H_{ik} = T^i_{jk} H_{ki} = T^i_{jk} T^k_{ij} T^i_{ki} T^i_{jk} = H_{ij} T^i_{jk},$$

that is,

$$(c) \quad T^i_{jk} H_{ik} = H_{ij} T^i_{jk}.$$

Finally, if A_h is any other vertex distinct from A_i, A_j, A_k, and the plane $A_iA_jA_k$ is projected from the point F_{hk} on to the plane $A_iA_jA_h$, the points $A_i, A_j, A_k, P_{ij}, F_{jk}, F_{ij}, F_{ik}$ project, respectively, into the points, $A_i, A_j, A_h, P_{ij}, F_{jh}, F_{ij}, F_{ih}$. Hence the configuration of lines in $A_iA_jA_k$ which determines the transformation H_{ij} is projected into the configuration of lines in $A_iA_jA_h$ which determines the transformation in that plane. Since P'_{ij} is projected into P'_{ij}, the transformation H_{ij} is independent of the third vertex A_k by which it is defined.

We may note, in passing, that if we are not in the special case, so that $E_{ij} \neq F_{ij}$, P'_{ij} can also be defined as $(E_{ij}, F_{ij})/P_{ij}$.

A second type of transformation is $T^i_{jk}T^i_{kh}$. We prove that

(ii) $T^i_{jk}T^i_{kh} = T^i_{jh}$. Let $T^i_{jk}(P_{ij}) = P_{ik}$, and $T^i_{kh}(P_{ik}) = P_{ih}$. We wish to prove that $T^i_{jh}(P_{ij}) = P_{ih}$. We assume that $P_{ij} \neq E_{ij}$, since in that case the result is trivial. Now, the triangles $P_{ij}P_{ik}P_{ih}$ and $E_{ij}E_{ik}E_{ih}$ are in perspective from A_i. Hence corresponding sides meet in collinear points. Two of these points are F_{jk}, F_{kh}. Hence $F_{jk}F_{kh}$ passes through the intersection of $P_{ij}P_{ih}$ and $E_{ij}E_{ih}$. But $E_{ij}E_{ih}$ and $F_{jk}F_{kh}$ meet only in F_{jh}. Therefore $P_{ij}P_{ih}$ passes through F_{jh}. That is

$$T^i_{jh}(P_{ij}) = P_{ih}.$$

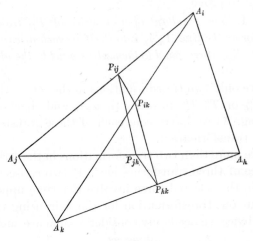

Fig. 30.

Finally, if i, j, h, k are all different, we prove that

(iii) $T^i_{jk}T^k_{ih} = T^i_{ih}T^h_{jk}$. Both transformations in question take ranges on A_iA_j into ranges on A_hA_k so that the points A_i, E_{ij}, A_j

are transformed into the points A_h, E_{hk}, A_k respectively. Let P_{ij} be any other point of $A_i A_j$, and let

$$T^i_{jk}(P_{ij}) = P_{ik}, \quad T^k_{ih}(P_{ik}) = P_{hk}.$$

If $T^j_{ih}(P_{ij}) = P_{jh}$, we wish to prove that $T^h_{jk}(P_{jh}) = P_{hk}$.

Now, $P_{ij}P_{jh}$ passes through F_{ih}, and $P_{ik}P_{hk}$ passes through F_{ih}. Hence these two lines (which are distinct if $P_{ij} \neq A_i$, as we have supposed) lie in a plane. Therefore $P_{ij}P_{ik}$ and $P_{jh}P_{hk}$ meet. Since one of these lines lies in the plane $A_i A_j A_k$, and the other in $A_h A_j A_k$, they can only meet on the line of intersection, which is given by $A_j A_k$. But since $P_{ij} \neq A_j$ the line $P_{ij}P_{ik}$ meets $A_j A_k$ only in F_{jk}. Hence $P_{jh}P_{hk}$ passes through F_{jk}. That is, $T^h_{jk}(P_{jh}) = P_{hk}$.

We use these three types of transformation to prove the main theorem of this section. Consider two series of T^i_{jk} transformations which transform a range on $A_p A_q$ into a range on $A_r A_s$ so that A_p, E_{pq}, A_q transform into A_r, E_{rs}, A_s respectively. We wish to prove that the resultant projectivities are identical. Let one series of transformations be

$$T^p_{ql} T^l_{mn} \ldots$$

and the other

$$T^p_{ql'} T^{l'}_{m'n'} \ldots.$$

Since

$$(T^p_{ql'} T^{l'}_{m'n'} \ldots)^{-1} = (\ldots T^{l'}_{n'm'} T^p_{l'q})$$

it is sufficient to prove

THEOREM I. *The resultant of any series of T^i_{jk} transformations which transforms the line $A_a A_b$ into itself in such a way that A_a, A_b (and therefore E_{ab}) correspond to themselves must be the identity transformation.*

If there are only two transformations in the series, they must be either $T^a_{bc} T^a_{cb}$ or $T^b_{ac} T^b_{ca}$ in order that A_a and A_b should be self-corresponding. As we have seen, each of these transformations is the identity transformation.

If there are more than two transformations in the series, consider any sequence of three transformations. If two consecutive transformations in the selected three involve the same upper index we can substitute one transformation for the pair, using the result of (ii) above. Hence we need only consider a sequence such as

$$T^i_{jk} T^k_{il} T^l_{km},$$

and consider the various possibilities.

(a) $l = j$, $m = i$. By (i) above the sequence can be replaced by H_{ij}. If this is preceded by any transformation of the series, this transformation must be either $T^i_{\cdot j}$ or $T^j_{\cdot i}$. In either case we may use the result of (i) (c) to move the H_{ij} transformation towards the head of the series of transformations. When it reaches this position it must be an H_{ab} transformation.

(b) $l = j$, $m \neq i$. Then

$$T^i_{jk} T^k_{ij} T^j_{km} = T^i_{jk} T^i_{km} T^m_{ij} \quad \text{(by (iii))}$$
$$= T^i_{jm} T^m_{ij} \quad \text{(by (ii))}.$$

(c) If $l \neq j$, we have, similarly,

$$T^i_{jk} T^k_{il} T^l_{km} = T^j_{il} T^l_{jk} T^l_{km} \quad \text{(by (iii))}$$
$$= T^j_{il} T^l_{jm}, \quad \text{(by (ii))}.$$

Hence, in all three cases, we can reduce the number of transformations in the sequence. Finally, the whole series of transformations must be reducible to one of the following forms:

$$(H_{ab})^\sigma, \quad (H_{ab})^\sigma T^a_{bc}, \quad (H_{ab})^\sigma T^a_{bc} T^c_{ab} \quad (\sigma = 0 \text{ or } 1).$$

Only the first of these transformations transforms A_a into A_a and A_b into A_b, and then only when $\sigma = 0$. Hence we can reduce the series of transformations to the identity transformation, and the theorem is proved.

This theorem enables us to establish a unique projectivity between ranges on any two lines $A_a A_b$ and $A_i A_j$, in which A_a, E_{ab}, A_b correspond respectively to A_i, E_{ij}, A_j. Such a projectivity will be used later and we shall denote it by T^{ab}_{ij}. Then $T^{ab}_{ab} = 1$, and $T^{ab}_{ba} = H_{ab}$.

7. The algebra of points on a line. In §5 we discussed two projectively invariant constructions. We now use these to construct a *field*, which will be used in a later section to introduce coordinates into our space.

The constructions depend on the choice of three distinct points O, E, U on a line l. We call the process of choosing these points the establishing of a *scale* on l. Our constructions determine points on l from any two points A, B, neither of which coincides with U. The points determined are always distinct from U. We have, therefore, two laws of composition for the points of l other than U. We consider these laws of composition separately.

Construction I is symmetric in A and B, and we denote the derived point T by $A + B$. We show that this law of addition is *associative*.

Let A, B, C be three points on l. The result is evident if any one of these points is at O, so we confine ourselves to the case in which they are all distinct from O. Perform the usual construction for

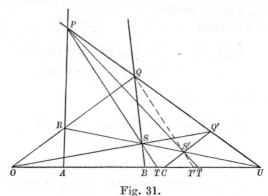

Fig. 31.

$T = A + B$, using the notation of §5. To construct $T + C$ we draw TSP through T and let OS meet UQ in Q', which is necessarily distinct from S. If CQ' meets US in S', then PS' meets l in $\bar{T}$, where

$$T + C = \bar{T}.$$

Using the same figure, QS' meets l in $T' = B + C$. We construct $A + T'$ by means of the lines ARP, $T'S'Q$, and ORQ. Then PS' meets l in $A + T'$. But this is $\bar{T}$. Hence

$$A + (B + C) = (A + B) + C.$$

We have already seen that if A is any point on l distinct from U,

$$A + O = A.$$

We show now that given any two points A, B of l (distinct from U), there is a point X of l, also distinct from U, such that

$$A + X = B.$$

It is sufficient to show that there is a point Y such that

$$A + Y = O.$$

For if Y has this property, the point

$$X = Y + B$$

satisfies our requirements. Let A' be the point $(O, U)/A$. Then, in the usual construction for harmonic conjugate, as in Fig. 32, the lines ARS, $A'PQ$ are drawn through A and A', and ORQ meets them in R, Q respectively. Also, UQ, UR meet them in S, P respectively, and PS meets l in $A + A'$. Hence

$$A + A' = O,$$

and A' is the required point Y. Since $A + Y = O$, we shall usually

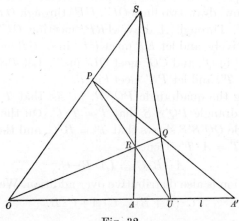

Fig. 32.

denote the point Y by $-A$, and write $B - A$ for $B + (-A)$. We have proved

THEOREM I. *The points of the line l other than U form a commutative group under the addition law.*

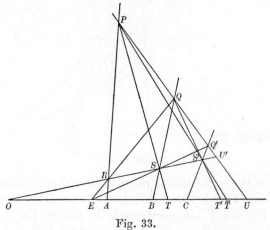

Fig. 33.

We now consider Construction II of §5, which also gives us a law of composition for the points of l other than U. We regard this as a *multiplication*, and write $T = A \cdot B$. Let us prove that multiplication is associative. It is easily verified that

$$A \cdot (B \cdot C) = (A \cdot B) \cdot C$$

if any one of the points A, B, C coincides with O or E, and we therefore suppose that none of the points A, B, C coincides with O or with E. Now, draw two lines OU', UU' through O and U, intersecting in U'. Through A draw ARP, meeting OU', UU' in R and P respectively, and let ER meet UU' in Q, QB meet OU' in S, ES meet UU' in Q', and CQ' meet OU' in S'. Let PS meet l in T, QS' meet l in T', and let PS' meet l in $\bar{T}$.

Considering the quadrangle $PQSR$, we see that $T = A \cdot B$, and from the quadrangle $PQ'S'S$ that $\bar{T} = T \cdot C$. On the other hand, the quadrangle $QQ'S'S$ shows that $T' = B \cdot C$, and the quadrangle $PQS'R$ that $\bar{T} = A \cdot T'$. Hence

$$A \cdot (B \cdot C) = (A \cdot B) \cdot C.$$

Multiplication is also distributive over addition. We prove that

$$C \cdot (A + B) = C \cdot A + C \cdot B.$$

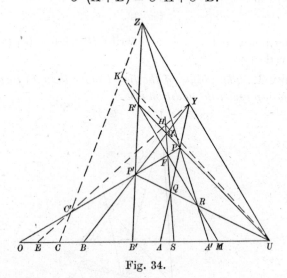

Fig. 34.

In a plane through l take a point Z, and then a point Y on the line ZU. Join YB, YA and ZC. Let YE meet ZC in C', and let OC' meet YB and YA respectively in P' and P. Let ZP' and ZP respectively meet OU in B' and A', and let UP and UP' meet ZP' and ZP respectively in R' and R, these same lines meeting YP' and YP respectively in Q' and Q.

Since corresponding sides of the triangles PQR, $P'Q'R'$ meet in the collinear points U, Z, Y, the converse of Desargues' Theorem shows that QQ' passes through the intersection F of PP' and RR'. Also, if $C'Y$, $C'Z$ meet QQ' and RR' respectively in H and K, then since corresponding sides of the triangles YHQ' and ZKR' meet in the collinear points F, P', C', it follows that KH passes through the intersection U of YZ and $Q'R'$.

We can now prove our theorem. Denoting the intersections of QQ' and RR' respectively with l by S and M, the quadrangle $QPQ'P'$ shows that $S = A + B$, and the quadrangle $C'FHK$ that $M = C \cdot S = C \cdot (A + B)$. On the other hand, consideration of the quadrangles $C'PYZ$, $C'P'YZ$ and $P'RPR'$ respectively tells us that $A' = C \cdot A$, $B' = C \cdot B$ and $M = A' + B'$ respectively. We have therefore shown that

$$C \cdot (A + B) = C \cdot A + C \cdot B.$$

In a similar fashion it may be proved that

$$(A + B) \cdot C = A \cdot C + B \cdot C.$$

We have already noted in § 5 that

$$A \cdot E = A = E \cdot A.$$

Hence the point E acts as *unity* under multiplication. Finally, if A is any point on l distinct from O (and U) we can construct an inverse A^* such that

$$A \cdot A^* = E = A^* \cdot A.$$

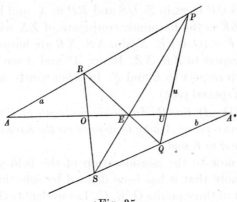

Fig. 35.

The construction of A^* is evident from the diagram, as is the proof of the properties of A^*.

These results show that the set of points on l, excluding U, can have two laws of composition associated with them, one a law of addition, the other a multiplication law, and that under these laws the points form a *field*. In this field O is the zero, E the unity. We sum these results in

THEOREM II. *Under the two laws of composition defined by Constructions I and II the points of the line l other than U form a field.*

Before passing on it is convenient to prove here a result, which we shall use later, concerning the construction of the inverse $A*$ of A.

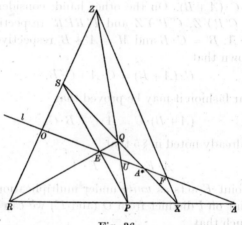

Fig. 36.

Let RS and QP meet in Z, QS and RP in X, and let ZX meet l in F. Since ZE is the harmonic conjugate of ZX with respect to ZP and ZR, $F = (O, U)/E$. Again, XS, XR are harmonically conjugate with respect to XE, XZ. Hence $A*$ and A are harmonically conjugate with respect to E and F. In other words, we have (if we are not in the special case)

THEOREM III. *If F is the harmonic conjugate of E with respect to O and U, the inverse of A may be defined as the harmonic conjugate of A with respect to E and F.*

Returning now to the consideration of the field we have constructed, we note that it has been defined by selecting on a line l an ordered set of three points O, E, U. Let us denote the field which is then defined by $K(O, E, U)$. If O', E', U' be any other ordered set of points on a line l', we may similarly construct a field $K(O', E', U')$. Now, there is a projectivity which relates a range on

l to a range on l', O, E, U corresponding to O', E', U' respectively. If points P, Q, ... of the first range (other than U) correspond to points P', Q', ... of the second range, then $P + Q$ corresponds to $P' + Q'$, and $P \cdot Q$ corresponds to $P' \cdot Q'$. For we have proved that Constructions I and II yield projectively invariant points. Hence, there is a one-to-one correspondence between the elements of the fields $K(O, E, U)$ and $K(O', E', U')$ which is, in fact, an *isomorphism*.

In particular, there is a projectivity which transforms l into itself, O, E, U being self-corresponding points. This defines an automorphism of $K(O, E, U)$ which is the identical correspondence only if the projectivity is the identical projectivity.

Since all the fields we can construct by establishing a scale on any line l in S_n are isomorphic, we can call any field isomorphic with them *the field of the geometry*. There is, of course, another field, for which addition is defined, as above, by Construction I, and multiplication by interchanging the roles of A and B in Construction II. This second field is the *skew-isomorph* [V, § 1] of the field of the geometry.

8. The representation of the incidence space as a $P_n^r(K)$.

We are now in a position to introduce coordinate systems into our space S_n. We first choose a reference system [§ 6], and use the notation already introduced. On any line $A_i A_j$ there are three points A_i, A_j, E_{ij}. We choose these as O, U, E, and define, as in the preceding section, a field by means of these points. All the fields obtained in this way are isomorphic, and the transformations T_{cd}^{ab} defined in § 6 establish, in a unique fashion, an isomorphism between the fields $K(A_a, E_{ab}, A_b)$ and $K(A_c, E_{cd}, A_d)$.

This means that if K denotes the field of our geometry, we have established without ambiguity, for every choice of a, b, a correspondence between the points of $A_a A_b$ (other than A_b) and the elements of K in which A_a corresponds to zero. The element of K which corresponds to the point P on $A_a A_b$ will be called *the coordinate of P in the scale* (A_a, E_{ab}, A_b); or more briefly, when there is no risk of ambiguity, *the coordinate of P*. The coordinate of E_{ab} is always 1.

If P is distinct from both A_a and A_b, and α is the coordinate of P in the scale (A_a, E_{ab}, A_b), the coordinate α^* of P in the scale (A_b, E_{ba}, A_a) is found as follows, when we are not in the special case.

The transformation T_{ba}^{ab} takes P into P^*, where P and P^* are harmonically conjugate with respect to E_{ab} and F_{ab} [§6], and of course this transformation takes P^* into P. But [§7, Th. III], if P and P^* are harmonically conjugate with respect to E_{ab} and F_{ab}, the corresponding elements of K are inverses. Since the coordinate of P^* in the scale (A_a, E_{ab}, A_b) is the coordinate of P in the scale (A_b, E_{ba}, A_a), the coordinate of P in this last scale is $\alpha^* = \alpha^{-1}$. Hence

THEOREM I. *If P is any point of $A_a A_b$ distinct from A_a and A_b, and α, α^* are its coordinates in the respective scales (A_a, E_{ab}, A_b) and (A_b, E_{ba}, A_a), then $\alpha\alpha^* = 1$.*

This theorem is also true in the special case, which has been excepted from the foregoing proof. To see this we first note that in the special case the configuration of Fig. 36 has the following properties: P, E, S are collinear points, and lie on the sides of the triangle OZU, therefore OP, ZE, US are concurrent. Let the point of concurrence be T. Also, Z, E, X are collinear. Now identify this configuration with that of Fig. 29, identifying O, U, Z, T with A_i, A_j, A_k, E_{ijk} respectively. Then E, P, S are identified with E_{ij}, E_{jk}, E_{ki} respectively. We saw in §6 that if P_{ij} is any point on $A_i A_j$, the point P'_{ij} which corresponds to P_{ij} in the transformation H_{ij} which makes A_i, E_{ij}, A_j correspond to A_j, E_{ji}, A_i respectively is obtained thus: $E_{jk}P_{ij}$ meets $E_{ik}P'_{ij}$ on $A_k E_{ij}$. Now, returning to Fig. 36, with the above identification, the point A' corresponding to A is constructed as follows: let AP meet ZE in X, then XS meets l in A'. But this shows that $A^* = A'$. Hence it follows that Theorem I remains true in the special case.

We now consider any point P of the given space, and we suppose, in the first instance, that P is not in any face of the simplex $A_0, ..., A_n$. If we use P as we used E in the constructions of §6 we obtain a series of points

$$P_i, \ P_{ij}, \ P_{ijk}, \ ...,$$

where $P_{i_0...i_k}$ lies in the space of k dimensions determined by $A_{i_0}, ..., A_{i_k}$, but not in any face of the simplex formed by these $k+1$ points. Since $P_{ij} = P_{ji}$ is on $A_i A_j$ and distinct from both A_i and A_j, it has a coordinate in each of the scales (A_i, E_{ij}, A_j) and (A_j, E_{ji}, A_i). Let these coordinates be p_{ji} and p_{ij} respectively. Then, by the above theorem,

$$p_{ij}p_{ji} = 1.$$

THEOREM II.* *If i, j, k are all distinct,*

$$p_{ik}p_{kj}p_{ji} = 1.$$

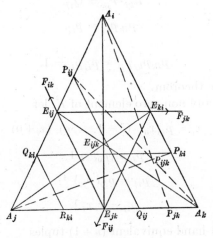

Fig. 37.

Let $F_{jk}P_{ki}$ meet A_iA_j in Q_{ki}, and let $F_{ki}Q_{ki}$ meet A_jA_k in R_{ki}. Clearly $T_{jk}^{ki}P_{ki} = R_{ki}$, and therefore the coordinate of R_{ki} in the scale (A_j, E_{jk}, A_k) is p_{ik}. Similarly, if $P_{ij}F_{ki}$ meets A_jA_k in Q_{ij}, then $T_{jk}^{ji}P_{ij} = Q_{ij}$, and the coordinate of Q_{ij} in the scale (A_j, E_{jk}, A_k) is p_{ij}.

With these preliminary remarks we prove the

Lemma. $Q_{ki}E_{jk}$ *intersects* $P_{ij}P_{jk}$ *on* A_iA_k.

The harmonic conjugate E_{jk} of F_{jk} with respect to A_j and A_k can be constructed by drawing the lines A_jA_i, A_kA_i and $F_{jk}Q_{ki}P_{ki}$. Hence A_jP_{ki} and A_kQ_{ki} intersect in a point X of A_iE_{jk}.

Now consider the triangles $E_{jk}P_{jk}A_i$ and $Q_{ki}P_{ij}A_k$. Corresponding sides intersect at the points P_{ijk}, X, A_j. These points are collinear, and the triangles are therefore in perspective. The vertex of perspective Y lies on A_iA_k, and is the intersection of $Q_{ki}E_{jk}$ and $P_{ij}P_{jk}$. This proves the lemma.

We now take (A_j, E_{jk}, A_k) as our scale on A_jA_k, and construct the product $R_{ki} \cdot P_{jk}$, as in Construction II. We use the quadrangle $F_{ki}YQ_{ki}P_{ij}$. The line A_jA_k meets the pairs of opposite sides of this

---

* We are indebted to Mr G. Kreisel of Trinity College, Cambridge, for assistance with the proofs of Theorems II and III, which do not involve the assumption of Pappus' Theorem.

quadrangle in the pairs of points A_j, A_k; R_{ki}, P_{jk}; and E_{jk}, Q_{ij}; and we find that consequently

$$R_{ki} \cdot P_{jk} = Q_{ij}.$$

Therefore $\qquad\qquad p_{ik} p_{kj} = p_{ij},$

or, by Th. I,

$$p_{ik} p_{kj} p_{ji} = p_{ij} p_{ji} = 1.$$

This proves the theorem.

Now, if x_0 is any non-zero element of K, let

$$x_i = p_{i0} x_0 \quad (i = 1, ..., n), \ (x_i \neq 0).$$

Then, since $\qquad\qquad p_{ij} p_{j0} p_{0i} = 1,$

that is, $\qquad\qquad p_{ij} = p_{i0} (p_{j0})^{-1},$

we see that $\qquad\qquad p_{ij} = x_i x_j^{-1}.$

The set of right-hand equivalent $(n+1)$-tuples

$$(x_0, x_1, ..., x_n)$$

determined by different x_0's are the *coordinates* of P with regard to the given reference system.

We now suppose that P lies in the space defined by $A_{i_0}, ..., A_{i_k}$, but does not lie in any face of the k-simplex defined by these points. If we complete the reference system in this space by means of the point $E_{i_0 ... i_k}$, we obtain, as above, a set of equivalent $(k+1)$-tuples $(x_{i_0}, ..., x_{i_k})$ as coordinates of P with respect to the system of reference in the k-space. The coordinates $(y_0, ..., y_n)$ of P with regard to the system of reference in S_n are defined as follows:

$$y_i = x_i \quad (i = i_0, ..., i_k),$$
$$y_i = 0 \quad (i \neq i_0, ..., i_k).$$

We see that this definition is consistent with our definition of the coordinates of P when P does not lie in any face of the simplex $A_0, ..., A_n$. In fact, if the coordinates of any point P are $(y_0, ..., y_n)$, a necessary and sufficient condition that $y_i = 0$ is that, for each $j \neq i$, the space defined by the set of points

$$A_0, ..., A_{i-1}, A_{i+1}, ..., A_{j-1}, A_{j+1}, ..., A_n, P$$

intersects the line $A_i A_j$ at the point A_j, or that this set is linearly dependent. For the intersection is the point P_{ij}, and in the scale (A_j, E_{ij}, A_i) the coordinate of P_{ij} is $p_{ij} = y_i y_j^{-1}$. If $P_{ij} = A_j$,

$$p_{ij} = y_i y_j^{-1} = 0,$$

and therefore $y_i = 0$. Also, a necessary and sufficient condition that P lies in the space defined by $A_{i_0}, \dots, A_{i_k}$, and not in any face of this simplex, is that the points

$$A_0, \dots, A_{i-1}, A_{i+1}, \dots, A_{j-1}, A_{j+1}, \dots, A_n, P \quad (i \neq i_0, \dots, i_k)$$

are linearly independent and determine a space which intersects $A_i A_j$ in A_j, where j takes the values $(i_0, \dots, i_k)$. Also, if P is not in the space $A_{i_{k+1}} \dots A_{i_n}$ the space $A_{i_{k+1}} \dots A_{i_n} P$ meets the space $A_{i_0} \dots A_{i_k}$ in a point $P_{i_0 \dots i_k}$ whose coordinates are $(z_0, \dots, z_n)$, where
$$z_{i_j} = y_{i_j} \ (j = 0, \dots, k), \quad z_{i_j} = 0 \ (j = k+1, \dots, n).$$

We leave the proofs of these last results to the reader.

We show now that *any set of right-hand equivalent $(n+1)$-tuples corresponds to one and only one point P of the space.*

Let $(x_0, \dots, x_n)$ be any $(n+1)$-tuple of the set. If

$$x_{i_{k+1}} = \dots = x_{i_n} = 0,$$

P must lie in the k-space defined by $A_{i_0}, \dots, A_{i_k}$. We may therefore suppose that no $x_i = 0$.

On $A_0 A_i$ take the scale (A_0, E_{0i}, A_i), and let P_i be the point on this line which has the coordinate $x_i x_0^{-1}$ in this scale. Then, by hypothesis, $P_i \neq A_i$ $(i = 0, \dots, n)$. *The n primes defined by the points $A_1, \dots, A_{i-1}, A_{i+1}, \dots, A_n, P_i$ have a single point P in common.* We prove this by induction on n.

When $n = 2$, the result is trivial, since two lines intersect in a point. We assume that the theorem is true for an S_{n-1}, in particular for that defined by $A_0, \dots, A_{n-1}$. Then the $n-1$ spaces S_{n-1}^i defined by
$$A_1, \dots, A_{i-1}, A_{i+1}, \dots, A_n, P_i \quad (i = 1, \dots, n-1)$$

intersect in a space S_r which, by hypothesis, meets the S_{n-1} defined by $A_0, \dots, A_{n-1}$ in a single point R; for S_{n-1}^i meets the S_{n-1} defined by $A_0, \dots, A_{n-1}$ in the S_{n-2} defined by $A_1, \dots, A_{i-1}, A_{i+1}, \dots, A_{n-1}, P_i$. This point R does not lie in any face of the simplex $A_0, \dots, A_{n-1}$. Again, $A_n R$ does not lie in the S_{n-1}^n defined by $A_1, \dots, A_{n-1}, P_n$. It therefore meets it in a single point, and this is the required point P. It is evident that the coordinates of P are $(x_0, \dots, x_n)$.

The condition for the collinearity of three points is our next subject. We prove

THEOREM III. *A necessary and sufficient condition that the points* $P = (x_0, ..., x_n)$, $Q = (y_0, ..., y_n)$ *and* $R = (z_0, ..., z_n)$ *be collinear is that the rank of the matrix*

$$\begin{pmatrix} x_0 & y_0 & z_0 \\ x_1 & y_1 & z_1 \\ \cdot & \cdot & \cdot \\ x_n & y_n & z_n \end{pmatrix} \tag{1}$$

be less than three.

If the rank is one, the three $(n+1)$-tuples given by the columns of this matrix are necessarily equivalent, and the three points P, Q, R coincide. If, conversely, they coincide, the rank is clearly one. We may therefore omit this case.

Similarly, in proving the necessity of the condition, we may omit the case when two of the points coincide.

Since the rank of the matrix is now two, at least, there are at least two linearly independent rows. Without loss of generality we may assume that the first two rows are linearly independent. A necessary and sufficient condition that the matrix is of rank two is that every other row of the matrix is linearly dependent on the first two rows.

(1) We first prove that the condition in the enunciation of Theorem III is necessary. By what we have just said, it is enough to prove that if P, Q, R are distinct collinear points such that the left-hand vectors (x_0, y_0, z_0), (x_1, y_1, z_1) are linearly independent, then any other row of the matrix (1), regarded as a left-hand vector, is linearly dependent on these two. The first step is to show that this simplified form of the hypothesis implies that the line PQR does not meet the space determined by $A_2, ..., A_{i-1}, A_{i+1}, ..., A_n$ $(i \geqslant 2)$. If P, Q, R all lie in this space, then

$$x_0 = x_1 = x_i = 0; \quad y_0 = y_1 = y_i = 0; \quad z_0 = z_1 = z_i = 0,$$

and therefore the first two rows of the matrix (1) consist of zeros, which is contrary to hypothesis. Next, suppose that the line PQR meets the space determined by $A_2, ..., A_{i-1}, A_{i+1}, ..., A_n$ in a single point. Then the S_{n-2} containing this space and the line PQR meets the plane $A_0 A_1 A_i$ in a single point, S, say. If P lies in the space $A_2 ... A_{i-1} A_{i+1} ... A_n$,

$$x_0 = x_1 = x_i = 0,$$

and if it does not, P_{01i} is determinate, and equal to S. A similar argument can be applied to Q and to R. Hence in all cases we have

$$x_j = t_j \lambda, \quad y_j = t_j \mu, \quad z_j = t_j \nu \quad (j = 0, 1, i),$$

where S is $(t_0, t_1, 0, \dots, 0, t_i, 0, \dots, 0)$. Therefore

$$\begin{pmatrix} x_0 & y_0 & z_0 \\ x_1 & y_1 & z_1 \\ x_i & y_i & z_i \end{pmatrix} = \begin{pmatrix} t_0 & 0 & 0 \\ t_1 & 0 & 0 \\ t_i & 0 & 0 \end{pmatrix} \begin{pmatrix} \lambda & \mu & \nu \\ 0 & 0 & 0 \\ 0 & 0 & 0 \end{pmatrix},$$

and is therefore a matrix of rank one. We conclude that the first two rows of the matrix (1) are linearly dependent, which is contrary to hypothesis.

Since the linear independence of (x_0, y_0, z_0) and (x_1, y_1, z_1) has been shown to imply that PQR does not meet the space determined by $A_2, A_3, \dots, A_{i-1}, A_{i+1}, \dots, A_n$, it follows that the collinear points $P_{01i}, Q_{01i}, R_{01i}$ are distinct. To simplify the notation we denote these points by P', Q', R'. We have now to show that the collinearity of these three points implies that the ith row of the matrix (1) is linearly dependent on the first two rows.

If the line $P'Q'R'$ lies on a side of the triangle $A_0 A_1 A_i$,

$$x_j = y_j = z_j = 0 \quad (j = 0, \text{ or } j = 1, \text{ or } j = i),$$

and the matrix

$$\begin{pmatrix} x_0 & y_0 & z_0 \\ x_1 & y_1 & z_1 \\ x_i & y_i & z_i \end{pmatrix} \tag{2}$$

is of rank two. If this is not the case, but $P'Q'R'$ passes through one vertex only of the simplex $A_0 A_1 A_i$, say the vertex A_j, let us first suppose that P', Q', R' are all different from A_j. Then

$$x_h x_k^{-1} = y_h y_k^{-1} = z_h z_k^{-1},$$

where (j, h, k) is some derangement of $(0, 1, i)$; for we obtain the same point on the side $A_k A_h$ if we project P', Q' or R' from A_j. Thus the matrix

$$\begin{pmatrix} x_j x_k^{-1} & y_j y_k^{-1} & z_j z_k^{-1} \\ x_h x_k^{-1} & y_h y_k^{-1} & z_h z_k^{-1} \\ 1 & 1 & 1 \end{pmatrix}$$

has two rows which are linearly dependent, as left-hand vectors;

its rank is therefore less than three. But this matrix is the product

$$\begin{pmatrix} x_j & y_j & z_j \\ x_h & y_h & z_h \\ x_k & y_k & z_k \end{pmatrix} \begin{pmatrix} x_k^{-1} & 0 & 0 \\ 0 & y_k^{-1} & 0 \\ 0 & 0 & z_k^{-1} \end{pmatrix},$$

that is, the product of the matrix (2), with its rows possibly deranged, by a regular matrix. Hence the rank of the matrix (2) must be less than three.

If, on the other hand, $P' = A_j$,

$$\begin{pmatrix} x_j & y_j & z_j \\ x_h & y_h & z_h \\ x_k & y_k & z_k \end{pmatrix} = \begin{pmatrix} 1 & y_j & z_j \\ 0 & y_h & z_h \\ 0 & y_k & z_k \end{pmatrix},$$

where

$$y_h y_k^{-1} = z_h z_k^{-1},$$

and we prove as before that the matrix (2) is of rank two.

We are therefore left with the case in which the line $P'Q'R'$ does not pass through a vertex of $A_0 A_1 A_i$. Let $l' = P'Q'R'$ meet the sides of $A_0 A_1 A_i$ in the points U_0, U_1, U_i, and let X be any point on l'. In the first instance let X be distinct from U_0, U_1 and U_i. Let $A_0 X$

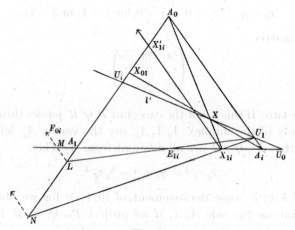

Fig. 38.

meet $A_1 A_i$ in X_{1i}, and $A_i X$ meet $A_0 A_1$ in X_{01}. Let $X_{1i} U_1$ meet $A_0 A_1$ in N, $E_{1i} U_1$ meet $A_0 A_1$ in L, and $F_{0i} L$ meet $A_1 A_i$ in M. Then, in this construction, the points U_0, U_1, U_i, L, M depend only on l', and not on the point X chosen on it.

Taking the scale (A_1, E_{1i}, A_i) on $A_1 A_i$ we construct the product $M \cdot X_{1i}$ as follows. Through M, X_{1i}, E_{1i} we draw the lines MF_{0i}, $X_{1i}U_1$ and $E_{1i}U_1$ respectively. Then, by the usual construction, $F_{0i}N$ meets A_1A_i in the required point $S = M \cdot X_{1i}$. If we denote the elements of the ground field K corresponding to the points Y of A_1A_i by y we have

$$mx_{i1} = s.$$

Passing from A_1A_i to A_1A_0 by the transformation T_{10}^{1i}, it follows that in the scale (A_1, E_{10}, A_0) the product $L \cdot X'_{1i} = N$. If, in the same scale, we construct $N + X_{01}$, using the quadrangle $XU_1A_iX_{1i}$, we see that $N + X_{01} = U_i$. That is

$$mx_{i1} + x_{01} = u_i.$$

It follows, that if X is the point $(\xi_0, \ldots, \xi_n)$,

$$m\xi_i + \xi_0 = u_i\xi_1. \tag{3}$$

We note that this formula holds when X is at U_0, U_1 or U_i. For, if $X = U_0$, $N = U_i$ and $L \cdot X'_{1i} = U_i$, so that $m\xi_i = u_i\xi_1$, and $\xi_0 = 0$. If $X = U_i$, $\xi_i = 0$, and $u_i = x_{01}$. Finally, if $X = U_1$, let $F_{1i}U_1$ meet A_0A_1 in U'_1. Then L and U'_1 are harmonically conjugate with respect to A_0 and A_1. But the elements of K which correspond to L and to U'_1 in the scale (A_1, E_{10}, A_0) are m and $u_1 = x_{0i}$ respectively. Hence $m = -x_{0i}$, and $\xi_1 = 0$, so that once again the formula is satisfied.

Since the formula (3) is true for all points on l', it is true, in particular, when X coincides with P', Q' and R' respectively. The rows of the matrix (2) are therefore linearly dependent, and so once again it is of rank two.

Applying this result for $i = 2, \ldots, n$ we deduce that if P, Q, R are collinear the rows of the matrix

$$\begin{pmatrix} x_0 & y_0 & z_0 \\ x_1 & y_1 & z_1 \\ \cdot & \cdot & \cdot \\ x_n & y_n & z_n \end{pmatrix}$$

are all linearly dependent on the first two rows. The rank of this matrix is therefore two. We have proved the necessity of our theorem, and we now prove its sufficiency.

(2) Let us suppose then that the rank of the matrix is less than three. We must show that P, Q, R are collinear. If the $(n+1)$-tuple defined by any column is equivalent to that defined by any other

column the points P, Q, R are not distinct, and the theorem is trivial. We need only consider, therefore, the cases in which P, Q, R are distinct.

The point $P = (x_0, ..., x_n)$ cannot lie in every face of the simplex. Suppose, for instance, that it does not lie in the face $A_1 ... A_n$. Then $x_0 \neq 0$. A necessary and sufficient condition that P, Q, R are collinear is that PQ and PR meet the face $A_1 ... A_n$ in the same point. If PQ, PR meet this face in Q', R', then by the first part of the theorem, proved above, Q' is linearly dependent on P, Q and satisfies the equation $y_0' = 0$, if we suppose that $Q' = (y_0', ..., y_n')$. Hence, by (1) above,

$$Q' = (0, y_1', ..., y_n') = (0, y_1 - x_1 x_0^{-1} y_0, ..., y_n - x_n x_0^{-1} y_0).$$

Similarly,

$$R' = (0, z_1', ..., z_n') = (0, z_1 - x_1 x_0^{-1} z_0, ..., z_n - x_n x_0^{-1} z_0).$$

Now, the matrix

$$\begin{pmatrix} x_0 & 0 & 0 \\ x_1 & y_1' & z_1' \\ \cdot & \cdot & \\ x_n & y_n' & z_n' \end{pmatrix} = \begin{pmatrix} x_0 & y_0 & z_0 \\ x_1 & y_1 & z_1 \\ \cdot & \cdot & \\ x_n & y_n & z_n \end{pmatrix} \begin{pmatrix} 1 & -x_0^{-1} y_0 & -x_0^{-1} z_0 \\ 0 & 1 & 0 \\ 0 & 0 & 1 \end{pmatrix}$$

is the product of the original matrix by a non-singular matrix, and therefore its rank is equal to that of the original matrix. By hypothesis, this rank is less than three. The columns of the first matrix are therefore linearly dependent. Since $x_0 \neq 0$ this can only be the case if the submatrix

$$\begin{pmatrix} y_1' & z_1' \\ \cdot & \cdot \\ y_n' & z_n' \end{pmatrix}$$

is of rank one, that is, if $Q' = R'$. Therefore P, Q, R are collinear, and both parts of Theorem III are proved.

THEOREM IV. *A necessary and sufficient condition that the points*

$$P_i = (x_{0i}, x_{1i}, ..., x_{ni}) \quad (i = 0, ..., r)$$

be linearly dependent is that the rank of the matrix

$$\begin{pmatrix} x_{00} & \cdot & x_{0r} \\ x_{10} & \cdot & x_{1r} \\ \cdot & \cdot & \cdot \\ x_{n0} & \cdot & x_{nr} \end{pmatrix} \quad (4)$$

be less than $r+1$.

We have proved this theorem when $r = 2$, and we therefore assume that it is true for r points, and use the principle of induction.

(1) *Necessity.* Suppose that the $r + 1$ points are linearly dependent. If any set of r of these points is also linearly dependent then, by the hypothesis of induction, the corresponding columns of the matrix (4) are linearly dependent. The rank of this matrix must then be less than $r + 1$.

If no set of r points is linearly dependent, the first r points of the set of $r + 1$ points determine a space S_{r-1} which contains the remaining point P_r. In this S_{r-1} the points $P_1, \ldots, P_{r-1}$ define an S_{r-2} which is met by the line $P_0 P_r$ in a point R, say. By the induction hypothesis we may write, with the usual symbolic notation [V, § 4],

$$R = \sum_{i=1}^{r-1} P_i \lambda_i,$$

and also $$R = -P_0 \lambda_0 - P_r \lambda_r.$$

Hence, $\sum_0^r P_i \lambda_i = 0$, and this means that the columns of the matrix (4) are linearly dependent, and therefore the rank of (4) is less than $r + 1$.

(2) *Sufficiency.* Let the symbolic relation $\sum_0^r P_i \lambda_i = 0$ express the linear dependence of the columns of the matrix (4). There must be at least two λ_i which are not zero. If there are only two, the corresponding P_i coincide. The theorem is evident if any of the P_i coincide. If more than two λ_i are not zero, say $\lambda_0, \lambda_1, \lambda_2$ are not zero, then the points $P_0 \lambda_0 + P_1 \lambda_1$, $-\sum_2^r P_i \lambda_i$ are coincident. Hence the points P_0, P_1 and $P_2, \ldots, P_r$ define intersecting spaces, and therefore by § 1, (6), p. 210, the points $P_0, P_1, \ldots, P_r$, are linearly dependent.

Just as in Chapter V we deduce that the points of a k-space S_k are precisely those which satisfy $n - k$ linearly independent left-hand linear equations.

We have now proved that an incidence space Σ_n has the property that its points can be put in one-to-one correspondence with the points of a projective number space $PN_n^r(K)$ in such a way that the points of Σ_n lying in an S_a correspond to the points of $PN_n^r(K)$ which satisfy $n - a$ linearly independent left-hand linear equations. Now let

$$y = Ax, \quad x = By \quad (AB = I_{n+1})$$

be a projective transformation of $PN_n^r(K)$. This gives us a new correspondence between the points of Σ_n and the points $(y_0, ..., y_n)$ of $PN_n^r(K)$. A necessary and sufficient condition for the collinearity of three points of Σ_n is still that the corresponding matrix of the y coordinates be of rank less than three, for the rank of a matrix is invariant under a non-singular transformation.

Now let A_i' $(i = 0, ..., n)$ be the points of Σ_n corresponding to those of $PN_n^r(K)$ with coordinates $(\delta_{i0}, ..., \delta_{in})$, and let E' be the point in Σ_n which corresponds to $(1, 1, ..., 1)$ in $PN_n^n(K)$. Then we can construct a new reference system in Σ_n, using $A_0', ..., A_n', E'$ in place of $A_0, ..., A_n, E$. Let P' be any point of Σ_n which is not in any face of the new simplex, and let the corresponding point in $PN_n^r(K)$ (more briefly, its *y-coordinates*) be $(y_0, ..., y_n)$. We show that we can construct a coordinate system for Σ_n, using the methods described above, in which the coordinates of P' are also $(y_0, ..., y_n)$.

First of all it is evident that if the prime

$$A_0' ... A_{i-1}' A_{i+1}' ... A_{j-1}' A_{j+1}' ... A_n' P'$$

meets the line $A_i' A_j'$ in P_{ij}', then the y-coordinates of P_{ij}' are

$$(0, ..., 0, y_i, 0, ..., y_j, 0, ..., 0) = (0, ..., 0, y_i y_j^{-1}, 0, ..., 1, 0, ..., 0).$$

There is, indeed, a one-to-one correspondence between the points of $A_i' A_j'$ (other than A_j') and the field K, given by the y-coordinates of the points, in which A_i' corresponds to 0, and E_{ij}' corresponds to 1. Let us now consider the effect of the fundamental constructions on the points of $A_i' A_j'$, choosing (A_i', E_{ij}', A_j') as the scale. By V, §7, we see that if the points Q, R of the line correspond respectively to the elements q, r of K, the points $Q + R$ and $Q \cdot R$ correspond to the elements $q + r$ and qr of K. Hence we can set up an isomorphism between the field determined by choosing the scale (A_i', E_{ij}', A_j') on $A_i' A_j'$ and the field K.

Now, if the y-coordinates of any point Q' on $A_i' A_j'$ are

$$(0, ..., 0, q, 0, ..., 1, 0, \quad ..., \quad 0),$$

let R' be the point on $A_i' A_k'$ with y-coordinates

$$(0, ..., 0, q, \; 0, ..., 0, ..., \quad 1, ..., 0).$$

Then $Q' R'$ meets $A_j' A_k'$ in the point F_{jk}' with coordinates

$$(0, ..., 0, 0, ..., \quad 1, ..., -1, ..., 0).$$

From these results it follows that if we choose the scale (A_0', E_{01}', A_1')

on one line, $A_0'A_1'$ say, and construct our field as in §7, the isomorphism between the field so constructed and the field K of the geometry can be set up so that the constructed coordinates of P_{01}' are the same as its y-coordinates. We may then use the transformations T_{jk}^i to assign coordinates to points on any edge $A_l'A_m'$ of the simplex of reference, and the constructed coordinates of these points are also the same as their y-coordinates. Hence the constructed coordinates of P' are the y-coordinates of P' for all points P'.

Our method of introducing coordinate systems into Σ_n allows us to establish a one-to-one correspondence between the points of Σ_n and those of a right-hand projective number space $PN_n^r(K)$, and, furthermore, as we have just seen, we can construct a new coordinate system corresponding to each projective transformation in $PN_n^r(K)$. But we cannot say, conversely, that every coordinate system obtained by the methods of this section necessarily arises from the original one by means of a projective transformation of $PN_n^r(K)$.

In fact, let us consider the coordinate system $(x_0, \ldots, x_n)$ constructed at the beginning of this section. This gives, of course, an isomorphism between the points P of A_0A_1 other than A_1 and the elements p of the field of the geometry, in which A_0 and E_{01} correspond to 0 and 1 respectively. There may, however, exist other isomorphisms between the points of A_0A_1 other than A_1 and the elements of K satisfying the same conditions, in which the point P corresponds to the element $\bar{p}$ of K, where $\bar{p}$ is not always the same as p. This isomorphism maps A_0 on the element 0, E_{01} on the element 1, the point $P+Q$ on $\overline{p+q}$, and $P \cdot Q$ on $\overline{pq}$. If we now construct a coordinate system as above, using the T_{jk}^i transformations, we may obtain a coordinate system for the incidence space which is not obtainable from $PN_n^r(K)$ by a projective transformation. For example, if K is the field of complex numbers, and $\bar{p}$ denotes the conjugate complex of p, the coordinates of a point $(x_0, \ldots, x_n)$ are $(\bar{x}_0, \ldots, \bar{x}_n)$ in the new coordinate system. This transformation is not a projectivity, since it transforms the line $x_2 = x_3 = \ldots = x_n = 0$ into itself and every real point of this line is a united point, whereas a projectivity on a line has only a finite number of united points.

Thus the space Σ_n can be represented as a projective space $P_n^r(K)$, and our method of establishing coordinates in Σ_n yields all the allowable coordinate systems of $P_n^r(K)$, but, possibly, other coordinate systems as well.

The reader may ask how, starting from the Propositions of Incidence, in which there is no mention of right or left, we arrive at a right-hand projective space, rather than a left-hand space. In particular, how is it that a left-hand projective space $P_n^l(K)$, which satisfies the Propositions of Incidence, can be represented as a right-hand projective space? The answer lies in our choice of the definition of $A \cdot B$ in § 7. We might have interchanged the parts played by A and B in the construction, and so arrived at the skew-isomorph of the field of the geometry. Using *this* field, we should have obtained a representation of $\varSigma_n$ as a *left*-hand projective space.

9. Restrictions on the geometry. We have shown that a space defined by the Propositions of Incidence can be represented as a projective space, as defined in Chapter V, and have, in fact, shown that the definitions of that chapter are identical with those of our present chapter. For the further development of the properties of a projective space it is now convenient to impose certain further conditions on the space. The imposition of these conditions is equivalent to restrictions being imposed on the field of the geometry.

A. *The field K is to be commutative.* There are several ways in which this condition can be expressed. By V, § 8, we see that an equivalent form of the restriction is to require that Pappus' Theorem is true in the geometry. In our next section we shall discuss alternative forms of the same restriction. In the meantime we prove

THEOREM I. *If Pappus' Theorem holds in an incidence space of two dimensions, then Desargues' Theorem is a true theorem in that space.*

After the discussion in V, § 6, it is sufficient to consider the 'general' case, in which the vertices of the two triangles ABC, $A'B'C'$ and the centre of perspective O are all distinct points. Let the inter-section of corresponding sides of ABC and $A'B'C'$ be P, Q, R.

Let QR cut OB in P', and let AP' meet $A'C'$ in L and OC in M. Also, let LB' cut AB in N. Now consider the two triads of collinear points OAA' and $LB'N$. By Pappus' Theorem ON and $A'L$ intersect on $P'R = QR$. Hence O, Q, N are collinear. Next, consider the triads OMC, ABN. By Pappus' Theorem MN and BC meet on QR. Finally, consider the triads $OMC', LB'N$. By Pappus'

Theorem $B'C'$ and MN meet on QR. Therefore BC and $B'C'$ pass through the point common to MN and QR. That is, Desargues'

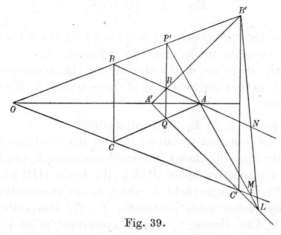

Fig. 39.

Theorem is true. In place of VIII (a) (p. 216), which postulates the truth of Desargues' Theorem for $n = 2$ (in the plane), we substitute a new postulate:

IX. Pappus' Theorem is true.

B. *The field K is to be without characteristic.* Let (O, E, U) be a scale on a line l, and define the set of points $E_1, E_2, \ldots$ (Fig. 40) by the relations
$$E_r = E_{r-1} + E_1, \quad E_1 = E.$$

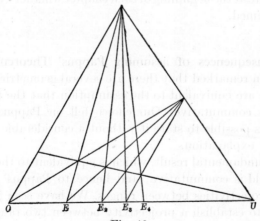

Fig. 40.

If the field is of characteristic p, the points $O, E_1, \ldots, E_{p-1}$ are all distinct, but $E_p = O$.

In particular, if $p = 2$, $E_2 = O$, and therefore $-E = E$. That is,

$$E = -E = (O, U)/E, \tag{1}$$

and we have the *special case* discussed in §4, in which the diagonal points of a complete quadrilateral are collinear.

Conversely, if we are in the special case the relation (1) holds, and $E_2 = O$, so that the field K is of characteristic 2. We now add the postulate

X. The points $E, E_2, E_3, \ldots$ are all distinct.

Finally, we sometimes wish to impose the condition that the field K be algebraically closed. The incidence space Σ_n can be represented as a projective space $P_n(K)$. We know [III, §4, Th. II] that there is a unique field $\bar{K}$ which is the intersection of all algebraically closed fields containing K. We can embed $P_n(K)$ in $P_n(\bar{K})$ [V, §3]. Hence Σ_n can be embedded in an essentially unique space $\bar{\Sigma}_n$ whose field is $\bar{K}$. We call $\bar{\Sigma}_n$ the *algebraic closure* of Σ_n. Our final postulate may then be stated as: *The space Σ_n coincides with its algebraic closure.* More simply we shall usually say

XI. The field of the geometry (or ground field) is algebraically closed.

In the rest of this work we shall always assume Postulates I–X. We shall state at the beginning of each chapter whether Postulate XI is to be assumed.

10. Consequences of assuming Pappus' Theorem.

It has already been remarked that there are several geometrical assumptions which are equivalent to the assumption that the field of the geometry is commutative. Our choice fell on Pappus' Theorem because it is possible to state it without a considerable amount of preliminary explanation.

A more fundamental result, which is equivalent to the condition that the field is commutative (and hence to Pappus' Theorem), concerns projectivities between ranges. We have seen [§3] that it is possible to establish a projectivity between two ranges so that three distinct points of the one range correspond to three distinct points of the other. On the other hand, if we are given four points A, B, C, D of one range, and four points A', B', C', D' of the other, there may be no projectivity in which A, B, C, D correspond, respectively, to A', B', C', D'. We now prove

THEOREM I. *A necessary and sufficient condition that a projectivity between two ranges be uniquely determined by the assignment of three pairs of corresponding points is that Pappus' Theorem be true.*

(1) *Necessity.* Suppose that a projectivity is uniquely determined when three pairs of corresponding points are given.

Let ABC, $A'B'C'$ be two triads of points on two lines l, l' which intersect at O. Let $B'C$, BC' meet in P, CA', $C'A$ meet in Q, and $A'B$, AB' meet in R.

(*a*) If the triads are in perspective from a point V then clearly the lines OP, OQ, OR all coincide with the harmonic conjugate of OV with respect to l and l'. Then P, Q, R are collinear, and Pappus' Theorem is true without any further condition.

Suppose, next, that the line joining two of the points P, Q, R, say Q and R, passes through O. Then if BB' meets AA' in V_3, OV_3 is the harmonic conjugate of OR with respect to l and l'. If CC' meets AA' in V_2, OV_2 is the harmonic conjugate of OQ with respect to l and l'. Hence $OV_3 = OV_2$, and therefore $V_3 = V_2$, the triads are in perspective, and P lies on QR.

(*b*) If the triads are not in perspective, we use the hypothesis that a projectivity is determined by the assignment of three corresponding pairs of points to deduce Pappus' Theorem. Let QR meet l in L, and l' in M'. Then the points L, M', O are all distinct, by what we have just proved. Let AA' meet QR in S. We denote the line $LM'QR$ by l^*.

By hypothesis there is a unique projectivity between the ranges on l and l' in which A, B, C correspond, respectively, to A', B', C'. This projectivity may therefore be defined by the perspectivities

$$(A, B, C, \ldots) \overset{A'}{\barwedge} (S, R, Q, \ldots) \overset{A}{\barwedge} (A', B', C', \ldots).$$

Now, regarding O as a point of l, there is a unique point of l' corresponding to it in the range on l'. Passing from l to l' via l^* by the above perspectivities, O becomes M', then M'. Similarly, the point L of l corresponds to O of l'. Since, by hypothesis, the projectivity is uniquely determined by the pairs A, A'; B, B' and C, C', the points L, M' are uniquely determined by the projectivity. The line l^* is therefore uniquely determined by the projectivity, and this line contains the points Q, R.

Now, if we choose B, B' as centres of perspective, we find that the line RP cuts l in the point L and l' in the point M'. That is, R and P also lie on l^*. Hence, P, Q, R are collinear, and Pappus' Theorem is true.

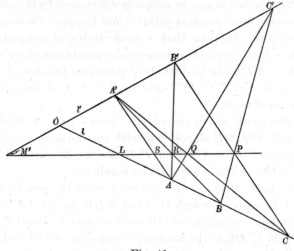

Fig. 41.

(2) *Sufficiency.* We now suppose that Pappus' Theorem is true. Before proving our theorem we must prove a

Lemma. If l, l' are distinct lines intersecting in O, and if ranges $(P, Q, R, O, …)$, $(P', Q', R', O, …)$ on l and l' are projectively related so that O on l corresponds to O on l', then the ranges are in perspective.

It is evident that if the ranges *are* in perspective O on l corresponds to O on l'. Now, we can pass from the range on l to that on l' by two perspectivities at most [§ 3]. There is nothing to prove if we can pass from one range to the other by a single perspectivity. Let there be two, then, and denote the intermediary line by l^*. If l^* passes through O, the ranges on l and l' are in perspective [§ 3, Th. III]. We suppose, then, that l^* meets l in P, l' in Q', and that P, Q', O are distinct points. We pass from the range on l to a range on l^* by a perspectivity with vertex L, and then from the range on l^* to that on l' by a perspectivity, vertex N. It is easily verified that P and Q' do not correspond in the projectivity. If $L = N$ the ranges on l, l' are in perspective, vertex $L = N$. If $L \neq N$, the line LN must pass through O, since O on l corresponds to O on l'. Let LQ' meet l in Q, NP meet l' in P', and let LQ' meet NP in M. If R is any other point of l, R' the corresponding point of the range on l', LR and NR' must meet in a point R^* of l^*. Now, applying Pappus' Theorem to the triads LON, PR^*Q', we see that RR'

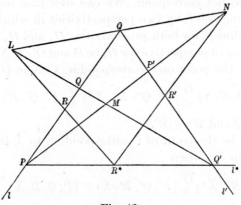

Fig. 42.

passes through M. Since R, R' is any pair of corresponding points, it follows that the ranges are in perspective from M, and the lemma is proved.

We now return to our main theorem. Let $(P, Q, R, ...)$, $(P', Q', R', ...)$ be ranges on two distinct lines l, l', and suppose that there are *two* projectivities Π_1 and Π_2 between the ranges which

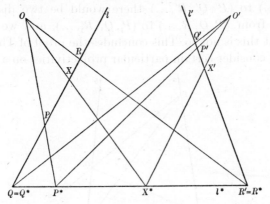

Fig. 43.

make P, Q, R correspond to P', Q', R' respectively. If a pair of corresponding points, say P and P', coincide at the intersection of l and l', then, by the lemma, Π_1 and Π_2 are both perspectivities with the intersection of QQ' and RR' as vertex of perspective. In this case $\Pi_1 = \Pi_2$. Since the three pairs of corresponding points are assumed to be distinct pairs we can select points on l and l', say Q and R', which are both distinct from the possible intersection of l and l', and do not correspond. We can now pass from the range on l to the range on l' by two perspectivities in which QR' is the intermediary line l^* for both projectivities Π_1 and Π_2 [§ 3, Th. IV]. Let the vertices of perspective for Π_1 be O and O'. If X is any other point of l, X' the point on l' corresponding to X in Π_1, then

$$(P, Q, R, X) \; \overset{O}{\overline{\wedge}} \; (P^*, Q^*, R^*, X^*) \; \overset{O'}{\overline{\wedge}} \; (P', Q', R', X'),$$

where $Q^* = Q$ and $R^* = R'$.

Now let $\bar{X}$ be the point of l' corresponding to X in Π_2, and let $O'\bar{X}$ meet l^* in $\bar{X}^*$. Then

$$(P^*, Q^*, R^*, \bar{X}^*) \; \overset{O'}{\overline{\wedge}} \; (P', Q', R', \bar{X}) \; \overline{\wedge} \; (P, Q, R, X) \quad \text{(in } \Pi_2).$$

Since $Q^* = Q$, the ranges $(P^*, Q^*, R^*, \bar{X}^*)$, (P, Q, R, X), by the lemma, must be in perspective. The vertex must be O. Hence $O, X, \bar{X}^*$ are collinear points. That is, $\bar{X}^* = X^*$, therefore $X' = \bar{X}$, and hence $\Pi_1 = \Pi_2$.

If the ranges $(P, Q, R, ...)$, $(P', Q', R', ...)$ are on the same line l, we project the second range on to a line l', obtaining a range $(P_1, Q_1, R_1, ...)$. If there were two distinct projectivities from $(P, Q, R, ...)$ to $(P', Q', R', ...)$ there would be two distinct projectivities from $(P, Q, R, ...)$ to $(P_1, Q_1, R_1, ...)$, and we have just shown that this is not so. This concludes the proof of Theorem I.

We now consider certain particular projectivities on a line l.

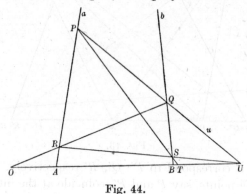

Fig. 44.

In Construction I of § 5 for $A + B$ let us keep A, O, U fixed, and also the lines a, u. This fixes P, and we suppose that Q is also fixed.

R is then fixed, and b is defined as QB. As B describes a range (B) on OU, S describes a range (S) on UR such that

$$(S) \; \frac{Q}{\barwedge} \; (B).$$

Similarly,
$$(T) \; \frac{P}{\barwedge} \; (S),$$

and therefore
$$(T) \; \barwedge \; (B).$$

If, in the usual way, we introduce coordinates on l, taking (O, E, U) as our scale, and if A has the coordinate α, B the coordinate x, and T the coordinate x', then

$$x' = x + \alpha. \tag{1}$$

We have shown that a transformation of this type between the points of l is a projectivity.

Next we consider Construction II, keeping O, E, U, A, P, Q and

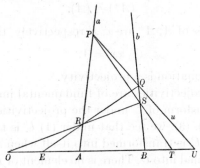

Fig. 45.

hence R fixed, and confine our attention to the case $A \neq O$. We take QB as b. Then B, S, T describe ranges on l, OR, l respectively, such that

$$(B) \; \frac{Q}{\barwedge} \; (S) \; \frac{P}{\barwedge} \; (T),$$

so that
$$(B) \; \barwedge \; (T).$$

Defining coordinates by the same scale, if the coordinates of A, B, T are α, x, x' respectively, then
$$x' = \alpha x, \tag{2}$$

and this transformation is also a projectivity.

Finally, in the construction [§ 7], p. 257, for the inverse $A*$ of A,

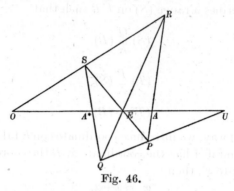

Fig. 46.

we keep O, E, U, Q, R fixed. Then $A*$, S, P, A describe ranges on l, OR, UQ, l, so that

$$(A*) \underset{\Lambda}{\overset{Q}{}} (S) \underset{\Lambda}{\overset{E}{}} (P) \underset{\Lambda}{\overset{R}{}} (A),$$

and $$(A*) \overline{\Lambda} (A).$$

If the coordinates of A, $A*$ are x, x' respectively, then

$$xx' = 1, \tag{3}$$

and this transformation is a projectivity.

These three projectivities are of fundamental importance. If we consider the transform of U under the projectivities, given respectively by (1), (2), (3), we see that under (1) U is transformed into itself; under (2) U is transformed into itself when $\alpha \neq 0$, and under (3) U is transformed into O. There is no element of K corresponding to U, but it is convenient to attach the symbol ∞ to U. The properties of this symbol are

(i) $\infty + \alpha = \infty$,

(ii) $\alpha\infty = \infty$ $(\alpha \neq 0)$,

(iii) $1/\infty = 0$,

$1/0 = \infty$.

These are the usual properties of 'infinity' assumed in elementary algebra.

We consider now, with reference to the coordinate system set up on l, the bilinear transformation

$$x' = \frac{ax+b}{cx+d}, \tag{4}$$

where a, b, c, d are in K, and are not all zero. If $ad = bc$ this transformation reduces to $x' =$ constant, where the constant is in K, or is ∞. Then x' does not depend on x, and we exclude this case. We now consider two cases.

(i) $c = 0$. Neither a nor d can be zero, and

$$x' = \frac{a}{d}x + \frac{b}{d}.$$

Writing $x_1 = ax/d$, this becomes

$$x' = x_1 + b/d, \quad x_1 = ax/d.$$

We can therefore pass from x to x' by a transformation of type (2), which takes x into x_1, followed by a transformation of type (1), which takes x_1 into x'. Since both transformations define projectivities, it is clear that (4) defines a projectivity when $c = 0$, $ad \neq 0$.

(ii) $c \neq 0$, $ad \neq bc$. We can pass from x to x' by the series of transformations

$$x_1 = cx, \quad x_2 = x_1 + d, \quad x_3 = \frac{1}{x_2}, \quad x_4 = \frac{(bc - ad)}{c}x_3, \quad x' = x_4 + \frac{a}{c}.$$

These are of types (2), (1), (3), (2), (1) respectively. Since each transformation represents a projectivity it follows that (4) represents a projectivity. Hence we have

THEOREM II. *A transformation given in a coordinate system on a line l by the equation*

$$x' = \frac{ax + b}{cx + d},$$

where a, b, c, d are in K and $ad \neq bc$, is a projectivity.

We now show that every projectivity on l can indeed be represented by an equation of the form given in the above theorem. We first see what happens to the point $x = \infty$ under the five projectivities into which $x' = (ax + b)/(cx + d)$ has been resolved. The first two leave it invariant, the third transforms it into 0, the fourth leaves 0 invariant, and the fifth transforms it into a/c. The point ∞ is therefore transformed into the point $x' = a/c$. Hence we derive a further property of the symbol ∞:

$$\frac{ax + b}{cx + d} = \frac{a}{c}, \quad \text{when} \quad x = \infty.$$

Now let us suppose that a given projectivity transforms the points $0, 1, \infty$ into the points p, q, r respectively. The transformation

$$x' = \frac{r(q-p)\,x + p(r-q)}{(q-p)\,x + (r-q)} \tag{5}$$

clearly transforms 0 into p, 1 into q, and, by virtue of the relation above, it also transforms ∞ into r. This transformation is also, by Theorem I, a projectivity, since

$$ad - bc = (q-p)\,(r-q)\,(r-p),$$

which is not zero if p, q, r are all distinct. But a projectivity is uniquely defined if we are given three pairs of corresponding points. The transformation (5) therefore represents the given projectivity, and we have proved

THEOREM III. *Any projectivity on l is given by an equation*

$$x' = \frac{ax + b}{cx + d},$$

where a, b, c, d are in K, and $ad \neq bc$.

As an immediate corollary to this theorem we see that the projectivity in which (x_1, x_1'), (x_2, x_2'), (x_3, x_3') are corresponding pairs is given by

$$\frac{(x - x_1)\,(x_2 - x_3)}{(x - x_3)\,(x_2 - x_1)} = \frac{(x' - x_1')\,(x_2' - x_3')}{(x' - x_3')\,(x_2' - x_1')}.$$

Let us now consider a change of coordinate system on l. Let x be the coordinate of a variable point in the original coordinate system for which (O, E, U) is a scale, so that these points are given by $x = 0, 1, \infty$ respectively. Let (O', E', U') be a new scale on l. This does not of itself fix a new coordinate system, since we still have to set up an isomorphism between the points on l other than U' and the elements of the ground field K so that O', E' correspond to 0, 1 respectively. There may be several ways of doing this. For example, if K is the field of complex numbers and we replace every element of K by the conjugate complex element we satisfy all the conditions and obtain a new coordinate system. But we can determine a particular isomorphism as follows. There exists a unique projectivity operating on the points of l which takes O, E, U into O', E', U' respectively. If this takes P into P' we associate with P' the element x which is the coordinate of P in the original coordinate system. This correspondence between the points of l and the elements of K is clearly an isomorphism, and the coordinates 0, 1 are associated with O', E' respectively.

We now find the coordinate y of a point X in the new coordinate system in terms of its coordinate x in the original system. If Y is the unique point of l such that

$$(O, E, U, Y) \barwedge (O', E', U', X),$$

then y is the coordinate of Y in the original coordinate system. Since the correspondence between X and Y is a projectivity,

$$y = \frac{ax+b}{cx+d},$$

by Theorem III, where a, b, c, d are in K, and $ad \neq bc$.

Next, consider a projectivity between two distinct lines l and l', such that

$$(O, E, U, P, \ldots) \barwedge (O', E', U', P', \ldots).$$

If a coordinate system exists on l for which (O, E, U) is a scale, then the projectivity between l and l' sets up a coordinate system for which (O', E', U') is a scale, corresponding points of the two ranges having equal coordinates. The projectivity is given by

$$x' = x$$

in the two coordinate systems chosen.

We have stressed the point that the selection of a scale (O, E, U) on a line does not, of itself, fix the coordinate system. But, having determined a coordinate system on any line l with respect to the scale (O, E, U), we can determine a unique coordinate system on any line l' with respect to any given scale (O', E', U') on that line, by using the unique projectivity which makes (O, E, U) correspond to (O', E', U') respectively, as above. The coordinate systems on l and l' related in this way may be described as related coordinate systems.

Let us fix, once and for all, a coordinate system on a definite line l of the given space. For brevity we shall call any coordinate system related to this chosen one on l a *related* system. If $A_0, \ldots, A_n, E$ is a reference system, and we use the related coordinate system on $A_i A_j$ for which the scale is (A_i, E_{ij}, A_j), we can introduce coordinates into the space as in §8. We call this coordinate system a *scale coordinate system* of the space.

Now let m be any line of the space. It cannot meet all the S_{n-2} spaces $A_{i_0} \ldots A_{i_{n-2}}$, spanned by vertices of the simplex of reference, and we may suppose that it does not meet that determined by $A_2, \ldots, A_n$. Then if it meets $x_0 = 0$ in P, $x_1 = 0$ in Q, the points P, Q are distinct. By suitably choosing the multipliers, we may take

$$P = (0, 1, p_2, \ldots, p_n),$$

and
$$Q = (1, 0, q_2, \ldots, q_n).$$

Let
$$R = (1, 1, p_2 + q_2, \ldots, p_n + q_n).$$

This point is on PQ and in the S_{n-1} determined by $A_2, \ldots, A_n, E$. Now let
$$X = (x_0, \ldots, x_n)$$

be any point of m other than P. Then $x_0 \neq 0$, and we can write

$$X = Q + P x_1 x_0^{-1} = Q + P\xi.$$

We now have a one-to-one correspondence between the points X of PQ other than P and the elements ξ of K. We show that *this correspondence is that determined by the related coordinate system on m with scale (Q, R, P).*

Project the range on m from the S_{n-2} formed by $A_2, \ldots, A_n$ on to the line $A_0 A_1$. The points Q, R, P project, respectively, into A_0, E_{01}, A_1, and X projects into the point $(1, \xi, 0, \ldots, 0)$, which has ξ as its scale coordinate. This proves the result.

Now let L, M, N be any three distinct points on m, and choose the multipliers of their coordinates so that

$$M = L + N.$$

Then, if
$$Q = L\alpha + N\gamma$$

and
$$P = L\beta + N\delta,$$

then
$$\alpha\delta - \beta\gamma \neq 0,$$

since P, Q are distinct. Also, the point X on m can be represented by the symbol
$$X = L + N\eta,$$

where
$$\eta = \frac{\gamma + \delta\xi}{\alpha + \beta\xi}.$$

Since this last relation is of type (4), it follows that *the correspondence between the points X of m and the elements η of K (and ∞) is that defined by the related coordinate system on m for which the scale is (L, M, N).*

Now carry out an allowable transformation of coordinates

$$x' = Ax \quad (A = (\alpha_{ij})).$$

If, in the original coordinate system,

$$L = (l_0, \dots, l_n),$$
$$N = (n_0, \dots, n_n),$$

and

$$X = (x_0, \dots, x_n),$$

where

$$x_i = l_i + n_i \eta \quad (i = 0, \dots, n),$$

the new coordinates of L, N, X are

$$L = (l'_0, \dots, l'_n),$$
$$N = (n'_0, \dots, n'_n),$$
$$X = (x'_0, \dots, x'_n),$$

where

$$l'_i = \sum_{j=0}^{n} \alpha_{ij} l_j,$$

$$n'_i = \sum_{j=0}^{n} \alpha_{ij} n_j,$$

$$x'_i = \sum_{j=0}^{n} \alpha_{ij} x_j,$$

and therefore

$$x'_i = l'_i + n'_i \eta \quad (i = 0, \dots, n).$$

Hence, the correspondence between the points X of m and the elements η of K (and ∞) is unaltered by an allowable transformation of coordinates. Since this result is true for every line of the space, it follows that an allowable transformation of the coordinate system merely changes the simplex of reference used to construct the scale coordinate system. Finally, since a scale coordinate system is uniquely defined when we are given the reference system $A_0, \dots, A_n, E$, and an allowable transformation is uniquely defined (save for a common multiplier) when the points with new coordinates $(1, 0, \dots, 0)$, $(0, 1, \dots, 0)$, $\dots$, $(0, 0, \dots, 1)$, $(1, 1, \dots, 1)$ are given, it follows that *the set of transformations of coordinate systems from one related system to another coincides with the set of allowable transformations of coordinates.*

CHAPTER VII

GRASSMANN COORDINATES

WE now return to the algebraic methods used in Chapter V. From now on we shall assume that the ground field K is commutative, and without characteristic. Indeed, the main reason for considering more general fields in Chapter V was that this cleared the way for the detailed analysis of the Propositions of Incidence which was made in Chapter VI. It is not necessary to assume in this chapter that K is algebraically closed, since all the algebraic operations which we shall use are rational.

1. Linear spaces. In V, § 4, we defined a linear space of k dimensions in $P_n^r(K)$, and in the subsequent sections we obtained certain elementary properties of linear spaces. We indicated how similar definitions and properties could be obtained for $P_n^l(K)$, and it was clear that the two sets of definitions and properties coincide when K is commutative. In this chapter it will not be necessary to indicate the ground field explicitly. We shall denote the space with which we are concerned by $[n]$. Linear spaces in it will be denoted by $S_a, S_b, \ldots$, the suffix denoting the dimension.

We recall that if

$$A^i = (\alpha_0^i, \ldots, \alpha_n^i) \quad (i = 0, \ldots, k)$$

in a given allowable coordinate system, the points $A^0, \ldots, A^k$ are linearly dependent if and only if the matrix

$$A = \begin{pmatrix} \alpha_0^0 & \cdot & \alpha_n^0 \\ \cdot & \cdot & \cdot \\ \alpha_0^k & \cdot & \alpha_n^k \end{pmatrix}$$

is of rank less than $k+1$. By definition, any point $(\alpha_0, \ldots, \alpha_n)$ is linearly dependent on $A^0, \ldots, A^k$ if and only if there exist elements $\lambda_0, \ldots, \lambda_k$ of K such that

$$\alpha_i = \sum_{j=0}^{k} \lambda_j \alpha_i^j \quad (i = 0, \ldots, n).$$

We saw also that in a linear space of k dimensions there exist sets of $k+1$ independent points, but no set of h independent points if $h > k+1$.

Now let $A^0, \ldots, A^k$ be a basis for S_k. The points $B^0, \ldots, B^k$ of S_k can be expressed in the form

$$B^i = \sum_{j=0}^{k} \lambda_j^i A^j \quad (i = 0, \ldots, k).$$

As we saw, the set of points $B^0, \ldots, B^k$ forms a basis for S^k if and only if the matrix

$$\Lambda = (\lambda_j^i)$$

is non-singular. If

$$B^i = (\beta_0^i, \ldots, \beta_n^i),$$

and

$$B = (\beta_j^i),$$

the space S_k spanned by $A^0, \ldots, A^k$ is determined, in an obvious sense, by the matrix A, or, when Λ is non-singular, by the matrix

$$B = \Lambda A.$$

Thus S_k is determined by a set of equivalent $(k+1) \times (n+1)$ matrices $A, B, \ldots$, equivalent matrices being such that we can pass from any one to any other by premultiplication by a non-singular square matrix.

Let us consider an allowable transformation of the coordinate system

$$x_i^* = \sum_{j=0}^{n} \tau_{ij} x_j \quad (i = 0, \ldots, n),$$

or

$$x^* = Px,$$

in matrix notation. If, in the new coordinate system,

$$A^i = (\alpha_0^{*i}, \ldots, \alpha_n^{*i}),$$

then

$$\alpha_j^{*i} = \sum_{k=0}^{n} \tau_{jk} \alpha_k^i,$$

and hence in the new coordinate system S_k is determined by the set of matrices equivalent to

$$A^* = (\alpha_j^{*i}) = AP'. \tag{1}$$

Thus in $[n]$ a linear space S_k is determined by a set of $(k+1) \times (n+1)$ matrices which are *equivalent* (in the sense described) in a given allowable coordinate system. The law of transformation for allowable transformations of coordinates is given by (1). However, for many purposes the identification of a space by means of a set of equivalent matrices is not the most convenient method, and it is our purpose in this chapter to consider a more suitable system of coordinates for the k-spaces of $[n]$. These coordinates were first introduced by Grassmann, and they coincide, when $k = 0$, with the coordinates already defined.

2.   Grassmann coordinates.

We choose an allowable coordinate system and keep it fixed. Then a given S_k of $[n]$ is determined by a set of equivalent $(k+1) \times (n+1)$ matrices $A, B, \ldots$ which are all, of course, of rank $k+1$. Suppose that

$$B = \Lambda A,$$

where Λ is a non-singular $(k+1) \times (k+1)$ matrix. We consider the $(k+1) \times (k+1)$ submatrix of A formed by selecting the columns with suffixes $i_0, i_1, \ldots, i_k$, and the corresponding submatrix of B. We have

$$\begin{pmatrix} \beta_{i_0}^0 & \cdot & \beta_{i_k}^0 \\ \beta_{i_0}^1 & \cdot & \beta_{i_k}^1 \\ \cdot & & \cdot \\ \beta_{i_0}^k & \cdot & \beta_{i_k}^k \end{pmatrix} = \Lambda \begin{pmatrix} \alpha_{i_0}^0 & \cdot & \alpha_{i_k}^0 \\ \alpha_{i_0}^1 & \cdot & \alpha_{i_k}^1 \\ \cdot & & \cdot \\ \alpha_{i_0}^k & \cdot & \alpha_{i_k}^k \end{pmatrix},$$

and taking determinants of both sides, we find that

$$\begin{vmatrix} \beta_{i_0}^0 & \cdot & \beta_{i_k}^0 \\ \cdot & \cdot & \cdot \\ \beta_{i_0}^k & \cdot & \beta_{i_k}^k \end{vmatrix} = |\Lambda| \begin{vmatrix} \alpha_{i_0}^0 & \cdot & \alpha_{i_k}^0 \\ \cdot & \cdot & \cdot \\ \alpha_{i_0}^k & \cdot & \alpha_{i_k}^k \end{vmatrix},$$

where $|\Lambda| = \det \Lambda$ is different from zero, and does not depend on the suffixes $i_0, \ldots, i_k$ chosen. We write this equation in the form

$$b_{i_0 \ldots i_k} = |\Lambda| \, a_{i_0 \ldots i_k}.$$

Since A is of rank $k+1$, for at least one set of suffixes $i_0, \ldots, i_k$,

$$a_{i_0 \ldots i_k} \neq 0,$$

and then $$b_{i_0 \ldots i_k} \neq 0.$$

Again, from the elementary properties of determinants,

$$a_{i_0 \ldots i_k} = 0$$

if the integers $i_0, \ldots, i_k$ are not all distinct; and if $j_0, \ldots, j_k$ is any derangement of the set $i_0, \ldots, i_k$,

$$a_{i_0 \ldots i_k} = \epsilon a_{j_0 \ldots j_k},$$

where $\epsilon = +1$ or -1 according as the derangement is even or odd.

From these considerations it is clear that the set of equivalent matrices $A, B, \ldots$, which determines S_k also determines a set of equivalent $\binom{n+1}{k+1}$-tuples $(\ldots, a_{i_0 \ldots i_k}, \ldots)$, $(\ldots, b_{i_0 \ldots i_k}, \ldots)$. We define the *Grassmann coordinates* of S_k to be any one of the equivalent $\binom{n+1}{k+1}$-tuples. Hitherto, in using the term *coordinates* in connection with points we have implied (i) that each point has a set of co-ordinates which is unique except for a common multiplier, and (ii) that *any* $(n+1)$-tuple gives the coordinates of some point. This property (ii) is not characteristic of Grassmann coordinates, and we shall see later that except when $k = 0$ or $k = n-1$ an $\binom{n+1}{k+1}$-tuple $(\ldots, a_{i_0 \ldots i_k}, \ldots)$ can only give the coordinates of an S_k when the $a_{i_0 \ldots i_k}$ satisfy certain algebraic relations. The property (i) of coordinates described above is, however, an essential one, and, before proceeding, it is of fundamental importance to show that *no two distinct spaces S_k, S_k' can have the same coordinates.* We do this by showing how to write down the equations of $n-k$ linearly independent primes through a given S_k, and remark that these equations depend only on the coordinates of S_k.

Suppose that S_k is determined by the basis

$$A^i = (\alpha_0^i, \ldots, \alpha_n^i) \quad (i = 0, \ldots, k),$$

and let the Grassmann coordinates of S_k be $(\ldots, p_{i_0 \ldots i_k}, \ldots)$. One at least of these coordinates is not zero. Suppose that

$$p_{j_0 \ldots j_k} \neq 0.$$

The condition that any point $(x_0, \ldots, x_n)$ should lie in S_k is that the matrix

$$\begin{pmatrix} \alpha_0^0 & \cdot & \alpha_n^0 \\ \cdot & \cdot & \cdot \\ \alpha_0^k & \cdot & \alpha_n^k \\ x_0 & \cdot & x_n \end{pmatrix}$$

should be of rank $k+1$. In this case the determinant of the sub-matrix formed from the columns with suffixes $i_0, \ldots, i_{k+1}$ must be zero. Expanding this determinant in terms of the last row, we get the equations

$$\sum_{h=0}^{k+1} (-1)^h x_{i_h} p_{i_0 \ldots i_{h-1} i_{h+1} \ldots i_{k+1}} = 0. \tag{1}$$

These equations, for all possible choices of $i_0, ..., i_{k+1}$, are either identically true, or define primes which contain all points of S_k. Hence the aggregate of these $\binom{n+1}{k+2}$ equations defines a linear space which contains S_k. In order to show that these equations actually define S_k itself it is therefore sufficient to show that amongst them there is a set of $n-k$ linearly independent equations.

We consider the equation of the set for which

$$(i_0, ..., i_{k+1}) = (j_0, ..., j_k, j),$$

where j is any integer $0 \leqslant j \leqslant n$ distinct from $j_0, ..., j_k$. This equation is

$$\sum_{h=0}^{k} (-1)^h x_{j_h} p_{j_0 ... j_{h-1} j_{h+1} ... j_k j} + (-1)^{k+1} x_j p_{j_0 ... j_k} = 0.$$

Since each Grassmann coordinate is skew-symmetric in its suffixes we may write the equation in the form

$$\sum_{h=0}^{k} (-1)^h x_{j_h} (-1)^{k-h} p_{j_0 ... j_{h-1} j j_{h+1} ... j_k} + (-1)^{k+1} x_j p_{j_0 ... j_k} = 0,$$

or $$x_j p_{j_0 ... j_k} - \sum_{h=0}^{k} x_{j_h} p_{j_0 ... j_{h-1} j j_{h+1} ... j_k} = 0. \qquad (2)$$

If $(j_0, ..., j_k, j_{k+1}, ..., j_n)$ is a derangement of $(0, ..., n)$, we consider the equations (2) for the values of j given by

$$j = j_{k+1}, ..., j_n.$$

The matrix of coefficients of these equations is an $(n-k) \times (n+1)$ matrix. It is of rank $n-k$; for the determinant of the submatrix corresponding to the columns with suffixes $j_{k+1}, ..., j_n$ is equal to $(p_{j_0 ... j_k})^{n-k}$, and this is not zero. It follows that the set of equations (2) defines $n-k$ linearly independent primes, and therefore defines S_k.

The equations of S_k are therefore determined by the Grassmann coordinates of S_k, and it follows that no two distinct k-spaces can have the same coordinates.

We conclude this section by considering the effect of an allowable transformation of coordinates in $[n]$ on the Grassmann coordinates of S_k. We saw in §1 that the transformation

$$x^* = Px \qquad (3)$$

transforms the matrix A which defines S_k into the matrix

$$A^* = AP'.$$

Hence

$$p^*_{i_0 \ldots i_k} = \begin{vmatrix} \alpha^{*0}_{i_0} & \cdot & \alpha^{*0}_{i_k} \\ \cdot & \cdot & \cdot \\ \alpha^{*k}_{i_0} & \cdot & \alpha^{*k}_{i_k} \end{vmatrix}$$

$$= \begin{vmatrix} \sum_h \tau_{i_0 h} \alpha^0_h & \cdot & \sum_h \tau_{i_k h} \alpha^0_h \\ \cdot & \cdot & \cdot \\ \sum_h \tau_{i_0 h} \alpha^k_h & \cdot & \sum_h \tau_{i_k h} \alpha^k_h \end{vmatrix}$$

$$= \sum_{h_0, \ldots, h_k} \begin{vmatrix} \tau_{i_0 h_0} & \cdot & \tau_{i_k h_0} \\ \cdot & \cdot & \cdot \\ \tau_{i_0 h_k} & \cdot & \tau_{i_k h_k} \end{vmatrix} \begin{vmatrix} \alpha^0_{h_0} & \cdot & \alpha^0_{h_k} \\ \cdot & \cdot & \cdot \\ \alpha^k_{h_0} & \cdot & \alpha^k_{h_k} \end{vmatrix},$$

by II, §8, Th. V, and this is equal to

$$\sum_{h_0, \ldots, h_k} \begin{vmatrix} \tau_{i_0 h_0} & \cdot & \tau_{i_k h_0} \\ \cdot & \cdot & \cdot \\ \tau_{i_0 h_k} & \cdot & \tau_{i_k h_k} \end{vmatrix} p_{h_0 \ldots h_k}. \tag{4}$$

Hence an allowable transformation of coordinates in $[n]$ induces a linear transformation of the Grassmann coordinates of a k-space. The matrix of this transformation has as its elements the minors of order $k+1$ which can be extracted from P. Let all minors which come from the same set of $k+1$ rows (or columns) of P be placed in the same row (or column), and let the priority of elements in rows or columns be decided on the principle by which words are ordered in a dictionary; that is, let the order be *lexicographical* order. The resulting $\binom{n+1}{k+1} \times \binom{n+1}{k+1}$ matrix is called the $(k+1)$th *compound* of P, and it is denoted by $P^{(k+1)}$. From the reasoning given above it follows easily that

$$(PQ)^{(k+1)} = P^{(k+1)} Q^{(k+1)}. \tag{5}$$

If $P = I_{n+1}$ (the unit matrix), evidently

$$P^{(k+1)} = I_{\binom{n+1}{k+1}}.$$

Hence, taking $Q = P^{-1}$, we see from (5) that

$$I_{\binom{n+1}{k+1}} = (I_{n+1})^{(k+1)} = P^{(k+1)} Q^{(k+1)},$$

and therefore the matrix $(P^{-1})^{(k+1)}$

is the inverse of $P^{(k+1)}$.

These compound matrices are of importance later on, when we consider them as defining a particular type of allowable transformation in an associated N-space, where $N + 1 = \binom{n+1}{k+1}$.

3. Dual Grassmann coordinates.

An S_k may be defined not only by $k + 1$ linearly independent points which lie in it, but also by means of $n - k$ linearly independent primes which pass through it. In a given allowable coordinate system let S_k have Grassmann coordinates

$$(\ldots, p_{i_0 \ldots i_k}, \ldots),$$

and let
$$\sum_{j=0}^{n} u_j^i x_j = 0 \quad (i = 1, \ldots, n-k) \tag{1}$$

be the equations of $n - k$ linearly independent primes which contain S_k. If

$$U = (u_j^i),$$

the equations (1) may be written in matrix form as

$$Ux = 0. \tag{1'}$$

These equations are the equations of S_k, and the $(n-k) \times (n+1)$ matrix U is of rank $n - k$, since the primes are linearly independent. Any prime through S_k has for its equation a linear combination of the equations (1), and $n - k$ such primes, given by the matrix equation
$$Vx = 0,$$

are linearly independent primes through S_k if and only if there exists a non-singular $(n-k) \times (n-k)$ matrix M such that

$$V = MU;$$

that is, in the terminology of § 2, if and only if U and V are equivalent matrices. Thus S_k can also be determined by a set of equivalent $(n-k) \times (n+1)$ matrices.

If, as in § 2, we consider the transformation of coordinates

$$x^* = Px, \tag{2}$$

the equations of S_k become

$$UP^{-1}x^* = 0,$$

and the set of equivalent matrices $U, V, \ldots$ becomes the set of equivalent matrices $UP^{-1}, VP^{-1}, \ldots$.

Again, the determinants of the $(n-k) \times (n-k)$ submatrices of the set of equivalent matrices U, V, ... determine a class of equivalent $\binom{n+1}{n-k}$-tuples. A representative member of the class can be determined from the matrix U. We write

$$p^{i_1 \cdots i_{n-k}} = \begin{vmatrix} u_{i_1}^1 & \cdot & u_{i_{n-k}}^1 \\ \cdot & \cdot & \cdot \\ u_{i_1}^{n-k} & \cdot & u_{i_{n-k}}^{n-k} \end{vmatrix} . \tag{3}$$

Then S_k is determined by the set of $\binom{n+1}{n-k}$-tuples

$$(\dots, p^{i_1 \cdots i_{n-k}}, \dots).$$

We call these *dual Grassmann coordinates*.

It is easy to show that no two distinct spaces S_k, S_k' give rise to the same set of dual coordinates. If $(x_0, \dots, x_n)$ is any point of S_k, then

$$\sum_{i=1}^{n-k} \sum_{j=0}^{n} \lambda_i u_j^i x_j = 0,$$

where $\lambda_1, \dots, \lambda_{n-k}$ are any elements of K. Now choose

$$\lambda_i = (-1)^i \begin{vmatrix} u_{j_1}^1 & \cdot & u_{j_{n-k-1}}^1 \\ \cdot & \cdot & \cdot \\ u_{j_1}^{i-1} & \cdot & u_{j_{n-k-1}}^{i-1} \\ u_{j_1}^{i+1} & \cdot & u_{j_{n-k-1}}^{i+1} \\ \cdot & \cdot & \cdot \\ u_{j_1}^{n-k} & \cdot & u_{j_{n-k-1}}^{n-k} \end{vmatrix},$$

and we obtain the equation

$$\sum_{j=0}^{n} p^{i_1 \cdots i_{n-k-1} j} x_j = 0. \tag{4}$$

If we give $j_1, \dots, j_{n-k-1}$ all possible values, (4) gives us a set of equations defining a linear space which contains S_k. As in the previous section we now show that there are $n-k$ linearly independent equations in the set, and deduce that the linear space coincides with S_k.

Since U is of rank $n-k$, there is at least one non-zero dual coordinate. Suppose that

$$p^{a_1 \cdots a_{n-k}} \neq 0,$$

and consider the $n-k$ equations obtained from (4) when $j_1, \ldots, j_{n-k-1}$ are selected from the set $a_1, \ldots, a_{n-k}$. If a_i is the element omitted in the selection, (4) becomes

$$\sum_{j=0}^{n} p^{a_1 \cdots a_{i-1} a_{i+1} \cdots a_{n-k} j} x_j = 0,$$

that is,

$$p^{a_1 \cdots a_{i-1} a_{i+1} \cdots a_{n-k} a_i} x_{a_i} + \sum_{j \neq a_1, \ldots, a_{n-k}} p^{a_1 \cdots a_{i-1} a_{i+1} \cdots a_{n-k} j} x_j = 0,$$

or $$p^{a_1 \cdots a_{n-k}} x_{a_i} + \sum_{j \neq a_1, \ldots, a_{n-k}} p^{a_1 \cdots a_{i-1} j a_{i+1} \cdots a_{n-k}} x_j = 0.$$

If we take $i = 1, \ldots, n-k$, we obtain $n-k$ linearly independent equations, since the determinant of the submatrix of the $(n-k) \times (n+1)$ matrix of coefficients which corresponds to the columns $a_1, \ldots, a_{n-k}$ is evidently

$$(p^{a_1 \cdots a_{n-k}})^{n-k},$$

and this is not zero. The dual coordinates of S_k therefore determine it uniquely.

These dual coordinates are closely related to the ordinary Grassmann coordinates defined in § 2. We now prove

THEOREM I. *Let $(i_0, \ldots, i_n)$ be any derangement of $(0, \ldots, n)$. Then if S_k has Grassmann coordinates $(\ldots, p_{i_0 \cdots i_k}, \ldots)$, and dual Grassmann coordinates $(\ldots, p^{i_{k+1} \cdots i_n}, \ldots)$, there exists a non-zero element ρ in K such that*

$$q_{i_0 \ldots i_k} \equiv \epsilon_{i_0 \ldots i_n} p^{i_{k+1} \cdots i_n} \equiv \rho p_{i_0 \ldots i_k}. \tag{5}$$

This equation defines $q_{i_0 \ldots i_k}$. The proof is in two stages. We show first of all, that the transformation (2) of coordinates in $[n]$ induces a non-singular linear transformation in the coordinates $q_{i_0 \ldots i_k}$, of the same kind as that induced in the coordinates $p_{i_0 \ldots i_k}$ [cf. § 2]. We then show that P can be chosen so that in the new coordinate system it is evident that

$$q^*_{i_0 \ldots i_k} \equiv \rho p^*_{i_0 \ldots i_k}$$

for some ρ. The theorem then follows from the fact that the coordinates $(\ldots, p^{*}_{i_0 \ldots i_k}, \ldots)$ and $(\ldots, q^{*}_{i_0 \ldots i_k}, \ldots)$ are transformed in the same way for each allowable transformation in $[n]$.

Since the transformation (2) transforms the equations of S_k into

$$U P^{-1} x^* = 0,$$

if
$$P = (\tau_{ij}), \quad \text{and} \quad P^{-1} = (\sigma_{ij}),$$

then

$$p^{*i_1 \cdots i_{n-k}} = \begin{vmatrix} \sum_j u^1_j \sigma_{ji_1} & \cdot & \sum_j u^1_j \sigma_{ji_{n-k}} \\ \cdot & \cdot & \cdot \\ \sum_j u^{n-k}_j \sigma_{ji_1} & \cdot & \sum_j u^{n-k}_j \sigma_{ji_{n-k}} \end{vmatrix}$$

$$= \sum_{j_1, \ldots, j_{n-k}} \begin{vmatrix} u^1_{j_1} & \cdot & u^1_{j_{n-k}} \\ \cdot & \cdot & \cdot \\ u^{n-k}_{j_1} & \cdot & u^{n-k}_{j_{n-k}} \end{vmatrix} \begin{vmatrix} \sigma_{j_1 i_1} & \cdot & \sigma_{j_1 i_{n-k}} \\ \cdot & \cdot & \cdot \\ \sigma_{j_{n-k} i_1} & \cdot & \sigma_{j_{n-k} i_{n-k}} \end{vmatrix}$$

$$= \sum_{j_1, \ldots, j_{n-k}} p^{j_1 \cdots j_{n-k}} \begin{vmatrix} \sigma_{j_1 i_1} & \cdot & \sigma_{j_1 i_{n-k}} \\ \cdot & \cdot & \cdot \\ \sigma_{j_{n-k} i_1} & \cdot & \sigma_{j_{n-k} i_{n-k}} \end{vmatrix}.$$

Hence

$$q^{*}_{i_0 \ldots i_k} = \epsilon_{i_0 \ldots i_n} p^{*i_{k+1} \cdots i_n}$$

$$= \epsilon_{i_0 \ldots i_n} \sum_{j_{k+1}, \ldots, j_n} p^{j_{k+1} \cdots j_n} \begin{vmatrix} \sigma_{j_{k+1} i_{k+1}} & \cdot & \sigma_{j_{k+1} i_n} \\ \cdot & \cdot & \cdot \\ \sigma_{j_n i_{k+1}} & \cdot & \sigma_{j_n i_n} \end{vmatrix}$$

$$= \epsilon_{i_0 \ldots i_n} \sum \epsilon_{j_0 \ldots j_n} q_{j_0 \ldots j_k} \begin{vmatrix} \sigma_{j_{k+1} i_{k+1}} & \cdot & \sigma_{j_{k+1} i_n} \\ \cdot & \cdot & \cdot \\ \sigma_{j_n i_{k+1}} & \cdot & \sigma_{j_n i_n} \end{vmatrix}$$

$$= \sum \delta^{i_0 \ldots i_n}_{j_0 \ldots j_n} q_{j_0 \ldots j_k} \begin{vmatrix} \sigma_{j_{k+1} i_{k+1}} & \cdot & \sigma_{j_{k+1} i_n} \\ \cdot & \cdot & \cdot \\ \sigma_{j_n i_{k+1}} & \cdot & \sigma_{j_n i_n} \end{vmatrix},$$

the summation being over all the $\binom{n+1}{k+1}$ *distinct* partitions $(j_0, \ldots, j_k)(j_{k+1}, \ldots, j_n)$ of $(j_0, \ldots, j_n)$. The sets $(i_0, \ldots, i_n)$, $(j_0, \ldots, j_n)$ are, of course, derangements of $(0, \ldots, n)$.

But [II, §8, Th. VIII],

$$\begin{vmatrix} \sigma_{j_{k+1}i_{k+1}} & \cdot & \sigma_{j_{k+1}i_n} \\ \cdot & \cdot & \cdot \\ \sigma_{j_n i_{k+1}} & \cdot & \sigma_{j_n i_n} \end{vmatrix} = \delta^{j_0\ldots j_n}_{i_0\ldots i_n} |P|^{-1} \begin{vmatrix} \tau_{i_0 j_0} & \cdot & \tau_{i_k j_0} \\ \cdot & \cdot & \cdot \\ \tau_{i_0 j_k} & \cdot & \tau_{i_k j_k} \end{vmatrix},$$

where $|P| = \det P$. Hence

$$q^*_{i_0\ldots i_k} = |P|^{-1} \sum_{j_0,\ldots,j_k} \begin{vmatrix} \tau_{i_0 j_0} & \cdot & \tau_{i_k j_0} \\ \cdot & \cdot & \cdot \\ \tau_{i_0 j_k} & \cdot & \tau_{i_k j_k} \end{vmatrix} q_{j_0\ldots j_k}. \tag{6}$$

Comparing this with the result of §2, (4) we see that the allowable transformation of coordinates in $[n]$ given by (2) induces the same linear transformation on the coordinates $(\ldots, q_{i_0\ldots i_k}, \ldots)$ as it does on the coordinates $(\ldots, p_{i_0\ldots i_k}, \ldots)$, save for a common non-zero factor.

Now, by V, §4, Th. V, there is an allowable coordinate system in $[n]$ in which the points $A^0, \ldots, A^k$, which form a basis for S_k, coincide with vertices $X^{*0}, \ldots, X^{*k}$ of the simplex of reference of an allowable coordinate system. Let us suppose that the transformation (2) is to this coordinate system. Then S_k is now given by the $(k+1) \times (n+1)$ matrix

$$\begin{pmatrix} 1 & 0 & \cdot & \cdot & \cdot & 0 \\ 0 & 1 & \cdot & \cdot & \cdot & 0 \\ \cdot & \cdot & \cdot & \cdot & \cdot & \cdot \\ 0 & 0 & \cdot & 1 & \cdot & 0 \end{pmatrix},$$

and therefore $p^*_{0\ldots k} = 1$, but $p^*_{i_0\ldots i_k} = 0$, unless the set $(i_0, \ldots, i_k)$ is a derangement of $(0, \ldots, k)$. Also, S_k is given by the equations

$$x_i = 0 \quad (i = k+1, \ldots, n),$$

that is, by the $(n-k) \times (n+1)$ matrix

$$\begin{pmatrix} 0 & \cdot & 1 & 0 & \cdot & \cdot \\ 0 & \cdot & 0 & 1 & \cdot & \cdot \\ \cdot & \cdot & \cdot & \cdot & \cdot & \cdot \\ 0 & \cdot & 0 & \cdot & \cdot & 1 \end{pmatrix},$$

and therefore $q^*_{0\ldots k} = p^{*k+1\ldots n} = 1$, but $q^*_{i_0\ldots i_k} = \pm p^{*i_{k+1}\ldots i_n} = 0$ if $(i_0, \ldots, i_k)$ is not a derangement of $(0, \ldots, k)$. In this special system of coordinates

$$q^*_{i_0\ldots i_k} = p^*_{i_0\ldots i_k},$$

and therefore, as explained above, we conclude that in any allowable coordinate system the relations (5) hold for a suitable ρ.

The Principle of Duality [V, § 5] throws further light on the relation between the Grassmann coordinates of an S_k and its dual Grassmann coordinates. If the points

$$A^i = (\alpha_0^i, \ldots, \alpha_n^i) \quad (i = 0, \ldots, k)$$

form a basis for S_k, the equations

$$\sum_{j=0}^{n} \alpha_j^i x_j = 0 \quad (i = 0, \ldots, k)$$

define the dual space Σ_{n-k-1}. Hence, if

$$(\ldots, p_{i_0 \ldots i_k}, \ldots) \quad \text{and} \quad (\ldots, p^{i_1 \ldots i_{n-k}}, \ldots)$$

are the Grassmann and dual Grassmann coordinates respectively of S_k, and

$$(\ldots, q_{i_0 \ldots i_{n-k-1}}, \ldots) \quad \text{and} \quad (\ldots, q^{i_1 \ldots i_{k+1}}, \ldots)$$

are the Grassmann and dual Grassmann coordinates of Σ_{n-k-1}, then evidently

$$q^{i_0 \ldots i_k} = \rho p_{i_0 \ldots i_k},$$

and therefore, by our theorem,

$$p^{i_1 \ldots i_{n-k}} = \sigma q_{i_1 \ldots i_{n-k}}.$$

Using these results it is possible to read off a property of Grassmann coordinates dual to any known property. For instance, it follows at once from the fact that the equations of S_k are [§ 3, (4)]

$$\sum_{j=0}^{n} p^{j_1 \ldots j_{n-k-1} j} x_j = 0,$$

that if the vector

$$(p_{j_1 \ldots j_{n-k-1} 0}, \, p_{j_1 \ldots j_{n-k-1} 1}, \, \ldots, \, p_{j_1 \ldots j_{n-k-1} n})$$

is not zero, it gives us the coordinates of a point in the S_{n-k-1} whose Grassmann coordinates are $(\ldots, q_{i_1 \ldots i_{n-k}}, \ldots)$. By giving the set of integers $(j_1, \ldots, j_{n-k-1})$ all possible values we obtain a set of points in S_{n-k-1} which contains a basis for this space.

4. Elementary properties of Grassmann coordinates.
The condition

$$p_{a_0 \ldots a_k} = 0,$$

for a given set of suffixes $(a_0, \ldots, a_k)$, is easily interpreted as a geometric property of the S_k which has the Grassmann coordinates $(\dots, p_{i_0 \dots i_k}, \dots)$. For if

$$A^i = (\alpha_0^i, \dots, \alpha_n^i) \quad (i = 0, \dots, k)$$

is a basis for S_k, the condition is

$$\begin{vmatrix} \alpha_{a_0}^0 & . & \alpha_{a_k}^0 \\ . & . & . \\ \alpha_{a_0}^k & . & \alpha_{a_k}^k \end{vmatrix} = 0.$$

From this statement of the condition we deduce the existence of elements $\lambda_0, \dots, \lambda_k$ of K, not all zero, such that

$$\sum_{i=0}^k \lambda_i \alpha_j^i = 0 \quad (j = a_0, \dots, a_k).$$

It follows that $\sum_{i=0}^k \lambda_i A^i$ is a point in S_k whose coordinates satisfy the conditions

$$x_{a_0} = x_{a_1} = \dots = x_{a_k} = 0.$$

These last equations define an S_{n-k-1}, a basis for which consists of $n - k$ vertices of the simplex of references. The condition we are examining is a sufficient condition for S_k to meet this S_{n-k-1}. Conversely, if S_k meets this S_{n-k-1}, one of the points, say A^k, of a basis for S_k can be chosen in S_{n-k-1}, and then

$$\alpha_{a_0}^k = \dots = \alpha_{a_k}^k = 0,$$

and therefore $p_{a_0 \dots a_k} = 0$.

This result can be generalised:

THEOREM I. *Let $a_0, \dots, a_s$ be $s+1$ distinct integers $(s+1 \leqslant k+1)$ chosen from the set $0, \dots, n$; and let S_{n-s-1} be the linear space whose equations are*

$$x_{a_0} = \dots = x_{a_s} = 0.$$

The necessary and sufficient conditions that S_k should meet S_{n-s-1} in a space of dimension at least $k - s$ are

$$p_{a_0 \dots a_s \, i_{s+1} \dots i_k} = 0$$

for all possible choices of $i_{s+1}, \dots, i_k$.

Clearly we need only consider sets $(i_{s+1}, \dots, i_k)$ which consist of distinct numbers, none of which is equal to any member of the set $(a_0, \dots, a_s)$. After what has been proved above we may also suppose that $s < k$.

Now let us assume that S_k and S_{n-s-1} have a linear space of at least $k-s$ dimensions in common. Then we can find $k-s+1$ linearly independent points of S_k in S_{n-s-1}, and we may include these in a basis for S_k, say as the points $A^s, A^{s+1}, \ldots, A^k$. Then

$$\alpha_j^i = 0 \quad (i = s, \ldots, k; \, j = a_0, \ldots, a_s).$$

It follows that in the matrix $A = (\alpha_j^i)$ which defines S_k the columns corresponding to the suffixes $a_0, \ldots, a_s$ have non-zero elements only in the first s rows. The rank of the submatrix formed by these columns is therefore not greater than s, and hence these columns, considered as vectors, are linearly dependent. Therefore the columns corresponding to suffixes $(a_0, \ldots, a_s, i_{s+1}, \ldots, i_k)$ are also linearly dependent, and finally

$$p_{a_0 \ldots a_s \, i_{s+1} \ldots i_k} = 0.$$

This proves the necessity of the condition. To prove its sufficiency we recall that any S_k intersects an S_{n-s-1} in a linear space of at least $k-s-1$ dimensions. Hence we can choose the points $A^{s+1}, \ldots, A^k$ to lie in S_{n-s-1}, so that

$$\alpha_j^i = 0 \quad (i = s+1, \ldots, k; \, j = a_0, \ldots, a_s).$$

Then evidently

$$p_{a_0 \ldots a_s \, i_{s+1} \ldots i_k} = \begin{vmatrix} \alpha_{a_0}^0 & \cdot & \alpha_{a_s}^0 \\ \cdot & \cdot & \cdot \\ \alpha_{a_0}^s & \cdot & \alpha_{a_s}^s \end{vmatrix} \begin{vmatrix} \alpha_{i_{s+1}}^{s+1} & \cdot & \alpha_{i_k}^{s+1} \\ \cdot & \cdot & \cdot \\ \alpha_{i_{s+1}}^k & \cdot & \alpha_{i_k}^k \end{vmatrix},$$

using elementary properties of determinants.

Not all the determinants

$$\begin{vmatrix} \alpha_{i_{s+1}}^{s+1} & \cdot & \alpha_{i_k}^{s+1} \\ \cdot & \cdot & \cdot \\ \alpha_{i_{s+1}}^k & \cdot & \alpha_{i_k}^k \end{vmatrix}$$

can be zero. If they were, the last $k-s$ rows of A would be linearly dependent. Since $k-s > 0$, this would imply that the rank of A was less than $k+1$, contrary to hypothesis. Hence the equations

$$p_{a_0 \ldots a_s \, i_{s+1} \ldots i_k} = 0$$

imply that

$$\begin{vmatrix} \alpha_{a_0}^0 & \cdot & \alpha_{a_s}^0 \\ \cdot & \cdot & \cdot \\ \alpha_{a_0}^s & \cdot & \alpha_{a_s}^s \end{vmatrix} = 0.$$

It follows that there exist elements $\lambda_0, ..., \lambda_k$ of K, which are not all zero, such that the point $\sum\limits_{i=0}^{s} \lambda_i A^i$, which is a point of S_k linearly independent of $A^{s+1}, ..., A^k$, lies in S_{n-s-1}. Hence S_k and S_{n-s-1} have at least $k-s+1$ linearly independent points in common, and therefore intersect in a space of at least $k-s$ dimensions. This completes the proof of the theorem.

We now show how to determine a basis for an S_k when we are given its Grassmann coordinates $(..., p_{i_0...i_k}, ...)$. Let $p_{a_0...a_k}$ be a non-zero coordinate, and define

$$x_j^i = p_{a_0...a_{i-1}j\,a_{i+1}...a_k} \quad (i = 0, ..., k; j = 0, ..., n). \tag{1}$$

Since
$$x_{a_i}^i = p_{a_0...a_k} \neq 0,$$

the $(n+1)$-tuple $\qquad B^i = (x_0^i, ..., x_n^i)$

represents a point, which we denote by B^i. Since

$$x_j^i = 0 \quad (j = a_0, ..., a_{i-1}, a_{i+1}, ..., a_k),$$

the point B^i lies in the S_{n-k} whose equations are

$$x_j = 0 \quad (j = a_0, ..., a_{i-1}, a_{i+1}, ..., a_k). \tag{2}$$

We show that B^i is the unique point of intersection of S_k with this S_{n-k}. Since

$$x_j^i = \begin{vmatrix} \alpha_{a_0}^0 & \cdot & \alpha_{a_{i-1}}^0 & \alpha_j^0 & \alpha_{a_{i+1}}^0 & \cdot & \alpha_{a_k}^0 \\ \cdot & \cdot & \cdot & \cdot & \cdot & \cdot & \cdot \\ \alpha_{a_0}^k & \cdot & \alpha_{a_{i-1}}^k & \alpha_j^k & \alpha_{a_{i+1}}^k & \cdot & \alpha_{a_k}^k \end{vmatrix}$$

$$= \sum_{h=0}^{k} (-1)^{h+i} \begin{vmatrix} \alpha_{a_0}^0 & \cdot & \alpha_{a_{i-1}}^0 & \alpha_{a_{i+1}}^0 & \cdot & \alpha_{a_k}^0 \\ \cdot & \cdot & \cdot & \cdot & \cdot & \cdot \\ \alpha_{a_0}^{h-1} & \cdot & \alpha_{a_{i-1}}^{h-1} & \alpha_{a_{i+1}}^{h-1} & & \alpha_{a_k}^{h-1} \\ \alpha_{a_0}^{h+1} & \cdot & \alpha_{a_{i-1}}^{h+1} & \alpha_{a_{i+1}}^{h+1} & & \alpha_{a_k}^{h+1} \\ \cdot & \cdot & \cdot & \cdot & \cdot & \cdot \\ \alpha_{a_0}^k & \cdot & \alpha_{a_{i-1}}^k & \alpha_{a_{i+1}}^k & \cdot & \alpha_{a_k}^k \end{vmatrix} \alpha_j^h$$

$$= \sum_{h=0}^{k} \lambda_h^i \alpha_j^h,$$

it follows that $B^i = \sum\limits_{h=0}^{k} \lambda_h^i A^h$ is a point of S_k. If S_k meets the S_{n-k} given by (2) in more than the point B^i, it has at least a line in common with it, and this line, lying in S_{n-k}, must meet the S_{n-k-1} given by

$$x_j = 0 \quad (j = a_0, ..., a_k).$$

This S_{n-k-1} would then meet S_k, and by Theorem I we should have

$$p_{a_0 \ldots a_k} = 0,$$

contrary to hypothesis. It follows that B^i is the unique point common to S_k and the S_{n-k} given by (2).

We now show that the points $B^0, \ldots, B^k$ defined in this way form a basis for S_k. Since each B^i lies in S_k it is sufficient to prove that the $k+1$ points are linearly independent; that is, that the matrix

$$X = \begin{pmatrix} x_0^0 & . & x_n^0 \\ . & . & . \\ x_0^k & . & x_n^k \end{pmatrix}$$

is of rank $k+1$. The submatrix of X whose columns correspond to the suffixes $a_0, \ldots, a_k$ is

$$\begin{pmatrix} p_{a_0 \ldots a_k} & 0 & . & 0 \\ 0 & p_{a_0 \ldots a_k} & . & 0 \\ . & . & . & . \\ 0 & . & . & p_{a_0 \ldots a_k} \end{pmatrix}$$

(since $x_{a_i}^i = p_{a_0 \ldots a_k}$), and this submatrix is non-singular, since $p_{a_0 \ldots a_k} \neq 0$. Hence X is of rank $k+1$, and the points $B^0, \ldots, B^k$ form a basis for S_k.

An immediate consequence of this result is the fact that there exists a non-zero element ρ in K such that

$$\rho p_{i_0 \ldots i_k} = \begin{vmatrix} x_{i_0}^0 & . & x_{i_k}^0 \\ . & . & . \\ x_{i_0}^k & . & x_{i_k}^k \end{vmatrix}$$

for all choices of $(i_0, \ldots, i_k)$. If we take

$$i_j = a_j \quad (j = 0, \ldots, k),$$

this equation becomes

$$\rho p_{a_0 \ldots a_k} = (p_{a_0 \ldots a_k})^{k+1},$$

and therefore

$$\rho = (p_{a_0 \ldots a_k})^k.$$

Again, suppose that $i_j = a_j$, except when $j = t, u, v, \ldots, w$, there being s elements in this last set. Then

$$\rho p_{i_0 \ldots i_k} = \begin{vmatrix} x_{a_0}^0 & . & x_{i_t}^0 & . & x_{i_u}^0 & . & x_{i_w}^0 & . & x_{a_k}^0 \\ . & . & . & . & . & . & . & . & . \\ x_{a_0}^k & . & x_{i_t}^k & . & x_{i_u}^k & . & x_{i_w}^k & . & x_{a_k}^k \end{vmatrix}.$$

In any column corresponding to the suffix a_i every element other than $x^i_{a_i}$ is zero. Since a determinant can be expanded in terms of the elements of such a column, and since $x^i_{a_i} = p_{a_0 \ldots a_k}$ is on the principal diagonal,

$$\rho p_{i_0 \ldots i_k} = (p_{a_0 \ldots a_k})^{k-s+1} \begin{vmatrix} x^t_{i_t} & . & x^t_{i_w} \\ . & . & . \\ x^w_{i_t} & . & x^w_{i_w} \end{vmatrix},$$

that is,

$$(p_{a_0 \ldots a_k})^{s-1} p_{i_0 \ldots i_k} = \begin{vmatrix} x^t_{i_t} & . & x^t_{i_w} \\ . & . & . \\ x^w_{i_t} & . & x^w_{i_w} \end{vmatrix}. \tag{3}$$

If we dualise these results we can obtain a basis for the primes which pass through S_k. But we may also use the results of § 2. If $(a_0, \ldots, a_n)$ is an even derangement of $(0, \ldots, n)$,

$$p^{a_{k+1} \ldots a_n} = p_{a_0 \ldots a_k} \neq 0,$$

by hypothesis. By § 2, (2) the equations

$$p_{a_0 \ldots a_k} x_i - \sum_{h=0}^{k} p_{a_0 \ldots a_{h-1} i a_{h+1} \ldots a_k} x_{a_h} = 0 \quad (i = a_{k+1}, \ldots, a_n)$$

are the equations of a dual basis for S_k. Since for the given values of i we may write

$$i = a_j \quad (j = k+1, \ldots, n),$$

and then

$$p_{a_0 \ldots a_{h-1} a_j a_{h+1} \ldots a_k} = -p^{a_{k+1} \ldots a_{j-1} a_h a_{j+1} \ldots a_n},$$

the equations become

$$p^{a_{k+1} \ldots a_n} x_{a_j} + \sum_{h=0}^{k} p^{a_{k+1} \ldots a_{j-1} a_h a_{j+1} \ldots a_n} x_{a_h} = 0 \quad (j = k+1, \ldots, n),$$

or, more simply,

$$\sum_{i=0}^{n} p^{a_{k+1} \ldots a_{j-1} i a_{j+1} \ldots a_n} x_i = 0 \quad (j = k+1, \ldots, n),$$

on inserting terms with zero coefficients. We write

$$u^i_j = p^{a_{k+1} \ldots a_{j-1} i a_{j+1} \ldots a_n}, \tag{4}$$

and the equations of S_k are then

$$\sum_{i=0}^{n} u^i_j x_i = 0 \quad (j = k+1, \ldots, n).$$

The matrix

$$U = \begin{pmatrix} u_{k+1}^0 & \cdot & u_{k+1}^n \\ \cdot & \cdot & \cdot \\ u_n^0 & \cdot & u_n^n \end{pmatrix}$$

defines S_k, and

$$\rho p^{i_{k+1} \cdots i_n} = \begin{vmatrix} u_{k+1}^{i_{k+1}} & \cdot & u_{k+1}^{i_n} \\ \cdot & \cdot & \cdot \\ u_n^{i_{k+1}} & \cdot & u_n^{i_n} \end{vmatrix}.$$

Since $u_j^{a_j} = p^{a_{k+1} \cdots a_n}$ $(j = k+1, \ldots, n),$

$$\rho p^{a_{k+1} \cdots a_n} = \begin{vmatrix} p^{a_{k+1} \cdots a_n} & 0 & \cdot & \cdot \\ 0 & p^{a_{k+1} \cdots a_n} & 0 & \cdot \\ \cdot & \cdot & \cdot & \cdot \\ 0 & \cdot & \cdot & p^{a_{k+1} \cdots a_n} \end{vmatrix}$$

$$= (p^{a_{k+1} \cdots a_n})^{n-k},$$

and therefore we may write our previous result in the form

$$(p^{a_{k+1} \cdots a_n})^{n-k-1} p^{i_{k+1} \cdots i_n} = \begin{vmatrix} u_{k+1}^{i_{k+1}} & \cdot & u_{k+1}^{i_n} \\ \cdot & \cdot & \cdot \\ u_n^{i_{k+1}} & \cdot & u_n^{i_n} \end{vmatrix}.$$

If $i_j = a_j$, except when $j = t, u, v, \ldots, w$, we find, as before, there being s elements in the set $(t, u, v, \ldots, w)$, that

$$(p^{a_{k+1} \cdots a_n})^{s-1} p^{i_{k+1} \cdots i_n} = \begin{vmatrix} u_t^{i_t} & \cdot & u_t^{i_w} \\ \cdot & \cdot & \cdot \\ u_w^{i_t} & \cdot & u_w^{i_w} \end{vmatrix}. \tag{5}$$

Finally, we note the following relations between the u_j^i defined in (4) and the x_j^i defined in (1) above.

(i) If $j > k$, and $i \leqslant k$,
$$u_j^{a_j} = p^{a_{k+1} \cdots a_n} = p_{a_0 \ldots a_k} = x_{a_i}^i;$$

(ii) if $i, j > k$, $i \neq j$, and $l, m \leqslant k$, $l \neq m$,
$$u_j^{a_i} = 0 = x_{a_m}^l;$$

(iii) if $i > k$, $j \leqslant k$,
$$u_i^{a_j} = p^{a_{k+1} \cdots a_{i-1} a_j a_{i+1} \cdots a_n}$$
$$= -p_{a_0 \ldots a_{j-1} a_i a_{j+1} \ldots a_n} = -x_{a_i}^j.$$

We now use these results to obtain necessary and sufficient conditions for a given S_h to meet a given S_k in a space of at least t dimensions.

5. Some results on intersections and joins. Let the coordinates of S_h be $(\ldots, p_{i_0 \ldots i_h}, \ldots)$ and let the *dual* coordinates of S_k be $(\ldots, q^{i_{k+1} \ldots i_n}, \ldots)$. We prove

THEOREM I. *Necessary and sufficient conditions that S_h and S_k have a linear space of dimension not less than t in common are*

$$\sum_{\lambda_1, \ldots, \lambda_s} q^{\alpha_{k+1} \ldots \alpha_{n-s} \lambda_1 \ldots \lambda_s} p_{\lambda_1 \ldots \lambda_s \beta_0 \ldots \beta_{h-s}} = 0 \tag{1}$$

for all choices of $\alpha_{k+1}, \ldots, \alpha_{n-s}$; $\beta_0, \ldots, \beta_{h-s}$, where $s = h - t + 1$. A sufficient set of conditions is obtained from (1) if we restrict our choices of $\alpha_{k+1}, \ldots, \alpha_{n-s}$ to all possible selections from $a_{k+1}, \ldots, a_n$, and $\beta_0, \ldots, \beta_{h-s}$ to all possible selections from $b_0, \ldots, b_h$, where $a_{k+1}, \ldots, a_n$ and $b_0, \ldots, b_h$ are sets of $n-k$ and $h+1$ numbers respectively chosen from the set $0, \ldots, n$ such that

$$q^{a_{k+1} \ldots a_n} p_{b_0 \ldots b_h} \neq 0. \tag{2}$$

Clearly if

$$q^{a_{k+1} \ldots a_n} p_{b_0 \ldots b_h} = 0$$

for all sets $(a_{n-s+1}, \ldots, a_n)$, $(b_{h-s+1}, \ldots, b_h)$, condition (1) is satisfied. We need only consider sets $a_{k+1}, \ldots, a_n$; $b_0, \ldots, b_h$, therefore, for which (2) is true.

If we now write

$$u_j^i = q^{a_{k+1} \ldots a_{j-1} i a_{j+1} \ldots a_n},$$

and

$$x_j^i = p_{b_0 \ldots b_{i-1} j b_{i+1} \ldots b_h},$$

the equations of S_k can be written

$$\sum_{i=0}^{n} u_j^i x_i = 0 \quad (j = k+1, \ldots, n),$$

and the points

$$x^i = (x_0^i, \ldots, x_n^i) \quad (i = 0, \ldots, h)$$

form a basis for S_h. Any point of S_h can be written in the form $\sum_0^h \lambda_a x^a$, and lies in S_k if and only if

$$\sum_{i=0}^{n} \sum_{a=0}^{h} u_j^i x_i^a \lambda_a = 0 \quad (j = k+1, \ldots, n). \tag{3}$$

These equations in $(\lambda_0, \ldots, \lambda_h)$ determine the $(h+1)$-tuples such that $\sum_0^h \lambda_a x^a$ lies in S_k. Hence a necessary and sufficient condition that

S_h and S_k meet in an S_t (at least) is that the equations (3) should have at least $t+1$ independent solutions. The rank of the matrix

$$\left(\sum_{i=0}^{n} u_j^i x_i^a \right)$$

must therefore be $h-t$, at most [II, § 6]. For this to be the case it is necessary and sufficient that every determinant of $s = h-t+1$ rows and columns extracted from this matrix should be zero. A set of necessary and sufficient conditions is therefore given by the equations

$$\begin{vmatrix} \sum_{\lambda=0}^{n} u_{i_1}^\lambda x_\lambda^{j_1} & \cdot & \sum_{\lambda=0}^{n} u_{i_1}^\lambda x_\lambda^{j_s} \\ \cdot & \cdot & \cdot \\ \sum_{\lambda=0}^{n} u_{i_s}^\lambda x_\lambda^{j_1} & \cdot & \sum_{\lambda=0}^{n} u_{i_s}^\lambda x_\lambda^{j_s} \end{vmatrix} = 0, \tag{4}$$

for all possible selections of $i_1, ..., i_s$ from $(k+1, ..., n)$ and of $j_1, ..., j_s$ from $(0, ..., h)$. The above determinant, by II, § 8, Th. V,

$$\doteq \sum_{\lambda_1, ..., \lambda_s} \begin{vmatrix} u_{i_1}^{\lambda_1} & \cdot & u_{i_1}^{\lambda_s} \\ \cdot & \cdot & \cdot \\ u_{i_s}^{\lambda_1} & \cdot & u_{i_s}^{\lambda_s} \end{vmatrix} \begin{vmatrix} x_{\lambda_1}^{j_1} & \cdot & x_{\lambda_1}^{j_s} \\ \cdot & \cdot & \cdot \\ x_{\lambda_s}^{j_1} & \cdot & x_{\lambda_s}^{j_s} \end{vmatrix}.$$

Now, by equation (5) of the preceding section,

$$\begin{vmatrix} u_{i_1}^{\lambda_1} & \cdot & u_{i_1}^{\lambda_s} \\ \cdot & \cdot & \cdot \\ u_{i_s}^{\lambda_1} & \cdot & u_{i_s}^{\lambda_s} \end{vmatrix} = \epsilon (q^{a_{k+1} \cdots a_n})^{s-1} q^{\alpha_{k+1} \cdots \alpha_{n-s} \lambda_1 \cdots \lambda_s},$$

where $\alpha_{k+1}, ..., \alpha_{n-s}$ is a selection of $n-k-s$ numbers of the set $a_{k+1}, ..., a_n$ which is uniquely determined by the set $i_1, ..., i_s$, no two distinct sets $i_1, ..., i_s$ giving the same selection $\alpha_{k+1}, ..., \alpha_{n-s}$, and ϵ is $+1$ or -1 and is uniquely determined by $i_1, ..., i_s$. Similarly, using equation (3) of the last section,

$$\begin{vmatrix} x_{\lambda_1}^{j_1} & \cdot & x_{\lambda_1}^{j_s} \\ \cdot & \cdot & \cdot \\ x_{\lambda_s}^{j_1} & \cdot & x_{\lambda_s}^{j_s} \end{vmatrix} = \epsilon' (p_{b_0 \ldots b_h})^{s-1} p_{\lambda_1 \ldots \lambda_s \beta_0 \ldots \beta_{h-s}},$$

where $\beta_0, ..., \beta_{h-s}$ is a selection from the set $b_0, ..., b_h$ which is uniquely determined by $j_1, ..., j_s$, and $\epsilon' = \pm 1$ is also uniquely determined by $j_1, ..., j_s$. We can therefore write, instead of (4),

$$\sum_{\lambda_1, ..., \lambda_s} \epsilon\epsilon' (q^{a_{k+1} \cdots a_n} p_{b_0 \ldots b_h})^{s-1} q^{\alpha_{k+1} \cdots \alpha_{n-s} \lambda_1 \cdots \lambda_s} p_{\lambda_1 \ldots \lambda_s \beta_0 \ldots \beta_{h-s}} = 0, \tag{5}$$

where the factor $\epsilon\epsilon'$, being independent of $\lambda_1, ..., \lambda_s$, may be ignored.

Using (2) it follows that the necessary and sufficient conditions (5) are equivalent to equations (1) for all choices of $\alpha_{k+1}, ..., \alpha_{n-s}$ from $a_{k+1}, ..., a_n$, and of $\beta_0, ..., \beta_{h-s}$ from $b_0, ..., b_h$. This proves the theorem.

We now obtain some formulae connected with the joins and intersections of linear spaces. Let S_h have the coordinates $(..., p_{i_0 ... i_h}, ...)$, S_k the coordinates $(..., q_{i_0 ... i_k}, ...)$, and, as usual, denote the dual coordinates of S_h by $(..., p^{i_{h+1} ... i_n}, ...)$ and those of S_k by $(..., q^{i_{k+1} ... i_n}, ...)$. Let

$$x^i = (x_0^i, ..., x_n^i) \quad (i = 0, ..., h)$$

be a basis for S_h, and

$$y^i = (y_0^i, ..., y_n^i) \quad (i = 0, ..., k)$$

be a basis for S_k. A necessary and sufficient condition that S_h and S_k meet is that there exist elements $\lambda_0, ..., \lambda_h$ and $\mu_0, ..., \mu_k$, not all zero, such that

$$\sum_0^h \lambda_i x^i = \sum_0^k \mu_i y^i.$$

A necessary and sufficient condition, therefore, is that the matrix

$$\begin{pmatrix} x_0^0 & \cdot & x_n^0 \\ \cdot & \cdot & \cdot \\ x_0^h & \cdot & x_n^h \\ y_0^0 & \cdot & y_n^0 \\ \cdot & \cdot & \cdot \\ y_0^k & \cdot & y_n^k \end{pmatrix} \tag{6}$$

should be of rank $h + k + 1$ at most, since the rows are to be linearly dependent. Hence all determinants of $h + k + 2$ rows and columns extracted from this $(h + k + 2) \times (n + 1)$ matrix must vanish. If we consider the determinant which corresponds to the columns with suffix $i_0, ..., i_{h+k+1}$, and expand it by Laplace's formula [II, §8, Th. II], we have

$$\sum_{j_0, ..., j_{h+k+1}} \delta_{i_0 ... i_{h+k+1}}^{j_0 ... j_{h+k+1}} p_{j_0 ... j_h} q_{j_{h+1} ... j_{h+k+1}} = 0.$$

It can be verified that these conditions are equivalent to those given by Theorem I.

If S_h and S_k do not meet, the points $x^0, ..., x^h, y^0, ..., y^k$ are linearly independent [V, §4], and determine the *join* of the two spaces.

Hence the determinants of $h+k+2$ rows and columns extracted from the matrix (6) are the Grassmann coordinates of the join of the two spaces. We may write these coordinates as $(\ldots, r_{i_0 \ldots i_{h+k+1}}, \ldots)$, where

$$r_{i_0 \ldots i_{h+k+1}} = \sum_{j_0, \ldots, j_{h+k+1}} \delta^{j_0 \ldots j_{h+k+1}}_{i_0 \ldots i_{h+k+1}} p_{j_0 \ldots j_h} q_{j_{h+1} \ldots j_{h+k+1}}. \tag{7}$$

Ignoring a common factor, we may also write these equations as

$$r_{i_0 \ldots i_{h+k+1}} = \sum_j \pm p_{j_0 \ldots j_h} q_{j_{h+1} \ldots j_{h+k+1}}, \tag{8}$$

where the summation is over all derangements $j_0, \ldots, j_{h+k+1}$ of $i_0, \ldots, i_{h+k+1}$, the positive sign being taken with even, and the negative sign with odd derangements.

Introducing the dual coordinates, we have

$$q_{j_{h+1} \ldots j_{h+k+1}} = (-1)^{(h+1)(k+1)} q^{j_0 \ldots j_h i_{h+k+2} \ldots i_n},$$

where $(j_0, \ldots, j_{h+k+1}, i_{h+k+2}, \ldots, i_n)$ is an even derangement of $(i_0, \ldots, i_n)$. Hence

$$r_{i_0 \ldots i_{h+k+1}} = r^{i_{h+k+2} \ldots i_n} = \sum_j (-1)^{(h+1)(k+1)} p_{j_0 \ldots j_h} q^{j_0 \ldots j_h i_{h+k+2} \ldots i_n}$$

$$= (-1)^{(h+1)(k+1)} \sum_j p_{j_0 \ldots j_h} q^{j_0 \ldots j_h i_{h+k+2} \ldots i_n}.$$

Ignoring the common factor ± 1, we may write this as

$$r^{i_{h+k+2} \ldots i_n} = \sum_j p_{j_0 \ldots j_h} q^{j_0 \ldots j_h i_{h+k+2} \ldots i_n}.$$

An alternative form is

$$r^{i_{h+k+2} \ldots i_n} = \sum_{j_0, \ldots, j_n} \pm p^{i_{h+k+2} \ldots i_n j_0 \ldots j_k} q^{j_{k+1} \ldots j_n}.$$

This follows from equation (8), the proof being left to the reader. By duality, or by an exactly similar argument, we show that if $h+k > n$, and

$$t^{i_1 \ldots i_{2n-h-k}} = \sum_j \delta^{i_1 \ldots i_{2n-h-k}}_{j_1 \ldots j_{2n-h-k}} p^{j_1 \ldots j_{n-h}} q^{j_{n-h+1} \ldots j_{2n-h-k}},$$

then
$$t^{i_1 \ldots i_{2n-h-k}} = 0 \quad (\text{all } i_1, \ldots, i_{2n-h-k})$$

is the condition that S_h and S_k meet in a space of more than $h+k-n$ dimensions, but if these spaces meet in a space of dimension $h+k-n$, the coordinates of their intersection are $(\ldots, t^{i_1 \ldots i_{2n-h-k}}, \ldots)$. Equivalent formulae can also be found for $t_{i_0 \ldots i_{h+k-n}}$.

We now obtain the coordinates of the projection, from a vertex S_h, of a space S_k on to a space S_{n-h-1}. We assume that S_h does not meet S_k. The projection is then the intersection of the *join* of S_h and S_k with S_{n-h-1}. The coordinates of the join of S_h and S_k are given by

$$r_{i_0 \ldots i_{h+k+1}} = \sum_j \delta_{i_0 \ldots i_{h+k+1}}^{j_0 \ldots j_{h+k+1}} p_{j_0 \ldots j_h} q_{j_{h+1} \ldots j_{h+k+1}},$$

and if the coordinates of S_{n-h-1} are $(\ldots, s^{i_0 \ldots i_h}, \ldots)$, the coordinates $(\ldots, t_{i_0 \ldots i_k}, \ldots)$ of the intersection of this join with S_{n-h-1} are given by the equations

$$t_{i_0 \ldots i_k} = \sum_j \sum_i \sum_m \delta_{i_0 \ldots i_h l_0 \ldots i_k}^{j_0 \ldots j_h m_0 \ldots m_k} p_{j_0 \ldots j_h} q_{m_0 \ldots m_k} s^{i_0 \ldots i_h}.$$

In the case $h = 0$ the coordinates of the projection of S_k from the point $b = (b_0, \ldots, b_n)$ on to the prime $\sum_0^n B_i x_i = 0$ can be obtained more simply. Let

$$x^i = (x_0^i, \ldots, x_n^i) \quad (i = 0, \ldots, k)$$

be a basis for S_k. Since b does not lie in S_k, the points $b, x^0, \ldots, x^k$ are linearly independent. Hence the points $y^0, \ldots, y^k$, where

$$y^i = \varDelta x^i - \left(\sum_j B_j x_j^i \right) b \quad (\varDelta = b_0 B_0 + \ldots + b_n B_n \neq 0)$$

are linearly independent. But since

$$\sum_j B_j y_j^i = \varDelta \sum_j B_j x_j^i - \left(\sum_j B_j x_j^i \right) \varDelta = 0,$$

the points $y^0, \ldots, y^k$ lie in the prime $\sum_i B_i x_i = 0$. Hence these points, which lie in the projection of S_k on to the prime, may be taken as a basis for the projection. Therefore

$$t_{i_0 \ldots i_k} = \begin{vmatrix} y_{i_0}^0 & \cdot & y_{i_k}^0 \\ y_{i_0}^1 & \cdot & y_{i_k}^1 \\ \cdot & \cdot & \cdot \\ y_{i_0}^k & \cdot & y_{i_k}^k \end{vmatrix}$$

$$= \begin{vmatrix} \varDelta x_{i_0}^0 - \lambda^0 b_{i_0} & \cdot & \varDelta x_{i_k}^0 - \lambda^0 b_{i_k} \\ \cdot & \cdot & \cdot \\ \varDelta x_{i_0}^k - \lambda^k b_{i_0} & \cdot & \varDelta x_{i_k}^k - \lambda^k b_{i_k} \end{vmatrix},$$

where
$$\lambda^i = \sum_j B_j x_j^i.$$

Expanding this determinant we obtain

$$t_{i_0 \ldots i_k} = \Delta^{k+1} \begin{vmatrix} x_{i_0}^0 & . & x_{i_k}^0 \\ . & & . \\ x_{i_0}^k & . & x_{i_k}^k \end{vmatrix} - \Delta^k \sum_j b_{ij} \begin{vmatrix} x_{i_0}^0 & . & x_{i_{j-1}}^0 & \lambda^0 & x_{i_{j+1}}^0 & . & x_{i_k}^0 \\ . & . & . & . & . & . & . \\ x_{i_0}^k & . & x_{i_{j-1}}^k & \lambda^k & x_{i_{j+1}}^k & . & x_{i_k}^k \end{vmatrix},$$

and substituting for λ^i we find that

$$t_{i_0 \ldots i_k} = \Delta^{k+1} p_{i_0 \ldots i_k} - \Delta^k \sum_j \sum_l b_{ij} B_l p_{i_0 \ldots i_{j-1} l i_{j+1} \ldots i_k}.$$

We have therefore proved

THEOREM III. *The coordinates* $(\ldots, t_{i_0 \ldots i_k}, \ldots)$ *of the projection of the k-space* $(\ldots, p_{i_0 \ldots i_k}, \ldots)$ *from the point* $(b_0, \ldots, b_n)$ *on to the prime*

$$B_0 x_0 + \ldots + B_n x_n = 0$$

are given by the equations

$$t_{i_0 \ldots i_k} = \Delta p_{i_0 \ldots i_k} - \sum_j \sum_l (-1)^j b_{ij} B_l p_{i_0 \ldots i_{j-1} l i_{j+1} \ldots i_k},$$

where
$$\Delta = B_0 b_0 + \ldots + B_n b_n.$$

6. Quadratic p-relations.

We have shown that any k-space S_k has a set of coordinates $(\ldots, p_{i_0 \ldots i_k}, \ldots)$ in a given allowable coordinate system, but it does not follow that a set of $\binom{n+1}{k+1}$ elements $p_{i_0 \ldots i_k}$ which are skew-symmetric in their suffixes, and are not all zero, are necessarily the coordinates of an S_k. Indeed, this is not the case, except when $k = 0$ or $k = n-1$. We must therefore consider what algebraic relations, if any, connect the coordinates of an S_k.

We first show that there can be no *linear* relation. Suppose that

$$\sum_{i_0, \ldots, i_k} u_{i_0 \ldots i_k} P_{i_0 \ldots i_k}$$

is a homogeneous linear form in the $\binom{n+1}{k+1}$ independent indeterminates $P_{i_0 \ldots i_k}$ (which are skew-symmetric in their suffixes) such that

$$\sum_{i_0, \ldots, i_k} u_{i_0 \ldots i_k} p_{i_0 \ldots i_k} = 0, \tag{1}$$

whenever $P_{i_0 \ldots i_k}$ is replaced by the coordinates $p_{i_0 \ldots i_k}$ of any k-space. We show that each coefficient $u_{i_0 \ldots i_k}$ must be zero. Let us show that $u_{a_0 \ldots a_k}$, for instance, is zero.

Consider the k-space defined by the $k+1$ points

$$x^i = (\delta_0^{a_i}, \ldots, \delta_n^{a_i}) \quad (i = 0, \ldots, k).$$

We see at once that

$$p_{i_0 \ldots i_k} = 0,$$

unless $i_0, \ldots, i_k$ is a derangement of $a_0, \ldots, a_k$, whilst $p_{a_0 \ldots a_k} = 1$. The relation (1) becomes

$$u_{a_0 \ldots a_k} = 0.$$

Thus we have

THEOREM I. *The coordinates of the k-spaces in $[n]$ do not satisfy any linear relation of the form*

$$\sum_{i_0, \ldots, i_k} u_{i_0 \ldots i_k} p_{i_0 \ldots i_k} = 0.$$

There are, however, relations of higher degree satisfied by the coordinates of every S_k in $[n]$. We assume that $k \neq 0$, and $k \neq n-1$, and denote by $F(P)$ a homogeneous polynomial in the $\binom{n+1}{k+1}$ independent indeterminates $P_{i_0 \ldots i_k}$ (which are skew-symmetric in their suffixes), and denote by $F(p)$ the result of replacing $P_{i_0 \ldots i_k}$ by the coordinates $p_{i_0 \ldots i_k}$ of an S_k. We seek non-zero forms $F(P)$ such that $F(p) = 0$ for every S_k in $[n]$.

Let $i_1, \ldots, i_k$ be k distinct numbers which are chosen from the set $0, \ldots, n$, and let $j_0, \ldots, j_{k+1}$ be $k+2$ distinct numbers chosen from the same set. We define

$$F_{i_1 \ldots i_k, j_0 \ldots j_{k+1}}(P) = \sum_{\lambda = 0}^{k+1} (-1)^\lambda P_{i_1 \ldots i_k j_\lambda} P_{j_0 \ldots j_{\lambda-1} j_{\lambda+1} \ldots j_{k+1}}, \quad (2)$$

and prove that

$$F_{i_1 \ldots i_k, j_0 \ldots j_{k+1}}(p) = 0$$

for every S_k.

Let

$$A^i = (\alpha_0^i, \ldots, \alpha_n^i) \quad (i = 0, \ldots, k)$$

be a basis for any given S_k. Then

$$F_{i_1 \ldots i_k, j_0 \ldots j_{k+1}}(p)$$

$$= \sum_{\lambda = 0}^{k+1} (-1)^\lambda \begin{vmatrix} \alpha_{i_1}^0 & . & \alpha_{i_k}^0 & \alpha_{j_\lambda}^0 \\ . & . & . & . \\ \alpha_{i_1}^k & . & \alpha_{i_k}^k & \alpha_{j_\lambda}^k \end{vmatrix} \begin{vmatrix} \alpha_{j_0}^0 & . & \alpha_{j_{\lambda-1}}^0 & \alpha_{j_{\lambda+1}}^0 & . & \alpha_{j_{k+1}}^0 \\ . & . & . & . & . & . \\ \alpha_{j_0}^k & . & \alpha_{j_{\lambda-1}}^k & \alpha_{j_{\lambda+1}}^k & . & \alpha_{j_{k+1}}^k \end{vmatrix}.$$

If A^μ is the cofactor of $\alpha_{j\lambda}^\mu$ in the determinant

$$\begin{vmatrix} \alpha_{i_1}^0 & . & \alpha_{i_k}^0 & \alpha_{j\lambda}^0 \\ . & . & . & . \\ \alpha_{i_1}^k & . & \alpha_{i_k}^k & \alpha_{j\lambda}^k \end{vmatrix},$$

we may write

$$F_{i_1\ldots i_k,\,j_0\ldots j_{k+1}}(p)$$

$$= \sum_{\mu=0}^{k} \sum_{\lambda=0}^{k+1} (-1)^\lambda A^\mu \alpha_{j\lambda}^\mu \begin{vmatrix} \alpha_{j_0}^0 & . & \alpha_{j_{\lambda-1}}^0 & \alpha_{j_{\lambda+1}}^0 & . & \alpha_{j_{k+1}}^0 \\ . & . & . & . & . & . \\ \alpha_{j_0}^k & . & \alpha_{j_{\lambda-1}}^k & \alpha_{j_{\lambda+1}}^k & . & \alpha_{j_{k+1}}^k \end{vmatrix}$$

$$= \sum_{\mu=0}^{k} A^\mu \begin{vmatrix} \alpha_{j_0}^\mu & . & \alpha_{j\lambda}^\mu & . & \alpha_{j_{k+1}}^\mu \\ \alpha_{j_0}^0 & . & \alpha_{j\lambda}^0 & . & \alpha_{j_{k+1}}^0 \\ . & . & . & . & . \\ \alpha_{j_0}^k & . & \alpha_{j\lambda}^k & . & \alpha_{j_{k+1}}^k \end{vmatrix}.$$

Since every determinant in the above sum has two rows equal, every term in the sum vanishes, and therefore

$$F_{i_1\ldots i_k,\,j_0\ldots j_{k+1}}(p) = 0. \tag{3}$$

This relation simplifies when the numbers $i_1, \ldots, i_k$ include some of $j_0, \ldots, j_{k+1}$. If

$$i_r = j_r \quad (r = 1, \ldots, k),$$

$$F_{i_1\ldots i_k,\,j_0\ldots j_{k+1}}(P) = P_{i_1\ldots i_k j_0} P_{i_1\ldots i_k j_{k+1}} + (-1)^{k+1} P_{i_1\ldots i_k j_{k+1}} P_{j_0 i_1\ldots i_k},$$

all other terms vanishing. Since the indeterminates are assumed to be skew-symmetric in the suffixes we have

$$F_{i_1\ldots i_k,\,j_0\ldots j_{k+1}}(P) = P_{i_1\ldots i_k j_0} P_{i_1\ldots i_k j_{k+1}} - P_{i_1\ldots i_k j_0} P_{i_1\ldots i_k j_{k+1}} = 0.$$

In this case there is no relation. We obtain non-trivial relations containing *three* terms if

$$j_0, \ldots, j_{k+1} = i_1, \ldots, i_{k-1}, l, m, n$$

respectively. Writing $i_k = h$, we find that

$$F_{i_1\ldots i_k,\,j_0\ldots j_{k+1}}(P) = (-1)^{k-1} P_{i_1\ldots i_{k-1} hl} P_{i_1\ldots i_{k-1} mn}$$
$$+ (-1)^k P_{i_1\ldots i_{k-1} hm} P_{i_1\ldots i_{k-1} ln} + (-1)^{k+1} P_{i_1\ldots i_{k-1} hn} P_{i_1\ldots i_{k-1} lm},$$

and therefore

$$p_{i_1\ldots i_{k-1} hl} p_{i_1\ldots i_{k-1} mn} + p_{i_1\ldots i_{k-1} hm} p_{i_1\ldots i_{k-1} nl}$$
$$+ p_{i_1\ldots i_{k-1} hn} p_{i_1\ldots i_{k-1} lm} = 0.$$

We now obtain an alternative form for the relations (3). If we write

$$i_0, \ldots, i_{s-1}, i_{s+1}, \ldots, i_k, i_s, j_0, \ldots, j_k$$

in place of
$$i_1, \ldots, i_s, \quad i_{s+1}, \ldots, i_k, j_0, j_1, \ldots, j_{k+1}$$

for any $0 \leqslant s \leqslant k$, the relation (3) becomes

$$F_{i_0 \ldots i_{s-1} i_{s+1} \ldots i_k, i_s j_0 \ldots j_k}(p)$$

$$= p_{i_0 \ldots i_{s-1} i_{s+1} \ldots i_k i_s} p_{j_0 \ldots j_k}$$

$$+ \sum_{\lambda=1}^{k+1} (-1)^\lambda p_{i_0 \ldots i_{s-1} i_{s+1} \ldots i_k j_{\lambda-1}} p_{i_s j_0 \ldots j_{\lambda-2} j_\lambda \ldots j_k} = 0,$$

or

$$(-1)^{k-s} p_{i_0 \ldots i_k} p_{j_0 \ldots j_k}$$

$$+ \sum_{\lambda=0}^{k} (-1)^{\lambda+k-s+1} p_{i_0 \ldots i_{s-1} j_\lambda i_{s+1} \ldots i_k} (-1)^\lambda p_{j_0 \ldots j_{\lambda-1} i_s j_{\lambda+1} \ldots j_k} = 0,$$

using the skew-symmetric property of the coordinates with respect to the interchange of suffixes. Hence (3) may always be written in the form

$$p_{i_0 \ldots i_k} p_{j_0 \ldots j_k} = \sum_{\lambda=0}^{k} p_{i_0 \ldots i_{s-1} j_\lambda i_{s+1} \ldots i_k} p_{j_0 \ldots j_{\lambda-1} i_s j_{\lambda+1} \ldots j_k}. \qquad (4)$$

The relations (3), or (4), will be referred to as *the quadratic p-relations*. We now prove

THEOREM II. *If* $(\ldots, p_{i_0 \ldots i_k}, \ldots)$ *be* $\binom{n+1}{k+1}$ *elements of K which are not all zero, which are skew-symmetric in the suffixes and which satisfy the quadratic p-relations, then there is a k-space which has coordinates* $(\ldots, p_{i_0 \ldots i_k}, \ldots)$.

If there is such a k-space it is, of course, unique. Since not all the coordinates are zero we may suppose that

$$p_{a_0 \ldots a_k} \neq 0.$$

It will simplify our notation if we assume that

$$a_i = i \quad (i = 0, \ldots, k).$$

It will be evident that the method of proof can be extended to any set $a_0, \ldots, a_k$. We have, then,

$$p_{0 \ldots k} \neq 0,$$

and since we are dealing with homogeneous coordinates we may assume that $p_{0\ldots k} = 1$. If

$$b_j^i = p_{0\ldots i-1\,j\,i+1\ldots k} \quad (i = 0,\ldots,k;\ j = 0,\ldots,n),$$

we shall prove that the $k+1$ points

$$B^i = (b_0^i,\ldots,b_n^i) \quad (i = 0,\ldots,k)$$

determine a k-space with the prescribed coordinates.

Since $b_i^i = p_{0\ldots k} = 1$ $(i = 0,\ldots,k)$, the submatrix formed by the first $k+1$ columns of the matrix (b_j^i) is the unit matrix. Hence this matrix has rank $k+1$, and the points $B^0,\ldots,B^k$ determine a k-space, which we call S_k. If

$$q_{i_0\ldots i_k} = \begin{vmatrix} b_{i_0}^0 & \cdot & b_{i_k}^0 \\ \cdot & \cdot & \cdot \\ b_{i_0}^k & \cdot & b_{i_k}^k \end{vmatrix},$$

the Grassmann coordinates of S_k are $(\ldots, q_{i_0\ldots i_k}, \ldots)$, and all that we must prove is that

$$q_{i_0\ldots i_k} = p_{i_0\ldots i_k} \quad (\text{all } i_0,\ldots,i_k).$$

Since the $p_{i_0\ldots i_k}$ are skew-symmetric in the suffixes, this result is independent of the order of the suffixes. Let the set $i_0,\ldots,i_k$ contain the integers $l_1, l_2, \ldots, l_s$ which are greater than k, and write the set

$$i_0,\ldots,i_k$$
$$= 0,\ldots,j_1-1,l_1,j_1+1,\ldots,j_2-1,l_2,j_2+1,\ldots,j_s-1,l_s,j_s+1,\ldots,k.$$

Since
$$b_j^i = \delta_j^i \quad (j \leqslant k),$$

the determinant which gives $q_{i_0\ldots i_k}$ can be simplified by expanding it in terms of the elements of any column whose suffix is in the natural order of the integers. This column contains only one non-zero term, and this is on the principal diagonal, and is unity. Hence, noting which row and column are removed by this simplification from the determinant we are considering, we eventually find that

$$q_{i_0\ldots i_k} = \begin{vmatrix} b_{l_1}^{j_1} & \cdot & b_{l_s}^{j_1} \\ \cdot & \cdot & \cdot \\ b_{l_1}^{j_s} & \cdot & b_{l_s}^{j_s} \end{vmatrix}. \tag{5}$$

Our theorem is now proved by induction on s.

If $s = 0$,
$$i_0,\ldots,i_k = 0,\ldots,k,$$

and
$$q_{i_0\ldots i_k} = 1 = p_{i_0\ldots i_k}.$$

If $s = 1$, $\qquad q_{i_0 \ldots i_k} = b_{l_1}^{j_1} = p_{0 \ldots j_1 - 1 \, l_1 \, j_1 + 1 \ldots k}$,

so that the theorem is also true when $s = 1$. We therefore assume that if $s < t$, $p_{i_0 \ldots i_k} = q_{i_0 \ldots i_k}$; that is,

$$p_{i_0 \ldots i_k} = \begin{vmatrix} b_{l_1}^{j_1} & \cdot & b_{l_s}^{j_1} \\ \cdot & \cdot & \cdot \\ b_{l_1}^{j_s} & \cdot & b_{l_s}^{j_s} \end{vmatrix}.$$

Now suppose that $s = t$. Since the $p_{i_0 \ldots i_k}$ satisfy the quadratic p-relations we have, from (4),

$$p_{i_0 \ldots i_k} p_{0 \ldots k} = \sum_{j=0}^{k} p_{i_0 \ldots i_{r-1} j \, i_{r+1} \ldots i_k} p_{0 \ldots j - 1 \, i_r \, j + 1 \ldots k},$$

where r is at our disposal ($0 \leqslant r \leqslant k$). Choose r so that $i_r = l_t$. Then

$$p_{i_0 \ldots i_{r-1} j \, i_{r+1} \ldots i_k} = 0,$$

unless $j = j_1, \ldots, j_t$, these being the only missing integers of the set $0, \ldots, k$. If now $j = j_\lambda$, say, $p_{i_0 \ldots i_{r-1} j_\lambda i_{r+1} \ldots i_k}$ has only $t - 1$ suffixes *not* chosen from $(0, \ldots, k)$, and hence, by the hypothesis of induction

$$p_{i_0 \ldots i_{r-1} j_\lambda i_{r+1} \ldots i_k} = \begin{vmatrix} b_{i_0}^0 & \cdot & b_{i_{r-1}}^0 & b_{j_\lambda}^0 & b_{i_{r+1}}^0 & \cdot & b_{i_k}^0 \\ \cdot & \cdot & \cdot & \cdot & \cdot & \cdot & \cdot \\ b_{i_0}^k & \cdot & b_{i_{r-1}}^k & b_{j_\lambda}^k & b_{i_{r+1}}^k & \cdot & b_{i_k}^k \end{vmatrix}$$

$$= \begin{vmatrix} b_{l_1}^{j_1} & \cdot & b_{l_{t-1}}^{j_1} & b_{j_\lambda}^{j_1} \\ \cdot & \cdot & \cdot & \\ b_{l_1}^{j_{\lambda-1}} & \cdot & b_{l_{t-1}}^{j_{\lambda-1}} & b_{j_\lambda}^{j_{\lambda-1}} \\ b_{l_1}^{j_\lambda} & \cdot & b_{l_{t-1}}^{j_\lambda} & b_{j_\lambda}^{j_\lambda} \\ b_{l_1}^{j_{\lambda+1}} & \cdot & b_{l_{t-1}}^{j_{\lambda+1}} & b_{j_\lambda}^{j_{\lambda+1}} \\ \cdot & \cdot & \cdot & \\ b_{l_1}^{j_t} & \cdot & b_{l_{t-1}}^{j_t} & b_{j_\lambda}^{j_t} \end{vmatrix}$$

$$= (-1)^{t+\lambda} \begin{vmatrix} b_{l_1}^{j_1} & \cdot & b_{l_{t-1}}^{j_1} \\ \cdot & \cdot & \cdot \\ b_{l_1}^{j_{\lambda-1}} & \cdot & b_{l_{t-1}}^{j_{\lambda-1}} \\ b_{l_1}^{j_{\lambda+1}} & \cdot & b_{l_{t-1}}^{j_{\lambda+1}} \\ \cdot & \cdot & \cdot \\ b_{l_1}^{j_t} & \cdot & b_{l_{t-1}}^{j_t} \end{vmatrix},$$

on expanding by the last column, the only non-zero element in which is $b_{j_\lambda}^{j_\lambda} = 1$. Now $p_{0\ldots k} = 1$, and, since $j = j_\lambda$ and $i_r = l_t$, we have $p_{0\ldots j-1\,i_r\,j+1\ldots k} = b_{l_t}^{j_\lambda}$, and so the quadratic p-relation gives us

$$p_{i_0\ldots i_k} = \sum_{\lambda=1}^{t} (-1)^{t+\lambda} b_{l_t}^{j_\lambda} \begin{vmatrix} b_{l_1}^{j_1} & . & b_{l_{t-1}}^{j_1} \\ . & . & . \\ b_{l_1}^{j_{\lambda-1}} & . & b_{l_{t-1}}^{j_{\lambda-1}} \\ b_{l_1}^{j_{\lambda+1}} & . & b_{l_{t-1}}^{j_{\lambda+1}} \\ . & . & . \\ b_{l_1}^{j_t} & . & b_{l_{t-1}}^{j_t} \end{vmatrix}$$

$$= \begin{vmatrix} b_{l_1}^{j_1} & . & b_{l_{t-1}}^{j_1} & b_{l_t}^{j_1} \\ . & . & . & . \\ b_{l_1}^{j_t} & . & b_{l_{t-1}}^{j_t} & b_{l_t}^{j_t} \end{vmatrix},$$

thus proving the theorem for $s = t$. This completes our proof of Theorem II.

We have thus obtained certain necessary and sufficient conditions to be satisfied in order that a set of elements $(\ldots, p_{i_0\ldots i_k}, \ldots)$ of K may be the coordinates of a k-space. In the course of doing this we have found certain conditions—the p-relations—satisfied by the coordinates of a k-space. This raises the question of other relations satisfied by the coordinates of a k-space, and the complete answer to this question is the subject of the next section.

7. The basis theorem. This section is devoted to the following theorem:

THEOREM I. *If $F(P)$ is any homogeneous polynomial in $P_{i_0\ldots i_k}$ such that*

$$F(p) = 0$$

for all S_k, then

$$F(P) = \sum_{i,j} A_{i_1\ldots i_k, j_0\ldots j_{k+1}}(P)\,F_{i_1\ldots i_k, j_0\ldots j_{k+1}}(P), \tag{1}$$

where $F_{i_1\ldots i_k, j_0\ldots j_{k+1}}(P)$ is the quadratic form defined in §6, (2), and $A_{i_1\ldots i_k, j_0\ldots j_{k+1}}(P)$ is a homogeneous polynomial in $P_{i_0\ldots i_k}$.

For the purpose of this proof we define a *generic k-space* in $[n]$ to be the k-space defined by $k+1$ points

$$(b_0^i, \ldots, b_n^i) \quad (i = 0, \ldots, k),$$

where the b_j^i are $(n+1)(k+1)$ independent indeterminates over the ground field K. Clearly, if $F(P)$ is any form such that

$$F\left(\left|\begin{array}{ccc} b_{i_0}^0 & . & b_{i_k}^0 \\ . & . & . \\ b_{i_0}^k & . & b_{i_k}^k \end{array}\right|\right) = 0,$$

this relation remains true when the b_j^i are specialised in any way; in particular, when the points $(b_0^i, ..., b_n^i)$ are specialised so that they become $k+1$ independent points of any assigned k-space. Hence

$$F(p) = 0$$

for every S_k. Conversely, if

$$F(p) = 0$$

for every S_k,

$$F\left(\left|\begin{array}{ccc} b_{i_0}^0 & . & b_{i_k}^0 \\ . & . & . \\ b_{i_0}^k & . & b_{i_k}^k \end{array}\right|\right)$$

vanishes for *all* specialisations of the b_j^i. Hence, regarding this last expression as a polynomial in the $(n+1)(k+1)$ indeterminates b_j^i, since it vanishes for all specialisations of these indeterminates, it vanishes identically [III, §8, Th. I]. Thus in order that $F(P)$ should satisfy the conditions of the theorem, it is necessary and sufficient that $F(p) = 0$, where $(..., p_{i_0...i_k}, ...)$ are the coordinates of a *generic* k-space.

Now let $F(P)$ be a form satisfying the conditions of the theorem. We group together all the power products in $F(P)$ which are isobaric in *each* of the suffixes $0, ..., n$; that is, we consider all the power products in which the suffix 0 appears λ_0 times, the suffix 1 appears λ_1 times, and so on. If the sum of such a set of terms is denoted by $f_{\lambda_0...\lambda_n}(P)$,

$$F(P) = \sum_\lambda f_{\lambda_0...\lambda_n}(P).$$

Now let b_j^i $(i = 0, ..., k; j = 0, ..., n)$ be $(n+1)(k+1)$ indeterminates, $\rho_0, ..., \rho_n$ $n+1$ additional indeterminates, and let

$$q_{i_0...i_k} = \left|\begin{array}{ccc} \rho_{i_0} b_{i_0}^0 & . & \rho_{i_k} b_{i_k}^0 \\ . & . & . \\ \rho_{i_0} b_{i_0}^k & . & \rho_{i_k} b_{i_k}^k \end{array}\right|$$

$$= \rho_{i_0} \rho_{i_1} \cdots \rho_{i_k} p_{i_0...i_k}.$$

Then $(\dots, p_{i_0 \dots i_k}, \dots)$ and $(\dots, q_{i_0 \dots i_k}, \dots)$ are coordinates of generic k-spaces. Hence

$$0 = F(q) = \sum_{\lambda} f_{\lambda_0 \dots \lambda_n}(q) = \sum \rho_{i_0}^{\lambda_0} \dots \rho_{i_n}^{\lambda_n} f_{\lambda_0 \dots \lambda_n}(p).$$

Since $\rho_0, \dots, \rho_n$ are independent indeterminates over $K(b_j^i)$, it follows that

$$f_{\lambda_0 \dots \lambda_n}(p) = 0$$

for each set $\lambda_0, \dots, \lambda_n$. Hence

THEOREM II. *Any form $F(P)$ which satisfies the conditions of Theorem I is the sum of forms isobaric in each of the suffixes $0, \dots, n$ which satisfy the conditions of Theorem I.*

In proving our first theorem we may therefore confine ourselves to forms $F(P)$ which are isobaric in each of the suffixes. We now proceed by double induction. First, we assume that k is fixed, and let n vary. If $n = k+1$, an S_k is a prime, given by a single linear equation

$$a_0 x_0 + \dots + a_{k+1} x_{k+1} = 0,$$

and its coordinates are

$$p_{0 \dots i-1 \, i+1 \dots k+1} = (-1)^{k-i+1} p^i = (-1)^{k-i+1} a_i.$$

Since the a_i can take arbitrary values independently, there is no non-zero form $F(P)$ such that

$$F(p) = 0$$

for every S_k in $[k+1]$.

We may therefore assume, as hypothesis of induction, that Theorem I is true for the coordinates of k-spaces in $[n-1]$. Equivalently, we may assume that the theorem is true for forms $F(P)$ in which none of the $P_{i_0 \dots i_k}$ actually present has n as a suffix.

We now suppose that $F(P)$, which is isobaric in each suffix, is isobaric of weight τ in the suffix n, and is of degree t in $P_{i_0 \dots i_k}$. By the hypothesis of induction made above, Theorem I is true if $\tau = 0$. We therefore make the further hypothesis of induction that the theorem is true for forms $F(P)$ which are isobaric of weight less than τ in the suffix n.

We write

$$\frac{\partial F(p)}{\partial p_{i_0 \dots i_k}}$$

to denote the result of replacing $P_{i_0 \dots i_k}$ by the coordinates $p_{i_0 \dots i_k}$ of an S_k in

$$\frac{\partial F(P)}{\partial P_{i_0 \dots i_k}}.$$

Let b_j^i $(i = 0, ..., k; \; j = 0, ..., n)$ be independent indeterminates, and let

$$p_{i_0 ... i_k} = \begin{vmatrix} b_{i_0}^0 & . & b_{i_k}^0 \\ . & . & . \\ b_{i_0}^k & . & b_{i_k}^k \end{vmatrix}.$$

Then if $G(P)$ is any form in $P_{i_0 ... i_k}$, $(G(p)$ does not necessarily vanish), we write

$$g(b) = G(p),$$

and we find that

$$\frac{\partial g(b)}{\partial b_j^i} = \sum_l B_{l_0 ... l_{k-1}}^i \frac{\partial G(p)}{\partial p_{l_0 ... l_{k-1} j}},$$

where

$$B_{l_0 ... l_{k-1}}^i = (-1)^{k+i} \begin{vmatrix} b_{l_0}^0 & . & b_{l_{k-1}}^0 \\ . & . & . \\ b_{l_0}^{i-1} & . & b_{l_{k-1}}^{i-1} \\ b_{l_0}^{i+1} & . & b_{l_{k-1}}^{i+1} \\ . & . & . \\ b_{l_0}^k & . & b_{l_{k-1}}^k \end{vmatrix}.$$

Hence

$$\sum_{i=0}^{k} b_h^i \frac{\partial g(b)}{\partial b_j^i} = \sum_{l_0, ..., l_{k-1}} p_{l_0 ... l_{k-1} h} \frac{\partial G(p)}{\partial p_{l_0 ... l_{k-1} j}}. \tag{2}$$

Since

$$f(b) = F(p) = 0,$$

and the b_j^i are independent indeterminates, $f(b)$ is identically zero, and therefore

$$\sum_{i=0}^{k} b_h^i \frac{\partial f(b)}{\partial b_n^i} = 0.$$

By (2) we can write this in the form

$$\sum_l p_{l_0 ... l_{k-1} h} \frac{\partial F(p)}{\partial p_{l_0 ... l_{k-1} n}} = 0.$$

Hence the n forms

$$\sum P_{l_0 ... l_{k-1} h} \frac{\partial F(P)}{\partial P_{l_0 ... l_{k-1} n}} \qquad (h = 0, ..., n-1)$$

satisfy the conditions of our theorem. Since each of them is isobaric in the suffix n of weight $\tau - 1$, we may write, by the hypothesis of induction,

$$\sum_l P_{l_0 ... l_{k-1} h} \frac{\partial F(P)}{\partial P_{l_0 ... l_{k-1} n}} = \sum A_{i_1 ... i_k, j_0 ... j_{k+1}}^h(P) \, F_{i_1 ... i_k, j_0 ... j_{k+1}}(P), \tag{3}$$

where $h = 0, ..., n-1$.

We propose to deduce (1) from (3) by operating on each side of (3) with

$$D_h = \sum_m P_{m_0 \ldots m_{k-1} n} \frac{\partial}{\partial P_{m_0 \ldots m_{k-1} h}}, \tag{4}$$

and then summing with respect to h from $h = 0$ to $h = n-1$. We first consider the effect of this operation on the left-hand side of (3).

$$\sum_{h=0}^{n-1} \sum_m P_{m_0 \ldots m_{k-1} n} \frac{\partial}{\partial P_{m_0 \ldots m_{k-1} h}} \left(\sum_l P_{l_0 \ldots l_{k-1} h} \frac{\partial F(P)}{\partial P_{l_0 \ldots l_{k-1} n}} \right)$$

$$= \sum_{h=0}^{n-1} \sum_l P_{l_0 \ldots l_{k-1} n} \frac{\partial F(P)}{\partial P_{l_0 \ldots l_{k-1} n}}$$

$$\quad + \sum_{h=0}^{n-1} \sum_m \sum_l P_{m_0 \ldots m_{k-1} n} P_{l_0 \ldots l_{k-1} h} \frac{\partial^2 F(P)}{\partial P_{m_0 \ldots m_{k-1} h} \partial P_{l_0 \ldots l_{k-1} n}}$$

$$= n\tau F(P)$$

$$\quad + \sum_{h=0}^{n} \sum_m \sum_l P_{m_0 \ldots m_{k-1} n} P_{l_0 \ldots l_{k-1} h} \frac{\partial^2 F(P)}{\partial P_{m_0 \ldots m_{k-1} h} \partial P_{l_0 \ldots l_{k-1} n}}$$

$$\quad - \sum_m \sum_l P_{m_0 \ldots m_{k-1} n} P_{l_0 \ldots l_{k-1} n} \frac{\partial^2 F(P)}{\partial P_{m_0 \ldots m_{k-1} n} \partial P_{l_0 \ldots l_{k-1} n}}$$

$$= [n\tau - \tau(\tau-1)] F(P)$$

$$\quad + \sum_{h=0}^{n} \sum_m \sum_l P_{m_0 \ldots m_{k-1} n} P_{l_0 \ldots l_{k-1} h} \frac{\partial^2 F(P)}{\partial P_{m_0 \ldots m_{k-1} h} \partial P_{l_0 \ldots l_{k-1} n}}, \tag{5}$$

using the isobaric property of $F(P)$, and Euler's theorem on homogeneous polynomials.

Now let $a_0, \ldots, a_k$ be a set of numbers chosen from $(0, \ldots, n)$, and consider the terms of the summation in (5) corresponding to

$$m_0, \ldots, m_{k-1} = a_0, \ldots, a_{i-1}, a_{i+1}, \ldots, a_k,$$
$$h = a_i.$$

Then the corresponding terms in the summation in (5) are

$$\sum_l \frac{\partial^2 F(P)}{\partial P_{a_0 \ldots a_k} \partial P_{l_0 \ldots l_{k-1} n}} \left[\sum_{i=0}^{k} P_{l_0 \ldots l_{k-1} a_i} P_{a_0 \ldots a_{i-1} n a_{i+1} \ldots a_k} \right]$$

$$= \sum_l \frac{\partial^2 F(P)}{\partial P_{a_0 \ldots a_k} \partial P_{l_0 \ldots l_{k-1} n}} P_{l_0 \ldots l_{k-1} n} P_{a_0 \ldots a_k}$$

$$\quad - \sum_l \frac{\partial^2 F(P)}{\partial P_{a_0 \ldots a_k} \partial P_{l_0 \ldots l_{k-1} n}} F_{l_0 \ldots l_{k-1}, n a_0 \ldots a_k}(P),$$

by § 6, (2).

Hence,

$$\sum_{h=0}^{n-1} D_h \sum_l P_{l_0 \ldots l_{k-1} h} \frac{\partial F(P)}{\partial P_{l_0 \ldots l_{k-1} n}}$$

$$= \tau(n-\tau+1) F(P) + \sum_a \sum_l P_{a_0 \ldots a_k} P_{l_0 \ldots l_{k-1} n} \frac{\partial^2 F(P)}{\partial P_{a_0 \ldots a_k} \partial P_{l_0 \ldots l_{k-1} n}}$$

$$- \sum_a \sum_l \frac{\partial^2 F(P)}{\partial P_{a_0 \ldots a_k} \partial P_{l_0 \ldots l_{k-1} n}} F_{l_0 \ldots l_{k-1}, n\, a_0 \ldots a_k}(P)$$

$$= \tau(n-\tau+1) F(P) + \sum_l P_{l_0 \ldots l_{k-1} n} \frac{\partial}{\partial P_{l_0 \ldots l_{k-1} n}} \left(\sum_a P_{a_0 \ldots a_k} \frac{\partial F(P)}{\partial P_{a_0 \ldots a_k}} \right)$$

$$- \sum_l P_{l_0 \ldots l_{k-1} n} \frac{\partial F(P)}{\partial P_{l_0 \ldots l_{k-1} n}}$$

$$- \sum_a \sum_l \frac{\partial^2 F(P)}{\partial P_{a_0 \ldots a_k} \partial P_{l_0 \ldots l_{k-1} n}} F_{l_0 \ldots l_{k-1}, n\, a_0 \ldots a_k}(P)$$

$$= \tau(n-\tau+1) F(P) + \tau t F(P)$$

$$- \tau F(P)$$

$$- \sum_a \sum_l \frac{\partial^2 F(P)}{\partial P_{a_0 \ldots a_k} \partial P_{l_0 \ldots l_{k-1} n}} F_{l_0 \ldots l_{k-1}, n\, a_0 \ldots a_k}(P)$$

$$= \tau(n+t-\tau) F(P)$$

$$- \sum_a \sum_l \frac{\partial^2 F(P)}{\partial P_{a_0 \ldots a_k} \partial P_{l_0 \ldots l_{k-1} n}} F_{l_0 \ldots l_{k-1}, n\, a_0 \ldots a_k}(P). \tag{6}$$

Since $t \geqslant \tau$, and we are assuming that $\tau > 0$, the coefficient of $F(P)$ in (6) is not zero.

We now consider the effect of operating on the right-hand side of (3). We have

$$D_h[A^h_{i_1 \ldots i_k, j_0 \ldots j_{k+1}}(P)\, F_{i_1 \ldots i_k, j_0 \ldots j_{k+1}}(P)]$$

$$= D_h[A^h_{i_1 \ldots i_k, j_0 \ldots j_{k+1}}(P)]\, F_{i_1 \ldots i_k, j_0 \ldots j_{k+1}}(P)$$

$$+ A^h_{i_1 \ldots i_k, j_0 \ldots j_{k+1}}(P)\, D_h[F_{i_1 \ldots i_k, j_0 \ldots j_{k+1}}(P)].$$

From this equation, and equations (3) and (6), we derive (1) if we can finally prove that

$$D_h[F_{i_1 \ldots i_k, j_0 \ldots j_{k+1}}(P)]$$

is expressible as a linear combination of forms $F_{a_1 \ldots a_k, b_0 \ldots b_{k+1}}(P)$ for all choices of $i_1, \ldots, i_k, j_0, \ldots, j_{k+1}$ and h.

(i) If h is different from $i_1, \ldots, i_k$ and from $j_0, \ldots, j_{k+1}$, clearly

$$D_h[F_{i_1 \ldots i_k, j_0 \ldots j_{k+1}}(P)] = 0.$$

(ii) If $h = i_1$, say, but $h \neq j_0, \ldots, j_{k+1}$, it is easily seen that

$$D_h[F_{i_1 \ldots i_k, j_0 \ldots j_{k+1}}(P)] = F_{n\, i_2 \ldots i_k, j_0 \ldots j_{k+1}}(P).$$

(iii) If $h = j_0$, say, but $h \neq i_1, \ldots, i_k$,

$$D_h[F_{i_1 \ldots i_k, j_0 \ldots j_{k+1}}(P)] = F_{i_1 \ldots i_k, n\, j_1 \ldots j_{k+1}}(P).$$

(iv) Finally, if $h = i_1 = j_0$, say,

$$D_h[F_{i_1 \ldots i_k, j_0 \ldots j_{k+1}}(P)] = F_{n\, i_2 \ldots i_k, j_0 \ldots j_{k+1}}(P) + F_{i_1 \ldots i_k, n\, j_1 \ldots j_{k+1}}(P).$$

This completes the proof of Theorem I.

CHAPTER VIII

COLLINEATIONS

In this chapter the ground field K is again assumed to be commutative and without characteristic. It will not be necessary at first to assume that it is algebraically closed but, later, results will be obtained on the explicit assumption that K is algebraically closed.

1. Projective transformations.

Let S_m, S_n be two distinct projective spaces over the field K, of dimensions m, n respectively. Fix an allowable coordinate system x in S_n and y in S_m. Then consider the set of equations

$$y_i = \sum_{j=0}^{n} a_{ij} x_j \quad (i = 0, \ldots, m;\ a_{ij} \text{ in } K),$$

which we usually write in matrix form as

$$y = Ax. \tag{1}$$

We may assume that the $(m+1) \times (n+1)$ matrix A is not the zero matrix. The equations (1) associate a point $(y_0, \ldots, y_m)$ of S_m with any point $(x_0, \ldots, x_n)$ of S_n which does not satisfy the equations

$$\sum_{j=0}^{n} a_{ij} x_j = 0 \quad (i = 0, \ldots, m).$$

These points, which we call the *exceptional* points of S_n, fill a linear space of dimension $n - r$, where r is the rank of A.

If $r = n + 1$ there are no exceptional points, and (1) is said to define a *non-singular projective transformation* of S_n on S_m. In order that such a transformation should be possible, we must have $m \geqslant n$.

If $r \leqslant n$, the equations (1) are said to define a *singular projective transformation* of S_n on S_m.

Now let

$$x = Px^* \tag{2}$$

define an allowable transformation of coordinates in S_n, and let

$$y = Qy^* \tag{3}$$

define an allowable transformation of coordinates in S_m. In the new coordinate systems the projective transformation (1) becomes

$$Qy^* = APx^*,$$

that is

$$y^* = Q^{-1}APx^*.$$

By II, §4, Th. II, we can find P and Q so that

$$Q^{-1}AP = \begin{pmatrix} I_r & 0 \\ 0 & 0 \end{pmatrix},$$

where r is the rank of A. Calling r the *rank of the transformation*, we have proved

THEOREM I. *By a suitable choice of coordinate systems in S_n and in S_m any projective transformation of rank r from S_n to S_m can be taken in the form*

$$y_i = x_i \quad (i = 0, ..., r-1), \qquad y_i = 0 \quad (i \geqslant r).$$

We call this form of the equations (1) the *canonical form*, and in discussing the geometry of a projective transformation it is usually convenient to use the canonical form of the equations of the transformation. Before doing this, we consider the points of S_m which lie in the prime

$$\sum_0^m v_i y_i = 0.$$

In the projective transformation (1) these are just the points which arise from the points of S_n lying in

$$\sum_0^n u_j x_j = 0,$$

where

$$u_j = \sum_{i=0}^m v_i a_{ij} \quad (j = 0, ..., n).$$

We write these last equations in matrix form as

$$u = A'v, \tag{4}$$

where A' is the transpose of the matrix A. These equations define *a projective transformation of the primes of S_m on the primes of S_n.* We call this transformation the *dual* of the projective transformation (1). The transformations of coordinates (2) and (3) induce the dual transformations

$$u^* = P'u, \quad v^* = Q'v,$$

respectively. Therefore the dual transformation (4) becomes, in the new coordinate systems,

$$u^* = P'u = P'A'v = P'A'(Q')^{-1}v^*$$
$$= (Q^{-1}AP)'v^*.$$

The relation between a projective transformation and its dual is therefore preserved under transformations of coordinates. This result is otherwise evident from the geometrical definition.

If the point transformation is in canonical form, the dual transformation is in the canonical form

$$u_i = v_i \quad (i = 0, ..., r-1), \qquad u_i = 0 \quad (i \geqslant r).$$

Before discussing the geometry of projective transformations for arbitrary m, n, r, we consider the simple case in which

$$m = n = r - 1.$$

The canonical forms are then

$$y_i = x_i \quad (i = 0, ..., n), \qquad u_i = v_i \quad (i = 0, ..., n).$$

To *each* point of S_n (prime of S_m) there corresponds a point of S_m (prime of S_n), and conversely. The inverse correspondence is also a projective transformation of S_m on S_n. Linearly independent points or primes correspond to linearly independent points or primes, and, similarly, linearly dependent points or primes correspond to linearly dependent points or primes. Hence, any S_k of S_n corresponds to a unique k-space S'_k of S_m, and any S'_k of S_m arises from a unique S_k of S_n. If S_k is determined by the points

$$(b_0^i, ..., b_n^i) \quad (i = 0, ..., k)$$

of S_n, and has Grassmann coordinates $(..., p_{i_0...i_k}, ...)$, S'_k is determined by the points

$$(b_0^i, ..., b_n^i) \quad (i = 0, ..., k)$$

in S_m. Hence its Grassmann coordinates are $(..., q_{i_0...i_k}, ...)$, where

$$q_{i_0...i_k} = \begin{vmatrix} b_{i_0}^0 & . & b_{i_k}^0 \\ . & . & . \\ b_{i_0}^k & . & b_{i_k}^k \end{vmatrix} = p_{i_0...i_k}.$$

It follows that the projective transformation carries the S_k with coordinates $(..., p_{i_0...i_k}, ...)$, into the S'_k of S_m with coordinates

$(..., p_{i_0 ... i_k}, ...)$, for any value of k. In particular, if $k = m-1$, the S_{n-1}
$$(u_0, ..., u_n)$$
of S_n is transformed into the S'_{m-1}
$$(u_0, ..., u_n)$$
of S_m, and this transformation of the primes of S_n into the primes of S_m is the inverse of the dual projective transformation of the primes defined above.

We now return to the study of the projective transformation of rank r of S_n on S_m, where m, n are arbitrary, and $r > 0$. We choose coordinate systems in both spaces so that the projective transformation is given in canonical form by the equations

$$\begin{aligned} y_i &= x_i \quad (i = 0, ..., r-1), \\ y_i &= 0 \quad (i \geqslant r). \end{aligned} \right\} \qquad (5)$$

The dual transformation is then given by the equations

$$\begin{aligned} u_i &= v_i \quad (i = 0, ..., r-1), \\ u_i &= 0 \quad (i \geqslant r). \end{aligned} \right\} \qquad (6)$$

The exceptional points of S_n, that is, those which have no transforms, are the points of the S_{n-r}

$$x_i = 0 \quad (i = 0, ..., r-1).$$

We call this the *singular space* of S_n. The locus of points in S_m which are transforms of points of S_n is given by the equations

$$y_i = 0 \quad (i \geqslant r),$$

and is therefore a linear space of $r-1$ dimensions, Σ_{r-1} say. This we call the *vertex* of the transformation.

Now consider the dual transformation (6). It is also of rank r, and the primes of S_m which have no transforms are given by

$$v_i = 0 \quad (i = 0, ..., r-1).$$

These primes intersect in the vertex Σ_{r-1}. Similarly, the primes of S_n which are transforms of primes in S_m are the primes which pass through the singular space S_{n-r}.

The equations (5) define a non-singular projective transformation T^* of the space S_{r-1} of S_n, given by the equations

$$x_i = 0 \quad (i \geqslant r),$$

on Σ_{r-1}, and the equations (6), for $i = 0, \ldots, r-1$, define the dual of T^*. The properties of this non-singular transformation from S_{r-1} to Σ_{r-1} follow at once from our previous discussion of the non-singular case of projective transformations.

We now consider how the properties of the transformation (5) follow from a knowledge of the properties of T^*. Two points $(x_0, \ldots, x_n)$ and $(x_0', \ldots, x_n')$ of S_n, which are not in the singular locus S_{n-r}, are transformed by (5) into the same point of S_m if and only if

$$x_i = \lambda x_i' \quad (i = 0, \ldots, r-1).$$

Geometrically this condition indicates that the points have the same projection from the singular locus S_{n-r} on S_{r-1}, this projection being $(x_0, \ldots, x_{r-1}, 0, \ldots, 0)$. Now, each point P of S_n which is not in S_{n-r} is joined to S_{n-r} by a space S_{n-r+1}. It follows that a point Q of S_n which is not in S_{n-r} has the same transform as P in S_m if and only if Q lies in the S_{n-r+1} defined by P. Thus, to any S_{n-r+1} in S_n which passes through the singular space S_{n-r} there corresponds a unique point in Σ_{r-1}, and conversely. We may call this correspondence between the S_{n-r+1} through S_{n-r} and the points of Σ_{r-1} a *projective* correspondence. It is easily seen that in this correspondence the $(n-r+1)$-spaces of S_n which pass through the singular locus S_{n-r} and lie in an $(n-r+k+1)$-space through the same S_{n-r} correspond to the points of a k-space in Σ_{r-1}. In particular, primes of S_n through the singular locus correspond to $(r-2)$-spaces in Σ_{r-1}.

The properties of the dual transformation (6) from S_m to S_n are obtained in a similar manner. If Π is any prime in S_m which does not contain the vertex Σ_{r-1}, and if Π' is the corresponding prime in S_n, which passes through the singular locus S_{n-r}, a necessary and sufficient condition that another prime Π_1 of S_m should have the same transform Π' as Π, is that Π and Π_1 meet the vertex Σ_{r-1} in the same $(r-2)$-space. To each S_{r-2} in Σ_{r-1} there corresponds a unique prime in S_n through the singular space S_{n-r}. This correspondence between the $(r-2)$-spaces in Σ_{r-1}, and the primes of S_n through the singular space S_{n-r} is precisely that obtained above by the direct transformation.

Now let us consider what happens when S_n and S_m, instead of being distinct spaces, are the same space, which we denote by $[n]$. Then the transformation (1) takes a point P of $[n]$ into another point P^* of $[n]$, and, more generally, an S_k of $[n]$ which does not meet the singular S_{n-r} is transformed into another S_k of $[n]$.

It is important not to confuse this type of transformation in $[n]$ with a transformation of coordinates. A transformation of coordinates is a relation between two sets of coordinates for the same point. The present correspondence is a relation between the sets of coordinates of two different points.

A transformation of type $y = Ax$ which transforms $[n]$ into itself is called a *collineation* in $[n]$. Projective geometry is the study of the properties of configurations which are *invariant* under collineations. In the study of collineations we can deduce, by what has been said above, properties of the transform of any configuration, but we have a new problem to consider, that of the *relation* of a configuration to its transform. The remainder of this chapter is devoted to a study of collineations.

2. Collineations. In the space $[n]$ over K we choose an allowable coordinate system and consider the collineation given by the equations

$$y_i = \sum_{j=0}^{n} a_{ij} x_j \quad (i = 0, \ldots, n),$$

or, in matrix notation,

$$y = Ax. \tag{1}$$

Let a transformation of coordinates in $[n]$ be given by

$$x = Px^*.$$

The coordinates of the points x, y are transformed into x^*, y^*, where

$$x = Px^*, \quad y = Py^*,$$

and therefore in the new coordinate system the collineation has the equations

$$y^* = P^{-1}APx^*.$$

The collineation dual to (1) is (cf. § 1)

$$u = A'v, \tag{2}$$

$u = (u_0, \ldots, u_n)$ being the prime which contains every point x whose transform y by (1) lies in $v = (v_0, \ldots, v_n)$. If A is non-singular, (2) can be written as

$$v = \tilde{A}u, \tag{3}$$

where $\tilde{A} = (A')^{-1}$ is the matrix complementary to A. The collineation (3) transforms a prime u into the prime v which contains the transforms y of all the points x of u, and no other points.

The transformation of coordinates

$$x = Px^*$$

changes (2) into
$$u^* = (P^{-1}AP)' v^*,$$

and (3) into
$$v^* = (\widetilde{P^{-1}AP}) u^*.$$

Having seen the effect of a transformation of coordinates on equations (1), (2) and (3) we now define *similar* collineations of [n]. Two collineations

$$y = Ax, \quad \text{and} \quad y = Bx$$

are *similar* if there exists a non-singular matrix P with elements in K such that
$$B = P^{-1}AP.$$

This relation is clearly reflexive and symmetric, and if

$$C = Q^{-1}BQ \quad (Q \text{ non-singular}),$$

then
$$C = (PQ)^{-1}A(PQ),$$

and hence the relation is also transitive. It is therefore an *equivalence* relation. The relation between similar collineations is simply that there exists a non-singular projective transformation

$$x = Px^*$$

of [n] into itself which transforms one collineation into the other.

Our main problems here are

(i) to determine necessary and sufficient conditions that two collineations be similar, and

(ii) to find a set of canonical forms for collineations in [n], that is, a set of collineations with the properties: (a) no two collineations of the set are equivalent; (b) every collineation is equivalent to one member of the set.

The canonical forms are chosen so that it is a simple matter to read off from them the geometrical properties of the collineations. We now prove

THEOREM I. *A necessary and sufficient condition that the collineations*

$$y = Ax, \quad y = Bx$$

should be similar is that the λ-matrices $A - \lambda I_{n+1}$ and $B - \lambda I_{n+1}$ should have the same invariant factors (or, in the case in which K is algebraically closed, the same elementary divisors).

By II, §9, Th. III, a necessary and sufficient condition that the λ-matrices $A - \lambda I_{n+1}$ and $B - \lambda I_{n+1}$ should be equivalent, in the sense of that section, is that they have the same invariant factors. When this is the case,

$$B - \lambda I_{n+1} = M(A - \lambda I_{n+1})\,N.$$

But by II, §9, Th. V, this equation implies the existence of non-singular matrices P, Q over K such that

$$B - \lambda I_{n+1} = P(A - \lambda I_{n+1})\,Q.$$

It follows that
$$B = PAQ,$$

and
$$I_{n+1} = PQ.$$

Hence
$$P = Q^{-1},$$

and therefore
$$B = Q^{-1}AQ.$$

Now let K be algebraically closed. We note first of all that

$$\det(A - \lambda I_{n+1}) \quad \text{and} \quad \det(B - \lambda I_{n+1})$$

are each polynomials of degree $n + 1$ containing the term

$$(-1)^{n+1}\lambda^{n+1}.$$

These polynomials are therefore not zero polynomials, and

$$\operatorname{rank}(A - \lambda I_{n+1}) = \operatorname{rank}(B - \lambda I_{n+1}) = n + 1.$$

Hence the form of Theorem I which is applicable when K is algebraically closed follows from II, §9, Th. IV.

Now let $E_1(\lambda), ..., E_{n+1}(\lambda)$ be the invariant factors of $A - \lambda I_{n+1}$, and let $E_i(\lambda)$ be of degree r_i. Since

$$(-1)^{n+1} \prod_{i=1}^{n+1} E_i(\lambda) = \det(A - \lambda I_{n+1}),$$

it follows that
$$\sum_{1}^{n+1} r_i = n + 1,$$

and since $E_i(\lambda)$ is a factor of $E_{i+1}(\lambda)$,

$$r_i \leqslant r_{i+1}.$$

We suppose that
$$r_1 = r_2 = ... = r_s = 0,$$

and that
$$r_{s+1} > 0.$$

Let
$$E_i(\lambda) = \lambda^{r_i} + a_{i1}\lambda^{r_i-1} + \ldots + a_{ir_i} \quad (i > s),$$

and consider the $r_i \times r_i$ matrix

$$B_i = \begin{pmatrix} 0 & 1 & 0 & . & 0 \\ 0 & 0 & 1 & . & 0 \\ . & . & . & & . \\ 0 & 0 & . & . & 1 \\ -a_{ir_i} & . & . & . & -a_{i1} \end{pmatrix}.$$

We prove that the invariant factors of $B_i - \lambda I_{r_i}$ are

$$1, 1, \ldots, 1, E_i(\lambda).$$

For consider the determinants of the submatrices of t rows and columns extracted from $B_i - \lambda I_{r_i}$. If $1 \leqslant t < r_i$ we consider the particular submatrix whose elements lie in the 1st, 2nd, ..., tth rows of $B_i - \lambda I_{r_i}$, and in the 2nd, 3rd, ..., $(t+1)$th columns of this matrix. It is clear that the determinant of this particular $t \times t$ submatrix is equal to unity. Hence the highest common factor of determinants of $t \times t$ submatrices extracted from $B_i - \lambda I_{r_i}$ is of degree zero, if $1 \leqslant t < r_i$. But if $t = r_i$,

$$\det(B_i - \lambda I_{r_i}) = (-1)^{r_i} E_i(\lambda).$$

This proves the result.

Now let B be the $(n+1) \times (n+1)$ matrix

$$B = \begin{pmatrix} B_{s+1} & 0 & . & 0 \\ 0 & B_{s+2} & . & 0 \\ . & . & . & . \\ 0 & 0 & . & B_{n+1} \end{pmatrix}. \tag{4}$$

We prove that the invariant factors of $B - \lambda I_{n+1}$ are

$$E_1(\lambda), \ldots, E_{s+1}(\lambda), \ldots, E_{n+1}(\lambda).$$

We can perform elementary transformations [II, §9] on the rows and columns of any submatrix $B_t - \lambda I_{r_t}(s+1 \leqslant t \leqslant n+1)$ of $B - \lambda I_{n+1}$ without altering the rows and columns of any other submatrix, since these submatrices have no rows or columns in common. Hence each submatrix can be reduced to its canonical form by elementary transformations on $B-\lambda I_{n+1}$. By another elementary transformation this matrix can be reduced to the matrix

$$\begin{pmatrix} I_s & 0 & . & 0 \\ 0 & E_{s+1}(\lambda) & . & 0 \\ . & . & . & . \\ 0 & . & . & E_{n+1}(\lambda) \end{pmatrix}.$$

Since $E_i(\lambda)$ is a factor of $E_{i+1}(\lambda)$, the highest common factor property of invariant factors makes it evident that the invariant factors of this last matrix are

$$1, 1, ..., 1, \ E_{s+1}(\lambda), ..., E_{n+1}(\lambda),$$

that is, $\quad E_1(\lambda), ..., E_s(\lambda), \ E_{s+1}(\lambda), ..., E_{n+1}(\lambda).$

Thus $B-\lambda I_{n+1}$ is equivalent to the matrix $A-\lambda I_{n+1}$, since it has the same invariant factors [II, §9, Th. III].

We shall take the canonical form for collineations similar to (1) as

$$y = Bx,$$

where B is given by (4). Hence we have

THEOREM II. *If the matrix $A-\lambda I_{n+1}$ has the invariant factors*

$$E_1(\lambda), ..., E_{n+1}(\lambda),$$

and if the matrix B is defined as in (4) above, the collineation

$$y = Ax \qquad (1)$$

is similar to the collineation $y = Bx$, and this latter form of the equations may be taken as the canonical form for collineations similar to (1).

When the ground field K is algebraically closed, and we use elementary divisors in place of invariant factors, it is usually more convenient to use another set of canonical forms for collineations. Let $A-\lambda I_{n+1}$ have the elementary divisors

$$(\lambda-\alpha_1)^{e_1}, ..., (\lambda-\alpha_k)^{e_k},$$

where, for the moment, it is not necessary to distinguish the α_i which are equal from those which are unequal. By the properties of elementary divisors obtained in II, §9,

$$e_i > 0 \quad (i = 1, ..., k),$$

and $\qquad e_1 + ... + e_k = n+1.$

Now let $C_e(\alpha)$ be the $e \times e$ matrix

$$C_e(\alpha) = \begin{pmatrix} \alpha & 1 & 0 & . & 0 \\ 0 & \alpha & 1 & . & 0 \\ . & . & . & . & . \\ 0 & . & . & \alpha & 1 \\ 0 & . & . & 0 & \alpha \end{pmatrix}.$$

Then the matrix $C_e(\alpha) - \lambda I_e$ has the one elementary divisor $(\lambda - \alpha)^e$.

For $$\det(C_e(\alpha) - \lambda I_e) = (\alpha - \lambda)^e,$$

whilst the determinant of the $(e-1) \times (e-1)$ submatrix obtained by omitting the last row and the first column of the matrix under consideration is equal to unity.

Now let C be the $(n+1) \times (n+1)$ matrix

$$C = \begin{pmatrix} C_{e_1}(\alpha_1) & 0 & . & 0 \\ 0 & C_{e_2}(\alpha_2) & . & 0 \\ . & . & . & . \\ 0 & . & . & C_{e_k}(\alpha_k) \end{pmatrix}. \tag{5}$$

By methods exactly similar to those used in the proof of Theorem II we can show that $C - \lambda I_{n+1}$ has the elementary divisors

$$(\lambda - \alpha_1)^{e_1}, \ldots, (\lambda - \alpha_k)^{e_k}.$$

This gives us

THEOREM III. *If* $A - \lambda I_{n+1}$ *has the elementary divisors*

$$(\lambda - \alpha_1)^{e_1}, \ldots, (\lambda - \alpha_k)^{e_k},$$

the collineation (1) *is similar to the collineation*

$$y = Cx,$$

where the matrix C *is constructed as in* (5) *with the given elementary divisors. This collineation serves as a canonical form for collineations similar to* (1).

It should be noted, however, that geometrically the two collineations

$$y = Ax,$$

and $$\rho y = Ax \quad (\rho \neq 0),$$

if given in the same allowable coordinate system, perform the same transformation on the points, lines, ..., of $[n]$. From this it follows that two collineations

$$y = Ax, \quad \text{and} \quad y = Bx$$

are similar in a geometrical sense if the elementary divisors of $A - \lambda I_{n+1}$ and of $B - \lambda I_{n+1}$ are

$$(\lambda - \alpha_1)^{e_1}, \ldots, (\lambda - \alpha_k)^{e_k},$$

and
$$(\lambda - \beta_1)^{f_1}, \ldots, (\lambda - \beta_k)^{f_k}$$

respectively, where, for a proper arrangement of these divisors,

$$e_i = f_i, \quad \beta_i = \mu \alpha_i \quad (i = 1, \ldots, k),$$

μ being a non-zero element of K.

In the remainder of this chapter we shall assume that the ground field K is algebraically closed.

3. United points and primes of a non-singular collineation.
If we are given a collineation in $[n]$ over an algebraically closed field K we may, as in §2, choose our allowable coordinate system so that the equations of the collineation are

$$y = Cx, \tag{1}$$

where

$$C = \begin{pmatrix} C_{e_1}(\alpha_1) & 0 & . & 0 \\ 0 & C_{e_2}(\alpha_2) & . & 0 \\ . & . & . & . \\ 0 & 0 & . & C_{e_k}(\alpha_k) \end{pmatrix},$$

and

$$C_e(\alpha) = \begin{pmatrix} \alpha & 1 & 0 & . & 0 \\ 0 & \alpha & 1 & . & 0 \\ . & . & . & . & . \\ . & . & . & \alpha & 1 \\ 0 & 0 & 0 & . & \alpha \end{pmatrix}.$$

The elementary divisors of the matrix $C - \lambda I_{n+1}$ are

$$(\lambda - \alpha_1)^{e_1}, \ldots, (\lambda - \alpha_k)^{e_k}.$$

It is usual to call them the elementary divisors of the collineation (1). We note that if the original collineation is

$$y = Ax,$$

there exists a non-singular matrix P such that

$$C = P^{-1}AP.$$

Hence
$$C - \lambda I_{n+1} = P^{-1}(A - \lambda I_{n+1})P,$$

and therefore

$$\det (C - \lambda I_{n+1}) = \det (A - \lambda I_{n+1})$$
$$= (-1)^{n+1} \prod_1^k (\lambda - \alpha_i)^{e_i}.$$

Hence, putting $\lambda = 0$,

$$\det C = \det A = \alpha_1^{e_1} \ldots \alpha_k^{e_k}.$$

We shall assume in this section that the collineation is *non-singular*, that is, that
$$\det A \neq 0.$$

It follows that each latent root α_i is different from zero.

In the canonical form (1) the submatrices $C_{e_i}(\alpha_i)$ may be arranged in any order along the principal diagonal of C, but it will be convenient to order them so that

(i) those submatrices $C_{e_i}(\alpha_i)$ which correspond to equal latent roots α_i come together, and

(ii) if $\alpha_i = \alpha_j$ and $e_i < e_j$ then $C_{e_i}(\alpha_i)$ precedes $C_{e_j}(\alpha_j)$.

We shall assume that the submatrices are arranged in this way in all future applications.

A point $(z_0, \ldots, z_n)$ of $[n]$ is called a *united point* of the collineation (1) if it is transformed into itself by the collineation. The condition for this is
$$Cz = \rho z,$$

where ρ is a non-zero element of K. The equations

$$(C - \rho I_{n+1})z = 0$$

have a solution $(z_0, \ldots, z_n)$ if and only if [II, § 8]

$$\det (C - \rho I_{n+1}) = 0.$$

Hence ρ *must be a latent root of the collineation*. Let us take $\rho = \alpha_1$, and suppose that
$$\alpha_1 = \alpha_2 = \ldots = \alpha_t,$$
$$\alpha_i \neq \alpha_t \quad (i > t).$$

The equations to determine the united points arising from $\rho = \alpha_1$ are

$$\left.\begin{aligned}
\alpha_1 z_0 &= \alpha_1 z_0 + z_1, \\
\alpha_1 z_1 &= \alpha_1 z_1 + z_2, \\
\cdot \quad &\cdot \quad \cdot \\
\alpha_1 z_{e_1-1} &= \alpha_1 z_{e_1-1},
\end{aligned}\right\} \tag{2·1}$$

$$\left.\begin{aligned}
\alpha_1 z_{e_1} &= \alpha_2 z_{e_1} + z_{e_1+1}, \\
\cdot \quad &\cdot \quad \cdot \quad \cdot \\
\alpha_1 z_{e_1+e_2-1} &= \alpha_2 z_{e_1+e_2-1},
\end{aligned}\right\} \tag{2·2}$$

$$\cdot \quad \cdot \quad \cdot \quad \cdot \quad \cdot \quad \cdot \quad \cdot$$

$$\left.\begin{aligned}
\alpha_1 z_{e_1+\ldots+e_{t-1}} &= \alpha_t z_{e_1+\ldots+e_{t-1}} + z_{e_1+\ldots+e_{t-1}+1}, \\
\cdot \quad &\cdot \quad \cdot \quad \cdot \quad \cdot \quad \cdot \\
\alpha_1 z_{e_1+\ldots+e_t-1} &= \alpha_t z_{e_1+\ldots+e_t-1},
\end{aligned}\right\} \tag{2·t}$$

$$\alpha_1 z_{e_1+\ldots+e_t} = \alpha_{t+1} z_{e_1+\ldots+e_t} + z_{e_1+\ldots+e_t+1},$$
$$\cdot \quad \cdot \quad \cdot \quad \cdot \quad \cdot \quad \cdot \quad \cdot$$
$$\alpha_1 z_n = \alpha_k z_n.$$

From equations (2·1) we have, successively,

$$z_1 = 0, \; z_2 = 0, \; \ldots, \; z_{e_1-1} = 0;$$

from (2·2) we have, successively, since $\alpha_1 = \alpha_2$,

$$z_{e_1+1} = 0, \; \ldots, \; z_{e_1+e_2-1} = 0;$$

from (2·t) we find that

$$z_{e_1+\ldots+e_{t-1}+1} = 0, \; \ldots, \; z_{e_1+\ldots+e_t-1} = 0;$$

if, finally, we consider the last equation and work backwards we find that

$$z_{e_1+\ldots+e_t+1} = 0, \; \ldots, \; z_n = 0.$$

Hence a united point $(z_0, \ldots, z_n)$ arising from the latent root α_1 necessarily has all its coordinates zero except

$$z_0, \; z_{e_1}, \; z_{e_1+e_2}, \; \ldots, \; z_{e_1+\ldots+e_{t-1}}.$$

Conversely, we can verify at once that if $(z_0, \ldots, z_n)$ has all its coordinates zero except those named above, it satisfies the equations (2), and is therefore a united point.

If $A_0, \ldots, A_n$ are the vertices of the simplex of reference of our coordinate system we deduce from these results that the united points corresponding to the latent root α_1 of C form the linear space of $t-1$ dimensions spanned by the points $A_0, A_{e_1}, A_{e_1+e_2}, \ldots, A_{e_1+\ldots+e_{t-1}}$. We call this space the *fundamental space* of the collineation corresponding to the latent root α_1.

The united points corresponding to any other latent root of C are found in a similar way. The following rule is immediately obtained:

THEOREM I. *Let α_i be any latent root of C, and let*

$$C_{e_q}(\alpha_q),\ C_{e_{q+1}}(\alpha_{q+1}),\ \ldots,\ C_{e_{q+s}}(\alpha_{q+s})$$

be the submatrices of C which correspond to latent roots equal to α_i. Then the united points corresponding to α_i form the fundamental space spanned by the points

$$A_{e_1+\ldots+e_{q-1}},\ A_{e_1+\ldots+e_q},\ \ldots,\ A_{e_1+\ldots+e_{q+s-1}},$$

and therefore lie in a space of dimension s.

Since each fundamental space is determined by a set of vertices of the simplex of reference, and since also no two sets corresponding to distinct latent roots have any vertices in common we deduce

THEOREM II. *The fundamental spaces defined by distinct latent roots have no points in common. Indeed, they are linearly independent; that is, if their dimensions are $m_1, \ldots, m_r$, their join is a space of $r-1+\sum_1^r m_i$ dimensions.*

Again, we see from Theorem I that the join of all the fundamental spaces is the space spanned by the vertices

$$A_0,\ A_{e_1},\ A_{e_1+e_2},\ \ldots,\ \ldots,\ A_{e_1+e_2+\ldots+e_{k-1}},$$

and is therefore a space of $k-1$ dimensions. Therefore

$$r-1+\sum_1^r m_i = k-1.$$

The join is the whole of $[n]$ if and only if $k = n+1$, that is, if and only if

$$e_1 = e_2 = \ldots = e_k = 1.$$

This case, in which all the elementary divisors are linear, will sometimes be referred to as the *non-special* case; the *special* case being that in which at least one of the elementary divisors is of degree greater than one.

The collineation (1) transforms any k-space S_k into another k-space S'_k, this space consisting of all points y which are transforms of the points x of S_k. The reasoning is exactly that used in the case of a non-singular projective correspondence between two distinct n-spaces. In particular, when $k = n-1$, if S_k is

$$u = (u_0, \ldots, u_n),$$

and S'_k is
$$v = (v_0, \ldots, v_n),$$

the correspondence is given by the equations

$$v = \tilde{C}u. \qquad (3)$$

The self-corresponding primes of this collineation are obtained by finding primes $w = (w_0, \ldots, w_n)$ such that

$$\rho w = \tilde{C}w \quad (\rho \neq 0).$$

We are thus led to consider the elementary divisors of the matrix

$$\tilde{C} - \lambda I_{n+1}.$$

Since

$$\tilde{C} = \begin{pmatrix} \tilde{C}_{e_1}(\alpha_1) & 0 & . & 0 \\ 0 & \tilde{C}_{e_2}(\alpha_2) & . & . \\ . & . & . & . \\ 0 & 0 & . & \tilde{C}_{e_k}(\alpha_k) \end{pmatrix},$$

and since

$$\tilde{C}_e(\alpha) = \begin{pmatrix} \alpha^{-1} & 0 & 0 & . & 0 \\ -\alpha^{-2} & \alpha^{-1} & 0 & . & 0 \\ \alpha^{-3} & -\alpha^{-2} & \alpha^{-1} & . & 0 \\ . & & & . & . \\ (-1)^{e-1}\alpha^{-e} & (-1)^{e-2}\alpha^{-e+1} & . & . & \alpha^{-1} \end{pmatrix},$$

it is easily calculated that the elementary divisors of $\tilde{C} - \lambda I_{n+1}$ are

$$(\lambda - \alpha_1^{-1})^{e_1}, \ldots, (\lambda - \alpha_k^{-1})^{e_k}.$$

However, it will simplify our notation if we observe that a necessary and sufficient condition that $\tilde{C}w = \rho w$ (for some $\rho \neq 0$) is that $C'w = \sigma w$ (for some $\sigma \neq 0$). Hence we need only consider the united primes of the dual transformation

$$u = C'v \qquad (4)$$

to obtain the united primes of the collineation (3). The elementary divisors of $C' - \lambda I_{n+1}$ are evidently the same as those of $C - \lambda I_{n+1}$, that is

$$(\lambda - \alpha_1)^{e_1}, \ldots, (\lambda - \alpha_k)^{e_k}.$$

Hence the following equations determine the united prime $(w_0, \ldots, w_n)$ corresponding to the latent root α_1:

$$\left.\begin{aligned}
\alpha_1 w_0 &= \alpha_1 w_0, \\
\alpha_1 w_1 &= w_0 + \alpha_1 w_1, \\
&\cdot \qquad \cdot \qquad \cdot \\
\alpha_1 w_{e_1-1} &= w_{e_1-2} + \alpha_1 w_{e_1-1},
\end{aligned}\right\} \tag{5.1}$$

$$\left.\begin{aligned}
\alpha_1 w_{e_1} &= \alpha_2 w_{e_1}, \\
\cdot \qquad \cdot \qquad &\cdot \qquad \cdot \qquad \cdot \\
\alpha_1 w_{e_1+e_2-1} &= w_{e_1+e_2-2} + \alpha_2 w_{e_1+e_2-1},
\end{aligned}\right\} \tag{5.2}$$

$$\begin{aligned}
\cdot \qquad &\cdot \qquad \cdot \\
\cdot \qquad &\cdot \qquad \cdot
\end{aligned}$$

$$\left.\begin{aligned}
\alpha_1 w_{e_1+\ldots+e_t-1} &= \alpha_t w_{e_1+\ldots+e_t-1}, \\
\cdot \qquad \cdot \qquad &\cdot \qquad \cdot \\
\alpha_1 w_{e_1+\ldots+e_t-1} &= w_{e_1+\ldots+e_t-2} + \alpha_t w_{e_1+\ldots+e_t-1},
\end{aligned}\right\} \tag{5.t}$$

$$\alpha_1 w_{e_1+\ldots+e_t} = \alpha_{t+1} w_{e_1+\ldots+e_t},$$

$$\cdot \qquad \cdot \qquad \cdot$$

$$\alpha_1 w_n = w_{n-1} + \alpha_k w_n.$$

From (5.1) we find, successively, that

$$w_{e_1-2} = 0, \; w_{e_1-3} = 0, \; \ldots, \; w_0 = 0,$$

and then, from (5.2), ..., (5.t), we find that, since $\alpha_1 = \ldots = \alpha_t$,

$$w_{e_1+e_2-2} = 0, \; \ldots, \; w_{e_1} = 0,$$

$$w_{e_1+\ldots+e_t-2} = 0, \; \ldots, \; w_{e_1+\ldots+e_t-1} = 0,$$

and finally that

$$w_i = 0 \quad (i \geqslant e_1 + \ldots + e_t).$$

Hence the united prime necessarily contains the points

$$A_0, \ldots, A_{e_1-2}, A_{e_1}, \ldots, A_{e_1+e_2-2}, \ldots,$$
$$A_{e_1+\ldots+e_t-1}, \ldots, A_{e_1+\ldots+e_t-2}, A_{e_1+\ldots+e_t}, \ldots, A_n,$$

and, conversely, any prime which contains these points satisfies (4).

These points determine a linear space S_{n-t}, and the primes through it form a *star* with *vertex* S_{n-t}. This star of primes is the dual of the set of united points in the space S_{t-1}, and the properties of the star may be determined by duality from the properties of the set of united points corresponding to the latent root α_1.

Corresponding to each distinct latent root of C' there is a star of united primes, and we see that there is a rule, similar to Theorem I, for determining the star of united primes corresponding to a given latent root.

THEOREM III. *If α_i is any latent root of C (or C') and*

$$C_{e_q}(\alpha_q),\ C_{e_{q+1}}(\alpha_{q+1}),\ ...,\ C_{e_{q+s}}(\alpha_{q+s})$$

are the submatrices of C which correspond to the latent root α_i of C, then the united primes corresponding to α_i form the star whose vertex is the join of the points

$$A_0, ..., A_{e_1+...+e_q-1}, A_{e_1+...+e_q}, ..., A_{e_1+...+e_{q+1}-2}, ...,$$
$$A_{e_1+...+e_{q+s}-1}, ..., A_{e_1+...+e_{q+s}-2}, A_{e_1+...+e_{q+s}}, ..., A_n.$$

We have agreed to place $C_{e_i}(\alpha_i)$ before $C_{e_j}(\alpha_j)$ in C if $\alpha_i = \alpha_j$ and $e_i < e_j$; suppose that

$$e_q = ... = e_{q+t} = 1; \quad e_{q+t+1}, ..., e_{q+s} > 1.$$

Then, by Theorems I and III we see that the space S_s of united points corresponding to the latent root α_i and the vertex S_{n-s-1} of the star of united primes arising from the same latent root intersect in the space S_{s-t-1} defined by the points

$$A_{e_1+...+e_{q+t}}, ..., A_{e_1+...+e_{q+s-1}}.$$

Similarly we observe that the space of united points arising from any latent root $\alpha_j\ (\alpha_j \neq \alpha_i)$ lies in the vertex of the star corresponding to the latent root α_i. Hence we have

THEOREM IV. *The fundamental space of united points arising from any given latent root α lies in the vertex of the fundamental star corresponding to any other latent root, and meets the vertex of the star corresponding to the same latent root α in a space of $p-1$ dimensions, where p is the number of non-linear elementary divisors of the type $(\lambda-\alpha)^e\ (e>1)$.*

As an immediate corollary, we deduce that *if a collineation is non-special the vertex of the fundamental star corresponding to any given latent root is the join of the fundamental spaces corresponding to the other latent roots.*

Now let S_{t-1} and S_{n-t} denote the fundamental space and the vertex of the fundamental star, respectively, corresponding to the latent root α_1 of C, and suppose that

$$1 = e_1 = \ldots = e_s < e_{s+1} \leqslant e_{s+2} \leqslant \ldots \leqslant e_t. \tag{6}$$

Let x be any point of $[n]$, let $y = Cx$, and

$$z = y - \alpha_1 x = (C - \alpha_1 I_{n+1})x. \tag{7}$$

Evidently z is collinear with x and y, and from (7) it is the transform of x under the collineation with matrix $C - \alpha_1 I_{n+1}$. Since $\det(C - \alpha_1 I_{n+1}) = 0$, this collineation is a *singular* collineation. The point z is uniquely defined by (7) unless

$$Cx = \alpha_1 x,$$

that is, unless x lies in S_{t-1}. If x is not in S_{t-1} then we see from (7) that the coordinates of z satisfy the equations

$$z_0 = z_1 = \ldots = z_{s-1} = z_{s+e_{s+1}-1} = \ldots = z_{s+e_{s+1}\ldots+e_t-1} = 0.$$

That is, z lies in S_{n-t}.

It is also easily seen that if x^* is any point of the space S_t which joins x to S_{t-1}, the transform of x^* by (7) is also z, and the correspondence between the t-spaces through S_{t-1} and the points z of S_{n-t} is a projective one. We prove this result, which should be compared with a similar result in §1, using the symbolic notation for points. If the points

$$P_0, P_1, \ldots, P_{t-1}$$

form a basis for S_{t-1}, then

$$C(P_i) = \alpha_1 P_i \quad (i = 0, \ldots, t-1).$$

Let P be any point not in S_{t-1}. Then any point x^* in the S_t joining P to S_{t-1} is given by

$$x^* = \sum_0^{t-1} \lambda_i P_i + \mu P,$$

for suitable λ_i, μ in K. Now

$$Cx^* = \sum_0^{t-1} \lambda_i C(P_i) + \mu C(P)$$

$$= \alpha_1 \sum_0^{t-1} \lambda_i P_i + \mu C(P),$$

and therefore

$$z = Cx^* - \alpha_1 x^* = \mu[C(P) - \alpha_1 P], \tag{8}$$

which is independent of the particular x^* chosen in the S_t. If P is chosen in an S'_{n-t} which does not meet S_{t-1}, then P determines and is uniquely determined by S_t. Since S_{t-1} is the join of the points $A_0, A_1, ..., A_{s-1}, A_s, A_{s+e_{s+1}}, ..., A_{s+e_{s+1}+...+e_{t-1}}$, we may take P to lie in the S'_{n-t} spanned by the remaining vertices of the simplex of reference. The equations (8) determine a unique point z in S_{n-t} if P is taken anywhere in S'_{n-t}. Conversely, if we write down these equations, assuming that z is in S_{n-t}, we see that we can solve for the coordinates of P, and that the solution is *unique* if we assume that P lies in S'_{n-t}. Hence the correspondence between t-spaces through S_{t-1} and the points z of S_{n-t} may be described as a projective correspondence.

Now let us consider the effect of the original collineation (1), $y = Cx$, on the S_t determined by P and the space of united points S_{t-1}. Since

$$y = Cx^* = \alpha_1 \sum_0^{t-1} \lambda_i P_i + \mu C(P),$$

the points of S_t are transformed into the points of the S'_t determined by the transform of P under (1) and S_{t-1}. Since

$$z = y - \alpha_1 x^* = \mu[C(P) - \alpha_1 P]$$

gives a point in S_{n-t} which is independent of the point x^* chosen in S_t, it follows that the correspondence between S_t and S'_t is a *perspectivity*, vertex z.

Now let us assume that in (6) we have $s < t$, so that the collineation (1) has non-linear elementary divisors corresponding to the latent root α_1. Then S_{t-1} and S_{n-t} have a space of $t-s-1$ dimensions, S_{t-s-1}, say, in common. If z is in S_{t-s-1}, and S_t is the unique t-space through S_{t-1} which corresponds to z in the projective transformation described above, the transform of S_t under (1) is in perspective with S_t, vertex z. Since this transform contains S_{t-1}, and z lies in S_{t-1}, *the transform must coincide with S_t.* Algebraically, if

$$z = (z_0, ..., z_n),$$

each z_i except

$$z_s, z_{s+e_{s+1}}, ..., z_{s+e_{s+1}+...+e_{t-1}}$$

is zero, and if we solve (8) for the coordinates $(x_0, ..., x_n)$ of P, not restricting P this time, we find that

$$P = (x_0, x_1, ..., x_{s-1}, x_s, z_s, 0, ..., 0, x_{s+e_{s+1}},$$
$$z_{s+e_{s+1}}, 0, ..., 0, ..., x_{s+e_{s+1}+...+e_{t-1}}, z_{s+e_{s+1}+...+e_{t-1}}, 0, ..., 0),$$

where each x_i can be chosen arbitrarily. These points P fill the space S_t which corresponds to z. This expression for the coordinates of P makes it evident that the collineation (1) transforms P into a point with coordinates of the same form. Hence, again, S_t is transformed into itself by (1).

If we anticipate Theorem VI, we can say that the collineation (1) *induces* a collineation in S_t. This induced collineation is such that S_t contains an S_{t-1} of united points corresponding to the latent root α_1. The *number* of elementary divisors $(\lambda - \alpha_1)^{f_i}$ must therefore be t. Since also $\sum_1^t f_i = t + 1$, there being no united points of (1) in S_t outside S_{t-1}, it follows that the elementary divisors of the induced collineation consist of $t - 1$ elementary divisors $(\lambda - \alpha_1)$, and one quadratic elementary divisor $(\lambda - \alpha_1)^2$.

We return now to the consideration of (7), x being any point of $[n]$ which is not in a fundamental space. Its transform by (1), that is, the point $y = Cx$, is distinct from x. We consider the ρ points

$$y - \alpha_i x \quad (i = 1, \dots, \rho),$$

where ρ is the number of *distinct* latent roots of C. These are the points in which the line xy meets the vertices of the fundamental stars corresponding, respectively, to the latent roots $\alpha_1, \dots, \alpha_\rho$. This range of points, together with the points x and y, is projectively related to any other range of $\rho + 2$ points constructed from the collineation (1) in the same way [VI, § 10]. We remark that if the line xy lies in a vertex of a fundamental star, the points x and $y = Cx$ must lie in the vertex. Conversely, if x lies in a vertex of a fundamental star, say in that corresponding to the latent root α_1, so that

$$x_0 = x_1 = \dots = x_{s-1} = x_{s+e_{s+1}-1} = \dots = x_{s+e_{s+1}+\dots+e_t-1} = 0,$$
then
$$y_0 = y_1 = \dots = y_{s-1} = y_{s+e_{s+1}-1} = \dots = y_{s+e_{s+1}+\dots+e_t-1} = 0,$$

so that y also lies in the vertex. The vertices, in fact, are all united spaces under the collineation (1). This is also evident from the fact that any prime through a vertex is a united prime, and the intersection of any number of united primes is necessarily a united space. Returning to the ranges of points discussed above, we have

THEOREM V. *If any point x of $[n]$ is transformed by the collineation $y = Cx$ into a point $y \neq x$, the line xy meets the vertex of each of the* *fundamental stars of the collineation. If x does not lie in a vertex, let* $A_1, ..., A_\rho$ *be the unique points of intersection of xy with the vertices. Then if y* is the transform by y = Cx of any other point x* which does not lie in a vertex, and y* ≠ x*, and if x*y* meets the fundamental vertices in* $A_1^*, ..., A_\rho^*$, *respectively, the ranges x, y,* $A_1, ..., A_\rho$, *and* $x^*, y^*, A_1^*, ..., A_\rho^*$, *are related.*

We conclude this section by noting two simple results which will frequently be used in the sequel.

THEOREM VI. *If a space* S_k *is transformed into itself by a collineation, the points of* S_k *may be regarded as transformed by a collineation in* S_k.

The property of a space S_k being transformed into itself under the collineation (1) is invariant under any allowable change of coordinates. For let one of the linear equations satisfied by S_k be, in matrix notation,

$$u'x = 0. \tag{9}$$

Then since the point $y = Cx$ continues to lie in S_k,

$$u'Cx = 0. \tag{10}$$

The allowable transformation of coordinates $x = Px^*$ transforms (9) into

$$v'x^* = 0, \tag{9}'$$

where $v = P'u$, and transforms (10) into

$$v'P^{-1}CPx^* = 0, \tag{10}'$$

which is just the condition that the prime given by (9)′ should pass not only through x^*, but through

$$y^* = P^{-1}CPx^*.$$

But this is the transform of (1) under the transformation of coordinates $x = Px^*$. Our initial result is therefore proved.

We may therefore choose the coordinate system so that the equations of S_k are

$$x_{k+1} = 0, ..., x_n = 0.$$

Then if the collineation in this coordinate system is

$$y_i = \sum_{j=0}^{n} a_{ij}x_j \quad (i = 0, ..., n),$$

we have the equations

$$\sum_{j=0}^{n} a_{ij}x_j = 0 \quad (i = k+1, ..., n)$$

for every point $(x_0, ..., x_k, 0, ..., 0)$ of S_k; that is, for all choices of $x_0, ..., x_k$. This implies that

$$a_{ij} = 0 \quad (i > k, j \leqslant k).$$

The transformation in S_k is given by the equations

$$y_i = \sum_{j=0}^{k} a_{ij} x_j \quad (i = 0, ..., k),$$

which is a collineation in S_k.

The only united points possessed by this induced collineation are the united points of the given collineation which lie in S_k.

THEOREM VII. *In any collineation there is at least one united point and one united prime.*

We need only prove the result for a united point, the result for a united prime following at once by duality. Since any collineation has at least one latent root, and since to each latent root there corresponds at least one united point, the theorem is evident. There are collineations with exactly one united point. As an example, consider the collineation

$$y = C_{n+1}(\alpha)\, x.$$

The elementary divisors are $(\lambda - \alpha)^{n+1}$, and the only united point is $(1, 0, ..., 0)$.

4. The united k-spaces of a non-singular collineation. A collineation

$$y = Ax \tag{1}$$

induces a transformation, given by VII, § 2, (4),

$$q_{i_0 ... i_k} = \sum_{j_0, ..., j_k} \begin{vmatrix} a_{i_0 j_0} & . & a_{i_0 j_k} \\ . & . & . \\ a_{i_k j_0} & . & a_{i_k j_k} \end{vmatrix} p_{j_0 ... j_k} \tag{2}$$

on the Grassmann coordinates of the k-spaces of $[n]$, and we could find the united k-spaces of the collineation (1) by considering the k-spaces which satisfy the equations

$$\sum_{j_0, ..., j_k} \begin{vmatrix} a_{i_0 j_0} & . & a_{i_0 j_k} \\ . & . & . \\ a_{i_k j_0} & . & a_{i_k j_k} \end{vmatrix} p_{j_0 ... j_k} = \sigma p_{i_0 ... i_k},$$

remembering that the coordinates $p_{i_0 \ldots i_k}$ satisfy the quadratic p-relations [VII, § 6, (4)]

$$p_{i_0 \ldots i_k} p_{j_0 \ldots j_k} = \sum_{\lambda=0}^{k} p_{i_0 \ldots i_{s-1} j_\lambda i_{s+1} \ldots i_k} p_{j_0 \ldots j_{\lambda+1} i_s j_{\lambda+1} \ldots j_k}.$$

This method of procedure is not, however, very convenient. One difficulty is that a qualitative description of the united points of the collineation (1) in $[n]$ is not, in itself, sufficient to allow us to determine qualitatively the united points of (2), regarded as a collineation in a space of $\binom{n+1}{k+1} - 1$ dimensions. For example, if $n = 3$, and

$$A = \begin{pmatrix} \alpha & 0 & 0 & 0 \\ 0 & \beta & 0 & 0 \\ 0 & 0 & \gamma & 0 \\ 0 & 0 & 0 & \delta \end{pmatrix},$$

where α, β, γ, δ are all distinct, we have a complete qualitative description of the united points of (1) in the statement that there are four united points, at the vertices of a simplex. But if $k = 1$, we obtain equations (2) in the form

$$q = Bp,$$

where B is the second compound $A^{(2)}$ of the matrix A, and may be written, [VII, § 2],

$$B = \begin{pmatrix} \alpha\beta & 0 & 0 & 0 & 0 & 0 \\ 0 & \alpha\gamma & 0 & 0 & 0 & 0 \\ 0 & 0 & \alpha\delta & 0 & 0 & 0 \\ 0 & 0 & 0 & \beta\gamma & 0 & 0 \\ 0 & 0 & 0 & 0 & \beta\delta & 0 \\ 0 & 0 & 0 & 0 & 0 & \gamma\delta \end{pmatrix}.$$

The collineation in [5] has six united points at the vertices of a simplex, if the elements which appear on the principal diagonal of B are all distinct. But if, say, $\alpha\beta = \gamma\delta$, the collineation has an infinite number of united points. These do not all satisfy the quadratic p-relations, and therefore do not all represent united lines in [3].

We therefore use a different method to find the united k-spaces of a collineation. We begin with the facts [§ 3, Ths. VI, VII] that if an

S_k is transformed into itself a collineation is induced in S_k, and this has at least one united point, which is a united point of the original collineation. Thus we need only consider those k-spaces which meet a fundamental space of the given collineation.

Let P be any point of the fundamental space corresponding to the latent root α_1. We seek the k-spaces through P which are united in the collineation. Our search will be greatly simplified by the following theorem:

THEOREM I. *If P is any united point of the collineation* (1) *an allowable coordinate system can be found in which the collineation is given in canonical form by the equations*

$$y = Cx, \tag{3}$$

where

$$C = \begin{pmatrix} C_{e_1}(\alpha_1) & 0 & . & 0 \\ 0 & C_{e_2}(\alpha_2) & . & 0 \\ . & . & . & . \\ 0 & 0 & . & C_{e_k}(\alpha_k) \end{pmatrix},$$

and P is a vertex of the simplex of reference.

As in §3 we assume that

$$\alpha_1 = \alpha_2 = \ldots = \alpha_t \neq \alpha_i \quad (i > t),$$

and that $e_i \leqslant e_j$ if $i < j \leqslant t$. By the results of §2, an allowable system of coordinates can be found in which the collineation is given in the canonical form (3). The fundamental space of united points corresponding to the latent root α_1 is defined by the vertices

$$A_0, \ A_{e_1}, \ \ldots, \ A_{e_1+\ldots+e_{t-1}},$$

of the simplex of reference. Let P lie in this fundamental space, so that

$$P = \lambda_0 A_0 + \lambda_1 A_{e_1} + \ldots + \lambda_{t-1} A_{e_1+\ldots+e_{t-1}}.$$

Let us suppose that
$$\lambda_i = 0 \quad (i < m-1),$$

but
$$\lambda_{m-1} \neq 0.$$

We find a transformation of coordinates which leaves (3) unchanged, and transforms P to the vertex $A^*_{e_1+\ldots+e_{m-1}}$ of the new simplex of reference.

The equations of the collineation (3) have been written out in detail in §3, (2). We are now concerned only with the particular set

$$
\left.
\begin{aligned}
y_{e_1+\ldots+e_{m-1}} &= \alpha_m x_{e_1+\ldots+e_{m-1}} + x_{e_1+\ldots+e_{m-1}+1}, \\
\cdot \qquad \cdot \qquad \cdot \qquad \cdot \qquad \cdot \qquad \cdot \\
y_{e_1+\ldots+e_m-1} &= \alpha_m x_{e_1+\ldots+e_m-1},
\end{aligned}
\right\} \qquad (4\cdot m)
$$

$$
\left.
\begin{aligned}
y_{e_1+\ldots+e_m} &= \alpha_{m+1} x_{e_1+\ldots+e_m} + x_{e_1+\ldots+e_m+1}, \\
\cdot \qquad \cdot \qquad \cdot \qquad \cdot \qquad \cdot \qquad \cdot \\
y_{e_1+\ldots+e_{m+1}-1} &= \alpha_{m+1} x_{e_1+\ldots+e_{m+1}-1},
\end{aligned}
\right\} \qquad (4\cdot m+1)
$$

$$
\cdot \qquad \cdot \qquad \cdot \qquad \cdot \qquad \cdot \qquad \cdot
$$

$$
\cdot \qquad \cdot \qquad \cdot \qquad \cdot \qquad \cdot \qquad \cdot
$$

$$
\left.
\begin{aligned}
y_{e_1+\ldots+e_{t-1}} &= \alpha_t x_{e_1+\ldots+e_{t-1}} + x_{e_1+\ldots+e_{t-1}+1}, \\
\cdot \qquad \cdot \qquad \cdot \qquad \cdot \qquad \cdot \qquad \cdot \\
y_{e_1+\ldots+e_t-1} &= \alpha_t x_{e_1+\ldots+e_t-1}.
\end{aligned}
\right\} \qquad (4\cdot t)
$$

We perform a transformation of coordinates which affects only the coordinates involved in the above equations. We write

$$
x^*_{e_1+\ldots+e_{i-1}+j}
$$
$$
= \lambda_{m-1} x_{e_1+\ldots+e_{i-1}+j} - \lambda_{i-1} x_{e_1+\ldots+e_{m-1}+j} \quad (j = 0, \ldots, e_m - 1),
$$

and $\quad x^*_{e_1+\ldots+e_{i-1}+j} = \lambda_{m-1} x_{e_1+\ldots+e_{i-1}+j} \quad (j = e_m, \ldots, e_i - 1),$

for each value of i from $i = m+1$ to $i = t$. We perform the same transformation on the y's.

The equations of the collineation in this new allowable coordinate system are obtained by multiplying the equations $(4 \cdot i)$ by λ_{m-1} and subtracting from each of the first e_m of them λ_{i-1} times the corresponding equation of the set $(4 \cdot m)$. The other equations of the collineation are unaltered. It follows at once that the new equations of the collineation are just the original equations with x^*, y^* written for x, y, that is,

$$
y^* = Cx^*.
$$

It is immediately verified that in the new coordinate system P is the vertex $A^*_{e_1+\ldots+e_{m-1}}$ of the new simplex of reference. Thus our theorem is proved.

We now assume that the united point P of the collineation (3) is the vertex $A_{e_1+\ldots+e_{m-1}}$ of the simplex of reference. Consider the line joining P to any point x of $[n]$. The collineation (3) transforms this line into the line joining P to the transform $y = Cx$ of x by (3),

since P is a united point. The two lines we are considering meet the
face of the simplex of reference

$$x_{e_1+...+e_{m-1}} = 0$$

in the points $(x_0, ..., x_{e_1+...+e_{m-1}-1}, 0, x_{e_1+...+e_{m-1}+1}, ..., x_n)$, and
$(y_0, ..., y_{e_1+...+e_{m-1}-1}, 0, y_{e_1+...+e_{m-1}+1}, ..., y_n)$. If $(\bar{x}_0, ..., \bar{x}_{n-1})$ and
$(\bar{y}_0, ..., \bar{y}_{n-1})$ denote the coordinates of these points in the coordinate
system whose simplex of reference contains the vertices which lie
in the face $x_{e_1+...+e_{m-1}} = 0$, namely

$$A_0, ..., A_{e_1+...+e_{m-1}-1}, A_{e_1+...+e_{m-1}+1}, ..., A_n,$$

the relation between $\bar{x}$ and $\bar{y}$ is

$$\bar{y} = \bar{C}\bar{x}, \tag{5}$$

where $\bar{C}$ is the $n \times n$ matrix obtained from C as follows:

(i) if $e_m = 1$ we obtain $\bar{C}$ from C by omitting the one row and
column of $C_{e_m}(\alpha_m)$;

(ii) if $e_m > 1$ we obtain $\bar{C}$ from C by replacing $C_{e_m}(\alpha_m)$ by $C_{e_m-1}(\alpha_m)$,
that is by omitting the $(e_1 + ... + e_{m-1} + 1)$th row and column of C.

It is clear that a united line through P is the join of P to a united
point of the collineation (5) in the prime

$$x_{e_1+...+e_{m-1}} = 0,$$

and conversely. More generally, any united k-space through P is
the join of P to a united $(k-1)$-space of the collineation (5) in the
face of the simplex of reference opposite P, and conversely. We thus
have a means of constructing a theory of the united k-spaces of a
non-singular collineation, by induction on k.

A formal statement, in all generality, of the theory of united
k-spaces is somewhat complicated, although it does not involve
any serious difficulties, either of an algebraic or of a geometrical
nature. It is usually simple enough to obtain the desired results in
any particular case. We shall confine ourselves here to a description
of the properties of the united *lines* of $[n]$. This involves a study of
the united *points* of the collineation (5).

We have seen that in the collineation (3) each submatrix $C_{e_i}(\alpha_i)$
corresponds to a vertex $A_{e_1+...+e_{i-1}}$ of the simplex of reference which
is a united point, and the fundamental space of united points corresponding to a latent root α_j is the join of the vertices corresponding
to submatrices $C_{e_i}(\alpha_i)$ for which $\alpha_i = \alpha_j$. All these corresponding

vertices except $P = A_{e_1+\ldots+e_{m-1}}$ lie in $x_{e_1+\ldots+e_{m-1}} = 0$. It is at once seen that if A_h is the vertex associated with the submatrix $C_{e_j}(\alpha_j)$ of C, where $j \neq m$, then A_h is also the vertex associated with the submatrix $C_{e_j}(\alpha_j)$ of $\bar{C}$. When we consider the vertex associated with $C_{e_m}(\alpha_m)$ (remembering that $\alpha_1 = \ldots = \alpha_m = \ldots = \alpha_t$) there are two cases:

(i) if $e_m = 1$ the matrix $C_{e_m}(\alpha_m)$ is simply struck out of C to form $\bar{C}$, and there is no associated vertex for the collineation (5).

(ii) if $e_m > 1$ we form $\bar{C}$ from C by replacing $C_{e_m}(\alpha_m)$ by $C_{e_m-1}(\alpha_m)$, and the vertex associated with this latter matrix is the point $A_{e_1+\ldots+e_{m-1}+1}$.

In case (i) the united points of (5) are just the united points of (3) which lie in $x_{e_1+\ldots+e_{m-1}} = 0$, and a point associated with any latent root α of $\bar{C}$ is also associated with the latent root α of C. In case (ii) the united points associated with the latent roots of $\bar{C}$ different from α_1 are the same as those associated with the corresponding latent roots of C. But the united points of (5) associated with α_1 form the $(t-1)$-space defined by the vertices

$$A_0, A_{e_1}, \ldots, A_{e_1+\ldots+e_{m-2}}, A_{e_1+\ldots+e_{m-1}+1}, A_{e_1+\ldots+e_m}, \ldots, A_{e_1+\ldots+e_{t-1}}.$$

Hence, recalling our original reason for investigating the united points of the collineation (5), we have

THEOREM II. *If the vertex $A_{e_1+\ldots+e_{m-1}}$ of the simplex of reference is associated with the submatrix $C_{e_m}(\alpha_m)$ of C, the united lines of (3) which pass through $A_{e_1+\ldots+e_{m-1}}$ either join the point to another united point of (3) or, in the case in which $e_m > 1$, they lie in the t-space which joins the fundamental space S_{t-1} of united points of (3), which passes through $A_{e_1+\ldots+e_{m-1}}$, to the vertex $A_{e_1+\ldots+e_{m-1}+1}$.*

If we consider the implications of this theorem for the case $e_m > 1$, we see that the t-space joining the fundamental S_{t-1} corresponding to the latent root α_1 to the vertex $A_{e_1+\ldots+e_{m-1}+1}$ must be united. This is immediately verifiable from the equations of the collineation. Since in connection with this new result the vertex $A_{e_1+\ldots+e_{m-1}+1}$ plays no special part, we evidently obtain a more general theorem thus: Let

$$1 = e_1 = \ldots = e_s < e_{s+1} \leqslant e_{s+2} \leqslant \ldots \leqslant e_t.$$

Then the S_t which joins S_{t-1} to any point in the space defined by the vertices

$$A_{e_1+\ldots+e_s+1}, A_{e_1+\ldots+e_{s+1}+1}, \ldots, A_{e_1+\ldots+e_{t-1}+1}$$

is united. This result should be compared with that in § 3, p. 341, which gave the coordinates of a point P in a united S_t through S_{t-1} as

$$P = (x_0, x_1, \ldots, x_{s-1}, x_s, z_s, 0, \ldots, 0, x_{s+e_{s+1}}, z_{s+e_{s+1}}, 0, \ldots, 0,$$
$$x_{s+e_{s+1}+\ldots+e_{t-1}}, z_{s+e_{s+1}+\ldots+e_{t-1}}, 0, \ldots, 0).$$

The two results are the same.

An immediate deduction from the above is

THEOREM III. *If a collineation is non-special the only united k-spaces are those determined by $k + 1$ united points.*

Finally, we remark that *if a collineation has a non-linear elementary divisor, then there is a united line which contains only one united point.* With the notation used above, if $s < t$ the line

$$A_{e_1+\ldots+e_s} A_{e_1+\ldots+e_s+1}$$

is united, and contains the one united point $A_{e_1+\ldots+e_s}$. This result will be found useful on later occasions.

Our discussion of the geometry of the united points and spaces of a non-singular collineation has made use of the indices $e_1, \ldots, e_k$, and of the equalities between the latent roots; the actual values of the latent roots do not enter into our results. The geometrical properties of the collineation are therefore sufficiently indicated if we give the numbers $e_1, \ldots, e_k$ (whose sum is $n + 1$) and indicate which of them refer to equal latent roots. We do this by writing the *Segre symbol* for the collineation. This consists of the $e_1, \ldots, e_k$ written inside square brackets in any order, subject only to the condition that indices which refer to equal latent roots are put together, and enclosed in round brackets. Thus in [3] there are the following types of non-singular collineation:

$$[1, 1, 1, 1] \quad [(1, 1), 1, 1] \quad [(1, 1), (1, 1)] \quad [(1, 1, 1), 1] \quad [(1, 1, 1, 1)],$$
$$[1, 1, 2] \quad [(1, 2), 1] \quad [(1, 1), 2] \quad [(1, 1, 2)],$$
$$[2, 2], \quad [(2, 2)],$$
$$[1, 3] \quad [(1, 3)],$$
$$[4].$$

Writing (x, y, z, t) instead of (x_0, x_1, x_2, x_3), and denoting the vertices of the simplex of reference by X, Y, Z, T, the canonical forms of these collineations are, respectively, as follows:

(i) $x' = \alpha x, \quad y' = \beta y, \quad z' = \gamma z, \quad t' = \delta t.$

The vertices X, Y, Z, T are the only united points, their joins the only united lines, and the faces of the simplex are the only united planes.

(ii) $x' = \alpha x, \quad y' = \alpha y, \quad z' = \gamma z, \quad t' = \delta t.$

The united points are the points of XY, and the points Z, T. A united line joins any two united points, and a united plane is a plane containing three independent united points. In particular, there is a pencil of united planes through ZT.

(iii) $x' = \alpha x, \quad y' = \alpha y, \quad z' = \gamma z, \quad t' = \gamma t.$

The united points lie on the lines XY and ZT, and the united lines and planes are obtained as in (ii). In particular, there are pencils of united planes through XY and ZT.

(iv) $x' = \alpha x, \quad y' = \alpha y, \quad z' = \alpha z, \quad t' = \delta t.$

The united points fill the plane XYZ, and the point T is also united. United lines and planes are found as in (ii). In particular, any plane through T is united.

(v) $x' = \alpha x, \quad y' = \alpha y, \quad z' = \alpha z, \quad t' = \alpha t.$

This is the identity transformation.

(vi) $x' = \alpha x, \quad y' = \beta y, \quad z' = \gamma z + t, \quad t' = \gamma t.$

The united points are X, Y, Z; the united lines are YZ, ZX, XY and also ZT. The united planes are YZT, XZT, XYZ.

(vii) $x' = \alpha x, \quad y' = \alpha y + z, \quad z' = \alpha z, \quad t' = \delta t.$

The fundamental spaces are XY and T. United lines either join two united points, or join a point of ZX to Y. The planes of the star with vertex YT are all united, and the plane XYZ is also united.

(viii) $x' = \alpha x, \quad y' = \alpha y, \quad z' = \gamma z + t, \quad t' = \gamma t.$

The united points are Z and the points of XY; united lines either join two united points, or coincide with ZT. The united planes are the planes through ZT, and the plane XYZ.

(ix) $x' = \alpha x, \quad y' = \alpha y, \quad z' = \alpha z + t, \quad t' = \alpha t.$

United points fill the plane XYZ; the united lines either lie in this plane or pass through Z. Any plane through Z is united.

(x) $x' = \alpha x + y, \quad y' = \alpha y, \quad z' = \beta z + t, \quad t' = \beta t.$

The united points are X, Z; the united lines are XY, XZ, ZT, and the united planes are XZT, XYZ.

(xi) $x' = \alpha x + y,\quad y' = \alpha y,\quad z' = \alpha z + t,\quad t' = \alpha t.$

The united points form the fundamental space XZ; the united lines join the points $(a, 0, c, 0)$ and $(0, a, 0, c)$. The united planes all pass through XZ.

(xii) $x' = \alpha x,\quad y' = \beta y + z,\quad z' = \beta z + t,\quad t' = \beta t.$

The united points are X, Y; the united lines XY and YZ, and the united planes YZT and XYZ.

(xiii) $x' = \alpha x,\quad y' = \alpha y + z,\quad z' = \alpha z + t,\quad t' = \alpha t.$

The united points form the fundamental space XY; the united lines lie in XYZ and pass through Y. The united planes form a star having YZ as vertex.

(xiv) $x' = \alpha x + y,\quad y' = \alpha y + z,\quad z' = \alpha z + t,\quad t' = \alpha t.$

X is the only united point, XY the only united line, and XYZ the only united plane.

5. Cyclic collineations.   As in V, § 2, Th. I, we see that the non-singular collineations in $[n]$ form a group. We now ask: what elements, if any, of this group are of finite order? That is, we seek to determine the non-singular collineations

$$y = Ax \tag{1}$$

which are such that for some integral value of m, $y = A^m x$ is the identity transformation. This is equivalent to the condition

$$A^m = kI \quad (k \neq 0).$$

When this condition is satisfied, (1) is said to be *cyclic*, of order m. The successive transforms $P_1, P_2, \ldots$ of any point P of $[n]$ form a finite set containing at most m points, since $P_m = P$. When $m = 2$ the collineation (1) is often called an *involutory* transformation of the points of $[n]$, and in the case $n = 1$ the pairs of points P, P_1 are said to be *in involution* on the line.

We show that if (1) is cyclic the elementary divisors of A must be linear. We saw at the end of § 4 that if A has a non-linear elementary divisor there exists a united line which contains only one united point. The collineation induced on a united line must also be cyclic, and its order must be a factor of m. If we choose the coordinate system so that the line is given by the equations

$$x_2 = 0, \ldots, x_n = 0,$$

we can also assume that the induced collineation is in canonical form. Since there is only one united point on the line the canonical form must be

$$y_0 = \alpha x_0 + x_1,$$
$$y_1 = \quad \alpha x_1,$$

corresponding to a non-linear elementary divisor. If we apply this collineation m times to (x_0, x_1) we obtain the collineation

$$y_0 = \alpha^m x_0 + m\alpha^{m-1} x_1,$$
$$y_1 = \alpha^m x_1.$$

This is the identical transformation if and only if

$$m\alpha^{m-1} = 0.$$

Since the ground field K is without characteristic, and $\alpha \neq 0$, this cannot happen. Therefore, if (1) is cyclic its elementary divisors are necessarily linear.

We now write the collineation (1) in canonical form, which is

$$y = \begin{pmatrix} \alpha_1 & 0 & 0 & . & 0 \\ 0 & \alpha_2 & 0 & . & 0 \\ . & . & . & . & . \\ 0 & 0 & 0 & . & \alpha_{n+1} \end{pmatrix} x,$$

since the elementary divisors are all linear. The condition that (1) be cyclic of order m is now easily seen to be

$$\alpha_i^m = k \quad (i = 1, \dots, n+1)$$

for some non-zero k. This result may be stated as

THEOREM I. *A necessary and sufficient condition that the collineation*

$$y = Ax$$

be cyclic of order m is that the elementary divisors of $A - \lambda I_{n+1}$ be linear, and the latent roots of A satisfy the equation

$$x^m = k,$$

where k is a non-zero element of the ground field.

The condition can also be expressed in terms of invariant factors:

THEOREM II. *A necessary and sufficient condition that the collineation*

$$y = Ax$$

be cyclic of order m is that the invariant factors of $A - \lambda I_{n+1}$ have no repeated factors and that each invariant factor be a factor of the polynomial $\lambda^m - k$, where k is some non-zero element of the ground field.

This last theorem also holds when the ground field K is not algebraically closed. Indeed, let A be a non-singular matrix over any field K without characteristic, and let us suppose that the collineation (1) is cyclic of order m. Then

$$A^m = kI_{n+1} \quad (k \text{ in } K).$$

Now let K' be an algebraic extension of K over which the characteristic polynomial of A is completely reducible. Each invariant factor of $A - \lambda I_{n+1}$ is then completely reducible. The reasoning used in proving § 2, Th. III, shows that over K' the collineation can be reduced to the canonical form used in the case of algebraically closed fields. The reasoning given above then shows that the conditions given in Theorem II are necessary and sufficient for the equality

$$A^m = kI_{n+1},$$

k being in K.

6. Some particular collineations. In this section we consider some particular collineations which are of geometrical interest, confining ourselves to the case in which the ground field K is algebraically closed. Some of the results we shall obtain are particular cases of theorems proved in § 3, in particular of Theorem V of that section.

We first consider the non-special collineation with only two fundamental spaces S_a and S_b of united points. Since the collineation is non-special, we have [§ 3, Th. II]

$$a + b + 1 = n.$$

The Segre symbol for the collineation is

$$[(1, 1, \ldots, 1), (1, 1, \ldots, 1)],$$

with $a + 1$ units in one bracket, $b + 1$ in the other. The collineation can be written, in canonical form, as

$$y_0 = \alpha x_0,$$
$$y_1 = \alpha x_1,$$
$$\cdot \quad \cdot \quad \cdot$$
$$y_a = \alpha x_a,$$
$$y_{a+1} = \beta x_{a+1},$$
$$\cdot \quad \cdot \quad \cdot$$
$$y_n = \beta x_n,$$

where $\alpha \neq \beta$. The line joining any point x which is not in S_a or S_b to its transform y meets S_a in the point $z = y - \beta x$, and S_b in the point $t = y - \alpha x$. If x^* is any other point of $[n]$ not in a united space, and y^*, z^*, t^* are constructed as above, we see that the ranges (x, y, z, t) and (x^*, y^*, z^*, t^*) are related.

We can construct this collineation geometrically, as follows. We assume that we are given the fundamental spaces S_a and S_b, that these do not meet, and that we are also given one pair P, Q of corresponding points which are not united points. Let PQ meet S_a in R and S_b in S. We find the point B corresponding to a given point A as follows. If A is in either united space, $B = A$. If this is not the case the join of A to S_a is a space of $a + 1$ dimensions, Σ_{a+1}, say. Since $a + 1 = n - b$, Σ_{a+1} meets S_b in a point, at least. If Σ_{a+1} met S_b in a space S_c ($c > 0$), then S_c, lying in Σ_{a+1}, would meet S_a, which also lies in Σ_{a+1}. Hence S_a would meet S_b, contrary to hypothesis. Hence Σ_{a+1} and S_b have only one point in common. Let this be D. Then AD, being a line in Σ_{a+1}, meets S_a, in C, say. Hence ACD is a line through A which meets both S_a and S_b. It is the only line of this kind. For if $AC'D'$ is another, C' in S_a, and D' in S_b, it contains two points A and C' of Σ_{a+1}, and therefore lies in Σ_{a+1}. Hence D' is common to Σ_{a+1} and S_b. Therefore $D' = D$, and $ACD = AC'D'$.

On ACD there is a unique point B such that

$$(A, B, C, D) \;\overline{\wedge}\; (P, Q, R, S).$$

This is the required point B.

Since the collineation is non-special, the united k-spaces of the correspondence are the spaces determined by $k + 1$ united points. There are no others [§4, Th. III]. Hence they join an $S_{a'}$ in S_a to an $S_{b'}$ in S_b, where

$$a' + b' + 1 = k \quad (a' \geqslant 0, b' \geqslant 0),$$

or they lie in S_a or in S_b. In particular, any prime through S_b (S_a) joins S_b (S_a) to an S_{a-1} (S_{b-1}) in S_a (S_b) and is therefore united. The spaces S_b and S_a are the vertices of the stars of united primes, as is evident from the dual transformation.

A particular case is that in which $\alpha + \beta = 0$. The collineation is then cyclic, of order 2. If P is transformed into Q, Q is transformed into P, and, with the notation used above, (P, Q, R, S) is a harmonic range. This is the *involutory* case.

Another special case of interest is that in which $a = 0$, $b = n - 1$. Our construction for the point corresponding to a given point becomes very simple. The collineation in this case is called an *homology*, and the special case of homology, when $\alpha + \beta = 0$, is called *involutory homology*.

We now turn to certain collineations in which there is only *one* fundamental space of united points, confining ourselves to those whose Segre symbol is $[(1, 1, ..., 1, 2)]$. We first consider the case in which $n = 1$. The equations are

$$y_0 = \alpha x_0 + x_1,$$
$$y_1 = \alpha x_1.$$

This is the same collineation, from the projective point of view, as

$$y_0 = x_0 + \alpha^{-1} x_1,$$
$$y_1 = x_1,$$

and since the elementary divisor of this last collineation is $(\lambda - 1)^2$ it follows that *any* collineation on a line with Segre symbol $[2]$ can be written in the form

$$y_0 = x_0 + x_1,$$
$$y_1 = x_1,$$

by a suitable choice of coordinate system. Hence these collineations are all projectively equivalent.

Conversely, if we are given a collineation on a line with one united point, X, say, and a pair of corresponding points P, Q, a transformation of the above type is determined. We assume that X, P, Q are distinct. There exists a transformation of coordinates such that in the new coordinate system $X = (1, 0)$, $P = (1, 1)$ and $Q = (2, 1)$. Let the collineation be given in this coordinate system by the equations

$$y_0 = \alpha x_0 + \beta x_1, \quad y_1 = \gamma x_0 + \delta x_1.$$

Then, since $(1, 0)$ is a united point, $\gamma = 0$. Since also it is the only united point, there is only one elementary divisor, of degree two. Therefore $\delta = \alpha$. Finally, since $(1, 1)$ is transformed into $(2, 1)$, we have $\alpha + \beta = 2\delta$, and therefore

$$\alpha = \beta = \delta.$$

The collineation is therefore projectively equivalent to

$$y_0 = x_0 + x_1,$$
$$y_1 = x_1.$$

Such a collineation is sometimes called a *displacement* on the line, its equation in non-homogeneous coordinates being

$$y = x + 1.$$

The collineation in $[n]$ of type $[(1, 1, ..., 1, 2)]$ has the equations

$$\left.\begin{aligned} y_0 &= \alpha x_0, \\ y_1 &= \alpha x_1, \\ \cdot \quad &\cdot \quad \cdot \quad \cdot \quad \cdot \\ y_{n-2} &= \alpha x_{n-2}, \\ y_{n-1} &= \alpha x_{n-1} + x_n, \\ y_n &= \alpha x_n. \end{aligned}\right\} \tag{1}$$

The united points form the fundamental space

$$x_n = 0.$$

If the equations of any united S_k are

$$\sum_{j=0}^{n} a_{ij} x_j = 0 \quad (i = 0, ..., n-k-1),$$

the equations (1) show that

$$\alpha \sum_{j=0}^{n} a_{ij} x_j + a_{in-1} x_n = 0 \quad (i = 0, ..., n-k-1)$$

for every point $(x_0, ..., x_n)$ of S_k. If $x_n = 0$ for every point of S_k then S_k lies in the fundamental space of (1). If x_n is not zero for every point of S_k we must have

$$a_{in-1} = 0 \quad (i = 0, ..., n-k-1),$$

if S_k is united. Hence S_k passes through the point

$$A = (0, 0, ..., 0, 1, 0).$$

Conversely, the equations show that if S_k passes through this point it is united [cf. §4].

From the equations (1) it is evident that if P is transformed by the collineation into Q,

$$Q = \alpha P + x_n A,$$

so that A, P, Q are collinear. If P is not a united point, so that A, P, Q are distinct, there is a collineation induced on the line. This has only one united point, the point A. Hence it is the displacement having A as united point which transforms P into Q. The displacement is thereby defined.

Now consider any S_{n-2} which lies in the fundamental space, but does not pass through A. Any prime through S_{n-2} is transformed into another prime through S_{n-2}. In particular, the join of P and S_{n-2} is transformed into the join of Q and S_{n-2}. Let any line through A meet the first prime in P' and the second in Q'. The collineation (1) transforms P' into the point on AP' which lies in the second prime, that is, into Q'. Thus, having chosen an S_{n-2} in the united space, and being given one pair of corresponding points P, Q, we can find a pair of corresponding points P', Q' on each line through A, and these determine the displacement on the line. The transformation (1) then transforms any point R into the point S into which R is transformed by the displacement on AR.

7. Singular collineations. We conclude this chapter with a brief account of the singular collineations in $[n]$. The reasoning of §2 shows that, if the ground field K be algebraically closed, the coordinate system can be chosen so that the collineation may be written in the canonical form

$$y = \begin{pmatrix} C_{e_1}(\alpha_1) & 0 & . & 0 \\ 0 & C_{e_2}(\alpha_2) & . & 0 \\ . & . & . & . \\ 0 & 0 & . & C_{e_k}(\alpha_k) \end{pmatrix} x, \tag{1}$$

where $\alpha_i \neq 0 \quad (i \leqslant h)$,

and $\alpha_i = 0 \quad (i > h)$,

so that the submatrices corresponding to zero latent roots are together at the end.

The discussion of united points given in §3 is valid, subject only to the modification that the fundamental space S_{k-h-1} corresponding to the latent root zero is now *the space of points which have no transform*; but the geometrical relation of this to the other fundamental spaces is as before.

Again, it is clear from (1) that the points of $[n]$ which have a transform are all transformed into points in the space S_{n-k+h} whose equations are

$$x_{e_1 + \ldots + e_{h+1} - 1} = 0, \, x_{e_1 + \ldots + e_{h+2} - 1} = 0, \, \ldots, \, x_n = 0. \tag{2}$$

In the case in which

$$e_{h+1} = e_{h+2} = \ldots = e_k = 1,$$

the spaces S_{k-h-1} and S_{n-k+h} have no points in common, and their join is $[n]$. The description of the collineation is particularly simple

in this case. Just as in §3 we see that there is a projective correspondence between the $(k-h)$-spaces through S_{k-h-1} and the
points of S_{n-k+h}. The collineation (1) may then be described as
follows:

A point x in S_{k-h-1} has no transform. If x does not lie in S_{k-h-1}
it is projected from S_{k-h-1} into the point

$$z = (x_0, \ldots, x_{n-k+h}, 0, \ldots, 0)$$

of S_{n-k+h}. In S_{n-k+h} we consider the non-singular collineation

$$y^* = \begin{pmatrix} C_{e_1}(\alpha_1) & 0 & . & 0 \\ 0 & C_{e_2}(\alpha_2) & . & 0 \\ . & . & . & . \\ 0 & 0 & . & C_{e_h}(\alpha_h) \end{pmatrix} z^*,$$

where $y^* = (y_0, \ldots, y_{n-k+h})$, and $z^* = (z_0, \ldots, z_{n-k+h})$. The point

$$y = (y^*, 0, \ldots, 0)$$

of S_{n-k+h} obtained from the transform of z^* is evidently the transform of x under the collineation (1).

If the indices $e_{h+1}, \ldots, e_k$ are not all equal to unity, the construction of (1) by a series of non-singular collineations and projections
is not quite so simple, because S_{k-h-1} and S_{n-k+h} have points in
common. We may, however, proceed thus:

Let Σ_{n-k+h} be the space given by

$$x_{e_1+\ldots+e_h} = 0, x_{e_1+\ldots+e_{h+1}} = 0, \ldots, x_{e_1+\ldots+e_{k-1}} = 0.$$

This has no points in common with the space S_{k-h-1}, which is
spanned by the vertices

$$A_{e_1+\ldots+e_h}, A_{e_1+\ldots+e_{h+1}}, \ldots, A_{e_1+\ldots+e_{k-1}}.$$

We project any point x not in S_{k-h-1} from S_{k-h-1} into a point $x_{(1)}$ of
Σ_{n-k+h}. Then

$$x_{(1)} = (x_0, \ldots, x_{e_1+\ldots+e_h-1}, \overbrace{0, x_{e_1+\ldots+e_h+1}, \ldots, x_{e_1+\ldots+e_{h+1}-1}}, 0,$$
$$x_{e_1+\ldots+e_{h+1}+1}, \ldots),$$

the zeros corresponding to the first rows of the submatrices

$$C_{e_{h+1}}(0), \ldots, C_{e_k}(0) \tag{3}$$

in (1). Since we wish to consider a collineation in Σ_{n-k+h}, we omit
the zero coordinates in $x_{(1)}$, and write

$$x_{(1)}^* = (x_0, \ldots, x_{e_1+\ldots+e_h-1}, x_{e_1+\ldots+e_h+1}, \ldots).$$

We now perform the non-singular collineation in Σ_{n-k+h},

$$x_{(2)}^* = \begin{pmatrix} I_{e_1} & 0 & . & . & . & 0 \\ 0 & I_{e_2} & . & . & . & . \\ . & . & . & . & . & . \\ 0 & . & I_{e_h} & . & . & 0 \\ 0 & . & 0 & D_{e_{h+1}-1} & . & . \\ . & . & . & . & . & . \\ 0 & . & . & . & . & D_{e_k-1} \end{pmatrix} x_{(1)}^*,$$

where $I_{e_1}, \dots, I_{e_h}$ are each unity matrices, and D_e is the (cyclic) $e \times e$ matrix,

$$D_e = \begin{pmatrix} 0 & 1 & 0 & . & 0 \\ 0 & 0 & 1 & . & 0 \\ . & . & . & . & . \\ 0 & . & . & . & 1 \\ 1 & 0 & . & . & 0 \end{pmatrix}.$$

The effect of the matrices D_e is to displace the first to the last coordinate in each batch of coordinates in $x_{(1)}^*$ which corresponds to a submatrix (3), so that

$$x_{(2)}^* = (x_0, \dots, x_{e_1+\dots+e_h-1}, x_{e_1+\dots+e_h+2}, \dots, x_{e_1+\dots+e_{h+1}-1}, x_{e_1+\dots+e_h+1}, \dots).$$

Now consider the $(k-h-1)$-space Σ_{k-h-1} whose equations are

$$x_0 = x_1 = \dots = x_{e_1+\dots+e_h-1} = 0,$$
$$x_{e_1+\dots+e_h+1} = \dots = x_{e_1+\dots+e_{h+1}-2} = 0,$$
$$x_{e_1+\dots+e_{h+1}+1} = \dots = x_{e_1+\dots+e_{h+2}-2} = 0,$$
$$\dots \quad \dots \quad \dots \quad \dots \quad \dots$$
$$x_{e_1+\dots+e_{k-1}+1} = \dots = x_{n-1} = 0,$$
$$x_{e_1+\dots+e_h} + x_{e_1+\dots+e_{h+1}-1} = 0,$$
$$x_{e_1+\dots+e_{h+1}} + x_{e_1+\dots+e_{h+2}-1} = 0,$$
$$\dots \quad \dots \quad \dots \quad \dots$$
$$x_{e_1+\dots+e_{k-1}} + x_n = 0.$$

This space evidently does not meet the S_{n-k+h} given by (2). If we project the point $x_{(2)}^*$ in Σ_{n-k+h} from Σ_{k-h-1} on to S_{n-k+h} (noting that Σ_{n-k+h} does not meet Σ_{k-h-1}) we obtain the point

$$x_{(3)} = (x_0, \dots, x_{e_1+\dots+e_h-1}, \overbrace{x_{e_1+\dots+e_h+1}, \dots, x_{e_1+\dots+e_{h+1}-1}}, 0, \dots),^{\dagger}$$

$\dagger$ If z is the point in Σ_{k-h-1} which is collinear with $x_{(2)}^*$ in Σ_{n-k+h} and $x_{(3)}$ in S_{n-k+h}, we see that $z = x_{(3)} - x_{(2)}^*$.

where in each batch of coordinates corresponding to a submatrix (3) the order is standard. Since $x_{(3)}$ is in S_{n-k+h}, the coordinate corresponding to the last row of each submatrix is absent. Hence, if we omit the zero coordinates in $x_{(3)}$, and write

$$x_{(3)}^{**} = (x_0, \ldots, x_{e_1+\ldots+e_h-1}, x_{e_1+\ldots+e_h+1}, \ldots, x_{e_1+\ldots+e_{h+1}-1}, \ldots),$$

the non-singular collineation in S_{n-k+h} given by

$$y^{**} = \begin{pmatrix} C_{e_1}(\alpha_1) & 0 & 0 & . & . & . & 0 \\ 0 & C_{e_2}(\alpha_2) & 0 & . & . & . & 0 \\ . & . & . & . & . & . & . \\ 0 & . & . & C_{e_h}(\alpha_h) & . & . & . \\ 0 & . & . & . & I_{e_{h+1}-1} & . & . \\ . & . & . & . & . & . & . \\ 0 & . & . & . & . & . & I_{e_k-1} \end{pmatrix} x^{**}$$

transforms $x_{(3)}^{**}$ into the transform of x by the collineation (1).

It will be noticed that in each of the various projections and collineations we have used above, a united point of (1) remains a united point. For the coordinates of a united point are of the form

$$(x_0, x_1, \ldots, x_{e_1+\ldots+e_h-1}, 0, 0, \ldots, 0),$$

and are therefore unaffected.

Finally, the Segre symbol can be extended to denote singular collineations. This is usually done by drawing a line above the indices e_i in the symbol which correspond to a zero latent root. It should be noted that there is only one line, and this covers a single index, or a single set of indices in a round bracket. Thus the singular collineations in [3] are, apart from the improper one with zero matrix, $y = 0$,

$[1,1,1,\overline{1}]$ $[(1,1),1,\overline{1}]$ $[(\overline{1,1}),1,1]$ $[(1,1)(\overline{1,1})]$ $[(1,1,1),\overline{1}]$ $[(\overline{1,1,1}),1]$,

$[1,\overline{1},2]$ $[1,1,\overline{2}]$ $[(\overline{1,1}),2]$ $[(1,1),\overline{2}]$,

$[\overline{1},(1,2)]$ $[1,(\overline{1,2})]$ $[(\overline{1,1,2})]$,

$[2,\overline{2}]$ $[(\overline{2,2})]$,

$[3,\overline{1}]$ $[\overline{3},1]$ $[(\overline{1,3})]$,

$[\overline{4}]$.

CHAPTER IX

CORRELATIONS

In this chapter we assume once more that the ground field K is commutative and without characteristic. We shall indicate in the various sections whether K is also assumed to be algebraically closed.

1. Correlations. Let S_m, S_n be two projective spaces of dimensions m and n respectively over K. In each of them choose an allowable coordinate system. Then, if

$$A = (a_{ij})$$

is an $(m+1) \times (n+1)$ matrix over K, the equations

$$v_i = \sum_{j=0}^{n} a_{ij} x_j \quad (i = 0, \dots, m),$$

that is, in matrix notation,

$$v = Ax, \tag{1}$$

determine a prime v, of equation

$$v_0 y_0 + \dots + v_m y_m = 0,$$

in S_m corresponding to any point x of S_n which does not satisfy the equations

$$Ax = 0.$$

If A is of rank r, the *exceptional* points in S_n, that is, those with no transform under (1), form a space of $n-r$ dimensions. The primes in S_m corresponding to non-exceptional points of S_n form a star of dimension $r-1$, and hence all pass through a space of $m-r$ dimensions in S_m. We denote these spaces of $n-r$ dimensions in S_n and $m-r$ dimensions in S_m by the symbols S_{n-r}, S_{m-r} respectively.

If P and Q are any non-singular matrices, of orders[†] $n+1$ and $m+1$ respectively, over K, the equations

$$x = Px^*, \quad y = Qy^*$$

determine allowable transformations of coordinates in S_n, S_m. The

---

† An $(n+1) \times (n+1)$ matrix is sometimes said to be of *order* $n+1$.

corresponding transformations of the prime coordinates in these spaces are given by the equations

$$u^* = P'u, \quad \text{and} \quad v^* = Q'v,$$

and (1) becomes

$$v^* = Q'APx^*$$

in the new coordinate systems.

Since A is assumed to be of rank r, we can determine P, Q so that

$$Q'AP = \begin{pmatrix} I_r & 0 \\ 0 & 0 \end{pmatrix}.$$

The relation (1) now becomes

$$v_i^* = x_i^* \quad (i = 0, \dots, r-1),$$
$$v_i^* = 0 \quad (i \geqslant r)$$

in the new coordinate systems. The space S_{n-r} is given by

$$x_0^* = \dots = x_{r-1}^* = 0,$$

and S_{m-r} by

$$y_0^* = \dots = y_{r-1}^* = 0.$$

By an argument similar to that used in VIII, § 1, we can show that the points of any $(n-r+1)$-space through S_{n-r} all correspond to the *same* prime through S_{m-r}, and there is a one-to-one correspondence between these $(n-r+1)$-spaces through S_{n-r} and the primes through S_{m-r}.

Now choose two $(r-1)$-spaces, S_{r-1} in S_n and S'_{r-1} in S_m, which have no intersection with S_{n-r} and S_{m-r} respectively. Then there is clearly a correspondence between the points of S_{r-1} and the primes $((r-2)$-spaces$)$ of S'_{r-1}, in which a point P of S_{r-1} corresponds to the intersection of S'_{r-1} with that prime of S_m through S_{m-r} which corresponds to P and to the join of P to S_{n-r}.

The properties of the correspondence (1) can evidently be obtained at once from the properties of the point-prime correspondence between S_{r-1} and S'_{r-1}. Hence we need only consider that case of (1) in which $r = m+1 = n+1$.

We then have a non-singular correlative correspondence between two distinct spaces of equal dimension, S_n and S_m. If the allowable coordinate systems in the two spaces are suitably chosen, the correspondence is given by the equations

$$v_i = x_i \quad (i = 0, \dots, m = n).$$

Linearly independent (dependent) points of S_n give rise to linearly independent (dependent) primes of S_m. Hence the points of S_n which lie in a linear space S_k are transformed into the primes of S_m which pass through an S_{m-k-1}. If $(..., p_{i_0...i_k}, ...)$ are the Grassmann coordinates of S_k it is evident that the coordinates of S_{m-k-1} are $(..., q^{i_0...i_k}, ...)$, where

$$q^{i_0...i_k} = p_{i_0...i_k}.$$

Indeed we can pass from S_n to S_m by the projective transformation

$$y_i = x_i \quad (i = 0, ..., m),$$

followed by the dual transformation in S_m itself. The enumeration of the properties of this correspondence is a simple matter, and need not detain us here.

In this chapter we are more concerned with the case in which the two spaces S_m and S_n coincide in a single space, which we denote by $[n]$. We choose an allowable coordinate system in $[n]$, and consider the equations

$$u_i = \sum_{j=0}^{n} a_{ij} x_j \quad (i = 0, ..., n), \tag{2}$$

that is, $\qquad\qquad u = Ax$,

in matrix notation. These equations relate a point x of $[n]$, which does not lie in the space whose equations are

$$Ax = 0,$$

to a prime u whose equation is

$$u_0 x_0 + ... + u_n x_n = 0.$$

Such a relation is called a *correlation* in $[n]$. If

$$x = Py$$

is an allowable transformation in $[n]$, the induced transformation of the prime coordinates is

$$u = \tilde{P}v,$$

where $\tilde{P}$ is the complement of P. Equations (2) then become

$$v = P'u$$
$$= P'Ax$$
$$= P'APy.$$

One of the main objects of this chapter is to obtain canonical forms for sets of equivalent matrices $A, B, \ldots$, equivalent under the relationship

$$B = P'AP,$$

where P is non-singular. This will enable us to write the equations of any given correlation in canonical form, so that we can examine its properties. But before doing this we examine certain preliminary notions concerning correlations which, besides being of interest in themselves, will be useful in our discussion of equivalent correlations.

The correlation (2) sets up a correspondence between points x and y of $[n]$ in which there corresponds to any point x all the points y of the prime u. The point y corresponds to x if and only if $y'u = 0$, that is, if and only if

$$y'Ax = 0. \tag{3}$$

The equation (3) is said to determine a *bilinear correspondence* between x and y, and the form $y'Ax$, which is linear in the indeterminates x and y, is called a *bilinear form*. From (3) we can always obtain (2). Since we can also write (3) as

$$x'A'y = 0,$$

we see that if y corresponds to x in the bilinear correspondence arising from (2), then x corresponds to y in the *dual correlation*

$$v = A'y. \tag{4}$$

Hence the points x whose associated primes under (2) contain a given point y lie in the prime v given by (4).

The correlation (2) and the dual correlation (4) suggest another correspondence, between points which give the same prime in (2) and (4),

$$A'y = Ax. \tag{5}$$

This correspondence can be interpreted geometrically as follows: if z is any point corresponding to x in the bilinear correspondence (3), then $z'Ax = 0$. Using (5), this becomes

$$z'A'y = 0, \quad \text{or} \quad y'Az = 0,$$

which shows that y corresponds to z in (3). In the case of a non-singular correlation, that is, when A is non-singular, (5) is the collineation

$$y = \tilde{A}Ax; \tag{6}$$

we call this the *associated collineation*.

If we transform the coordinates by the equations

$$x = Px^*,$$

writing

$$B = P'AP,$$

(2), (3), (4) and (5) become, respectively,

$$u^* = Bx^*,$$

$$y^{*\prime}Bx^* = 0,$$

$$v^* = B'y^*,$$

and

$$B'y^* = Bx^*.$$

Hence *the bilinear correspondence, dual correlation and, when defined, the associated collineation are invariantly related to the given correlation.*

The study of the correlation (2) will be greatly simplified if, at the same time, we consider the associated correspondences given by (3), (4) and (5). We begin by considering the special case in which the correlation (2) is identical with the dual correlation (4); that is

$$A'x = \rho Ax$$

for all points x in $[n]$, ρ being some non-zero element of K. Then

$$A' = \rho A.$$

Forming the transpose of these equations, we obtain

$$A = \rho A'.$$

Hence

$$A = \rho^2 A.$$

Therefore

$$\rho = \pm 1.$$

When $\rho = 1$, so that $A' = A$, the matrix A is a *symmetric* matrix. The correlation (2) is then called a *polarity*. When $\rho = -1$, so that $A' = -A$, and A is *skew-symmetric*, (2) is called a *null-polarity*. We shall find it convenient to consider the properties of polarities and null-polarities in some detail before considering the properties of correlations in general.

We conclude this introductory section by remarking that we may consider, if we wish, a correspondence between two (possibly identical) spaces S_n and S_m in which primes in S_n determine points in S_m by means of the equations

$$y_i = \sum_{j=0}^{n} b_{ij} u_j \quad (i = 0, ..., m),$$

or

$$y = Bu. \tag{7}$$

It is clear that the properties of such a prime-point transformation can be obtained from the properties of the point-prime transformation we are discussing, and it is not necessary to discuss prime-point transformations separately. We note, however, that when $m = n$ and both A and B are non-singular, the point-prime transformation (1) determines the prime-point transformation

$$x = A^{-1}v$$

from S_m to S_n, and the prime-point transformation (7) determines a point-prime transformation

$$u = B^{-1}y$$

from S_m to S_n.

2. Polarities.

Let
$$u = Ax \tag{1}$$

be the equations of a polarity in an allowable coordinate system in $[n]$. The bilinear correspondence which arises from (1) is

$$y'Ax = x'Ay = 0.$$

Any two points ξ, η which are specialisations of x, y such that

$$\eta'A\xi = \xi'A\eta = 0$$

are said to be *conjugate* points in the polarity (1); if a point is conjugate to itself, it is *self-conjugate* in the polarity. If ξ, η are conjugate points, the prime $A\xi$ corresponding to ξ contains η, and the prime $A\eta$ corresponding to η contains ξ.

We begin our study of the polarity (1) by obtaining an allowable coordinate system in $[n]$ in which the equations of the polarity can be written in a standard form. There are several methods by which we may proceed. The one we shall follow is one which will prove useful later in this chapter. Our method involves the bilinear form

$$y'Ax = \sum_{i=0}^{n} \sum_{j=0}^{n} a_{ij} y_i x_j \tag{2}$$

in the two sets of indeterminates $(x_0, \ldots, x_n)$ and $(y_0, \ldots, y_n)$, and only uses transformations of coordinates of a very restricted type. We shall, for the purpose of the present reduction, say that an allowable transformation of coordinates in $[n]$ given by

$$x = Px^*$$

is of *restricted type* if the elements of the matrix P above the principal diagonal are all zero. Using the rules given in Chapter II for constructing products and inverses of matrices, we can prove at once that the product of two transformations of restricted type is also a transformation of restricted type, and the inverse of a (non-singular) transformation of restricted type is also a transformation of restricted type. We now prove

THEOREM I. *By a suitable transformation*

$$x = Px^*, \quad y = Py^*$$

of restricted type, the bilinear form $y'Ax$ can be reduced to the form

$$(y_{i_0}^* x_{i_1}^* + y_{i_1}^* x_{i_0}^*) + (y_{i_2}^* x_{i_3}^* + y_{i_3}^* x_{i_2}^*) + \ldots + (y_{i_{2r-2}}^* x_{i_{2r-1}}^* + y_{i_{2r-1}}^* x_{i_{2r-2}}^*)$$
$$+ c_{2r} y_{i_{2r}}^* x_{i_{2r}}^* + \ldots + c_n y_{i_n}^* x_{i_n}^*,$$

where $(i_0, \ldots, i_n)$ is a derangement of $(0, \ldots, n)$, r is a suitable integer such that $0 \leqslant r \leqslant \frac{1}{2}(n+1)$, and $c_{2r}, \ldots, c_n$ are in K.

There is nothing to prove if $n = 0$, and we therefore proceed by induction on n, assuming that the theorem is true for bilinear forms in the indeterminates $(x_0, \ldots, x_m)$ and $(y_0, \ldots, y_m)$, where $m < n$.

Case (i). If $a_{in} = a_{ni} = 0$ for all values of i,

$$y'Ax = \sum_{i=0}^{n-1} \sum_{j=0}^{n-1} a_{ij} y_i x_j.$$

By hypothesis there exists a transformation

$$x_i = \sum_{j=0}^{n-1} q_{ij} \xi_j, \quad y_i = \sum_{j=0}^{n-1} q_{ij} \eta_j \quad (i = 0, \ldots, n-1)$$

of restricted type which reduces the bilinear form

$$\sum_{i=0}^{n-1} \sum_{j=0}^{n-1} a_{ij} y_i x_j$$

to the form required by the theorem. Then the transformation

$$x = Px^*, \quad y = Py^*,$$

where

$$P = \begin{pmatrix} q_{00} & \cdot & \cdot & 0 & 0 \\ q_{10} & q_{11} & \cdot & \cdot & \cdot \\ \cdot & \cdot & \cdot & \cdot & \cdot \\ \cdot & \cdot & q_{n-2\,n-2} & 0 & \cdot \\ q_{n-1\,0} & \cdot & \cdot & q_{n-1\,n-1} & 0 \\ 0 & \cdot & \cdot & 0 & 1 \end{pmatrix}$$

is of restricted type, and reduces $y'Ax$ to the required form, with $i_n = n$, and $c_n = 0$.

Case (ii). $a_{nn} \neq 0$. We may write

$$y'Ax = \sum_{i=0}^{n} \sum_{j=0}^{n} a_{ij} y_i x_j$$

$$= a_{nn}^{-1} \left(\sum_{i=0}^{n} a_{in} y_i \right) \left(\sum_{i=0}^{n} a_{ni} x_i \right) + \sum_{i=0}^{n-1} \sum_{j=0}^{n-1} a_{nn}^{-1} (a_{nn} a_{ij} - a_{in} a_{nj}) y_i x_j.$$

Since $a_{in} = a_{ni}$, the transformations

$$x = Q^{-1} \xi, \quad y = Q^{-1} \eta,$$

where

$$Q = \begin{pmatrix} 1 & 0 & . & . & 0 \\ 0 & 1 & . & . & 0 \\ . & . & . & . & . \\ 0 & 0 & . & 1 & 0 \\ a_{0n} & a_{1n} & . & a_{n-1n} & a_{nn} \end{pmatrix}$$

are of restricted type, and reduce $y'Ax$ to

$$c_n \eta_n \xi_n + \sum_{i=0}^{n-1} \sum_{j=0}^{n-1} b_{ij} \eta_i \xi_j,$$

where $c_n = a_{nn}^{-1}$, and $b_{ij} = a_{nn}^{-1}(a_{nn} a_{ij} - a_{in} a_{nj})$. By the hypothesis of induction we can perform a restricted transformation on $(\xi_0, ..., \xi_{n-1})$ and $(\eta_0, ..., \eta_{n-1})$ so that

$$\sum_{i=0}^{n-1} \sum_{j=0}^{n-1} b_{ij} \eta_i \xi_j$$

is a form of the kind required by the theorem and then, just as in Case (i), we deduce a transformation of restricted type which reduces

$$\sum_{i=0}^{n-1} \sum_{j=0}^{n-1} b_{ij} \eta_i \xi_j + c_n \eta_n \xi_n$$

to the required form. Since the product of two transformations of restricted type is also of restricted type, the form $y'Ax$ is reduced to the required form by a transformation of restricted type.

Case (iii). $a_{nn} = 0$, $a_{in} = a_{ni} \neq 0$ for some values of i. Let k be the largest value of i for which $a_{in} \neq 0$. Then

$$y'Ax = y_n\left(\sum_{i=0}^{k} a_{ni}x_i\right) + \left(\sum_{i=0}^{k} a_{in}y_i\right)x_n + \sum_{i=0}^{n-1}\sum_{j=0}^{n-1} a_{ij}y_i x_j$$

$$= y_n\xi_k + x_n\eta_k + \sum_{i=0}^{n-1}\sum_{j=0}^{n-1} a_{ij}y_i x_j,$$

where

$$\xi_k = \sum_{i=0}^{k} a_{ni}x_i.$$

From this last equation, we have

$$x_k = -\sum_{i=0}^{k-1} a_{nk}^{-1}a_{ni}x_i + a_{nk}^{-1}\xi_k.$$

Replacing x_k by this expression in the indeterminates $x_0, \ldots, x_{k-1}, \xi_k$, and making a similar substitution for y_k, we find that

$$y_n\xi_k + x_n\eta_k + \sum_{i=0}^{n-1}\sum_{j=0}^{n-1} a_{ij}y_i x_j$$

$$= y_n\xi_k + x_n\eta_k + \sum_{j=0}^{n-1}{}' a_{kj}y_k x_j + \sum_{i=0}^{n-1}{}' a_{ik}y_i x_k$$

$$+ a_{kk}y_k x_k + \sum_{i=0}^{n-1}{}'\sum_{j=0}^{n-1}{}' a_{ij}y_i x_j{}^\dagger$$

$$= \left(\sum_{i=0}^{n-1}{}' b_i y_i + y_n\right)\xi_k + \eta_k\left(\sum_{i=0}^{n-1}{}' b_i x_i + x_n\right) + a_{kk}a_{nk}^{-2}\xi_k\eta_k$$

$$+ \sum_{i=0}^{n-1}{}'\sum_{j=0}^{n-1}{}' b_{ij}y_i x_j \qquad (b_{ij} = b_{ji}),$$

where the b_i, b_{ij} are elements of K easily determined by direct substitution. Now, the transformation

$$\xi_k = \sum_{i=0}^{k} a_{ni}x_i,$$

$$\xi_n = \sum_{i=0}^{n-1}{}' b_i x_i + x_n + \tfrac{1}{2}a_{kk}a_{nk}^{-2}\sum_{i=0}^{k} a_{ni}x_i,$$

$$\xi_i = x_i \quad (i = 0, \ldots, k-1, k+1, \ldots, n-1),$$

$\dagger$ In the summations $\sum_{i=0}^{n-1}{}'$ the value $i = k$ is omitted.

is of restricted type, and therefore its inverse is of restricted type. The form above becomes

$$\eta_n\xi_k+\eta_k\xi_n+\sideset{}{'}\sum_{i=0}^{n-1}\sideset{}{'}\sum_{j=0}^{n-1}b_{ij}\eta_i\xi_j$$

under the inverse transformation. We now apply our hypothesis of induction to $\sideset{}{'}\sum_{i=0}^{n-1}\sideset{}{'}\sum_{j=0}^{n-1}b_{ij}\eta_i\xi_j$. This is reduced to the form required in the theorem by a transformation of restricted type on

$$(\xi_0,\ldots,\xi_{k-1},\xi_{k+1},\ldots,\xi_{n-1}).$$

If the new indeterminates are

$$(\bar{\xi}_0,\ldots,\bar{\xi}_{k-1},\bar{\xi}_{k+1},\ldots,\bar{\xi}_{n-1}),$$

and we add to the equations of transformation the two equations

$$\xi_k=\bar{\xi}_k,$$
$$\xi_n=\bar{\xi}_n$$

in their correct position, the new matrix is still of restricted type, and we have reduced $y'Ax$ by a sequence of restricted transformations to the required form. Thus our theorem is proved.

The use of transformations of restricted type is of purely auxiliary importance, and when we are concerned with only one symmetric bilinear form $y'Ax$ we can obtain a simpler standard form by using allowable transformations which are not of the restricted type. We first carry out the transformation

$$x_{i_0}^*=\xi_{i_0}^*+\xi_{i_1}^*,$$
$$x_{i_1}^*=\xi_{i_0}^*-\xi_{i_1}^*,$$
$$\cdot\qquad\cdot\qquad\cdot$$
$$x_{i_{2r-2}}^*=\xi_{i_{2r-2}}^*+\xi_{i_{2r-1}}^*,$$
$$x_{i_{2r-1}}^*=\xi_{i_{2r-2}}^*-\xi_{i_{2r-1}}^*,$$
$$x_j^*=\xi_j^*\quad(j=i_{2r},\ldots,i_n)$$

on the standard form obtained in Theorem I. It becomes

$$\sum_{j=0}^{n}c_j\eta_{i_j}^*\xi_{i_j}^*,$$

where $\qquad c_{2i}=2\qquad(i=0,\ldots,r-1),$

and $\qquad c_{2i+1}=-2\qquad(i=0,\ldots,r-1).$

Remembering that $(i_0, ..., i_n)$ is a permutation of $(0, ..., n)$, we finally use a transformation which merely amounts to a permutation of the indeterminates and we have

$$y'Ax = \sum_{i=0}^{s} d_i Y_i X_i,$$

where $d_0, ..., d_s$ are not zero. If the resultant of all the transformations used is the transformation

$$x = RX, \quad y = RY,$$

then

$$R'AR = \begin{pmatrix} d_0 & 0 & . & . & . & 0 \\ 0 & d_1 & . & . & . & 0 \\ . & . & . & . & . & . \\ 0 & . & d_s & . & . & 0 \\ . & . & . & 0 & . & 0 \\ . & . & . & . & . & . \\ . & . & . & . & . & 0 \end{pmatrix},$$

and therefore the rank of A is $s+1$. Hence we have

THEOREM II. (a) *By a suitable choice of the allowable coordinate system any symmetric bilinear form $y'Ax$ can be reduced to*

$$\sum_{i=0}^{s} d_i Y_i X_i,$$

where $s+1$ is the rank of A.

(b) *By a suitable choice of an allowable coordinate system the polarity $u = Ax$ can be reduced to the equations*

$$U_i = d_i X_i \quad (i = 0, ..., n),$$

where $d_0, ..., d_s$ are not zero, but $d_{s+1} = ... = d_n = 0$, the rank of A being $s+1$.

When the ground field K is algebraically closed we may use a further transformation

$$X_i^* = d_i^{\frac{1}{2}} X_i \quad (i = 0, ..., s), \qquad X_i^* = X_i \quad (i = s+1, ..., n).$$

The effect of this is to replace each d_i $(i \leqslant s)$ in the above Theorem by 1. Hence we have

THEOREM III. *If the ground field K is algebraically closed, the only projective invariant of a polarity is its rank. By a suitable choice of the allowable coordinate system the equations of a polarity of rank $s+1$ may be taken as*

$$u_i = x_i \quad (i = 0, ..., s), \qquad u_i = 0 \quad (i = s+1, ..., n).$$

The system of allowable coordinates which reduces a polarity to the form given in Theorem III is not uniquely determined, as the following discussion will show. We assume that the matrix A in (1) is of rank $s+1$, and that $s \geqslant 0$. Let

$$P^{(0)} = (x_0^0, \ldots, x_n^0) = x^{(0)}$$

be any point which is not self-conjugate with respect to the polarity (1). Then

$$x^{(0)\prime} A x^{(0)} \neq 0. \tag{3}$$

The equation

$$x^{(0)\prime} A x = 0 \tag{4}$$

determines a prime. This prime contains the S_{n-s-1} given by

$$A x = 0,$$

coinciding with it if $s = 0$. By virtue of (3) the point $P^{(0)}$ does not lie in the prime (4). We may therefore choose n independent points in this prime, say,

$$P^{(i)} = (x_0^i, \ldots, x_n^i) = x^{(i)} \quad (i = 1, \ldots, n),$$

which, together with $P^{(0)}$, form a simplex. We take this simplex as a simplex of reference for a new coordinate system, noting, first of all, that

$$x^{(0)\prime} A x^{(i)} = 0 \quad (i = 1, \ldots, n).$$

Let the equation of the bilinear correspondence determined by (1) in the new coordinate system be

$$y^{*\prime} B x^* = 0 \quad (B = (b_{ij})).$$

Then if $x^{*(i)}$ is the transform of $x^{(i)}$,

$$x^{*(0)\prime} B x^{*(i)} = 0 \quad (i = 1, \ldots, n).$$

But

$$x^{*(i)} = (\delta_{i0}, \ldots, \delta_{in}) \quad (i = 0, \ldots, n).$$

Hence

$$b_{0i} = 0 \quad (i = 1, \ldots, n).$$

Since

$$x^{*(0)\prime} B x^{*(0)} \neq 0,$$

it follows that

$$b_{00} \neq 0.$$

Hence

$$y^{*\prime} B x^* = b_{00} y_0 x_0 + \sum_{i=1}^{n} \sum_{j=1}^{n} b_{ij} y_i^* x_j^*,$$

and the matrix

$$\begin{pmatrix} b_{11} & \cdot & b_{1n} \\ \cdot & \cdot & \cdot \\ b_{n1} & \cdot & b_{nn} \end{pmatrix}$$

must be of rank s. Repeating the process just described for the bilinear form

$$\sum_{i=1}^{n} \sum_{j=1}^{n} b_{ij} y_i^* x_j^*,$$

we arrive at the following result:

THEOREM IV. *If a polarity is of rank $s+1$ we can construct a simplex of reference, referred to which the polarity has its equation in canonical form, as follows:*

(i) *there exists a point $P^{(0)}$ which is not self-conjugate with regard to the polarity;*

(ii) *there exists a point $P^{(1)}$ which is not self-conjugate with regard to the polarity and is conjugate to $P^{(0)}$;*

. . . .

$(i+1)$ *there exists a point $P^{(i)}$ which is not self-conjugate with regard to the polarity, and is conjugate to $P^{(0)}, ..., P^{(i-1)}$;*

. . . .

$(s+1)$ *there exists a point $P^{(s)}$ which is not self-conjugate with regard to the polarity, and is conjugate to $P^{(0)}, ..., P^{(s-1)}$;*

$(s+2)$ *now let $P^{(s+1)}, ..., P^{(n)}$ be $n-s$ independent points of the space S_{n-s-1} whose points have no corresponding prime in the polarity. Then we can take $P^{(0)}, ..., P^{(n)}$ as simplex of reference, and, choosing the multipliers suitably, the equations of the polarity become*

$$u_i = x_i \quad (i = 0, ..., s), \qquad u_i = 0 \quad (i = s+1, ..., n).$$

The properties of a polarity are easily read off from the canonical form found above. In particular we observe that the properties of the polarity we have been considering,

$$\left. \begin{aligned} u_i &= x_i \quad (i = 0, ..., s), \\ u_i &= 0 \quad (i = s+1, ..., n), \end{aligned} \right\} \tag{5}$$

can be deduced immediately from those of the non-singular polarity

$$u_i = x_i \quad (i = 0, ..., s) \tag{6}$$

in the space S_s whose equations are

$$x_{s+1} = ... = x_n = 0.$$

The space S_{n-s-1}, whose equations are now

$$x_0 = ... = x_s = 0,$$

is called the *vertex* of the polarity. No point in this space has a corresponding prime in the polarity (5). Since the prime corresponding to any point not in S_{n-s-1} passes through S_{n-s-1}, it follows that a point of S_{n-s-1} is conjugate to any point of $[n]$ not in S_{n-s-1}. It also follows immediately, from the equations, that two points P and Q of $[n]$ which are not in S_{n-s-1} are conjugate with regard to (5) if and only if their projections from S_{n-s-1} on to S_s are conjugate with regard to (6).

The geometrical meaning of polarities will become clearer when we discuss conjugate points in the chapter on Quadrics in vol. II. We need only remark here that points which are conjugate with regard to the polarity

$$u = Ax$$

are also conjugate with regard to the quadric

$$x'Ax = 0,$$

and conversely, the relation between the points being the same in each case.

The non-singular polarity (6) transforms the points of an S_k whose Grassmann coordinates are $(\ldots, p_{i_0 \ldots i_k}, \ldots)$ into the primes through an S_{s-k-1} whose dual coordinates are $(\ldots, q^{i_0 \ldots i_k}, \ldots)$, where

$$q^{i_0 \ldots i_k} = p_{i_0 \ldots i_k}.$$

This is evident from the equations (6). Conversely, the transform of the points of S_{s-k-1} is the set of primes through S_k. The spaces S_k and S_{s-k-1} are said to be conjugate in the polarity. Every point in the one space is conjugate to every point in the other space. We now prove

THEOREM V. *If S_k and S_{s-k-1} are conjugate in a non-singular polarity, a necessary and sufficient condition that they should meet is that S_k should contain a point P which is conjugate with regard to every point of S_k.*

Let
$$y^{(i)} = (y_0^i, \ldots, y_s^i) \quad (i = 0, \ldots, k)$$

be $k+1$ independent points of S_k. The equations of S_{s-k-1} are given by the equations

$$\sum_{j=0}^{s} y_j^i x_j = 0 \quad (i = 0, \ldots, k).$$

If S_{s-k-1} contains a point of S_k, say the point

$$x = \sum_{a=0}^{k} \lambda_a y^{(a)},$$

the equations in $\lambda_0, \ldots, \lambda_k$,

$$\sum_{a=0}^{k} \sum_{j=0}^{s} y_j^i y_j^a \lambda_a = 0 \quad (i = 0, \ldots, k),$$

must have a solution. But the condition that there exists a proper set $\lambda_0, \ldots, \lambda_k$ such that the equations above are satisfied is precisely the condition that the point

$$x = \sum_0^k \lambda_i y^{(i)}$$

is conjugate to each of the points $y^{(0)}, \ldots, y^{(k)}$. The point x is then conjugate to every point of S_k. This proves the theorem, which is evident geometrically.

If we follow the point-prime polarity

$$u = Ax$$

by the prime-point polarity

$$y = Bu,$$

the result is the collineation

$$y = BAx.$$

We conclude our discussion of polarities by proving, in the case when the ground field K is algebraically closed,

THEOREM VI. *Any collineation in* [n] *can be expressed as the result of a point-prime polarity followed by a non-singular prime-point polarity.*

We choose our coordinate system so that the collineation is given in canonical form

$$y = Cx,$$

where

$$C = \begin{pmatrix} C_{e_1}(\alpha_1) & 0 & . & 0 \\ 0 & C_{e_2}(\alpha_2) & . & 0 \\ . & . & . & . \\ 0 & 0 & . & C_{e_k}(\alpha_k) \end{pmatrix},$$

and $C_e(\alpha)$ is the $e \times e$ matrix

$$C_e(\alpha) = \begin{pmatrix} \alpha & 1 & 0 & . & . & 0 \\ 0 & \alpha & 1 & . & . & 0 \\ . & . & . & . & . & . \\ 0 & . & . & . & \alpha & 1 \\ 0 & . & . & . & 0 & \alpha \end{pmatrix}.$$

Now let

$$B = \begin{pmatrix} B_{e_1} & 0 & . & 0 \\ 0 & B_{e_2} & . & 0 \\ . & . & . & . \\ 0 & 0 & . & B_{e_k} \end{pmatrix},$$

where B_e is the $e \times e$ matrix

$$B_e = \begin{pmatrix} 0 & 0 & . & 0 & 1 \\ 0 & 0 & . & 1 & 0 \\ . & . & . & . & . \\ 0 & 1 & . & 0 & 0 \\ 1 & 0 & . & 0 & 0 \end{pmatrix}.$$

Then

$$A = BC = \begin{pmatrix} B_{e_1} C_{e_1}(\alpha_1) & 0 & . & 0 \\ 0 & B_{e_2} C_{e_2}(\alpha_2) & . & 0 \\ . & . & . & . \\ 0 & 0 & . & B_{e_k} C_{e_k}(\alpha_k) \end{pmatrix}.$$

But $B_e C_e(\alpha)$ is the $e \times e$ matrix

$$\begin{pmatrix} 0 & 0 & . & 0 & \alpha \\ 0 & 0 & . & \alpha & 1 \\ . & . & . & . & . \\ 0 & \alpha & . & 0 & 0 \\ \alpha & 1 & . & 0 & 0 \end{pmatrix},$$

which is symmetric. Hence A is symmetric. Now B is not only symmetric, but also non-singular, and, indeed,

$$B = B^{-1}.$$

The collineation $y = Cx$ is the result of the polarity

$$u = Ax$$

followed by the non-singular prime-point polarity

$$y = Bu.$$

3. Null-polarities. The properties of null-polarities may be discussed along lines similar to those followed in § 2 in the discussion of polarities. We first consider the reduction, by means of a suitable choice of allowable coordinate system, of the equations of a null-polarity to a standard form. We prove the analogue of § 2, Th. I, using the same restricted type of transformation.

THEOREM I. *By means of a transformation*

$$x = Px^*, \quad y = Py^*$$

of restricted type, a skew-symmetric bilinear form $y'Ax$ can be reduced to the form

$$(y_{i_0}^* x_{i_1}^* - y_{i_1}^* x_{i_0}^*) + (y_{i_2}^* x_{i_3}^* - y_{i_3}^* x_{i_2}^*) + \ldots + (y_{i_{2r-2}}^* x_{i_{2r-1}}^* - y_{i_{2r-1}}^* x_{i_{2r-2}}^*),$$

where $(i_0, \ldots, i_{2r})$ are $2r$ distinct numbers chosen from the set $(0, \ldots, n)$.

If $n = 1$,
$$y'Ax = a_{01}(y_0 x_1 - y_1 x_0).$$

When $a_{01} = 0$ there is nothing to prove. If $a_{01} \neq 0$, we take

$$P = \begin{pmatrix} 1 & 0 \\ 0 & a_{01}^{-1} \end{pmatrix},$$

and
$$a_{01}(y_0 x_1 - y_1 x_0) = y_0^* x_1^* - y_1^* x_0^*.$$

This proves the theorem when $n = 1$, and we now proceed by induction. There are only two cases to consider in this theorem, since $a_{nn} = 0$, the matrix A being skew-symmetric.

Case (i) If $a_{in} = 0$ for all i, the theorem follows immediately from the hypothesis of induction (cf. § 2, Th. I).

Case (ii). If not all a_{in} are zero, let $k < n$ be the largest value of i such that $a_{in} \neq 0$. Then

$$y'Ax = y_n \left(\sum_{i=0}^{k} a_{ni} x_i \right) + \left(\sum_{i=0}^{k} a_{in} y_i \right) x_n + \sum_{i=0}^{n-1} \sum_{j=0}^{n-1} a_{ij} y_i x_j.$$

Now let

$$\xi_k = \sum_{i=0}^{k} a_{ni} x_i,$$

$$\xi_i = x_i \quad (i = 0, \ldots, k-1, k+1, \ldots, n).$$

This is a restricted transformation. Its inverse is

$$x_k = -a_{nk}^{-1} \sum_0^{k-1} a_{ni}\xi_i + a_{nk}^{-1}\xi_k,$$

$$x_i = \xi_i \quad (i = 0, ..., k-1, k+1, ..., n),$$

which is also of restricted type. Since we can write

$$y'Ax = y_n\left(\sum_{i=0}^k a_{ni}x_i\right) - \left(\sum_{i=0}^k a_{ni}y_i\right)x_n + \sum_{i=0}^{n-1}{}' \sum_{j=0}^{n-1}{}' a_{ij}y_i x_j$$

$$+ \sum_{j=0}^{n-1}{}' a_{kj}y_k x_j - \sum_{j=0}^{n-1}{}' a_{kj}y_j x_k,^\dagger$$

we have, after transformation,

$$y'Ax = \eta_n\xi_k - \eta_k\xi_n + \sum_{i=0}^{n-1}{}' \sum_{j=0}^{n-1}{}' a_{ij}\eta_i\xi_j$$

$$+ \left(\sum_{j=0}^{n-1}{}' a_{kj}\xi_j\right)\left(-a_{nk}^{-1}\sum_{i=0}^{k-1} a_{ni}\eta_i + a_{nk}^{-1}\eta_k\right)$$

$$- \left(\sum_{j=0}^{n-1}{}' a_{kj}\eta_j\right)\left(-a_{nk}^{-1}\sum_{i=0}^{k-1} a_{ni}\xi_i + a_{nk}^{-1}\xi_k\right)$$

$$= \left(\eta_n + \sum_{i=0}^{n-1}{}' b_i\eta_i\right)\xi_k - \eta_k\left(\xi_n + \sum_{i=0}^{n-1}{}' b_i\xi_i\right) + \sum_{i=0}^{n-1}{}' \sum_{j=0}^{n-1}{}' b_{ij}\eta_i\xi_j,$$

where the b_i, b_{ij} are easily calculated elements of K. We now use the restricted transformation

$$\xi_i^* = \xi_i \quad (i = 0, ..., n-1),$$

$$\xi_n^* = \xi_n + \sum_{i=0}^{n-1}{}' b_i\xi_i,$$

and

$$y'Ax = \eta_n^*\xi_k^* - \eta_k^*\xi_n^* + \sum_{i=0}^{n-1}{}' \sum_{j=0}^{n-1}{}' b_{ij}\eta_i^*\xi_j^*.$$

The rest of the argument follows from the hypothesis of induction, and is exactly as in § 2, Th. I. The theorem is then proved.

Since the rank of $P'AP$ is equal to the rank of A, and the rank of the bilinear form described in the theorem is $2r$, it follows that the rank of A is $2r$.

$\dagger$ In the summations $\sum'_i$, the value $i = k$ is omitted.

By a further transformation, not of restricted type, which merely rearranges the indeterminates, the bilinear form $y'Ax$ can finally be reduced to the form

$$\sum_{i=0}^{r-1} (Y_{2i} X_{2i+1} - Y_{2i+1} X_{2i}).$$

When we state this result in terms of null-polarities we have

THEOREM II. *A null-polarity has only one projective invariant, its rank, which must be even. If the rank is $2r$ the coordinate system can be chosen so that the equations of the null-polarity are*

$$\left.\begin{aligned} u_{2i} &= x_{2i+1}, \\ u_{2i+1} &= -x_{2i}, \end{aligned}\right\} \quad (i = 0, ..., r-1), \tag{1}$$
$$u_j = 0 \quad (j \geqslant 2r).$$

It is easy to show that the reduction to this form is not unique, but we do not stop to prove this explicitly.

An essential difference between the null-polarity and the polarity is that *every point x is conjugate to itself in a null-polarity.* For, if A is skew-symmetric,

$$x'Ax = (x'Ax)' = x'A'x = -x'Ax,$$

and therefore $x'Ax = 0.$

In other words the prime $u = Ax$ always contains the point x.

If two points x, y are conjugate, so that

$$y'Ax = -x'Ay = 0,$$

then any two points $\lambda x + \mu y$ and $\rho x + \sigma y$ on their join are also conjugate. For

$$(\lambda x' + \mu y') A (\rho x + \sigma y)$$
$$= \lambda \rho x'Ax + \lambda \sigma x'Ay + \mu \rho y'Ax + \mu \sigma y'Ay = 0.$$

Hence every line in $[n]$, joining a pair of points which are conjugate in the null-polarity, contains an infinite number of pairs of conjugate points. We also have

$$0 = y'Ax = \sum_{i=0}^{n} \sum_{j=0}^{n} a_{ij} y_i x_j = \sum_{i<j} a_{ij}(y_i x_j - y_j x_i)$$
$$= \sum_{i<j} a_{ij} p_{ij}, \tag{2}$$

where $(..., p_{ij}, ...)$ are the Grassmann coordinates of the line joining the two conjugate points x, y. Conversely, if x and y are two points of a line whose coordinates $(..., p_{ij}, ...)$ satisfy a relation

$$\sum_{i<j} b_{ij} p_{ij} = 0,$$

then we may write this as

$$\sum_{i=0}^{n} \sum_{j=0}^{n} b_{ij} y_i x_j = y' B x = 0,$$

where

$$b_{ij} = -b_{ji} \quad (i > j),$$

and

$$b_{ii} = 0.$$

Hence a null-polarity is associated with a system of lines (called a *linear complex*) whose Grassmann coordinates satisfy the relation (2), and conversely any linear complex is associated with a unique null-polarity. The geometry of a null-polarity is, essentially, the geometry of a linear complex and, as such, belongs to Line Geometry.

A null-polarity can only be non-singular when n is odd, and then $r = \frac{1}{2}(n+1)$. Let us briefly consider this case. We take the equations in canonical form.

$$\left. \begin{aligned} u_{2i} &= x_{2i+1}, \\ u_{2i+1} &= -x_{2i}, \end{aligned} \right\} \quad (i = 0, ..., r-1).$$

If

$$y^{(i)} = (y_0^i, ..., y_n^i) \quad (i = 0, ..., k),$$

are $k+1$ independent points of $[n]$ which determine an S_k, the equations of the conjugate S_{n-k-1} common to the transforms of all the points of S_k are

$$\sum_{j=0}^{r-1} (y_{2j+1}^i x_{2j} - y_{2j}^i x_{2j+1}) = 0 \quad (i = 0, ..., k).$$

This S_{n-k-1} meets S_k if these equations are satisfied by

$$x = \sum_{0}^{k} \lambda_i y^{(i)},$$

that is, if the equations

$$\sum_{h=0}^{k} \sum_{j=0}^{r-1} (y_{2j+1}^i y_{2j}^h - y_{2j}^i y_{2j+1}^h) \lambda_h = 0 \quad (i = 0, ..., k) \tag{3}$$

have a proper solution $(\lambda_0, ..., \lambda_k)$. The $(k+1) \times (k+1)$ matrix

$$(\alpha_{ih}) = \left(\sum_{j=0}^{r-1} (y_{2j+1}^i y_{2j}^h - y_{2j}^i y_{2j+1}^h) \right)$$

is skew-symmetric, and is therefore singular if $k+1$ is odd. Thus there is always a proper solution of (3), and therefore S_k meets S_{n-k-1}, when k is even. On the other hand, if k is odd the matrix (α_{ih}) may be non-singular, and then S_k does not meet S_{n-k-1}. This may be seen by taking

$$y^{(i)} = (\delta_{i0}, \ldots, \delta_{in}) \quad (i = 0, \ldots, k),$$

that is, by considering an S_k determined by the first $k+1$ vertices of the simplex of reference. In fact the equations of S_{n-k-1} are then

$$x_1 = x_0 = 0, \quad x_3 = x_2 = 0, \quad \ldots, \quad x_k = x_{k-1} = 0,$$

and this does not meet the S_k we have selected.

An S_k is called *self-conjugate* if it coincides with its conjugate S_{n-k-1}. This can only occur if $k = n-k-1$. We then have $k = r-1$. If this condition is satisfied there are k-spaces which are self-conjugate. For instance, the k-space determined by the first, third, fifth, ..., nth vertices of the simplex of reference is self-conjugate. In fact, the equations of the conjugate S_k are

$$x_0 = x_2 = \ldots = x_{n-1} = 0.$$

Let us find the condition that the space S_k whose coordinates are $(\ldots, p_{i_0 \ldots i_k}, \ldots)$ is self-conjugate. Since the method does not use the canonical form of the null-polarity, we assume that the null-polarity is given by the equations

$$u = Ax. \tag{4}$$

Clearly, a necessary and sufficient condition that S_k be self-conjugate is that any two points in S_k should be conjugate. Hence, any line in S_k must belong to the linear complex

$$\sum_{i<j} a_{ij} p_{ij} = 0.$$

Now any line in S_k is the intersection of S_k and an S_{n-k+1}. Let $(\ldots, q^{i_0 \ldots i_{k-2}}, \ldots)$ be the dual coordinates of an S_{n-k+1}. If this S_{n-k+1} meets S_k in a space of more than one dimension we have

$$\sum_{i_0, \ldots, i_{k-2}} p_{ij i_0 \ldots i_{k-2}} q^{i_0 \ldots i_{k-2}} = 0$$

for all values of i, j, but if the intersection is a line, its coordinates are $(\ldots, r_{ij}, \ldots)$, where [VII, § 5]

$$r_{ij} = \sum_{i_0, \ldots, i_{k-2}} p_{ij i_0 \ldots i_{k-2}} q^{i_0 \ldots i_{k-2}}.$$

It follows that a necessary and sufficient condition that S_k be self-conjugate is that

$$\sum_{i<j} \sum_{i_0,\ldots,i_{k-2}} a_{ij} p_{iji_0\ldots i_{k-2}} q^{i_0\cdots i_{k-2}} = 0$$

for all choices of elements $q^{i_0\cdots i_{k-2}}$ which are coordinates of an S_{n-k+1}. But we can always find an S_{n-k+1} for which every Grassmann coordinate except an assigned one is zero. We can therefore write the necessary and sufficient conditions that S_k be self-conjugate as

$$\sum_{i<j} a_{ij} p_{iji_0\ldots i_{k-2}} = 0,$$

for all choices of $i_0, \ldots, i_{k-2}$.

A point-prime null-polarity

$$u = Ax,$$

followed by a prime-point null-polarity

$$y = Bu$$

leads to the collineation $\quad y = BAx.$

If n is even, both A and B are singular, and the collineation is also singular. Hence we cannot expect to represent a non-singular collineation in this way. We may ask whether the representation is possible when n is odd. Similarly, we may enquire whether any collineation can be represented as the resultant of a point-prime null-polarity (polarity) followed by a prime-point polarity (null-polarity). In each case it is seen that certain conditions must be satisfied by the elementary divisors of the collineation, and that these are necessary and sufficient for the desired representation. Since the method of investigating the problems is the same in each case, we only consider one of them in detail, merely stating the results in the other cases.

THEOREM III. *If n is odd and the ground field K is algebraically closed, a necessary and sufficient condition that a collineation in $[n]$,*

$$y = Cx,$$

can be represented as the result of a point-prime null-polarity

$$u = Ax$$

followed by a non-singular prime-point null-polarity

$$y = Bu$$

is that the elementary divisors of $C - \lambda I_{n+1}$ can be arranged in equal pairs: $(\lambda - \alpha_1)^{e_1}, (\lambda - \alpha_1)^{e_1}; (\lambda - \alpha_2)^{e_2}, (\lambda - \alpha_2)^{e_2}; \ldots.$

We take C in the canonical form

$$C = \begin{pmatrix} C_{e_1}(\alpha_1) & 0 & . & 0 \\ 0 & C_{e_2}(\alpha_2) & . & 0 \\ . & . & . & . \\ 0 & 0 & . & C_{e_k}(\alpha_k) \end{pmatrix},$$

and find the conditions that there exist skew-symmetric matrices A, B such that

$$C = BA. \qquad (5)$$

An elementary argument shows that a *necessary* condition on C is that there is another elementary divisor $(\lambda - \alpha)^f$ corresponding to any elementary divisor $(\lambda - \alpha)^e$ of $C - \lambda I_{n+1}$. Let $P = B^{-1}$. Then the elementary divisors of $C - \lambda I_{n+1}$ are also the elementary divisors of

$$PC - \lambda P I_{n+1} = A - \lambda P,$$

which is a skew-symmetric matrix. Hence, if $\lambda = \alpha$ is a latent root of C, the rank of $A - \alpha P$, and hence the rank of $C - \alpha I_{n+1}$, is $n + 1 - 2\rho$, where ρ is an integer [Th. II]. There must therefore be 2ρ elementary divisors of the form

$$(\lambda - \alpha)^{e_1}, \ldots, (\lambda - \alpha)^{e_{2\rho}}.$$

This does not prove, however, that the numbers $e_1, \ldots, e_{2\rho}$ can be arranged in equal pairs, as is required by our theorem, and a more detailed argument is required to prove this.

We divide A and $P = B^{-1}$ into blocks of a size suggested by the canonical form of C. We write

$$A = \begin{pmatrix} A^{11} & . & A^{1k} \\ . & . & . \\ A^{k1} & . & A^{kk} \end{pmatrix},$$

and

$$P = B^{-1} = \begin{pmatrix} P^{11} & . & P^{1k} \\ . & . & . \\ P^{k1} & . & P^{kk} \end{pmatrix},$$

where A^{ij} and P^{ij} are $e_i \times e_j$ matrices. Since A and P are skew-symmetric,

$$(A^{ij})' = -(A^{ji}), \quad \text{and} \quad (P^{ij})' = -(P^{ji}). \qquad (6)$$

Since $PC = A$, multiplication of the appropriate matrices shows that we must have
$$P^{ij}C_{e_j}(\alpha_j) = A^{ij}.$$

Using (6), we find that
$$(A^{ij})' = (P^{ij}C_{e_j}(\alpha_j))' = C'_{e_j}(\alpha_j)\,(P^{ij})' = -C'_{e_j}(\alpha_j)\,P^{ji}.$$

But
$$(A^{ij})' = -A^{ji} = -P^{ji}C_{e_i}(\alpha_i)$$

for all values of i, j. Hence
$$C'_{e_j}(\alpha_j)\,P^{ji} = P^{ji}C_{e_i}(\alpha_i). \tag{7}$$

We use this result to determine the form of the submatrices P^{ji}. Write
$$P^{ji} = \begin{pmatrix} p_{11} & \cdot & p_{1\,e_i} \\ \cdot & \cdot & \cdot \\ p_{e_j 1} & \cdot & p_{e_j e_i} \end{pmatrix},$$

and define
$$p_{0h} = 0 \quad (h = 1, ..., e_i), \qquad p_{h0} = 0 \quad (h = 1, ..., e_j).$$

Equating elements in the hth row and kth column on both sides of (7) we have
$$\alpha_j p_{hk} + p_{h-1\,k} = \alpha_i p_{hk} + p_{h\,k-1} \quad (h = 1, ..., e_j;\, k = 1, ..., e_i). \tag{8}$$

Suppose, first of all, that $\alpha_i \neq \alpha_j$. Then, if $h = k = 1$ in (8), we get
$$(\alpha_i - \alpha_j)\,p_{11} = 0,$$

and therefore
$$p_{11} = 0.$$

Next, if $h = 1$, $k = 2$, (8) becomes
$$(\alpha_i - \alpha_j)\,p_{12} + p_{11} = 0,$$

and so
$$p_{12} = 0.$$

Proceeding along the first row of P^{ji}, then along the second row, and so on, we find that
$$P^{ji} = 0,$$

if $\alpha_i \neq \alpha_j$.

On the other hand, if $\alpha_i = \alpha_j$, (8) becomes
$$p_{h-1\,k} = p_{h\,k-1} \quad (h = 1, ..., e_j;\, k = 1, ..., e_i).$$

If $e_i \leqslant e_j$, all elements on lines parallel to the line joining p_{1e_i} to $p_{e_i 1}$ are equal, and if $e_i \geqslant e_j$ all elements on lines parallel to the line joining p_{1e_j} to $p_{e_j 1}$ are equal. Since also, if $e_i \leqslant e_j$,

$$p_{hk} = p_{h+k\,0} = 0 \quad (h+k \leqslant e_j),$$

and if $e_i \geqslant e_j$,

$$p_{hk} = p_{0\,h+k} = 0 \quad (h+k \leqslant e_i),$$

we obtain two forms for the submatrix P^{ji}:

$e_i \leqslant e_j$;

$$P^{ji} = \begin{pmatrix} 0 & . & . & . & . & 0 \\ . & . & . & . & . & \\ . & . & . & . & . & 0 \\ 0 & . & . & 0 & a \\ 0 & . & . & . & b \\ 0 & 0 & a & b & c \\ 0 & a & b & c & . \\ a & b & c & . & . \end{pmatrix}, \tag{9}$$

$e_i \geqslant e_j$;

$$P^{ji} = \begin{pmatrix} 0 & . & . & . & . & . & 0 & a \\ 0 & . & . & . & . & 0 & a & b \\ 0 & . & . & . & 0 & a & b & c \\ . & . & . & . & . & . & . & . \\ 0 & . & 0 & a & b & c & . & . \end{pmatrix}. \tag{9}$$

Thus the matrix P is divided into diagonal blocks of square matrices

$$P = \begin{pmatrix} P^1 & 0 & . & 0 \\ 0 & P^2 & . & 0 \\ . & . & . & . \\ 0 & 0 & . & P^r \end{pmatrix}$$

corresponding to sets of equal latent roots

$$(\alpha_1, ..., \alpha_{k_1})\,(\alpha_{k_1+1}, ..., \alpha_{k_2}) ... (\alpha_{k_{r-1}+1}, ..., \alpha_{k_r}),$$

where $k_r = k$. It is easily seen that the matrix A is similarly divided into diagonal blocks since

$$PC = A$$

Writing

$$A = \begin{pmatrix} A^1 & 0 & . & 0 \\ 0 & A^2 & . & 0 \\ . & . & . & . \\ 0 & 0 & . & A^r \end{pmatrix},$$

we may write the relation between the three matrices A, P, C as

$$P^i \begin{pmatrix} C_{e_{k_{i-1}+1}}(\alpha_{k_{i-1}+1}) & 0 & . & 0 \\ 0 & C_{e_{k_{i-1}+2}}(\alpha_{k_{i-1}+2}) & . & 0 \\ . & . & . & . \\ 0 & 0 & . & C_{e_{k_i}}(\alpha_{k_i}) \end{pmatrix} = A^i. \quad (10)$$

In order that P be non-singular, each submatrix P^i must be non-singular. We therefore consider whether there exists a non-singular matrix P^i made up of matrices of the form (9), such that both P^i and A^i are skew-symmetric. The latent roots which occur in the set $(\alpha_{k_{i-1}+1}, ..., \alpha_{k_i})$ are all equal, and our concern is with the suffixes $(e_{k_{i-1}+1}, ..., e_{k_i})$. To simplify the notation we omit the indices and sub-suffixes in (10), and write the relation as

$$P \begin{pmatrix} C_{e_1}(\alpha_1) & 0 & . & 0 \\ 0 & C_{e_2}(\alpha_2) & . & 0 \\ . & . & . & . \\ 0 & 0 & . & C_{e_k}(\alpha_k) \end{pmatrix} = A,$$

where $\alpha_1 = \alpha_2 = ... = \alpha_k$, and we assume that $e_1 \leqslant e_2 \leqslant ... \leqslant e_k$. We have

$$P = \begin{pmatrix} P^{11} & . & P^{1k} \\ . & . & . \\ P^{k1} & . & P^{kk} \end{pmatrix},$$

where the elements P^{ji} are $e_j \times e_i$ matrices given by (9). Since P is to be skew, it follows from (9) that

$$P^{ii} = 0 \quad (i = 1, ..., k).$$

Again, as in (6), $\qquad P^{ij} + (P^{ji})' = 0.$

If $e_i = e_j$, we see from (9) that

$$P^{ij} = (P^{ij})', \quad (11)$$

and therefore $\qquad P^{ij} = -P^{ji}.$

We now form a new matrix

$$Q = (q_{ij})$$

from P, by picking out the element q_{ij} at the bottom left-hand corner of P^{ij}. Then Q is a $k \times k$ matrix, and from (9) we see that

$$q_{ij} = 0 \quad (\text{if } e_i < e_j),$$

but, if $e_i = e_j$, $\qquad\qquad q_{ij} = -q_{ji},$

from (11). Now, if

$$e_1 = \ldots = e_{a_1} < e_{a_1+1} = \ldots = e_{a_1+a_2} < \ldots = e_{a_1+\ldots+a_s} = e_k,$$

so that the indices $e_1, \ldots, e_k$, which are assumed to be arranged in ascending order of magnitude, fall into s sets of equal indices,

$$Q = \begin{pmatrix} Q^{11} & 0 & . & 0 \\ . & Q^{22} & . & 0 \\ . & . & . & . \\ . & . & . & Q^{ss} \end{pmatrix},$$

where Q^{ii} is an $a_i \times a_i$ matrix, and all the submatrices above the principal diagonal are zero matrices. Since

$$\det Q = \prod_1^s \det Q^{ii},$$

Q is singular unless all the matrices Q^{ii} are non-singular. Since Q^{ii} is a skew-symmetric matrix, it is only non-singular when a_i is even. We now show that Q cannot be singular unless P is singular. For if Q is singular, its columns are linearly dependent. But if we replace the elements of Q in their original positions in P, we see that the remaining elements of the column of P which contains q_{ij} are all zero. Hence if the columns of Q are linearly dependent the columns of P which contain elements q_{ij} are also linearly dependent. Therefore if Q is singular, P is singular. Since we assumed P to be non-singular it follows that the a_i are even, and we have proved the necessity of the conditions of the theorem, that the elementary divisors of $C - \lambda I_{n+1}$ can be arranged in equal pairs:

$$(\lambda - \alpha_1)^{e_1}, \ (\lambda - \alpha_1)^{e_1}; \quad (\lambda - \alpha_2)^{e_2}, \ (\lambda - \alpha_2)^{e_2}; \quad \ldots.$$

The sufficiency of the conditions is proved more easily. Assuming that $k = 2h$, and that

$$e_1 = e_2, \; e_3 = e_4, \; \ldots, \; e_{2h-1} = e_{2h},$$

we write, in equation (10),

$$P^i = \begin{pmatrix} 0 & E_{e_1} & 0 & 0 & \cdot & \cdot & 0 \\ -E_{e_1} & 0 & 0 & 0 & \cdot & \cdot & 0 \\ 0 & 0 & 0 & E_{e_3} & \cdot & \cdot & \cdot \\ 0 & 0 & -E_{e_3} & 0 & \cdot & \cdot & 0 \\ \cdot & \cdot & \cdot & \cdot & \cdot & \cdot & \cdot \\ 0 & \cdot & \cdot & \cdot & \cdot & 0 & E_{2h} \\ 0 & \cdot & \cdot & \cdot & \cdot & -E_{2h} & 0 \end{pmatrix},$$

where E_i is the $i \times i$ matrix

$$E_i = \begin{pmatrix} 0 & 0 & \cdot & 0 & 1 \\ 0 & \cdot & \cdot & 1 & 0 \\ \cdot & \cdot & \cdot & \cdot & \cdot \\ 1 & 0 & \cdot & \cdot & 0 \end{pmatrix}.$$

It is clear that P^i is non-singular and skew-symmetric, and by elementary calculation we see that the matrix A^i defined by (10) is also skew-symmetric. We have therefore constructed the matrices A and $B = P^{-1}$ required, and have proved our theorem.

Other results, involving a combination of a null-polarity and a polarity, are most easily stated in terms of the properties of matrices.

THEOREM IV. *Given a matrix C, necessary and sufficient conditions that there exist matrices A, B (where A is skew-symmetric, and B is non-singular and symmetric), such that*

$$C = BA$$

are that the elementary divisors of $C - \lambda I_{n+1}$ corresponding to non-zero latent roots can be arranged in pairs $(\lambda - \alpha)^e$, $(\lambda + \alpha)^e$, and the elementary divisors λ^f corresponding to a zero latent root are even in number for any given even value of f.

THEOREM V. *Given a matrix C, necessary and sufficient conditions that there exist matrices A, B (where A is symmetric and B is non-singular and skew-symmetric), such that*

$$C = BA$$

are that the elementary divisors of $C - \lambda I_{n+1}$ corresponding to a non-zero latent root of C can be arranged in pairs $(\lambda - \alpha)^e$, $(\lambda + \alpha)^e$, and the elementary divisors λ^f corresponding to a zero latent root are even in number for any given odd value of f.

4. Simple correlations. We now consider correlations in $[n]$ which are neither polarities nor null-polarities. We assume that the ground field K is algebraically closed, and investigate the conditions in which the correlation

$$u = Ax \tag{1}$$

can be transformed to

$$v = By$$

by a non-singular transformation

$$x = Py, \quad \text{or equivalently} \quad u = \tilde{P}v,$$

of point or prime-coordinates respectively. We may regard the transformation as a collineation in $[n]$ instead of a transformation of coordinates, if we wish to do so.

Algebraically, this is the problem of determining when a non-singular matrix P can be found such that

$$B = P'AP. \tag{2}$$

If (2) holds,

$$B' = P'A'P,$$

and therefore, if λ is an indeterminate,

$$B - \lambda B' = P'(A - \lambda A')P,$$

so that the matrices $A - \lambda A'$ and $B - \lambda B'$ have the same rank and elementary divisors. This gives a *necessary* condition for the existence of a matrix P satisfying (2). We now show that *it is also a sufficient condition when the matrices $A - \lambda A'$ and $B - \lambda B'$ are non-singular*.

We can choose an element d (not ± 1) in K such that

$$C = A - dA' \quad \text{and} \quad D = B - dB'$$

are non-singular. If $A - \lambda A'$ and $B - \lambda B'$ (which are both of rank $n + 1$) have the same elementary divisors, so have

$$C - \mu C' \quad \text{and} \quad D - \mu D',$$

μ being an indeterminate over K related to λ by the equation

$$(1 + d\mu)\lambda = d + \mu.$$

If there exists a non-singular matrix P such that

$$D = P'CP,$$

then

$$B = (1-d^2)^{-1}[D+dD']$$
$$= (1-d^2)^{-1} P'[C+dC']P$$
$$= P'AP.$$

Now let us suppose that $C-\mu C'$ and $D-\mu D'$ have the same elementary divisors. Since C' and D' are non-singular, there exist [II, §9, Th. V] non-singular matrices R and S such that

$$D = RCS, \quad \text{and} \quad D' = RC'S.$$

From the second equation we have

$$D = S'CR',$$

and therefore

$$RCS = S'CR';$$

that is,

$$XC = CX',$$

where

$$X = \tilde{S}R.$$

From

$$XC = CX'$$

we derive

$$X^2C = XCX' = C(X')^2,$$

and

$$X^3C = XC(X')^2 = C(X')^3,$$

and finally

$$X^nC = C(X')^n.$$

Hence, if $f(\lambda)$ is any polynomial in $K[\lambda]$,

$$f(X)\,C = Cf(X').$$

But [II, §10, Th. II] there exists a polynomial $f(\lambda)$ such that if

$$Y = f(X), \quad \text{and therefore} \quad YC = CY',$$

then

$$Y^2 = X.$$

Now,

$$D = S'CR'$$
$$= S'CX'S$$
$$= S'C(Y')^2 S$$
$$= S'CY'Y'S$$
$$= (S'Y)\,C(Y'S).$$

Defining

$$P = Y'S,$$

we have proved that

$$D = P'CP.$$

Hence we have

THEOREM I. *If A and B are two $(n+1) \times (n+1)$ matrices which are such that $A - \lambda A'$ and $B - \lambda B'$ are non-singular, λ being an indeterminate, then a necessary and sufficient condition that there should exist a non-singular matrix P such that*

$$B = P'AP$$

is that $A - \lambda A'$ and $B - \lambda B'$ have the same elementary divisors.

In the case in which A (and therefore B) is non-singular, we deduce as an immediate corollary

THEOREM II. *A necessary and sufficient condition that the two non-singular correlations*

$$u = Ax, \quad u = Bx$$

should be equivalent is that the associated collineations

$$y = \tilde{A}Ax, \quad y = \tilde{B}Bx$$

should be similar collineations.

The next question which suggests itself is: can we find an $(n+1) \times (n+1)$ matrix A such that $A - \lambda A'$ has *assigned* elementary divisors? It is easily seen that this is not always possible. Let the elementary divisors of $A - \lambda A'$ be

$$(\lambda - \alpha_1)^{e_1}, \ldots, (\lambda - \alpha_k)^{e_k}.$$

If $\alpha_i \neq 0$, and $(\lambda - \alpha_i)^{e_i}$ is a factor of each determinant of $A - \lambda A'$ of order j, then $(\lambda - \alpha_i^{-1})^{e_i}$ is a factor of each determinant of $A' - \lambda A$ of order j, and the converse of this statement is also true. Now, the transpose of $A - \lambda A'$ is $A' - \lambda A$, and the transpose of a λ-matrix has the same elementary divisors as the original matrix. Hence it follows that if $(\lambda - \alpha_i)^{e_i}$ is an elementary divisor of $A - \lambda A'$ $(\alpha_i \neq 0)$, so is $(\lambda - \alpha_i^{-1})^{e_i}$.

Again, if $\alpha_1 = \alpha_2 = \ldots = \alpha_r = 0$, so that $\lambda^{e_1}, \ldots, \lambda^{e_r}$ are the elementary divisors of $A - \lambda A'$ corresponding to a zero latent root, we deduce from the fact that

$$\det(A - \lambda A') = \det(A' - \lambda A)$$

that the characteristic polynomial of $A - \lambda A'$ is of degree

$$n + 1 - \sum_1^r e_i.$$

It therefore follows that

$$\sum_1^k e_i = n + 1 - \sum_1^r e_i.$$

We have thus found some necessary conditions to be satisfied by the elementary divisors of $A - \lambda A'$. If $\alpha_i \neq \pm 1$, the elementary divisors (other than λ^{e_i}) can be arranged in pairs, a typical pair being $(\lambda - \alpha_i)^{e_i}$, $(\lambda - \alpha_i^{-1})^{e_i}$, but when $\alpha_i = \pm 1$ the elementary divisor $(\lambda - \alpha_i)^{e_i}$ may, possibly, be paired with itself. We now prove

THEOREM III. *Sufficient conditions that there exists a matrix A such that $A - \lambda A'$ has assigned elementary divisors are*

(i) *the elementary divisors other than those of type λ^e can be arranged in pairs* $(\lambda - \alpha_i)^{f_i}$, $(\lambda - \alpha_i^{-1})^{f_i}$ $(\alpha_i \neq \pm 1)$;

(ii) *if the elementary divisors are*

$$\lambda^{e_1}, \dots, \lambda^{e_r}, \ (\lambda - \alpha_1)^{f_1}, \ (\lambda - \alpha_1^{-1})^{f_1}, \ \dots, \ (\lambda - \alpha_s)^{f_s}, \ (\lambda - \alpha_s^{-1})^{f_s},$$

then
$$2 \sum_1^r e_i + 2 \sum_1^s f_i = n + 1.$$

Let $D_f(\alpha)$ be the $2f \times 2f$ matrix

$$
D_f(\alpha) = \begin{pmatrix}
0 & . & . & 0 & 0 & . & . & . & \alpha \\
. & . & . & . & . & . & . & \alpha & 1 \\
. & . & . & . & . & . & . & 1 & 0 \\
. & . & . & . & . & . & . & . & . \\
0 & . & . & 0 & \alpha & 1 & . & . & 0 \\
0 & . & . & 1 & 0 & . & . & . & 0 \\
. & . & 1 & 0 & 0 & . & . & . & 0 \\
. & . & . & . & . & . & . & . & . \\
1 & 0 & . & . & 0 & . & . & . & 0
\end{pmatrix}.
$$

Then $D_f(\alpha) - \lambda D_f'(\alpha)$

$$
= \begin{pmatrix}
0 & . & . & 0 & 0 & . & . & . & \alpha - \lambda \\
. & . & . & . & . & . & . & \alpha - \lambda & 1 \\
. & . & . & . & . & . & . & 1 & 0 \\
. & . & . & . & . & . & . & . & . \\
0 & . & . & 0 & \alpha - \lambda & 1 & . & . & . \\
0 & . & . & 1 - \lambda\alpha & 0 & 0 & . & . & 0 \\
. & . & . & -\lambda & 0 & . & . & . & 0 \\
. & . & . & . & . & . & . & . & . \\
1 - \lambda\alpha & -\lambda & . & . & 0 & . & . & . & 0
\end{pmatrix}.
$$

Except for numerical factors, the determinant of this matrix is
$$(\lambda - \alpha)^f (\lambda\alpha - 1)^f,$$
whilst the determinant of the $(2f-1) \times (2f-1)$ submatrix obtained by crossing out the first column and $(f+1)$th row is
$$(\lambda - \alpha)^f \lambda^{f-1},$$
and the determinant of the $(2f-1) \times (2f-1)$ submatrix obtained by crossing out the first row and the $(f+1)$th column is
$$(\lambda\alpha - 1)^f.$$
Hence the highest common factor of all determinants of submatrices of order $2f-1$ is 1, since we have assumed that $\alpha \neq \pm 1$, and when $\alpha \neq 0$ the elementary divisors of $D_f(\alpha) - \lambda D'_f(\alpha)$ are therefore
$$(\lambda - \alpha)^f \quad \text{and} \quad (\lambda - \alpha^{-1})^f.^\dagger$$
If $\alpha = 0$ the above argument shows that the only elementary divisor is λ^f. It follows that

$$A = \begin{pmatrix} D_{e_1}(0) & 0 & \cdot & \cdot & \cdot \\ 0 & D_{e_2}(0) & \cdot & \cdot & \cdot \\ \cdot & \cdot & D_{e_r}(0) & \cdot & \cdot \\ \cdot & \cdot & \cdot & D_{f_1}(\alpha_1) & \cdot \\ \cdot & \cdot & \cdot & \cdot & \cdot \\ 0 & \cdot & \cdot & \cdot & D_{f_s}(\alpha_s) \end{pmatrix} \qquad (3)$$

is a matrix such that $A - \lambda A'$ has the assigned elementary divisors.

Whenever the conditions of Theorem III hold we shall take
$$u = Ax$$
(where A is given by (3) above) as the canonical form of a correlation having the assigned elementary divisors. For $A - \lambda A'$ is non-singular, and we can apply Theorem I.

The conditions of Theorem III have also been shown to be necessary in the case when $A - \lambda A'$ is non-singular and has no elementary divisors of the form $(\lambda \pm 1)^e$. In this case
$$A + A' \quad \text{and} \quad A - A'$$
are both non-singular. We call this *the simple case*, and we have

THEOREM IV. *In the case of a simple correlation the conditions of the previous theorem are both necessary and sufficient.*

† If $\alpha = \pm 1$, we find that the elementary divisors are $(\lambda \pm 1)^f$, $(\lambda \pm 1)^f$, but we must use a different argument.

We observe that if n is even, $A - A'$, being skew, is necessarily singular, and the simple case does not arise. We could extend the notion of a simple correlation to include the case in which $A - \lambda A'$ has elementary divisors $(\lambda \pm 1)^e$, provided that these can be arranged in pairs, but it turns out to be more convenient to proceed with the transformation of the most general type of correlation in $[n]$ to canonical form.

5. Transformation of the general correlation.

In this section we show how to obtain a canonical form for any correlation in $[n]$ which does not fall into the categories already considered. Such a correlation, which is not necessarily a polarity, a null-polarity, or a simple correlation will be called a *general* correlation. We treat the problem of transforming (or *reducing*)

$$u = Ax$$

to a canonical form as a purely algebraic one, working with the bilinear form $y'Ax$ associated with the correlation.

Let B and C be, respectively, the symmetric and skew-symmetric parts of A: that is, let

$$B = \tfrac{1}{2}(A + A'), \quad C = \tfrac{1}{2}(A - A').$$

When A is transformed to $P'AP$, B is transformed to

$$\tfrac{1}{2}(P'AP + P'A'P) = P'BP,$$

and C is transformed to

$$\tfrac{1}{2}(P'AP - P'A'P) = P'CP.$$

Hence our problem may be regarded as that of the determination of canonical forms for the simultaneous reduction of the symmetric and skew-symmetric forms

$$y'Bx, \quad y'Cx.$$

If B and C are both non-singular, we are in the *simple* case considered in §4, and we may use the canonical form given there for $A = B + C$. When, in the notation of §4,

$$A = D_e(\alpha),$$

$$y'Bx = \tfrac{1}{2}(\alpha+1)\left[(y_0 x_{2e-1} + y_{2e-1} x_0) + \dots + (y_{e-1} x_e + y_e x_{e-1})\right]$$
$$+ \tfrac{1}{2}\left[(y_1 x_{2e-1} + y_{2e-1} x_1) + \dots + (y_{e-1} x_{e+1} + y_{e+1} x_{e-1})\right],$$

and

$$y'Cx = \tfrac{1}{2}(\alpha-1)\left[(y_0 x_{2e-1} - y_{2e-1} x_0) + \dots + (y_{e-1} x_e - y_e x_{e-1})\right]$$
$$+ \tfrac{1}{2}\left[(y_1 x_{2e-1} - y_{2e-1} x_1) + \dots + (y_{e-1} x_{e+1} - y_{e+1} x_{e-1})\right].$$

We shall denote these expressions by

$$\beta(\alpha, e) \quad \text{and} \quad \gamma(\alpha, e)$$

respectively. When A is in the canonical form

$$\begin{pmatrix} D_{e_1}(\alpha_1) & 0 & . & 0 \\ 0 & D_{e_2}(\alpha_2) & . & 0 \\ . & . & . & . \\ 0 & 0 & . & D_{e_k}(\alpha_k) \end{pmatrix},$$

the form $y'Bx$ is equal to a sum of forms such as $\beta(\alpha, e)$, differing only in the α, e and in the indeterminates $(y_0, ..., y_{2e-1})$, $(x_0, ..., x_{2e-1})$ involved. Similarly, $y'Cx$ is equal to a sum of forms such as $\gamma(\alpha, e)$. We shall write

$$y'Bx = \sum_i \beta(\alpha_i, e_i), \quad y'Cx = \sum_i \gamma(\alpha_i, e_i)$$

to express these facts. When we use this notation it is to be understood that each $\beta(\alpha_i, e_i)$ is paired with a $\gamma(\alpha_i, e_i)$ having the same α_i, e_i, and involving the same indeterminates, in the same order, and that two terms $\beta(\alpha_i, e_i)$ and $\beta(\alpha_j, e_j)$ have no indeterminates in common. Similarly, $\gamma(\alpha_i, e_i)$ and $\gamma(\alpha_j, e_j)$ have no indeterminates in common. The results of § 4 can now be stated as

THEOREM I. *If B and C are each non-singular, the symmetric and skew-symmetric forms $y'Bx$ and $y'Cx$ can be simultaneously reduced to the canonical forms $\sum\limits_i \beta(\alpha_i, e_i)$ and $\sum\limits_i \gamma(\alpha_i, e_i)$.*

We must now extend this theorem to the case in which B or C is singular. We introduce five different pairs of forms

(i) $\quad \beta_1(e) = (y_0 x_{2e-1} + y_{2e-1} x_0) + (y_1 x_{2e-2} + y_{2e-2} x_1) + ...$
$$+ (y_{e-1} x_e + y_e x_{e-1}),$$

$\quad \gamma_1(e) = (y_1 x_{2e-1} - y_{2e-1} x_1) + (y_2 x_{2e-2} - y_{2e-2} x_2) + ...$
$$+ (y_{e-1} x_{e+1} - y_{e+1} x_{e-1}),$$

where $\qquad\qquad\qquad \gamma_1(1) = 0;$

(ii) $\quad \beta_2(e) = (y_1 x_{2e-1} + y_{2e-1} x_1) + (y_2 x_{2e-2} + y_{2e-2} x_2) + ...$
$$+ (y_{e-1} x_{e+1} + y_{e+1} x_{e-1}),$$

$\quad \gamma_2(e) = (y_0 x_{2e-1} - y_{2e-1} x_0) + (y_1 x_{2e-2} - y_{2e-2} x_1) + ...$
$$+ (y_{e-1} x_e - y_e x_{e-1}),$$

where $\qquad\qquad\qquad \beta_2(1) = 0;$

(iii) $\beta_3(e) = (y_0 x_{2e-2} + y_{2e-2} x_0) + (y_1 x_{2e-3} + y_{2e-3} x_1) + \ldots$
$$+ (y_{e-2} x_e + y_e x_{e-2}) + y_{e-1} x_{e-1},$$

$\gamma_3(e) = (y_1 x_{2e-2} - y_{2e-2} x_1) + (y_2 x_{2e-3} - y_{2e-3} x_2) + \ldots$
$$+ (y_{e-1} x_e - y_e x_{e-1}),$$

where $\qquad \beta_3(1) = y_0 x_0, \quad$ and $\quad \gamma_3(1) = 0;$

(iv) $\beta_4(e) = (y_1 x_{2e-1} + y_{2e-1} x_1) + (y_2 x_{2e-2} + y_{2e-2} x_2) + \ldots$
$$+ (y_{e-1} x_{e+1} + y_{e+1} x_{e-1}) + y_e x_e,$$

$\gamma_4(e) = (y_0 x_{2e-1} - y_{2e-1} x_0) + (y_1 x_{2e-2} - y_{2e-2} x_1) + \ldots$
$$+ (y_{e-1} x_e - y_e x_{e-1}),$$

where $\qquad \beta_4(1) = y_1 x_1;$

(v) $\beta_5(e) = (y_0 x_{2e} + y_{2e} x_0) + (y_1 x_{2e-1} + y_{2e-1} x_1) + \ldots$
$$+ (y_{e-1} x_{e+1} + y_{e+1} x_{e-1}),$$

$\gamma_5(e) = (y_1 x_{2e} - y_{2e} x_1) + (y_2 x_{2e-1} - y_{2e-1} x_2) + \ldots$
$$+ (y_e x_{e+1} - y_{e+1} x_e).$$

Our object is to obtain the following generalisation of Theorem I:

THEOREM II. *If B, C are, respectively, symmetric and skew-symmetric $(n+1) \times (n+1)$ matrices, the bilinear forms $y'Bx$, $y'Cx$ can be simultaneously transformed to*

$$\sum_i \beta(\alpha_i, e_i) + \sum_j \beta_1(e_j) + \sum_k \beta_2(e_k) + \sum_l \beta_3(e_l) + \sum_m \beta_4(e_m) + \sum_h \beta_5(e_h),$$

and

$$\sum_i \gamma(\alpha_i, e_i) + \sum_j \gamma_1(e_j) + \sum_k \gamma_2(e_k) + \sum_l \gamma_3(e_l) + \sum_m \gamma_4(e_m) + \sum_h \gamma_5(e_h)$$

respectively, with the conventions previously introduced for the pairing of the terms and for the indeterminates involved in the two expressions.

We consider the equations

$$Bx = 0, \tag{1}$$
$$Cx = 0. \tag{2}$$

Let these define, respectively, linear spaces S_{r_1-1}, S_{r_2-1} of dimensions $r_1 - 1$, $r_2 - 1$, and let these spaces intersect in a space S_{r_0-1} of $r_0 - 1$ dimensions. We transform our coordinates, choosing a new simplex of reference in the following way. In S_{r_0-1} take r_0 independent points $A_{n-r_0+1}, \ldots, A_n$. In S_{r_1-1} there exist $r_1 - r_0$ further independent points $A_{n-r_1+1}, ..., A_{n-r_0}$, and in S_{r_2-1} there are $r_2 - r_0$ independent points which are independent of $A_{n-r_0+1}, ..., A_n$, say

$$A_{n-r_1-r_2+r_0+1}, ..., A_{n-r_1}.$$

The points $A_{n-r_1-r_2+r_0+1}, ..., A_n$ are linearly independent, and define the join of the spaces S_{r_1-1}, S_{r_2-1}. We complete the new simplex of reference by choosing $n-r_1-r_2+r_0+1$ points in $[n]$ which are independent of those already chosen, denoting them by

$$A_0, ..., A_{n-r_1-r_2+r_0}.$$

In the new coordinate system S_{r_0-1} has the equations

$$x_0 = ... = x_{n-r_0} = 0,$$

S_{r_1-1} has the equations

$$x_0 = ... = x_{n-r_1} = 0, \qquad\qquad (3)$$

and S_{r_2-1} has the equations

$$x_0 = ... = x_{n-r_1-r_2+r_0} = x_{n-r_1+1} = ... = x_{n-r_0} = 0.$$

In this coordinate system $y'Bx$ is a form in the indeterminates $(x_0, ..., x_{n-r_1})$, $(y_0, ..., y_{n-r_1})$ only, and $y'Cx$ is a form in the indeterminates

$$(x_0, ..., x_{n-r_1-r_2+r_0}, x_{n-r_1+1}, ..., x_{n-r_0}),$$
$$(y_0, ..., y_{n-r_1-r_2+r_0}, y_{n-r_1+1}, ..., y_{n-r_0})$$

only. In proving our theorem we shall use a series of transformations of coordinates, but we shall arrange matters so that at every stage the equations of S_{r_0-1}, S_{r_1-1} and S_{r_2-1} are given in the new coordinate system by (3). The reader will readily verify that any transformation of coordinates which ensures this result is of the form

$$\xi = Px, \quad \eta = Py,$$

where

$$P = \begin{pmatrix} D & 0 & 0 & 0 \\ E & F & 0 & 0 \\ G & 0 & H & 0 \\ L & M & N & K \end{pmatrix},$$

the matrices in the first, second, third and fourth rows (columns) having $n-r_1-r_2+r_0+1$, r_2-r_0, r_1-r_0 and r_0 rows (columns) respectively.

Our proof of Theorem II will be by induction on the number of indeterminates x_i, y_j involved, and for the purpose of the induction it is found convenient to impose a further restriction on P by requiring that the elements of F and H above the principal diagonal are zero, and that $K = I_{r_0}$. The transformation is then called a *permissible transformation*.

We shall prove that $y'Bx, y'Cx$ can be reduced to the forms given in the enunciation of Theorem II *by a permissible transformation*, after the preliminary transformation has been made.

We commence our induction proof by considering the case $n = 1$. Let
$$y'Bx = ay_0x_0 + b(y_0x_1 + y_1x_0) + cy_1x_1,$$
$$y'Cx = k(y_0x_1 - y_1x_0),$$

before any preliminary transformation is carried out. We have three cases to consider:

(i) If B and C are non-singular, $r_0 = r_1 = r_2 = 0$. No preliminary transformation is required, and any non-singular transformation is a permissible one. The result follows from the consideration of the simple case treated in § 4.

(ii) If $B = 0, C \neq 0, r_1 = 2, r_0 = r_2 = 0$, and $y'Cx$ is not essentially altered by the preliminary transformation. The permissible transformation
$$\xi = \begin{pmatrix} 1 & 0 \\ 0 & k \end{pmatrix} x$$

transforms $y'Cx$ to $\gamma_2(1)$, and $y'Bx$ to $\beta_2(1)$.

If $C = 0, B \neq 0, r_2 = 2, r_0 = r_1 = 1$ or $r_0 = r_1 = 0$. If $r_1 = 1$, a preliminary transformation reduces $y'Bx$ to the form ay_0x_0, and the permissible transformation
$$\xi = \begin{pmatrix} a^{\frac{1}{2}} & 0 \\ 0 & 1 \end{pmatrix} x$$

completes the reduction to $\beta_3(1)$. We take $y'Cx$ in its transformed form as $\gamma_3(1)$. If $r_1 = 0$ we need no preliminary transformation, and the restricted transformation of § 2, Th. I, which is permissible in this case, transforms $y'Bx$ to the form $x_0y_1 + x_1y_0$ (which is $\beta_1(1)$, and can be paired with $\gamma_1(1)$), or to the form $ay_0x_0 + cy_1x_1$. This last form can be reduced by a permissible transformation to the form $y_0x_0 + y_1x_1$. Thus we have the reduction $y'Bx = \beta_3(1) + \beta_3'(1)$, $y'Cx = \gamma_3(1) + \gamma_3'(1)$.

(iii) The only remaining case is that in which C is not singular, and therefore k is not zero, and B is singular, but not zero, so that $ac = b^2$. Then $r_0 = r_2 = 0$, $r_1 = 1$, and the preliminary transformation reduces the forms $y'Bx$, $y'Cx$ to forms of the type

$$dy_0x_0 \quad \rho(y_0x_1 - y_1x_0),$$

where d and ρ are not zero. The transformation

$$\xi = \begin{pmatrix} -d^{\frac{1}{2}} & 0 \\ 0 & \rho d^{-\frac{1}{2}} \end{pmatrix} x$$

is permissible, and reduces the two bilinear forms to

$$\xi_0\eta_0, \quad \eta_1\xi_0 - \eta_0\xi_1,$$

which are $\beta_4(1)$, $\gamma_4(1)$ respectively.

We may therefore assume as hypothesis of induction that Theorem II holds for a pair of forms $y'Bx$, $y'Cx$ which can be expressed in terms of the indeterminates $(y_0, ..., y_m)$, $(x_0, ..., x_m)$, where $m < n$.

Now, our preliminary transformation expresses $y'Bx$, $y'Cx$ in terms of the indeterminates $(y_0, ..., y_{n-r_0})$, $(x_0, ..., x_{n-r_0})$, and not in terms of fewer indeterminates. By the hypothesis of induction we can reduce these forms to canonical forms, as required by Theorem II, by a permissible transformation if (i) $r_0 > 0$, and (ii) the indeterminates $(y_0, ..., y_{n-r_0})$, $(x_0, ..., x_{n-r_0})$ are subjected to a preliminary transformation. But no preliminary transformation is necessary since, in the new coordinate system $r_0' = 0$, $r_1' = r_1 - r_0$, $r_2' = r_2 - r_0$, and, if $n' = n - r_0$, the equations of $S_{r_0'-1}$ are

$$x_0 = ... = x_{n'} = 0,$$

those of $S_{r_1'-1}$ are

$$x_0 = ... = x_{n'-r_1'} = 0,$$

and those of $S_{r_2'-1}$ are

$$x_0 = ... = x_{n'-r_1'-r_2'} = x_{n'-r_1'+1} = ... = x_{n'} = 0,$$

in accordance with (3). Hence the permissible transformation

$$\begin{pmatrix} \xi_0 \\ \cdot \\ \xi_{n-r_0} \end{pmatrix} = \begin{pmatrix} D & 0 & 0 \\ E & F & 0 \\ G & 0 & H \end{pmatrix} \begin{pmatrix} x_0 \\ \cdot \\ x_{n-r_0} \end{pmatrix}$$

transforms the bilinear forms in the indeterminates $(y_0, ..., y_{n-r_0})$,

$(x_0, ..., x_{n-r_0})$ into the required forms. Since we obtain from this the permissible transformation

$$\xi = \begin{pmatrix} D & 0 & 0 & 0 \\ E & F & 0 & 0 \\ G & 0 & H & 0 \\ 0 & 0 & 0 & I_{r_0} \end{pmatrix} x$$

on the indeterminates $(y_0, ..., y_n)$, $(x_0, ..., x_n)$, which also reduces $y'Bx$, $y'Cx$ to canonical form, our theorem is proved if $r_0 > 0$. We may therefore now confine ourselves to the case $r_0 = 0$.

Now suppose that $r_1 > 0$. A preliminary transformation gives us

$$y'Bx = \sum_0^{n-r_1} b_{ij} y_i x_j,$$

$$y'Cx = \sum_0^n{}' c_{ij} y_i x_j,$$

where $\sum_0^n{}'$ denotes summation over the values

$$0, ..., n - r_1 - r_2; \quad n - r_1 + 1, ..., n \tag{4}$$

of the suffixes i, j. In order to avoid the inconvenience of having to introduce new symbols for the indeterminates with each successive transformation, we shall start each step of the argument afresh with the indeterminates $(x_0, ..., x_n)$, $(y_0, ..., y_n)$, except in cases where this would cause misunderstanding.

Using the transformation of §3 applied to $y'Cx$, we have to consider only Case (ii), in which not all $c_{in} = 0$, since, if $c_{in} = 0$ for all values of i, $r_0 > 0$, contrary to hypothesis. The restricted transformations of that section are permissible, because of the absence of terms c_{ij} in $y'Cx$ in which either i or j lies between $n - r_1 - r_2 + 1$ and $n - r_1$, both values inclusive. Hence, using the same symbols as above, a permissible transformation reduces our bilinear forms to

$$y'Bx = \sum_0^{n-r_1} b_{ij} y_i x_j,$$

$$y'Cx = \sum_0^{n-1}{}' c_{ij} y_i x_j + (y_n x_k - y_k x_n),$$

where k is one of the suffixes given by (4), and $\sum_0^{n-1}{}'$ omits the suffixes n and k, besides those already mentioned. We now have two cases:

Case (i). $k > n - r_1$. The forms

$$\sum_0^{n-r_1} b_{ij} y_i x_j, \quad \sum_0^{n-1}{}' c_{ij} y_i x_j$$

are forms in the indeterminates

$$(x_0, \ldots, x_{k-1}, x_{k+1}, \ldots, x_{n-1}), \quad (y_0, \ldots, y_{k-1}, y_{k+1}, \ldots, y_{n-1})$$

for which $r_0' = 0, \quad r_1' = r_1 - 2, \quad r_2' = r_2, \quad n' = n - 2,$

and we see that these forms require no further preliminary transformation. By the hypothesis of induction, they can be reduced to canonical forms by a permissible transformation, and it is easily seen that a permissible transformation on the indeterminates $(x_0, \ldots, x_{k-1}, x_{k+1}, \ldots, x_{n-1})$ is still permissible when we add to the equations of transformation the further equations

$$\xi_k = x_k, \quad \xi_n = x_n,$$

in their proper place. Since

$$\beta_2(1) = 0, \quad \gamma_2(1) = y_i x_j - y_j x_i,$$

the theorem is proved in the case $k > n - r_1$.

Case (ii). $k \leqslant n - r_1$. Since $c_{kn} y_k x_n$ was a term in the prepared form $y'Cx$, we must have $k \leqslant n - r_1 - r_2$. Since a transformation of coordinates which permutes $x_0, \ldots, x_{n-r_1-r_2}$, but does not affect the remaining x_i, is permissible we may, after a suitable permissible transformation, take $k = 0$. We now write

$$\left.\begin{aligned} y'Bx &= y_0 \xi + \eta x_0 + \sum_1^{n-r_1} b_{ij} y_i x_j, \\ y'Cx &= y_n x_0 - y_0 x_n + \sum_1^{n-1}{}' c_{ij} y_i x_j, \end{aligned}\right\} \tag{5}$$

where the summation $\sum_1^{n-1}{}'$ is over the values

$$1, \ldots, n - r_1 - r_2, n - r_1 + 1, \ldots, n - 1$$

of the suffixes i, j, and

$$\xi = \sum_0^{n-r_1} b_i x_i, \quad \eta = \sum_0^{n-r_1} b_i y_i,$$

where $2b_0 = b_{00}$, and $b_{0i} = b_i$.

Now, by hypothesis, the matrix

$$\begin{pmatrix} 2b_0 & b_1 & b_2 & . & b_{n-r_1} \\ b_1 & b_{11} & b_{12} & . & b_{1\,n-r_1} \\ . & . & . & . & . \\ b_{n-r_1} & b_{n-r_1 1} & . & . & b_{n-r_1\,n-r_1} \end{pmatrix} \tag{6}$$

is of rank $n-r_1+1$. We first prove that this implies that the submatrix

$$\begin{pmatrix} b_{11} & . & b_{1\,n-r_1} \\ . & . & . \\ b_{n-r_1 1} & . & b_{n-r_1\,n-r_1} \end{pmatrix} \tag{7}$$

is of rank $n-r_1$ or $n-r_1-1$. For, suppose that the rank of (7) were less than $n-r_1-1$. Then there would exist at least two distinct relations

$$\sum_{i=1}^{n-r_1} \lambda_i b_{ij} = 0 \quad (j = 1, ..., n-r_1),$$

$$\sum_{i=1}^{n-r_1} \mu_i b_{ij} = 0 \quad (j = 1, ..., n-r_1),$$

connecting the rows of (7). If ρ, σ are chosen so that

$$\rho \sum_1^{n-r_1} \lambda_i b_i + \sigma \sum_1^{n-r_1} \mu_i b_i = 0,$$

then the multiples

$$0, \rho\lambda_1 + \sigma\mu_1, ..., \rho\lambda_{n-r_1} + \sigma\mu_{n-r_1}$$

of the first, second, ..., $(n-r_1+1)$th rows respectively of (6) are linearly dependent, and (6) is singular, contrary to hypothesis.

Case (ii a). Suppose that the matrix (7) is of rank $n-r_1$, and consider the forms

$$\sum_1^{n-r_1} b_{ij} y_i x_j, \quad \sum_1^{n-1}{}' c_{ij} y_i x_j.$$

For these forms in the indeterminates $(x_1, ..., x_{n-1})$, $(y_1, ..., y_{n-1})$ we have

$$n' = n-2, \quad r_1' = r_1-1, \quad r_2' = r_2.$$

Hence no preliminary transformation is necessary, and by hypothesis there is a permissible transformation which reduces these to canonical form. The equations of transformation, together with the equations

$$\xi_0 = x_0, \quad \xi_n = x_n$$

are seen to define a permissible transformation of the indeterminates $(x_0, \ldots, x_n)$. Before making this transformation, however, we make the permissible transformation

$$x_0 = \bar{x}_0,$$
$$x_i = \bar{x}_i - c_i \bar{x}_0 \quad (i = 1, \ldots, n - r_1),$$
$$x_i = \bar{x}_i \quad (i = n - r_1 + 1, \ldots, n)$$

on the *original* forms (5), our object being to simplify the term $y_0 \xi + \eta x_0$ before carrying out the final permissible transformation described above. We find that

$$y'Bx = \bar{y}_0 \left(b_0 \bar{x}_0 + \sum_1^{n-r_1} b_i \bar{x}_i - \bar{x}_0 \sum_1^{n-r_1} b_i c_i \right)$$

$$+ \bar{x}_0 \left(b_0 \bar{y}_0 + \sum_1^{n-r_1} b_i \bar{y}_i - \bar{y}_0 \sum_1^{n-r_1} b_i c_i \right)$$

$$+ \sum_1^{n-r_1} b_{ij} (\bar{y}_i - c_i \bar{y}_0)(\bar{x}_j - c_j \bar{x}_0)$$

$$= 2 b_0 \bar{x}_0 \bar{y}_0 + \bar{y}_0 \bar{\xi} + \bar{\eta} \bar{x}_0 + \sum_1^{n-r_1} b_{ij} \bar{y}_i \bar{x}_j$$

$$- \bar{y}_0 \left(\sum_1^{n-r_1} b_{ij} c_i \bar{x}_j \right) - \left(\sum_1^{n-r_1} b_{ij} \bar{y}_i c_j \right) \bar{x}_0$$

$$+ \left(\sum_1^{n-r_1} b_{ij} c_i c_j - 2 \sum_1^{n-r_1} b_i c_i \right) \bar{y}_0 \bar{x}_0,$$

and

$$y'Cx = \bar{y}_n \bar{x}_0 - \bar{y}_0 \bar{x}_n + \sum_1^{n-r_1-r_2} c_{ij} (\bar{y}_i - c_i \bar{y}_0)(\bar{x}_j - c_j \bar{x}_0)$$

$$+ \sum_{n-r_1+1}^{n-1} c_{ij} \bar{y}_i \bar{x}_j$$

$$= \bar{y}_n \bar{x}_0 - \bar{y}_0 \bar{x}_n$$

$$+ \sum_1^{n-1}{}' c_{ij} \bar{y}_i \bar{x}_j - \bar{y}_0 \sum_1^{n-r_1-r_2} c_{ij} c_i \bar{x}_j - \bar{x}_0 \sum_1^{n-r_1-r_2} c_{ij} c_j \bar{y}_i,$$

since $\bar{x}_0 \bar{y}_0 \sum_1^{n-r_1-r_2} c_{ij} c_i c_j = 0$. In the first expression we have written

$$\bar{\xi} = \sum_1^{n-r_1} b_i \bar{x}_i, \quad \bar{\eta} = \sum_1^{n-r_1} b_i \bar{y}_i.$$

Now, since the matrix (7) is non-singular, we can choose the constants $c_1, \ldots, c_{n-r_1}$ so that

$$\sum_{j=1}^{n-r_1} b_{ij} c_j = b_i \quad (i = 1, \ldots, n-r_1).$$

This simplifies the expression for $y'Bx$ to

$$2b_0 \bar{x}_0 \bar{y}_0 + \sum_1^{n-r_1} b_{ij} \bar{y}_i \bar{x}_j - \left(\sum_1^{n-r_1} b_i c_i\right) \bar{x}_0 \bar{y}_0$$

$$= p\bar{y}_0 \bar{x}_0 + \sum_1^{n-r_1} b_{ij} \bar{y}_i \bar{x}_j,$$

say. Now make the further permissible transformation

$$x_i^* = \bar{x}_i \quad (i = 0, \ldots, n-1),$$

$$x_n^* = \bar{x}_n + \sum_1^{n-r_1-r_2} c_{ij} c_i \bar{x}_j.$$

We then have

$$y'Bx = py_0^* x_0^* + \sum_1^{n-r_1} b_{ij} y_i^* x_j^*,$$

$$y'Cx = y_n^* x_0^* - y_0^* x_n^* + \sum_1^{n-1}{}' c_{ij} y_i^* x_j^*.$$

Now p cannot be zero, otherwise B would be of rank $n-r_1$, instead of $n-r_1+1$. Hence, by another permissible transformation which consists of replacing $p^{\frac{1}{2}} x_0^*$ by x_0^*, we may take $p = 1$. *Now* apply the hypothesis of induction to the forms

$$\sum_1^{n-r_1} b_{ij} y_i^* x_j^*, \quad \sum_1^{n-1}{}' c_{ij} y_i^* x_j^*$$

and, as explained above, we deduce a permissible transformation of the indeterminates $(x_0^*, \ldots, x_n^*)$, $(y_0^*, \ldots, y_n^*)$ which gives us

$$y'Bx = y_0^* x_0^* + \Sigma \beta(\alpha_i, e_i) + \Sigma\Sigma \beta_i(e_j),$$
$$y'Cx = y_n^* x_0^* - y_0^* x_n^* + \Sigma \gamma(\alpha_i, e_i) + \Sigma\Sigma \gamma_i(e_j).$$

Since these forms may finally be written

$$y'Bx = \beta_4(1) + \Sigma \beta(\alpha_i, e_i) + \Sigma\Sigma \beta_i(e_j),$$
$$y'Cx = \gamma_4(1) + \Sigma \gamma(\alpha_i, e_i) + \Sigma\Sigma \gamma_i(e_j),$$

this completes the proof of Case (ii$a$).

Case (ii*b*). Suppose that the matrix (7) is of rank $n - r_1 - 1$. Then the equations
$$\sum_{j=1}^{n-r_1} b_{ij} x_j = 0 \quad (i = 1, ..., n - r_1)$$

have just one solution. Apply the methods of § 2 to reduce $\sum_1^{n-r_1} b_{ij} y_i x_j$ to canonical form. The restricted transformation of that section can evidently be amplified to a permissible transformation of the indeterminates $(x_0, ..., x_n)$, $(y_0, ..., y_n)$. Now consider the canonical $(n - r_1) \times (n - r_1)$ matrix corresponding to the reduced form $\sum_1^{n-r_1} b_{ij} y_i x_j$. Since this matrix is of rank $n - r_1 - 1$, it is clear that one row consists entirely of zeros. That is, preserving the same notation,
$$b_{ih} = 0 \quad (i = 1, ..., n - r_1),$$

for some value of h $(1 \leqslant h \leqslant n - r_1)$, so that the one solution of the equations above is now
$$(\delta_0^h, ..., \delta_n^h).$$

We have two cases to consider: $h \leqslant n - r_1 - r_2$, $h > n - r_1 - r_2$.

Case (ii*b*$_1$). $h > n - r_1 - r_2$. We have, with the previous notation,
$$y' B x = y_0 \xi + \eta x_0 + \sum_1^{n-r_1}{}^* b_{ij} y_i x_j,$$
$$y' C x = y_n x_0 - y_0 x_n + \sum_1^{n-1}{}' c_{ij} y_i x_j,$$

where the summation Σ^* omits the value h. We now proceed as in Case (ii*a*), making the substitution
$$x_0 = \bar{x}_0,$$
$$x_i = \bar{x}_i - c_i \bar{x}_0 \quad (i = 1, ..., h-1, h+1, ..., n-r_1),$$
$$x_h = \bar{x}_h,$$
$$x_i = \bar{x}_i \quad (i = n - r_1 + 1, ..., n).$$

This is a permissible transformation, and gives us
$$y' B x = \bar{x}_0 \bar{y}_0 \left[-2 \sum_1^{n-r_1}{}^* b_i c_i + \sum_1^{n-r_1}{}^* b_{ij} c_i c_j \right] + \sum_1^{n-r_1}{}^* b_{ij} \bar{y}_i \bar{x}_j$$
$$+ b_h (\bar{y}_0 \bar{x}_h + \bar{y}_h \bar{x}_0) + \bar{y}_0 \sum_0^{n-r_1}{}^* b_i \bar{x}_i + \bar{x}_0 \sum_0^{n-r_1}{}^* b_i \bar{y}_i$$
$$- \bar{y}_0 \sum_1^{n-r_1}{}^* b_{ij} c_i \bar{x}_j - \bar{x}_0 \sum_1^{n-r_1}{}^* b_{ij} c_j \bar{y}_i.$$

We can choose $c_1, ..., c_{h-1}, c_{h+1}, ..., c_{n-r_1}$ so that

$$\sum_{1}^{n-r_1}{}^* b_{ij} c_j = b_i,$$

the matrix of coefficients having rank $n - r_1 - 1$, and then

$$y'Bx = \bar{y}_0(p\bar{x}_0 + q\bar{x}_h) + (p\bar{y}_0 + q\bar{y}_h)\bar{x}_0 + \sum_{1}^{n-r_1}{}^* b_{ij}\bar{y}_i\bar{x}_j.$$

Since B is of rank $n - r_1 + 1$, q cannot be zero. At this stage we have

$$y'Cx = \bar{y}_n\bar{x}_0 - \bar{y}_0\bar{x}_n$$
$$+ \sum_{1}^{n-1}{}' c_{ij}\bar{y}_i\bar{x}_j - \bar{y}_0 \sum_{1}^{n-r_1-r_2} c_{ij}c_i\bar{x}_j - \bar{x}_0 \sum_{1}^{n-r_1-r_2} c_{ij}c_j\bar{y}_i,$$

since $n - r_1 - r_2 < h \leqslant n - r_1$. The permissible transformation

$$x_i^* = \bar{x}_i \quad (i = 0, ..., n-1),$$
$$x_n^* = \bar{x}_n + \sum_{1}^{n-r_1-r_2} c_{ij}c_i\bar{x}_j$$

leaves $y'Bx$ unaltered, and transforms $y'Cx$ into

$$y'Cx = y_n^* x_0^* - y_0^* x_n^* + \sum_{1}^{n-1}{}' c_{ij}y_i^* x_j^*.$$

As a final transformation on

$$y'Bx = y_0^*(px_0^* + qx_h^*) + (py_0^* + qy_h^*)x_0^* + \sum_{1}^{n-r_1}{}^* b_{ij}y_i^* x_j^*,$$

we write

$$\xi_i = x_i^* \quad (i = 0, ..., h-1, h+1, ..., n),$$
$$\xi_h = px_0^* + qx_h^*.$$

This is a permissible transformation, and gives us

$$y'Bx = \eta_0\xi_h + \eta_h\xi_0 + \sum_{1}^{n-r_1}{}^* b_{ij}\eta_i\xi_j,$$

$$y'Cx = \eta_n\xi_0 - \eta_0\xi_n + \sum_{1}^{n-1}{}' c_{ij}\eta_i\xi_j.$$

We now make use of the hypothesis of induction to reduce

$$\sum_{1}^{n-r_1}{}^* b_{ij}\eta_i\xi_j \quad \text{and} \quad \sum_{1}^{n-1}{}' c_{ij}\eta_i\xi_j$$

to canonical forms by a permissible transformation on the indeterminates $(\xi_1, ..., \xi_{h-1}, \xi_{h+1}, ..., \xi_{n-1})$, $(\eta_1, ..., \eta_{h-1}, \eta_{h+1}, ..., \eta_{n-1})$, noting that no preliminary transformation is necessary. For this set of indeterminates,

$$n' = n-3, \quad r'_1 = r_1-1, \quad r'_2 = r_2-1,$$

and the transformation induces a permissible one of $(\xi_0, ..., \xi_n)$, $(\eta_0, ..., \eta_n)$. We have, finally,

$$y'Bx = y_h x_0 + y_0 x_h + \Sigma \beta(\alpha_i, e_i) + \Sigma\Sigma \beta_i(e_j),$$
$$y'Cx = y_n x_0 - y_0 x_n + \Sigma \gamma(\alpha_i, e_i) + \Sigma\Sigma \gamma_i(e_j),$$

that is,

$$y'Bx = \beta_5(1) + \Sigma \beta(\alpha_i, e_i) + \Sigma\Sigma \beta_i(e_j),$$
$$y'Cx = \gamma_5(1) + \Sigma \gamma(\alpha_i, e_i) + \Sigma\Sigma \gamma_i(e_j).$$

Case (iib_2). $h \leqslant n-r_1-r_2$. By means of a permissible transformation, which interchanges the suffixes 1 and h, we have, preserving the notation,

$$y'Bx = y_0 \xi + \eta x_0 + \sum_2^{n-r_1} b_{ij} y_i x_j,$$

$$y'Cx = y_n x_0 - y_0 x_n + \sum_1^{n-1}{}' c_{ij} y_i x_j.$$

In considering Cases (ii$a$) and (iib_1) we left the forms

$$\Sigma b_{ij} y_i x_j \quad \text{and} \quad \Sigma c_{ij} y_i x_j$$

unaltered until the end, and then reduced them to canonical form. In this case it is necessary to reduce the forms

$$\sum_2^{n-r_1} b_{ij} y_i x_j \quad \text{and} \quad \sum_1^{n-1}{}' c_{ij} y_i x_j$$

to canonical form at this stage. In applying the hypothesis of induction to the two forms, we take the indeterminates in the order

$$x_2, ..., x_{n-r_1-r_2}, x_{n-r_1-r_2+1}, ..., x_{n-r_1}, x_1, x_{n-r_1+1}, ..., x_{n-1}.$$

We see that for these indeterminates,

$$n' = n-2, \quad r'_1 = r_1, \quad r'_2 = r_2,$$

and no preliminary transformation is necessary. Furthermore, a permissible transformation in these indeterminates induces a permissible transformation in $(x_0, ..., x_n)$, $(y_0, ..., y_n)$. For the submatrix H which appears in the matrix of a permissible transformation has only zeros above its principal diagonal, and therefore the equations of such a transformation are, as far as the displaced indeterminate x_1 is concerned,

$$\xi_1 = \sum_2^{n-r_1-r_2} a_i x_i + b x_1.$$

Hence, when x_1 is replaced, and the additional equations

$$\xi_0 = x_0,$$
$$\xi_n = x_n$$

are added, we have a permissible transformation of $(x_0, ..., x_n)$, $(y_0, ..., y_n)$. At this stage we have

$$y'Bx = y_0\xi + \eta x_0 + \Sigma \beta(\alpha_i, e_i) + \Sigma\Sigma \beta_i(e_j),$$
$$y'Cx = y_n x_0 - y_0 x_n + \Sigma \gamma(\alpha_i, e_i) + \Sigma\Sigma \gamma_i(e_j),$$

where ξ, η involve the same set of indeterminates as before the transformation, with different coefficients. For simplicity we preserve our previous notation, and write

$$y'Bx = y_0\xi + \eta x_0 + \sum_2^{n-r_1} b_{ij} y_i x_j,$$

$$y'Cx = y_n x_0 - y_0 x_n + \sum_1^{n-1}{}' c_{ij} y_i x_j,$$

where $\sum_2^{n-r_1} b_{ij} y_i x_j$ and $\sum_1^{n-1}{}' c_{ij} y_i x_j$ are in canonical form. We now proceed as in Case (ii b_1), this time taking $h = 1$, and obtain

$$y'Bx = y_0 x_1 + y_1 x_0 + \sum_2^{n-r_1} b_{ij} y_i x_j,$$

$$y'Cx = y_n x_0 - y_0 x_n + \sum_1^{n-1}{}' c_{ij} y_i x_j,$$

where the coefficients b_{ij}, c_{ij} are unchanged by these final transformations. Hence we have

$$y'Bx = y_0 x_1 + y_1 x_0 + \Sigma \beta(\alpha_i, e_i) + \Sigma\Sigma \beta_i(e_j),$$
$$y'Cx = y_n x_0 - y_0 x_n + \Sigma \gamma(\alpha_i, e_i) + \Sigma\Sigma \gamma_i(e_j).$$

The indeterminates x_1, y_1 occur in

$$\Sigma \gamma(\alpha_i, e_i) + \Sigma\Sigma \gamma_i(e_j),$$

but not in

$$\Sigma \beta(\alpha_i, e_i) + \Sigma\Sigma \beta_i(e_j).$$

It follows that x_1, y_1 appear in some term $\gamma_i(e_j)$. On the other hand, x_0, y_0, x_n, y_n do not appear in either of these two expressions. Suppose that x_1, y_1 appear in

$$\gamma_i(e_j) = (y_1 x_{a_1} - y_{a_1} x_1) + (y_{a_2} x_{a_3} - y_{a_3} x_{a_2}) + \dots.$$

The corresponding

$$\beta_i(e_j) = (y_{a_1} x_{a_2} + y_{a_2} x_{a_1}) + \dots,$$

where $a_1, a_2, \dots$ are different from $0, 1, n$. Now, we may write

$$(y_0 x_1 + y_1 x_0) + (y_{a_1} x_{a_2} + y_{a_2} x_{a_1}) + \dots = \beta_i(e_j + 1),$$
$$(y_n x_0 - y_0 x_n) + (y_1 x_{a_1} - y_{a_1} x_1) + \dots = \gamma_i(e_j + 1),$$

the terms in $\beta_i(e_j + 1)$, $\gamma_i(e_j + 1)$ being taken in the order

$$x_n, \; x_0, \; x_1, \; x_{a_1}, \; x_{a_2}, \; \dots.$$

This completes the proof of Theorem II when $r_1 > 0$.

We suppose now that $r_0 = r_1 = 0$, $r_2 > 0$. The analysis in this case is similar to that followed when $r_1 > 0$, and it will only be necessary to indicate the changes. After our preliminary transformation we have

$$y'Bx = \sum_0^n b_{ij} y_i x_j, \quad y'Cx = \sum_0^{n-r_2} c_{ij} y_i x_j.$$

We may assume that not all $b_{in} = 0$, for in that case the hypothesis of induction would apply immediately. Hence the permissible transformations of §2 give us either

$$y'Bx = \sum_0^{n-1} b_{ij} y_i x_j + k y_n x_n \quad (k \neq 0),$$

and

$$y'Cx = \sum_0^{n-r_2} c_{ij} y_i x_j,$$

or

$$y'Bx = {\sum_0^{n-1}}' b_{ij} y_i x_j + (y_n x_k + y_k x_n),$$

and

$$y'Cx = \sum_0^{n-r_2} c_{ij} y_i x_j.$$

In the former case the permissible transformation

$$\bar{x}_i = x_i \quad (i = 0, \dots, n-1), \qquad \bar{x}_n = k^{\frac{1}{2}} x_n$$

enables us to take $k = 1$, and by applying the hypothesis of induction to $\sum_0^{n-1} b_{ij} y_i x_j$, $\sum_0^{n-r_2} c_{ij} y_i x_j$, we finally obtain

$$y'Bx = \Sigma \beta(\alpha_i, e_i) + \Sigma\Sigma \beta_i(e_j) + \beta_3(1),$$
$$y'Cx = \Sigma \gamma(\alpha_i, e_i) + \Sigma\Sigma \gamma_i(e_j) + \gamma_3(1).$$

We now consider the second alternative:

Case (i). $k > n - r_2$. This is dealt with in exactly the same way as Case (i) above, interchanging the roles of B and C. We find that

$$y'Bx = \Sigma \beta(\alpha_i, e_i) + \Sigma\Sigma \beta_i(e_j) + \beta_1(1),$$
$$y'Cx = \Sigma \gamma(\alpha_i, e_i) + \Sigma\Sigma \gamma_i(e_j) + \gamma_1(1).$$

Case (ii). If $k \leqslant n - r_2$, the interchange of suffixes 0 and k is a permissible transformation, and we may write

$$y'Bx = \sum_1^{n-1} b_{ij} y_i x_j + (y_n x_0 + y_0 x_n),$$

$$y'Cx = \sum_0^{n-r_2} c_{ij} y_i x_j.$$

The methods followed above, for $r_1 > 0$, still apply, interchanging the roles of B and C, but since C is skew-symmetric and therefore always of even rank, only Case (ii$b$) appears. Case (iib_1) gives us

$$y'Bx = \Sigma \beta(\alpha_i, e_i) + \Sigma\Sigma \beta_i(e_j) + \beta_5(1),$$
$$y'Cx = \Sigma \gamma(\alpha_i, e_i) + \Sigma\Sigma \gamma_i(e_j) + \gamma_5(1).$$

Case (iib_2) leads to a result exactly similar to Case (iib_2) above.

Finally, if $r_0 = r_1 = r_2 = 0$, we are in the simple case, and the reduction of §4 applies.

6. Canonical forms for correlations.

Having completed the reduction of the forms $y'Bx$, $y'Cx$ to the canonical forms

$$y'Bx = \sum_1^r \beta(\alpha_i, e_i) + \sum_{i=1}^5 \sum_{j=1}^{s_i} \beta_i(e_j^i),$$

$$y'Cx = \sum_1^r \gamma(\alpha_i, e_i) + \sum_{i=1}^5 \sum_{j=1}^{s_i} \gamma_i(e_j^i),$$

we arrange the indeterminates involved more conveniently so that the $2e_i$ indeterminates involved in $\beta(\alpha_i, e_i)$ and $\gamma(\alpha_i, e_i)$ are

$$x_{2(e_1 + \ldots + e_{i-1})}, \ldots, x_{2(e_1 + \ldots + e_i) - 1},$$

and

$$y_{2(e_1 + \ldots + e_{i-1})}, \ldots, y_{2(e_1 + \ldots + e_i) - 1}.$$

We then order those in $\beta_i(e_j)$, $\gamma_i(e_j)$ so that their suffixes exceed the suffixes of the indeterminates in $\beta_a(e_b)$, $\gamma_a(e_b)$ if $a < i$, or if $b < j$ when $a = i$. We now consider the matrix of $A = B + C$. We have at once

$$A = \begin{pmatrix} D_{e_1}(\alpha_1) & & & & & & & \\ & \ddots & & & & & & \\ & & D_{e_r}(\alpha_r) & & & & & \\ & & & F_1(e_1^1) & & & & \\ & & & & \ddots & & & \\ & & & & & F_1(e_{s_1}^1) & & \\ & & & & & & F_2(e_1^2) & \\ & & & & & & & \ddots & \\ & & & & & & & & F_5(e_{s_5}^5) \\ & & & & & & & & & 0 \end{pmatrix}, \quad (1)$$

the diagonal submatrices being defined as follows:

$D_e(\alpha)$ is defined in the proof of Th. III, §4. It is a $2e \times 2e$ matrix, and $D_e(\alpha) - \lambda D'_e(\alpha)$ has the elementary divisors $(\lambda - \alpha)^e$, $(\lambda - \alpha^{-1})^e$ if $\alpha \neq 0$, and λ^e if $\alpha = 0$.

$F_i(e)$ $(i = 1, \ldots, 5)$ is the matrix of the bilinear form

$$\beta_i(e) + \gamma_i(e).$$

It is a simple matter to verify that these matrices are:

(i) $F_1(e) = $

The methods already used for determining elementary divisors show that $F_1(e) - \lambda F'_1(e)$ has $(\lambda - 1)^e$, $(\lambda - 1)^e$ as its elementary divisors.

(ii) $F_2(e) =$

$$
\begin{pmatrix}
 & & & & & & & & 1 \\
 & & & & & & & 1 & 1 \\
 & & & & & & 1 & 1 & \\
 & & & & & \cdot & \cdot & & \\
 & & & & 1 & 1 & & & \\
\hline
 & & -1 & & & & & & \\
 & & -1 & 1 & & & & & \\
 & \cdot & & \cdot & & & & & \\
 -1 & 1 & & & & & & & \\
 -1 & 1 & & & & & & &
\end{pmatrix},
$$

and $F_2(e) - \lambda F'_2(e)$ has the elementary divisors $(\lambda+1)^e$, $(\lambda+1)^e$.

(iii) $F_3(e) =$

$$
\begin{pmatrix}
 & & & & & & & & 1 \\
 & & & & & & & 1 & 1 \\
 & & & & & & 1 & 1 & \\
 & & & & & 1 & 1 & & \\
 & & & & \cdot & \cdot & & & \\
 & & & & 1 & 1 & & & \\
\hline
 & & & 1 & 1 & & & & \\
\hline
 & & 1 & -1 & & & & & \\
 & 1 & -1 & & & & & & \\
 \cdot & \cdot & & & & & & & \\
 1 & & & & & & & & \\
 1 & -1 & & & & & & &
\end{pmatrix},
$$

and $F_3(e) - \lambda F'_3(e)$ has the one elementary divisor $(\lambda-1)^{2e-1}$.

(iv) $F_4(e) =$

$$
\begin{pmatrix}
 & & & & & & & & 1 \\
 & & & & & & & 1 & 1 \\
 & & & & & & 1 & 1 & \\
 & & & & \cdot & \cdot & & & \\
 & & & & 1 & 1 & & & \\
\hline
 & & -1 & & 1 & & & & \\
 & & -1 & 1 & & & & & \\
 & \cdot & & \cdot & & & & & \\
 & -1 & 1 & & & & & & \\
 -1 & 1 & & & & & & &
\end{pmatrix},
$$

and $F_4(e) - \lambda F'_4(e)$ has the elementary divisor $(\lambda+1)^{2e}$. Finally,

(v) $F_5(e) =$

$$\left(
\begin{array}{ccccc|ccccc}
 & & & & & & & & & 1 \\
 & & & & & & & & 1 & 1 \\
 & & & & & & & 1 & 1 & \\
 & & & & & & \cdot & \cdot & & \\
 & & & & & 1 & 1 & & & \\
\hline
 & & & & & 0 & 1 & & & \\
\hline
 & & & & 1 & -1 & & & & \\
 & & & 1 & -1 & & & & & \\
 & & \cdot & \cdot & & & & & & \\
 & 1 & & & & & & & & \\
1 & -1 & & & & & & & & \\
\end{array}
\right),$$

and the $(2e+1) \times (2e+1)$ matrix $F_5(e) - \lambda F_5'(e)$ (λ indeterminate) is of rank $2e$.

Now, if $A - \lambda A'$ is non-singular for indeterminate λ, there are no zero matrices on the diagonal of (1), nor are there any $F_5(e)$ matrices. We can now give Th. III, §4 in its complete form as

THEOREM I. *Necessary and sufficient conditions that there exists a matrix A such that $A - \lambda A'$ is non-singular and has assigned elementary divisors are:*

(i) *the elementary divisors, other than those of type λ^e, $(\lambda - 1)^f$, $(\lambda + 1)^g$ can be arranged in pairs $(\lambda - \alpha_i)^{f_i}$, $(\lambda - \alpha_i^{-1})^{f_i}$;*

(ii) *the elementary divisors $(\lambda - 1)^f$, for a given even integer f, are even in number;*

(iii) *the elementary divisors $(\lambda + 1)^g$, for a given odd integer g, are even in number;*

(iv) *if the elementary divisors are $\lambda^{e_1}, \ldots, \lambda^{e_a}$, $(\lambda - 1)^{f_1}, \ldots, (\lambda - 1)^{f_b}$, $(\lambda + 1)^{g_1}, \ldots, (\lambda + 1)^{g_c}$, $(\lambda - \alpha_1)^{h_1}, (\lambda - \alpha_1^{-1})^{h_1}, \ldots, (\lambda - \alpha_d)^{h_d}$, $(\lambda - \alpha_d^{-1})^{h_d}$, then*

$$2 \sum_1^a e_i + \sum_1^b f_i + \sum_1^c g_i + 2 \sum_1^d h_i = n + 1.$$

The necessity of these conditions is an immediate consequence of the reduction to a canonical form and of the results given above, which give the elementary divisors of the various submatrices in the canonical matrix (1). The sufficiency of the conditions is evident, because we can construct a matrix A as given by (1), after grouping the elementary divisors into suitable pairs.

The canonical form (1) may be simplified to some extent. We observe that $F_1(e) - \lambda F_1'(e)$ has the same elementary divisors $(\lambda - 1)^e$, $(\lambda - 1)^e$ as $D_e(1)$. Hence, by § 4, Th. I, there exists a non-singular matrix P such that

$$P' F_1(e) P = D_e(1).$$

For similar reasons we can find non-singular matrices Q, R, S such that

$$Q' F_2(e) Q = D_e(-1),$$

$$R' \begin{pmatrix} F_3'e) & 0 \\ 0 & F_3(e) \end{pmatrix} R = D_{2e-1}(1),$$

and

$$S' \begin{pmatrix} F_4(e) & 0 \\ 0 & F_4(e) \end{pmatrix} S = D_{2e}(-1).$$

Hence, by a further transformation of coordinates, we can assume that (1) contains no submatrices $F_1(e)$ or $F_2(e)$, and that for given f_i, g_i there is at most one $F_3(e)$, and one $F_4(e)$. In future we shall suppose that this has been done.

We now consider the case in which $A - \lambda A'$ is singular, for indeterminate λ. In the canonical form of A the number of zero rows (and columns) is r_0, where $n - r_0 + 1$ is the rank of the matrix

$$\begin{pmatrix} B \\ C \end{pmatrix},$$

and therefore $n - r_0 + 1$ is also the rank of the matrix

$$\begin{pmatrix} A \\ A' \end{pmatrix}.$$

This rank is invariant under transformations of coordinates, since

$$\begin{pmatrix} P'AP \\ (P'AP)' \end{pmatrix} = \begin{pmatrix} P'AP \\ P'A'P \end{pmatrix} = P' \begin{pmatrix} A \\ A' \end{pmatrix} P.$$

If the canonical matrix A contains k matrices $F_5(e)$, we see that the rank of $A - \lambda A'$ is $n - r_0 + 1 - k$. Hence k is also an invariant of A. We now prove that the e_i^5 which appear in the submatrices $F_5(e_i^5)$, and which determine the number of terms in $y'Ax$ corresponding to each submatrix $F_5(e_i^5)$, are also invariants of A. We assume that $k > 0$.

We consider the linearly dependent rows of the matrix

$$(A - \lambda A') x,$$

writing
$$X_i = \sum_{j=0}^{n-r_0} (a_{ij} - \lambda a_{ji}) x_j \quad (i = 0, \ldots, n-r_0).$$

These linear forms have k independent relations connecting them, say

$$\phi \equiv \sum_{j=0}^{n-r_0} d_j(\lambda) X_j = 0, \tag{2}$$

where we may assume that the $d_j(\lambda)$ are polynomials in λ. Amongst all possible relations of the form (2) we consider those in which the maximum of the degrees in λ of the polynomials $d_0, \ldots, d_{n-r_0}$ is least. Let this smallest maximum be m_1, and suppose that there are q_1 relations (2) of this degree, say

$$\phi_1, \ldots, \phi_{q_1}.$$

We now consider all relations (2) which are not of the form

$$\sum_{1}^{q_1} a_i(\lambda) \phi_i,$$

and amongst these we again consider those of lowest degree, which degree we denote by m_2. If

$$\phi_{q_1+1}, \ldots, \phi_{q_2}$$

is a basis for this set of polynomials, we then consider those relations (2) of lowest degree which are not expressible in the form

$$\sum_{i=1}^{q_2} a_i(\lambda) \phi_i,$$

and so on. We obtain a set of polynomials

$$\phi_1, \ldots, \phi_{q_\rho},$$

which form a basis for the relations (2). We prove that the integers $q_1, \ldots, q_\rho, m_1, \ldots, m_\rho$ are invariants under allowable transformations of coordinates. If

$$x = P\overline{x}$$

is such a transformation, the relation

$$\Sigma d_j(\lambda) X_j = 0$$

becomes
$$\Sigma d_i(\lambda) q_{ij} \overline{X}_j = 0,$$

where
$$Q = (q_{ij}) = \tilde{P}.$$

Since q_{ij} is in K, the degree of any relation is unaltered by an allowable transformation. This proves the invariance of $q_1, ..., q_\rho$, $m_1, ..., m_\rho$. We now associate these integers with the e_i^5.

In the canonical form (1) the only submatrices G such that $G - \lambda G'$ is singular are the k matrices $F_5(e_i^5)$. Since all the submatrices are on the principal diagonal of A, we obtain relations (2) only from the $F_5(e_i^5)$ matrices, and there is *one* relation corresponding to each matrix. Let $F_5(e_j^5)$ have rows and columns corresponding to the indeterminates

$$x_m, ..., x_{m+2e} \quad (e = e_j^5).$$

Then
$$X_m = (1-\lambda)\,x_{m+2e},$$
$$X_{m+1} = (1-\lambda)\,x_{m+2e-1} + (1+\lambda)\,x_{m+2e},$$
$$X_{m+2} = (1-\lambda)\,x_{m+2e-2} + (1+\lambda)\,x_{m+2e-1},$$
$$\cdot \quad \cdot \quad \cdot \quad \cdot \quad \cdot \quad \cdot \quad \cdot$$
$$X_{m+e-1} = (1-\lambda)\,x_{m+e+1} + (1+\lambda)\,x_{m+e+2},$$
$$X_{m+e} = (1+\lambda)\,x_{m+e+1},$$
$$X_{m+e+1} = (1-\lambda)\,x_{m+e-1} - (1+\lambda)\,x_{m+e},$$
$$\cdot \quad \cdot \quad \cdot \quad \cdot \quad \cdot \quad \cdot \quad \cdot$$
$$X_{m+2e} = (1-\lambda)\,x_m - (1+\lambda)\,x_{m+1}.$$

The relation of least degree connecting $X_m, ..., X_{m+2e}$ is
$$\psi_j \equiv (1+\lambda)^e X_m - (1+\lambda)^{e-1}(1-\lambda)\,X_{m+1}$$
$$- (1+\lambda)^{e-2}(1-\lambda)^2 X_{m+2} \cdots \pm (1-\lambda)^e X_{m+e} = 0,$$

and $\psi_1, ..., \psi_k$ form a basis for the relations (2). We deduce that if $e_1^5 \leqslant e_2^5 \leqslant ... \leqslant e_k^5$, then

$$e_1^5 = e_2^5 = ... = e_{q_1}^5 = m_1 < e_{q_1+1}^5 = ... = e_{q_2}^5 = m_2 < ...$$
$$= e_{q_\rho}^5 = m_\rho \quad (q_\rho = k),$$

and therefore the integers $e_1^5, ..., e_k^5$ are invariants of A under allowable transformations of coordinates.

We sum up our results in

THEOREM II. *Let A be any $(n+1) \times (n+1)$ matrix, let (A, A') be of rank $n-r+1$, let $A - \lambda A'$ be of rank $n-r+1-k$, and let*

$$\psi_1, ..., \psi_k$$

be a basis of polynomials of minimum degree for the relations connecting the rows of $(A - \lambda A')x$. Let the degree of ψ_i be m_i, and suppose that

$$m_1 = \ldots = m_{q_1} = n_1 < m_{q_1+1} = \ldots = m_{q_2} = n_2 < \ldots$$
$$= m_{q_\rho} = n_\rho \quad (q_\rho = k).$$

Let the elementary divisors of $A - \lambda A'$ be

$$\lambda^{e_1}, \ldots, \lambda^{e_a}, \quad (\lambda-1)^{2f_1-1}, \ldots, (\lambda-1)^{2f_b-1}, \quad (\lambda+1)^{2g_1}, \ldots, (\lambda+1)^{2g_c},$$
$$(\lambda-\alpha_1)^{h_1}, (\lambda-\alpha_1^{-1})^{h_1}, \ldots, (\lambda-\alpha_d)^{h_d}, (\lambda-\alpha_d^{-1})^{h_d}, \text{ where } \alpha_i \text{ may be } \pm 1,$$
and $f_1 < f_2 < \ldots < f_b$, $g_1 < g_2 < \ldots < g_c$.

Then

$$2\Sigma e + \Sigma(2f-1) + 2\Sigma g + 2\Sigma h = n - r + 1 - k,$$

and there exists a non-singular matrix P such that the correlation $u = Ax$ is transformed into the correlation $v = By$ by the transformation $x = Py$, where

$$
B = P'AP
$$

$$
= \begin{vmatrix}
D_{e_1}(0) & & & & & & & & & & & \\
& D_{e_a}(0) & & & & & & & & & & \\
& & D_{h_1}(\alpha_1) & & & & & & & & & \\
& & & \ddots & & & & & & & & \\
& & & & D_{h_d}(\alpha_d) & & & & & & & \\
& & & & & F_3(f_1) & & & & & & \\
& & & & & & \ddots & & & & & \\
& & & & & & & F_3(f_b) & & & & \\
& & & & & & & & F_4(g_1) & & & \\
& & & & & & & & & \ddots & & \\
& & & & & & & & & & F_4(g_c) & \\
& & & & & & & & & & & F_5(m_1) \\
& & & & & & & & & & & & \ddots \\
& & & & & & & & & & & & & F_5(m_{q_\rho}) \\
& & & & & & & & & & & & & & 0
\end{vmatrix},
$$

$q_\rho = k$, *and the zero matrix has r rows and columns.*

7. Some geometrical properties of correlations. We begin with a *simple* correlation [§ 4],

$$u = Ax, \tag{1}$$

this having been defined as one for which $A + A'$ and $A - A'$ are both non-singular. The canonical form is given by (1), where

$$A = \begin{pmatrix} D_{e_1}(0) & & & & & \\ & D_{e_2}(0) & & & & \\ & & \ddots & & & \\ & & & D_{e_r}(0) & & \\ & & & & D_{f_1}(\alpha_1) & \\ & & & & & \ddots \\ & & & & & & D_{f_s}(\alpha_s) \end{pmatrix}.$$

A point x has no transform if it lies in the space given by

$$Ax = 0. \tag{2}$$

Remembering that $D_e(\alpha)$ is the $2e \times 2e$ matrix

$$D_e(\alpha) = \begin{pmatrix} & & & & & & \alpha \\ & & & & & \alpha & 1 \\ & & & & \alpha & 1 & \\ & & & \ddots & \ddots & & \\ & & \alpha & 1 & & & \\ & 1 & 0 & & & & \\ 1 & 0 & & & & & \\ \ddots & \ddots & & & & & \\ 1 & 0 & & & & & \end{pmatrix},$$

it is easily seen that the space given by (2) is of $r-1$ dimensions, being spanned by the vertices

$$X_{e_1}, \; X_{2e_1+e_2}, \; \dots, \; X_{2(e_1+\dots+e_{r-1})+e_r},$$

of the simplex of reference. This space may be called the *fundamental space* of the correlation corresponding to the zero latent root of $A - \lambda A'$. Similar working shows us that the transform of any point which has a transform is a prime which always passes through the space spanned by

$$X_0, \; X_{2e_1}, \; X_{2(e_1+e_2)}, \; \dots, \; X_{2(e_1+\dots+e_{r-1})}.$$

This is also a space of $r-1$ dimensions which, we see at once, is the space defined by the equations

$$A'x = 0. \tag{3}$$

We may regard this as the fundamental space corresponding to the *infinite* latent root of $A - \lambda A'$. We note that the spaces defined by (2) and (3) do not meet.

The space given by

$$(A - \alpha_i A')x = 0,$$

where α_i is a latent root of $A - \lambda A'$, is called the fundamental space of the correlation corresponding to α_i. Recalling that the *dual* correlation is

$$v = A'y, \tag{4}$$

we see that a necessary and sufficient condition that a point x should have the same transform under (1) and (4) is that it should lie in a fundamental space corresponding to a latent root of $A - \lambda A'$. Let us consider the space defined by

$$(A - \alpha_1 A')x = 0,$$

and assume that

$$0 \neq \alpha_1 = \alpha_2 = \ldots = \alpha_t,$$

and

$$\alpha_i \neq \alpha_1 \quad (i > t).$$

We see that this space is an S_{t-1}, defined by the vertices

$$X_{2\Sigma e + f_1},\ X_{2\Sigma e + 2f_1 + f_2},\ \ldots,\ X_{2\Sigma e + 2(f_1 + \ldots + f_{t-1}) + f_t}.$$

The correlation (1) transforms the points of this S_{t-1} into the primes which pass through the S_{n-t} given by the equations

$$x_{2\Sigma e + f_1 - 1} = 0,\ x_{2\Sigma e + 2f_1 + f_2 - 1} = 0,\ \ldots,\ x_{2\Sigma e + 2(f_1 + \ldots + f_{t-1}) + f_t - 1} = 0.$$

This S_{n-t} contains the S_{t-1}, and also contains every fundamental space corresponding to a latent root of $A - \lambda A'$ distinct from α_1^{-1}. The fundamental space corresponding to α_1^{-1} is seen to be an S_{t-1}^* spanned by the vertices

$$X_{2\Sigma e},\ X_{2\Sigma e + 2f_1},\ X_{2\Sigma e + 2(f_1 + f_2)},\ \ldots,\ X_{2\Sigma e + 2(f_1 + \ldots + f_{t-1})}.$$

Hence S_{n-t} and S_{t-1}^* meet in a space which is spanned by the vertices

$$X_{2\,\Sigma e+2(f_1+\ldots+f_i)},\ X_{2\,\Sigma e+2(f_1+\ldots+f_{i+1})},\ \ldots,\ X_{2\,\Sigma e+2(f_1+\ldots+f_{t-1})},$$

where we have assumed that $f_1, f_2, \ldots, f_t$ are so arranged that

$$f_1 = \ldots = f_i = 1,$$

and $$f_{i+1}, f_{i+2}, \ldots, f_t > 1.$$

We now turn to the general correlation discussed in §6. In the simple case discussed above, the possibility of latent roots equal to ± 1 was excluded. Such latent roots arise here. Before finding the fundamental space corresponding to $\lambda = 1$ we remark that in discussing the geometrical properties of any correlation we are led to consider certain loci:

(i) the locus of points which lie in their transforms under (1). These are the points whose coordinates $x = (x_0, \ldots, x_n)$ satisfy the equation
$$x'u = x'Ax = 0.$$

This equation may also be written

$$(x'Ax)' = x'A'x = 0,$$

or $$x'Bx = 0, \qquad (5)$$

where $B = \frac{1}{2}(A + A')$ is the symmetric part of A.

(ii) the locus of points which have the same transform under (1) and (4). These points satisfy the equations

$$(A - \alpha A')x = 0, \qquad (6)$$

where α is any latent root of $A - \lambda A'$, and were considered in the simple case. If x is any solution of (6),

$$x'Ax = \alpha x'A'x = \alpha x'Ax.$$

Hence, if $\alpha \neq 1$, $$x'Ax = 0,$$

and therefore every point which lies in a fundamental space corresponding to a latent root $\alpha \neq 1$ satisfies equation (5).

We assume that A is in the canonical form described in §6, and suppose that $\alpha = 1$ in equations (6). These become

$$Cx = 0, \qquad (7)$$

where C is the skew-symmetric part of A. In solving these equations we observe that the only submatrices of A which yield any non-zero coordinates are those submatrices G, say, such that $G - G'$ is a singular matrix. These are the submatrices

$$D_e(1), \quad F_3(e), \quad F_5(e).$$

It is therefore sufficient to consider the case in which

$$A = \begin{pmatrix} D_{e_1}(1) & & & & & & & \\ & \ddots & & & & & & \\ & & D_{e_a}(1) & & & & & \\ & & & F_3(f_1) & & & & \\ & & & & \ddots & & & \\ & & & & & F_3(f_b) & & \\ & & & & & & F_5(g_1) & \\ & & & & & & & \ddots \\ & & & & & & & & F_5(g_c) \\ & & & & & & & & & 0 \end{pmatrix}.$$

By direct calculation we find that a basis for the solutions of (7) is given by the set of vertices

$$X_0, \; X_{e_1}, \; X_{2e_1}, \; X_{2e_1+e_2}, \; \ldots, \; X_{2(e_1+\ldots+e_{a-1})+e_a} \quad (2a \text{ points}),$$

$$X_{\Sigma 2e}, \; X_{\Sigma 2e+2f_1-1}, \; \ldots, \; X_{\Sigma 2e+2(f_1+\ldots+f_{b-1})-(b-1)} \quad (b \text{ points}),$$

$$X_{2\Sigma e+2\Sigma f-b}, \; X_{2\Sigma e+2\Sigma f-b+2g_1+1}, \; \ldots, \; X_{2\Sigma e+2\Sigma f-b+2(g_1+\ldots+g_{c-1})+(c-1)}$$
$$(c \text{ points}),$$

$$X_m, \; X_{m+1}, \; \ldots, \; X_n \quad (m = 2\Sigma e + 2\Sigma f + 2\Sigma g - b + c).$$

The point $P = \Sigma \lambda_i X_i$, where the summation is over the suffixes contained in the above table, lies on the locus

$$x'Ax = \Sigma a_{ij} x_i x_j = 0$$

if and only if

$$2(\lambda_0 \lambda_1 + \ldots + \lambda_{2d-2}\lambda_{2d-1}) + \sum_{i=0}^{d'-1} \lambda_{2(e_1+\ldots+e_a)+i}^2 = 0,$$

where

$$e_1 = \ldots = e_d = 1, \; e_{d+1} > 1, \text{ and } f_1 = \ldots = f_{d'} = 1, f_{d'+1} > 1.$$

A correlation may be singular for several reasons. If we consider the canonical form, we see that A is singular if

   (i) there are zero matrices on the principal diagonal;
   (ii) there are submatrices $D_e(0)$ on the principal diagonal;
   (iii) there are submatrices $F_5(e)$ present; and
   (iv) if there is a combination of (i), (ii) and (iii).

If a correlation is singular because of (i) only, we shall say that it is of the *first kind*. If it is singular because of (ii) and (iii) only, we shall say that it is of the *second kind*.

If a correlation is singular on account of (i), by itself, or on account of (iv), the canonical form is

$$\begin{pmatrix} A_1 & 0 \\ 0 & 0 \end{pmatrix},$$

where A_1 is an $(m+1) \times (m+1)$ matrix such that the correlation

$$u = A_1 x \tag{8}$$

in the S_m whose equations are

$$x_{m+1} = \ldots = x_n = 0$$

is either non-singular, or singular only because of (ii) and (iii) above. If S_{n-m-1} is the space

$$x_0 = \ldots = x_m = 0,$$

no point of this space has a transform under the given correlation in $[n]$, but the transform of any other point, if it exists, passes through S_{n-m-1}. We thus obtain the following construction for the given correlation in $[n]$; if P is any point not in S_{n-m-1}, project P from S_{n-m-1} into the point P' of S_m. Let Π' be the transform of P' by the correlation (8) in S_m, and let Π be the prime joining Π' to S_{n-m-1}. Then Π is the transform of P by the given correlation in $[n]$.

From this result it follows that the geometry of any correlation in $[n]$ can be deduced from the geometry of a correlation of the second kind. The properties of a singular correlation of the second kind are most easily discussed by showing that such a correlation can be represented as the product of a non-singular collineation (of a kind which is, geometrically, particularly simple) and a correlation (in the same space) of the first kind. We do this below. Ultimately, therefore, the properties of singular correlations can be made to depend on those of non-singular correlations in a subspace.

Let
$$u = Ax$$

be a correlation of the second kind, where we suppose that A is in canonical form and, to simplify our notation, we omit the submatrices $D_e(\alpha)(\alpha \neq 0)$, $F_3(e)$, $F_4(e)$. Let $D_{e_1}(0), \ldots, D_{e_t}(0)$ be the

diagonal submatrices corresponding to the latent root $\lambda = 0$, and let
$$F_5'(g_1), \ldots, F_5'(g_c)$$
be the diagonal submatrices of type $F_5(e)$. The space of points having no transform in the correlation is defined by the equations
$$Ax = 0.$$

By direct calculation this space is seen to be the S_{t+c-1} spanned by the t points
$$X_{e_1}, X_{2e_1+e_2}, \ldots, X_{2(e_1+\ldots+e_{t-1})+e_t},$$
and the c points whose coordinates are of the form
$$(0, 0, \ldots, 0, \underbrace{1, 1, \ldots, 1}_{g_i+1}, 0, \ldots, 0).$$

Each one of these c points arises from a submatrix $F_5(g_i)$, and the non-zero coordinates are $g_i + 1$ in number, their position corresponding to that of the first $g_i + 1$ rows of $F_5(g_i)$ in the matrix A.

Again, the primes which correspond to points in $[n]$ with a transform all pass through the space S_{t+c-1}' spanned by the t points
$$X_0, X_{2e_1}, \ldots, X_{2(e_1+\ldots+e_{t-1})},$$
and the c points
$$(0, 0, \ldots, 0, \underbrace{1, -1, 1, -1, \ldots, \pm 1}_{g_i+1}, 0, \ldots, 0).$$

Here also, each one of these c points arises from a submatrix $F_5(g_i)$, and the non-zero coordinates, which alternate in sign, are $g_i + 1$ in number, their position corresponding to that of the first $g_i + 1$ rows of $F_5(g_i)$ in the matrix A. This space S_{t+c-1}' is evidently defined by the equations
$$A'x = 0.$$

It is immediately verified that S_{t+c-1} and S_{t+c-1}' do not meet. This may also be seen from the fact that if the equations
$$Ax = 0 \quad \text{and} \quad A'x = 0$$
have a common solution, the integer r_0 introduced into our discussion, p. 415, of the canonical form is not zero, and therefore zero matrices appear on the principal diagonal of A, contradicting our hypothesis that the correlation is of the second kind.

When we consider the points which have the same transform in the dual correlation as in the given one, we have only to concern ourselves with the submatrices $F_5(g_1), \dots, F_5(g_c)$, since $D_e(0) - \lambda D_e'(0)$ is non-singular if $\lambda \neq 0$. Now

$$[F_5(g_i) - \lambda F_5'(g_i)]\, x = 0$$

has a solution for each value of λ. We see that *all* such solutions lie in the space

$$x_0 = x_1 = \dots = x_{2(e_1 + \dots + e_i) - 1} = 0,$$

$$x_{2\,\Sigma e + g_i + 1} = \dots = x_{2\,\Sigma e + 2g_i} = 0, \qquad (10)$$

$$\cdot \qquad \cdot \qquad \cdot \qquad \cdot \qquad \cdot \qquad \cdot \qquad \cdot$$

$$x_{2\,\Sigma e + 2(g_1 + \dots + g_{c-1}) + (c-1) + g_c + 1} = \dots = x_{2\,\Sigma e + 2\,\Sigma g + c - 1} = 0,$$

where $2\,\Sigma e + 2\,\Sigma g + c - 1 = n + 1$.

Now consider the collineation

$$\left.\begin{aligned} y_i &= x_{e_1 + i} \\ y_{e_1 + i} &= x_i \end{aligned}\right\} \quad (i = 0, \dots, e_1 - 1), \qquad (11{\cdot}1)$$

$$\left.\begin{aligned} y_{2e_1 + i} &= x_{2e_1 + e_2 + i} \\ y_{2e_1 + e_2 + i} &= x_{2e_1 + i} \end{aligned}\right\} \quad (i = 0, \dots, e_2 - 1), \qquad (11{\cdot}2)$$

$$\cdot \qquad \cdot \qquad \cdot \qquad \cdot \qquad \cdot \qquad \cdot \qquad \cdot$$

$$\left.\begin{aligned} y_{2(e_1 + \dots + e_{t-1}) + i} &= x_{2(e_1 + \dots + e_{t-1}) + e_t + i} \\ y_{2(e_1 + \dots + e_{t-1}) + e_t + i} &= x_{2(e_1 + \dots + e_{t-1}) + i} \end{aligned}\right\} \quad (i = 0, \dots, e_t - 1), \ (11{\cdot}t)$$

$$\left.\begin{aligned} y_{2(e_1 + \dots + e_t) + 2i} &= x_{2(e_1 + \dots + e_t) + 2i}, \\ y_{2(e_1 + \dots + e_t) + 2i + 1} &= -x_{2(e_1 + \dots + e_t) + 2i + 1}, \end{aligned}\right\} \qquad (11{\cdot}t')$$

where in $(11{\cdot}t')$ the suffix i varies so that the equations range over all the remaining coordinates. This collineation is evidently an involutory collineation. If we write it in matrix form as

$$y = Cx, \qquad (11)$$

then

$$C^2 = I_{n+1}.$$

It transforms S_{c+t-1} into S_{c+t-1}', and leaves the space defined in (10) invariant. Now consider the correlation

$$u = ACy. \qquad (12)$$

Since

$$u = (AC)(Cx) = ACy = Ax,$$

our given correlation of the second kind is now expressed as the product of the non-singular collineation (11) and the correlation (12). We show that the correlation (12) is of the first kind. In fact, actual multiplication of the matrices involved shows that the matrix AC is *symmetric*, and therefore the correlation (12) is necessarily of the first kind. The vertex of the primes u in the correlation (12) is S'_{c+t-1}, since the solutions of

$$(AC)'y = 0$$

are the solutions of

$$A'y = 0,$$

the matrix C being non-singular.

We conclude with some remarks on non-singular correlations. These are most easily discussed by means of the associated collineation

$$y = \tilde{A}Ax. \tag{13}$$

The points, lines, etc., which have the same transform under (1) and the dual correlation are precisely the united points, lines, etc., of (13), and we have discussed the methods of obtaining these in Chapter VIII. We recall the theorem established in §4, that the elementary divisors of $\tilde{A}A - \lambda I_{n+1}$, which are those of $A - \lambda A'$, cannot be chosen arbitrarily, but if $\lambda = \alpha$ ($\alpha \neq \pm 1$) is a latent root, so is $\lambda = \alpha^{-1}$. Applying VIII, §3, Th. V, gives us an interesting geometrical result. Let x be any point of $[n]$ which is not a united point, and y its transform under (13). The line xy meets all the fundamental spaces of the collineation (13), the point of intersection with the fundamental space corresponding to the latent root α being

$$A_\alpha = y - \alpha x.$$

We see that the points

$$A_\alpha, \quad A_{\alpha-1}$$

are in involution, and if $\lambda = \pm 1$ are latent roots of the collineation, the points A_1, A_{-1} are the united points of the involution.

As we have already seen, the correlation $u = Ax$, when A is non-singular, gives a prime-point transformation

$$y = \tilde{A}v. \tag{14}$$

For if x lies in the prime v, u passes through the point y, where

$$u'y = x'A'y = x'v.$$

We can develop a similar theory for this prime-point correlation, which is, indeed, the same correlation as $u = Ax$. In particular, the correlation *associated* with (14) is

$$w = A\tilde{A}v,$$

and since
$$(\widetilde{\tilde{A}A}) = A\tilde{A},$$

this is the dual form of (13).

Finally, some aspects of the elementary theory of quadrics are of interest in connection with the theory of correlations. If the prime u which is the transform of the point x *contains* the point x, this point satisfies the equation

$$x'u = x'Ax = 0,$$

or, equivalently,
$$x'Bx = 0, \tag{15}$$

where
$$B = \tfrac{1}{2}(A + A').$$

We call the locus of points given by (15) the *incidence quadric* associated with the correlation $u = Ax$. Similarly, the primes v which contain their transforms under (14) satisfy the equation

$$v'Dv = 0, \tag{16}$$

where
$$D = \tfrac{1}{2}(\tilde{A} + A^{-1}).$$

We see that
$$B = A'DA.$$

Let us assume that the correlation $u = Ax$, besides being non-singular, is such that B and D are non-singular. The point-equation of the locus (16) is
$$x'D^{-1}x = 0.$$

For this to coincide with the incidence quadric (15) we must have

$$kD^{-1} = B$$

for some k in K. We determine the simple non-singular correlations for which the 'envelope' incidence quadric (16) is the dual of the incidence quadric (15).

The above condition is

$$4kI_{n+1} = (A^{-1} + \tilde{A})(A + A')$$
$$= 2I_{n+1} + \tilde{A}A + A^{-1}A',$$

or
$$\tilde{A}A + (\tilde{A}A)^{-1} = 2(2k-1)I_{n+1}.$$

Let
$$Y = \tilde{A}A.$$

Our last condition is

$$Y^2 - 2(2k-1)\,Y + I_{n+1} = 0.$$

Hence, since $Y \neq \lambda I_{n+1}$, the *minimum function* of the matrix Y is [cf. II, § 10]

$$\psi(\lambda) = \lambda^2 - 2(2k-1)\,\lambda + 1.$$

By II, § 10, Th. III, the last invariant factor of $Y - \lambda I_{n+1}$ is $\psi(\lambda)$, and therefore all invariant factors divide $\psi(\lambda)$. We consider the following possibilities:

(i) $2k - 1 \neq \pm 1$. If α, α^{-1} are the roots of $\psi(\lambda) = 0$, neither of these roots is equal to ± 1. The elementary divisors of $Y - \lambda I_{n+1}$, as we remarked in § 4, occur in the pairs $(\lambda - \alpha)^{e_1}$, $(\lambda - \alpha^{-1})^{e_1}$. Since the product of all the elementary divisors is of degree $n + 1$, it follows that $n + 1$ is even. Finally, since the last invariant factor is simply $(\lambda - \alpha)(\lambda - \alpha^{-1})$, the elementary divisors of $Y - \lambda I_{n+1}$ consist of $\frac{1}{2}(n+1)$ elementary divisors $(\lambda - \alpha)$, and an equal number of elementary divisors $(\lambda - \alpha^{-1})$. Hence A can be reduced to the form

$$A = \begin{pmatrix} D_1(\alpha) & & & \\ & D_1(\alpha) & & \\ & & \ddots & \\ & & & D_1(\alpha) \end{pmatrix},$$

where, in the usual notation,

$$D_1(\alpha) = \begin{pmatrix} 0 & \alpha \\ 1 & 0 \end{pmatrix}.$$

Conversely, it is easily verified that if A is taken in this form, with any α which is neither zero nor ± 1, then

$$kD^{-1} = B \quad (k \neq 0),$$

where

$$k = \frac{(\alpha + 1)^2}{4\alpha}.$$

(ii) $2k - 1 = 1$. The minimum function is now $(\lambda - 1)^2$, and the elementary divisors of $Y - \lambda I_{n+1}$ are all of the form $(\lambda - 1)$ or $(\lambda - 1)^2$. Since, by § 6, Th. I, there must be an *even* number of elementary divisors of the latter type, A can be reduced to the form

$$A = \begin{pmatrix} F_1(2) & & & & & & \\ & F_1(2) & & & & & \\ & & \ddots & & & & \\ & & & F_1(2) & & & \\ & & & & 1 & & \\ & & & & & 1 & \\ & & & & & & \ddots \\ & & & & & & & 1 \end{pmatrix},$$

where [§ 6, (i)]

$$F_1(2) = \begin{pmatrix} 0 & 0 & 0 & 1 \\ 0 & 0 & 1 & 1 \\ 0 & 1 & 0 & 0 \\ 1 & -1 & 0 & 0 \end{pmatrix}.$$

We may again verify that if A is given in this form it satisfies all our requirements.

(iii) $2k - 1 = -1$. The minimum function is $(\lambda + 1)^2$, and $\lambda = -1$ is a latent root of the matrix Y. It follows that

$$B = \tfrac{1}{2}(A + A')$$

is singular, contrary to our hypothesis.

BIBLIOGRAPHICAL NOTES

Book I

A considerable part of the material of Chapters I–IV will be found in works on Modern Algebra, such as Albert (**1**), Dickson (**5**), Macaulay (**9**) and van der Waerden (**10**). As far as we know, the development of the theory of linear dependence over a non-commutative field, given in Chapter II, is new, and the algebraic theory of Jacobians given in § 7 of Chapter III has not previously been published. In Chapter IV we have preferred to use the term *resultant-forms* instead of the literal translation *inertia-forms* of the Trägheitsformen introduced by Hurwitz.

Book II

Chapter V. The method given here for defining a projective space has been used by Lefschetz (**8**) for the case of a commutative field, and is derived from Veblen and Whitehead (**11**). The development for a non-commutative field given here has not previously been published.

Chapter VI. Much has been written on the axiomatic foundations of projective geometry. For a full account of these writings, the reader is referred to the article by Enriques (**6**) and to Baker (**2**). The method followed here bears most resemblance to that adopted by Veblen and Young (**12**), but differs from their treatment in the choice of the initial axioms, and in the introduction of coordinate systems before the imposition of limitations which effectively restrict the field from which the coordinates are taken. The development in Chapter II of the theory of linear dependence over a non-commutative field was designed to make this treatment possible.

Chapter VII. The use of coordinates to distinguish linear spaces originated with Grassmann and was developed into line-geometry by Plücker. References will be found in the article by Segre (**7**), and an account is given in Bertini (**3**). Properties of determinants which are in effect Grassmann coordinates play an important part in the algebraic theory of invariants. The basis theorem of § 7 was first proved by Mertens. Our proof is similar to that given by Weitzenböck [*Proc. K. Akad. Wetensch. Amsterdam*, vol. XXXIX, p. 503 (1936)].

Chapter VIII. The geometrical theory of collineations has been fully discussed by Segre. For references see Segre (**7**). An account is given in Bertini (**3**). The treatment given here is more algebraic than either of these.

Chapter IX. The account of correlations given here is based on the simultaneous consideration of symmetric and skew-symmetric bilinear forms, which derives from the treatment of two quadratic forms given in Bromwich (**4**), who bases his work on that of Kronecker. For the geometrical aspects reference should be made to Segre (**7**).

BIBLIOGRAPHY

(1) ALBERT, A. A. *Modern Higher Algebra* (Cambridge, 1938).

(2) BAKER, H. F. *Principles of Geometry*, vol. I (Cambridge, 1922).

(3) BERTINI, E. *Geometria Proiettiva degli Iperspazi* (Messina, 1923).

(4) BROMWICH, T. J. I'A. *Quadratic Forms and their Classification by means of Invariant Factors* (Cambridge, 1906).

(5) DICKSON, L. E. *Modern Algebraic Theories* (Chicago, 1926).

(6) *Ency. der Math. Wissenschaften*, III, A, B 1, F. Enriques.

(7) *Ency. der Math. Wissenschaften*, III, C 7, C. Segre.

(8) LEFSCHETZ, S. *Lectures on Algebraic Geometry* (Princeton, 1937).

(9) MACAULAY, F. S. *Algebraic Theory of Modular Systems* (Cambridge, 1916).

(10) VAN DER WAERDEN, B. L. *Moderne Algebra* (Berlin, 1930).

(11) VEBLEN, O. and WHITEHEAD, J. H. C. *The Foundations of Differential Geometry* (Cambridge, 1932).

(12) VEBLEN, O. and YOUNG, J. W. *Projective Geometry*, vol. I (Boston, 1910).

INDEX

(The numbers refer to the page where the term occurs for the first time in the book or is defined)

436